Heat and Thermodynamics

HEAT and
THERMODYNAMICS

An Intermediate Textbook
for Students of Physics,
Chemistry, and Engineering

MARK W. ZEMANSKY, PH.D.

Professor of Physics, The City College of New York

FOURTH EDITION

1957 McGRAW-HILL BOOK COMPANY, INC.

New York   Toronto   London

DEDICATED TO
ADELE C. ZEMANSKY

Preface

This book is designed as an intermediate textbook to supply the needs of students who are in the first stage of preparation for a career in physics, chemistry, or engineering. The only prerequisites are a course in general college physics and one in calculus. Mathematical theorems beyond the scope of a first course in calculus are derived and explained in the body of the text at the places where they are needed.

The first ten chapters deal with the fundamental ideas of temperature, work, internal energy, heat, reversibility, and entropy, with examples and applications mostly to ideal gases. The treatment is simple, with occasional glimpses of more rigorous methods for the more sophisticated students. The remaining nine chapters deal with physical, chemical, and engineering applications in greater detail. The properties of chemical, linear, surface, electric, and magnetic systems are introduced in the beginning and used in general discussions instead of being reserved for special treatment at the end.

An attempt has been made to reduce the number of occasions in which the student is asked to refer back to a previous equation. In fact, only a few equations are numbered. Important equations are referred to either by name or by writing them in full. This procedure is dictated by the realistic attitude that a student, asked to refer to previous equations too often, will simply refuse and read on without understanding.

Methods of measurement are explained throughout the book and actual numerical data are given in numerous tables and graphs. These values have been brought up to date as much as possible. Problems are listed at the end of each chapter. By the use of script capitals to denote intensive variables or generalized forces (except pressure), it has been found possible to make the notation fairly consistent with that published by the Committee on Letter Symbols and Abbreviations of the American Association of Physics Teachers.

Many modern applications of thermodynamics are included in this book, for example, the Giauque temperature scale, the Onsager method of treating irreversible coupled flows and its application to a thermocouple, a treatment of dielectric phenomena, of the piezoelectric effect, and of second-order phase transitions, and almost the entire subject of low temperature physics. Chemical reactions are discussed in terms of the important variable, the "degree of reaction" in a manner similar to that of de Donder. The phase rule is derived carefully and discussed in some detail.

A list of the books which have been consulted and from which the author has profited greatly is given in the Bibliography. Particular mention should be made of the writings of Guggenheim and of Simon. It is a pleasure to acknowledge indebtedness to many colleagues and friends who have contributed ideas, corrections, problems, simplifications, and clarifications. Chief among these are Harold C. Berry, Henry A. Boorse, Joseph H. Keenan, Francis W. Sears, Henry Semat, Sir Francis Simon, and Hugh C. Wolfe.

MARK W. ZEMANSKY

Contents

Notation

Notation

$\mathcal{B}$	Magnetic induction
$\mathcal{E}$	Electromotive force
$\mathcal{F}$	Tension
$\mathcal{H}$	Magnetic field intensity
$\mathcal{R}$	Radiance
$\mathcal{S}$	Surface tension
$\mathcal{V}$	Velocity
$\mathcal{Y}$	Generalized force

Boldface Capitals

$\mathbf{G}$	Gibbs function of a heterogeneous system
$\mathbf{V}$	Volume of a heterogeneous system
$\mathbf{S}$	Entropy of a heterogeneous system

Special Symbols

đ	Inexact differential sign
ln	Natural logarithm
log	Common logarithm
T^*	Magnetic temperature

Greek Letters

α	Linear expansivity
β	Volume expansivity
γ	Ratio of heat capacities
δ	Linear compressibility
Δ	Finite difference
ϵ	Degree of reaction
ϵ_r	Relative permittivity (dielectric coefficient)
η	Efficiency, viscosity
θ	Absolute temperature
Θ	Debye characteristic temperature
λ	Wavelength
μ	Joule-Kelvin coefficient, chemical potential
ν	Stoichiometric coefficient
π	Peltier coefficient
ρ	Density
σ	Thomson coefficient, Stefan-Boltzmann constant
τ	Time, period
φ	Number of phases
ω	Coefficient of performance

1
Temperature

1.1. Macroscopic Point of View. The study of any special branch of physics starts with a separation of a restricted region of space or a finite portion of matter from its surroundings. The portion which is set aside (in the imagination) and on which the attention is focused is called the *system*, and everything outside the system which has a direct bearing on its behavior is known as the *surroundings*. When a system has been chosen, the next step is to describe it in terms of quantities that will be helpful in discussing the behavior of the system or its interactions with the surroundings, or both. There are in general two points of view that may be adopted, the *macroscopic* point of view and the *microscopic* point of view.

Let us take as a system the contents of a cylinder of an automobile engine. A chemical analysis would show a mixture of gasoline vapor and air before explosion, and after the mixture has been ignited there would be combustion products describable in terms of certain chemical compounds. A statement of the relative amounts of these substances is a description of the *composition* of the system. At any moment, the system whose composition has just been described occupies a certain *volume*, depending on the position of the piston. The volume can be easily measured and, in the laboratory, is recorded automatically by means of an appliance indirectly connected with the piston. Another quantity that is indispensable in the description of our system is the *pressure* of the gases in the cylinder. After explosion this pressure is large; after exhaust it is small. In the laboratory, a pressure gauge may be used to measure the changes of pressure and to make an automatic record as the engine operates. Finally, there is one more quantity without which we should have no adequate idea of the operation of the engine. This quantity is the *temperature;* as we shall see, in many instances, it can be measured just as simply as the other quantities.

We have described the materials in a cylinder of an automobile engine by specifying four quantities: composition, volume, pressure, and temperature. These quantities refer to the gross characteristics, or large-

1

scale properties, of the system and provide a *macroscopic description*. They are therefore called *macroscopic coordinates*. The quantities that must be specified to provide a macroscopic description of other systems are, of course, different; but macroscopic coordinates in general have the following characteristics in common:

1. They involve no special assumptions concerning the structure of matter.

2. Only a few coordinates are needed for a macroscopic description.

3. Macroscopic coordinates are suggested more or less directly by our sense perceptions.

4. Macroscopic coordinates can in general be directly measured.

In short, a macroscopic description of a system involves the specification of a *few fundamental measurable properties* of a system. The student will recognize that, in elementary physics, the macroscopic point of view is adopted in most cases, although no consistent attempt is made to adopt it at all times. To understand clearly the distinction between the macroscopic point of view and the microscopic, let us give a simple microscopic description of a gas in a containing vessel.

1.2. Microscopic Point of View. We shall assume that a gas consists of an enormous number N of particles called molecules, all having the same mass and each moving with a velocity independent of the others. The position of any molecule is specified by the three cartesian coordinates x, y, and z, and the velocity by the three components v_x, v_y, and v_z. Therefore, to describe the position and velocity of a molecule, six numbers are required. A microscopic description of the state of the gas consists of the specification of these six numbers for each of the N molecules. This may be accomplished in a manner that suggests Huygens' method in the elementary treatment of diffraction. The student will recall that, in the study of simple problems in diffraction, a wave front is subdivided into small regions called Fresnel zones and that the effect of the whole wave front at some point in space is obtained by considering the effect of each zone separately. In an analogous manner, we imagine a six-dimensional space called a *phase space* whose coordinates are x, y, z, v_x, v_y, v_z. Suppose the phase space is divided into a large number of small regions called *cells*. Each cell in the phase space corresponds to a limited region of position and velocity and therefore to a certain average energy.

A simple microscopic description of the gas is given by stating that

1. There are n_1 molecules in cell 1 with average energy e_1.

2. There are n_2 molecules in cell 2 with average energy e_2.

The total number of molecules is evidently equal to

$$N = n_1 + n_2 + \cdots ,$$

and the total energy U is given by

$$U = n_1 e_1 + n_2 e_2 + \cdots .$$

This type of description is used in an important branch of physics called *statistical mechanics*. It is not necessary to pursue the matter further to understand that a microscopic description involves the following characteristics:

1. Assumptions are made concerning the structure of matter; e.g., the existence of molecules is assumed.

2. Many quantities must be specified.

3. The quantities specified are not suggested by our sense perceptions.

4. These quantities cannot be measured.

1.3. Macroscopic vs. Microscopic. Although it might seem that the two points of view are hopelessly different and incompatible, there is nevertheless a relation between them; and when both points of view are applied to the same system, they must agree in the end. The relation between the two points of view lies in the fact that the few directly measurable properties whose specification constitutes the macroscopic description are really averages over a period of time of a large number of microscopic characteristics. For example, the macroscopic quantity, pressure, is the average rate of change of momentum due to all the molecular collisions made on a unit of area. Pressure, however, is a property that is perceived by our senses. We feel the effects of pressure. Pressure was experienced, measured, and used long before physicists had reason to believe in the existence of molecular impacts. If the molecular theory is changed or discarded at some time in the future, the concept of pressure will still remain and will still mean the same thing to all normal human beings. Herein lies an important distinction between the macroscopic and microscopic points of view. The few measurable macroscopic properties are as sure as our senses. They will remain unchanged as long as our senses remain the same. The microscopic point of view, however, goes much further than our senses. It postulates the existence of molecules, their motion, collisions, etc. It is constantly being changed, and we can never be sure that the assumptions are justified until we have compared some deduction made on the basis of these assumptions with a similar deduction based on the macroscopic point of view.

1.4. Scope of Thermodynamics. It has been emphasized that a description of the gross characteristics of a system by means of a few of its measurable properties, suggested more or less directly by our sense perceptions, constitutes a macroscopic description. Such descriptions are the starting point of all investigations in all branches of physics. For example, in dealing with the mechanics of a rigid body, the macroscopic point of view is adopted in that only the external aspects of the rigid body are considered. The position of its center of mass is specified with reference to coordinate axes at a particular time. Position and time and a combination of both, such as velocity, constitute some of the macroscopic quantities used in mechanics and are called *mechanical coordinates*. The mechanical coordinates serve to determine the potential and the kinetic energy of the rigid body with reference to the coordinate axes, i.e., the kinetic and the potential energy of the body as a whole. These two types of energy constitute the *external*, or *mechanical*, *energy* of the rigid body. It is the purpose of mechanics to find such relations between the position coordinates and the time as are consistent with Newton's laws of motion.

In thermodynamics, however, the attention is directed to the *interior* of a system. A macroscopic point of view is adopted, but only those macroscopic quantities are considered which have a bearing on the internal state of a system. It is the function of experiment to determine the quantities that are necessary and sufficient for such a purpose. *Macroscopic quantities having a bearing on the internal state of a system are called thermodynamic coordinates.* Such coordinates serve to determine the *internal energy* of a system. It is the purpose of thermodynamics to find general relations among the thermodynamic coordinates that are consistent with the fundamental laws of thermodynamics.

A system that may be described in terms of thermodynamic coordinates is called a *thermodynamic system*. In engineering, the important thermodynamic systems are a gas, such as air; a vapor, such as steam; a mixture, such as gasoline vapor and air; and a vapor in contact with its liquid, such as liquid and vaporized ammonia. Chemical thermodynamics deals with the above systems and, in addition, with solids, surface films, and electric cells. Physical thermodynamics includes, in addition to the above, such systems as stretched wires, electric capacitors, thermocouples, and magnetic substances.

1.5. Thermal Equilibrium. We have seen that a macroscopic description of a gaseous mixture may be given by specifying such quantities as the composition, the mass, the pressure, and the volume. Experiment shows that, for a given composition and for a constant mass, many different values of pressure and volume are possible. If the pressure is kept constant, the volume may vary over a wide range of values, and vice versa. In other words, the pressure and the volume are independent coordinates. Similarly, experiment shows that, for a wire of constant mass, the tension and the length are independent coordinates, whereas, in the case of a surface film, the surface tension and the area may be varied independently. Some systems that, at first sight, seem quite complicated, such as an electric cell with two different electrodes and an electrolyte, may still be described with the aid of only two independent coordinates. On the other hand, some systems composed of a number of homogeneous parts require the specification of two independent coordinates for each homogeneous part. Details of various thermodynamic systems and their thermodynamic coordinates will be given in Chap. 2. For the present, to simplify our discussion, we shall deal only with systems of constant mass and composition, each requiring *only one pair* of independent coordinates for its description. This involves no essential loss of generality and results in a considerable saving of words. In referring to any nonspecified system, we shall use the symbols Y and X for the pair of independent coordinates.

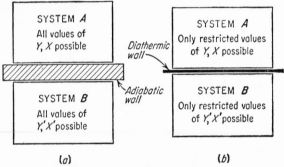

FIG. 1.1. Properties of adiabatic and diathermic walls.

A state of a system in which Y and X have definite values which remain constant so long as the external conditions are unchanged is called an *equilibrium* state. Experiment shows that the existence of an equilibrium state in one system depends on the proximity of other systems and on the nature of the wall separating them. Walls are said to be either adiabatic or diathermic. If a wall is *adiabatic* [see Fig. 1.1(a)], a state Y, X for system A and Y', X' for system B may coexist as equilibrium states for *any* attainable values of the four quantities, provided only that the wall is able to withstand the stress associated with the difference between the two sets of coordinates. Thick layers of wood, asbestos, felt, etc., are good experimental approximations to adiabatic walls. If the two systems are separated by a *diathermic* wall [see Fig. 1.1(b)], the values of Y, X and Y', X' will change spontaneously until an equilibrium state of the combined system is attained. The two systems are then said to be in *thermal equilibrium* with each other. The commonest diathermic wall is a thin metallic sheet. *Thermal equilibrium is the state achieved by two (or more) systems, characterized by restricted values of the coordinates of the systems, after they have been in communication with one another through a diathermic wall.*

Imagine two systems A and B separated from each other by an adiabatic wall but each in contact with a third system C through diathermic walls, the whole assembly being surrounded by an adiabatic wall as shown in Fig. 1.2(a). Experiment shows that the two systems will come to thermal equilibrium with the third and that no further change will occur if the adiabatic wall separating A and B is then replaced by a diathermic wall [Fig. 1.2(b)]. If, instead of allowing both systems A and B to come to equilibrium with C at the same time, we first have equilibrium between A and C and then equilibrium between B and C (the state of system C

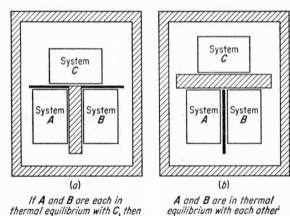

(a)

**If A and B are each in
thermal equilibrium with C, then**

(b)

**A and B are in thermal
equilibrium with each other**

Fig. 1.2. The zeroth law of thermodynamics. (Adiabatic walls are designated by cross shading, diathermic walls by heavy lines.)

being the same in both cases), then, when A and B are brought into communication through a diathermic wall, they will be found to be in thermal equilibrium. We shall use the expression "two systems are in thermal equilibrium" to mean that the two systems are in states such that, if the two *were* connected through a diathermic wall, the combined system *would be* in thermal equilibrium.

These experimental facts may then be stated concisely in the following form: *Two systems in thermal equilibrium with a third are in thermal equilibrium with each other.* Following R. H. Fowler, we shall call this postulate the *zeroth law of thermodynamics.*

1.6. Temperature Concept. Consider a system A in the state Y_1, X_1 in thermal equilibrium with a system B in the state Y_1', X_1'. If system A is removed and its state changed, there will be found another state Y_2, X_2 in which it is in thermal equilibrium with the *original* state Y_1', X_1' of system B. Experiment shows that there exists a whole set of states $Y_1, X_1; Y_2, X_2; Y_3, X_3; \ldots$ every one of which is in thermal equi-

librium with this *same* state Y_1', X_1' of system B and which, by the zeroth
law, are in thermal equilibrium with one another.   We shall suppose that
all such states, when plotted on a Y-X diagram, lie on a curve such as I in
Fig. 1.3, which we shall call an *isotherm*.   *An isotherm is the locus of all
points representing states at which a system is in thermal equilibrium with
one state of another system.*   We make no assumption as to the continuity
of the isotherm, although experiments on simple systems indicate usually
that at least a portion of an isotherm is a continuous curve.

Similarly, with regard to system B, we find a set of states Y_1', X_1';
Y_2', X_2'; . . . all of which are in thermal equilibrium with one state
(Y_1, X_1) of system A, and therefore in thermal equilibrium with one
another.   These states are plotted on the Y'-X' diagram of Fig. 1.3 and
lie on the isotherm I'.   From the zeroth law, it follows that all the states

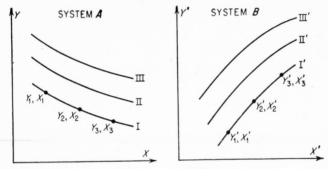

Fig. 1.3. Isotherms of two different systems.

on isotherm I of system A are in thermal equilibrium with all the states
on isotherm I' of system B.   We shall call curves I and I' *corresponding
isotherms* of the two systems.

If the experiments outlined above are repeated with different starting
conditions, another set of states of system A lying on curve II may be
found, every one of which is in thermal equilibrium with every state of
system B lying on curve II'.   In this way, a family of isotherms, I, II,
III, etc., of system A and a corresponding family I', II', III', etc., of
system B may be found.   Furthermore, by repeated applications of the
zeroth law, corresponding isotherms of still other systems C, D, etc.,
may be obtained.

All states of corresponding isotherms of all systems have something
in common, namely, that they are in thermal equilibrium with one
another.   The systems themselves, in these states, may be said to possess a property that ensures their being in thermal equilibrium with one
another.   We call this property *temperature*.   *The temperature of a system is a property that determines whether or not a system is in thermal equilibrium with other systems.*

The temperature of all systems in thermal equilibrium may be represented by a number. The establishment of a temperature scale is merely the adoption of a set of rules for assigning one number to one set of corresponding isotherms and a different number to a different set of corresponding isotherms. Once this is done, the necessary and sufficient condition for thermal equilibrium between two systems is that they have the same temperature. Also, when the temperatures are different, we may be sure that the systems are not in thermal equilibrium.

The preceding operational treatment of the concept of temperature merely expresses the fundamental idea that the temperature of a system is a property which eventually attains the same value as that of other systems when all these systems are put in contact or separated by thin metallic walls within an enclosure of thick asbestos walls. The student will recognize that this concept is identical with the everyday idea of temperature as a measure of the hotness or coldness of a system, since, so far as our senses may be relied upon, the hotness of all objects becomes the same after they have been together long enough. However, it was necessary to express this simple idea in technical language in order to be able to establish a rational set of rules for measuring temperature and also to provide a solid foundation for the study of thermodynamics and statistical mechanics.

1.7. Measurement of Temperature. To establish an empirical temperature scale, we select some system with coordinates Y and X as a

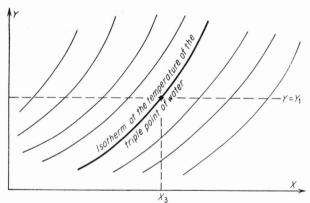

Fig. 1.4. Setting up a temperature scale involves the assignment of numerical values to the isotherms of an arbitrarily chosen standard system, or thermometer.

standard, which we call a *thermometer*, and adopt a set of rules for assigning a numerical value to the temperature associated with each of its isotherms. To every other system in thermal equilibrium with the thermometer, we assign the same number for the temperature. The simplest

procedure is to choose any convenient path in the Y-X plane such as that
shown in Fig. 1.4 by the dashed line $Y = Y_1$ which intersects the isotherms at points each of which has the same Y coordinate but a different X coordinate. The temperature associated with each isotherm is
then taken to be a convenient function of the X at this intersection point.
The coordinate X is called the *thermometric property*, and the form of the
thermometric function $\theta(X)$ determines the temperature scale. There are
five important kinds of thermometer, each with its own thermometric
property, as shown in Table 1.1.

TABLE 1.1. THERMOMETERS AND THERMOMETRIC PROPERTIES

Thermometer	Thermometric property	Symbol
Gas kept at constant volume....................	Pressure	P
Gas kept at constant pressure..................	Volume	V
Electric resistor (under constant pressure and tension).......................................	Electric resistance	R
Thermocouple (under constant pressure and tension).......................................	Thermal emf	$\mathscr{E}$
Liquid column in a glass capillary..............	Length	L

Let X stand for any one of the thermometric properties listed in
Table 1.1, and let us arbitrarily choose for the temperature common to
the thermometer *and to all systems in thermal equilibrium with it* the following linear function of X:

$$\theta(X) = aX \qquad (\text{const. } Y),$$

where a is an arbitrary constant. It follows that two temperatures on
this "linear X scale" are to each other as the ratio of the corresponding
X's, or

$$\frac{\theta(X_1)}{\theta(X_2)} = \frac{X_1}{X_2}. \tag{1}$$

To determine the temperature $\theta(X)$ of a system, either of two procedures
may be adopted:

1. *Method in Use before 1954.* Apply Eq. (1) to a thermometer placed
first in contact with the system whose temperature $\theta(X)$ is to be measured, and then in contact with an arbitrarily chosen standard system in
an easily reproducible state where the temperature is $\theta(X_1)$. Thus

$$\frac{\theta(X_1)}{\theta(X)} = \frac{X_1}{X}. \tag{2}$$

Apply Eq. (1) to the thermometer at the temperature $\theta(X)$, and at the
temperature of another arbitrarily chosen standard system in another

easily reproducible state where the temperature is $\theta(X_2)$. Thus

$$\frac{\theta(X_2)}{\theta(X)} = \frac{X_2}{X}. \tag{3}$$

Subtracting Eq. (3) from Eq. (2),

$$\frac{\theta(X_1) - \theta(X_2)}{\theta(X)} = \frac{X_1 - X_2}{X}$$

and solving for $\theta(X)$, we get

$$\theta(X) = \frac{\theta(X_1) - \theta(X_2)}{X_1 - X_2} X \qquad (\text{const. } Y).$$

Now assign an arbitrary number of "degrees" to the temperature interval $\theta(X_1) - \theta(X_2)$. Then $\theta(X)$ can be calculated from the three measurements: X, X_1, X_2.

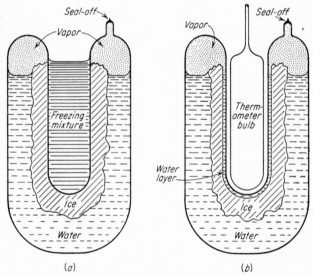

FIG. 1.5. Triple-point cell, (a) with freezing mixture in the central well to freeze a layer of ice; (b) with a thermometer in the well, which melts a thin layer of ice nearby.

An easily reproducible state of an arbitrarily chosen standard system is called a fixed point. Before 1954 there were two fixed points: (1) the temperature at which pure ice coexisted in equilibrium with air-saturated water at one atmosphere pressure (the ice point); and (2) the temperature of equilibrium between pure water and pure steam at one atmosphere pressure (the steam point). The temperature interval between these two fixed points was chosen to be 100 degrees. A critical discussion of this abandoned method will be given in Art. 1.12.

    2. *Method after 1954. Only one fixed point is chosen,* namely, the

temperature and pressure at which ice, liquid water, and water vapor coexist in equilibrium, a state known as the *triple point of water*. We choose arbitrarily for the temperature at this fixed point 273.16 degrees Kelvin, abbreviated 273.16°K. (The reason for the use of Kelvin's name will be made clear later.) Thus, designating the triple point of water by the subscript 3, we have, from Eq. (1),

$$\frac{\theta(X)}{\theta(X_3)} = \frac{X}{X_3},$$

with

$$\theta(X_3) = 273.16°K.$$

Hence,

$$\theta(X) = 273.16° \frac{X}{X_3} \quad (\text{const. } Y).$$

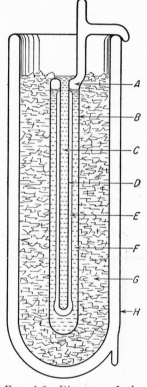

The temperature of the triple point of water is the *standard fixed point* of thermometry. To achieve the triple point, water of the highest purity is distilled into a vessel depicted schematically in Fig. 1.5. When all air has been removed, the vessel is sealed off. With the aid of a freezing mixture in the inner well, a layer of ice is formed around the well, as shown in Fig. 1.5(*a*). When the freezing mixture is replaced by a thermometer bulb, a thin layer of ice is melted nearby, as shown in Fig. 1.5(*b*). So long as the solid, liquid, and vapor phases coexist in equilibrium, the system is at the triple point. The actual shape of the apparatus used by the U.S. National Bureau of Standards is shown in Fig. 1.6.

Fig. 1.6. Diagram of the NBS triple-point cell (*B, D*) in use in an ice bath (*G*) within a Dewar flask (*H*). *A*, water vapor; *C*, thermometer well; *E*, ice mantle; *F*, liquid water.

1.8. Comparison of Thermometers. Applying the principles outlined in the preceding paragraphs to the five thermometers listed in Table 1.1, we have five different ways of measuring temperature. Thus, for a gas at constant volume,

$$\theta(P) = 273.16° \frac{P}{P_3} \quad (\text{const. } V);$$

for a gas at constant pressure,

$$\theta(V) = 273.16° \frac{V}{V_3} \quad (\text{const. } P);$$

for an electric resistor,

$$\theta(R) = 273.16° \frac{R}{R_3};$$

for a thermocouple,

$$\theta(\mathcal{E}) = 273.16° \frac{\mathcal{E}}{\mathcal{E}_3};$$

and for a liquid-in-glass thermometer,

$$\theta(L) = 273.16° \frac{L}{L_3}.$$

Now imagine a series of tests in which the temperature of a given system is measured simultaneously with each of the five thermometers. Results of such a test would show that there is considerable difference among the readings of the various thermometers. Further tests show that different varieties of the same kind of thermometer yield different results. The smallest variation, however, is found among different gas thermometers. In particular, the constant-volume hydrogen thermometer and the constant-volume helium thermometer agree more closely than the others. For this reason a gas is chosen as the standard thermometric substance.

1.9. Gas Thermometer. A schematic diagram of a constant-volume gas thermometer is shown in Fig. 1.7. The materials, construction, and dimensions differ in the various bureaus and institutes throughout the world where these instruments are used and depend on the nature of the gas and the temperature range for which the thermometer is intended. The gas is contained in the bulb B, which communicates with the mercury column M through a capillary. The volume of the gas is kept constant by adjusting the height of the mercury column M until the

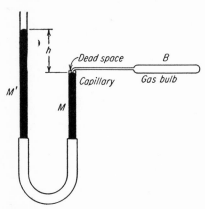

FIG. 1.7. Constant-volume gas thermometer.

mercury level just touches the tip of the projection of the capillary into the space above M, known as the "dead space," or "nuisance volume." The mercury column M is adjusted by raising or lowering the tube M'. The difference in height h between the two mercury columns M and M' is measured when the bulb is surrounded by the system whose temperature is to be measured, and when it is surrounded by water at the triple point. It is clear that the pressure of the gas under any conditions is given by

$$P = \text{atmospheric pressure} \pm h,$$

the plus sign to be used when the top of M' is above the top of M.

The various values of the pressure must be corrected to take account of the following sources of error:

1. The gas present in the dead space (and in any other nuisance volumes) is at a temperature different from that in the bulb.

2. The gas in the capillary connecting the bulb with the manometer has a temperature gradient, i.e., it is not at a uniform temperature.

3. The bulb, capillary, and nuisance volumes undergo changes of volume when the temperature and pressure change.

4. If the diameter of the capillary is comparable with the mean free path of the molecules of the gas, a pressure gradient exists in the capillary (Knudsen effect).

5. Some gas is adsorbed on the walls of the bulb and capillary, the lower the temperature, the greater the adsorption.

6. There are effects due to temperature and compressibility of the mercury in the manometer.

Some of these sources of error may be eliminated by proper design of the gas thermometer. Others are taken into account by elaborate calculations. Some of these corrections will be made clear in Chap. 6 when the properties of gases are discussed more fully. For the present, let us assume that the corrections have been made and that the temperature is calculated from the equation

$$\theta(P) = 273.16° \frac{P}{P_3} \qquad (\text{const. } V).$$

The constant-volume gas thermometer is superior to the constant-pressure instrument with regard to simplicity of construction, ease of operation, and reliability of correction, and therefore the constant-volume thermometer is used almost exclusively in present-day work.

1.10. Ideal Gas Temperature. Suppose that an amount of gas is introduced into the bulb of a constant-volume gas thermometer so that the pressure P_3, when the bulb is surrounded by water at its triple point, is equal to 1000 mm Hg. Keeping the volume V constant, suppose the following procedures are carried out:

1. Surrounding the bulb with steam condensing at 1 atm pressure, determine the gas pressure P_s and calculate

$$\theta(P_s) = 273.16° \frac{P_s}{1000}.$$

2. Remove some of the gas so that P_3 has a smaller value, say 500 mm Hg. Determine the new value of P_s and calculate a new value

$$\theta(P_s) = 273.16° \frac{P_s}{500}.$$

3. Continue reducing the amount of gas in the bulb so that P_3 and P_s have smaller and smaller values, P_3 having values of, say, 250 mm Hg, 100 mm Hg, etc. At *each* value of P_3, calculate the corresponding $\theta(P_s)$.

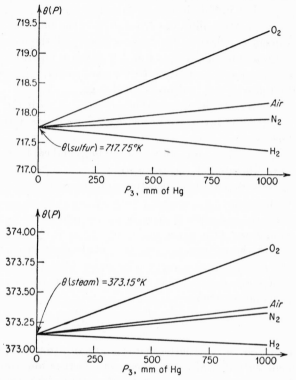

FIG. 1.8. Readings of a constant-volume gas thermometer for the temperature of condensing steam and for that of condensing sulfur, when different gases are used at various values of P_3.

4. Plot $\theta(P_s)$ against P_3 and extrapolate the resulting curve to the axis where $P_3 = 0$. Read from the graph

$$\lim_{P_3 \to 0} \theta(P_s).$$

The results of a series of tests of this sort are plotted in Fig. 1.8 for four different gases in order to measure $\theta(P)$ not only of condensing steam but also of condensing sulfur. The graph conveys the information that, although the readings of a constant-volume gas thermometer depend upon the nature of the gas at ordinary values of P_3, *all gases indicate the same temperature as P_3 is lowered and made to approach zero.*

A similar series of tests may be made with a constant-pressure gas thermometer. The constant pressure P may first be taken to be 1000 mm Hg, then 500 mm Hg, etc., and at each value of P, the corresponding value of $\theta(V)$ may be calculated. Again, experiment shows that all gases indicate the same value of $\theta(V)$ as P approaches zero.

We therefore define the *ideal gas temperature* θ by either of the two equations

$$
\theta =
\begin{cases}
273.16° \lim_{P_3 \to 0} \left(\dfrac{P}{P_3} \right) & \text{(const. } V\text{)}, \\[2ex]
273.16° \lim_{P \to 0} \left(\dfrac{V}{V_3} \right) & \text{(const. } P\text{)}.
\end{cases}
$$

Although the ideal gas temperature scale is independent of the properties of any one particular gas, it still depends on the properties of gases in general. To measure a low temperature, a gas must be used at that low temperature. The lowest ideal gas temperature that can be measured with a gas thermometer is about 1°K, provided low-pressure helium is used. *The temperature* $\theta = 0$ *remains as yet undefined.*

In Chap. 9 the Kelvin temperature scale, which is independent of the properties of any particular substance, will be developed. It will be shown that, in the temperature region in which a gas thermometer may be used, the ideal gas scale and the Kelvin scale are identical. In anticipation of this result we write °K after an ideal gas temperature. It will also be shown in Chap. 9 how the absolute zero of temperature is defined on the Kelvin scale. Until then, the phrase "absolute zero" will have no meaning. It should be remarked that the statement, found in so many textbooks of elementary physics, that, at the temperature $\theta = 0$, all molecular activity ceases is entirely erroneous. First, such a statement involves an assumption connecting the purely macroscopic concept of temperature and the microscopic concept of molecular motion. If we want our theory to be general, this is precisely the sort of assumption that must be avoided. Second, when it is necessary in statistical mechanics to correlate temperature to molecular activity, it is found that classical statistical mechanics must be modified with the aid of quantum mechanics and that, when this modification is carried out, the molecules of a substance at absolute zero have a *finite* amount of kinetic energy, known as the zero-point energy.

1.11. Celsius Temperature Scale. The Celsius temperature scale employs a degree of the same magnitude as that of the ideal gas scale but its zero point is shifted so that *the Celsius temperature of the triple point of water is* 0.01 *degree Celsius*, abbreviated 0.01°C. Thus, if t denotes the

Celsius temperature,

$$t = \theta - 273.15°.$$

Thus, the Celsius temperature t_s at which steam condenses at 1 atm pressure is

$$t_s = \theta_s - 273.15°,$$

and reading θ_s from Fig. 1.8,

$$t_s = 373.15° - 273.15°$$

or $\qquad\qquad t_s = 100.00°C.$

Helium is the most useful gas for thermometric purposes for two reasons. At high temperatures helium does not diffuse through platinum, whereas hydrogen does. Furthermore, helium becomes a liquid at a temperature lower than any other gas, and therefore a helium thermometer may be used to measure temperatures lower than those which can be measured with any other gas thermometer. The accurate measurement of an ideal gas or Celsius temperature requires months of painstaking

TABLE 1.2. TEMPERATURES OF FIXED POINTS

Fixed points		Temp., °C	Temp., °K
Standard	**Triple point of water**	**0.01**	**273.16**
Basic	NBP of oxygen (oxygen point)	−182.97	90.18
	Equilibrium of ice and air-saturated water (ice point)	0.00	273.15
	NBP of water (steam point)	100.00	373.15
	NBP of sulfur (sulfur point)	444.60	717.75
	NMP of antimony (antimony point)	630.50	903.65
	NMP of silver (silver point)	960.80	1233.95
	NMP of gold (gold point)	1063.00	1336.15
Secondary	NBP of helium	−268.93	4.22
	NBP of hydrogen	−252.78	20.37
	NBP of neon	−246.09	27.06
	NBP of nitrogen	−195.81	77.34
	NMP of mercury	−38.86	234.29
	Transition point of sodium sulfate	32.38	305.53
	NBP of naphthalene	217.96	491.11
	NMP of tin	231.85	505.00
	NBP of benzophenone	305.90	579.05
	NMP of cadmium	320.90	594.05
	NMP of lead	327.30	600.45
	NMP of zinc	419.50	692.65

laboratory work and mathematical computation and, when completed, is an international event. Such work is published in a physical journal and eventually is listed in tables of physical constants. The temperatures of the normal boiling points (NBP) and normal melting points (NMP) of a number of materials have been measured, and the results are tabulated in Table 1.2. The fixed points designated in the table as basic are used to calibrate other thermometers in a manner that will be described in Art. 1.15.

1.12. Temperature Scales before 1954. The temperature scales in use before 1954 required for their specification two fixed points, the ice point and the steam point. The difference between the steam point and the ice point temperatures was arbitrarily assigned the value of 100 deg. All other thermometric principles were the same as those just described. Thus, the ratio of the ideal gas steam temperature θ_s and the ideal gas ice temperature θ_i was expressed in terms of measurements with a constant-volume gas thermometer in the usual way,

$$\frac{\theta_s}{\theta_i} = \lim_{P_i \to 0} \left(\frac{P_s}{P_i}\right) \qquad \text{(const. } V\text{).}$$

Subtracting unity from both sides of this equation, we get

$$\frac{\theta_s - \theta_i}{\theta_i} = \lim_{P_i \to 0} \left(\frac{P_s}{P_i}\right) - 1,$$

and substituting for $\theta_s - \theta_i$ its arbitrarily assigned value of 100°, the result is obtained that

$$\theta_i = \frac{100°}{\lim\limits_{P_i \to 0} \left(\dfrac{P_s}{P_i}\right) - 1}.$$

Hundreds of attempts were made all over the world to measure θ_i with great accuracy—without much success. The main difficulty was the realization of the equilibrium between air-saturated water and pure ice required by the definition of the ice point. When ice melts, it surrounds itself with pure water and prevents intimate contact of ice and air-saturated water. The steam point was also very sensitive to minute changes of pressure. As a result, values of θ_i seemed to lie between the limits 273.13 and 273.17°, the British and Dutch physicists favoring low values, while the German and the American physicists favored the higher ones.

If θ is the ideal gas temperature of a system whose temperature is to be measured, then

$$\frac{\theta}{\theta_i} = \lim_{P_i \to 0} \left(\frac{P}{P_i}\right),$$

and, beside the unavoidable error in the measurement of the right-hand side, there was still the uncertainty in the value of θ_i.

The same uncertainty existed in the Celsius temperature t (formerly called the "centigrade" temperature in America and in Great Britain), where t was defined by the equation

$$t = \theta - \theta_i.$$

To convert Celsius temperatures into ideal gas temperatures, or vice versa, was quite unsatisfactory, particularly at very low temperatures. Thus, suppose the normal boiling point of helium was reported to be $t = -268.93°C$, and no value of θ_i was given. Using the low value of θ_i, θ was found to be $4.20°K$, whereas with the higher value of θ_i, θ would be $4.24°K$, a discrepancy of 1 per cent. In the important temperature range below $-272°C$, the percentage error became seriously large. The choice of a value of θ_i was often a question of personal judgment rather than exact measurement. If both t and θ_i were measured in the same laboratory, different apparatus was needed for each measurement, for a cryostat designed to hold liquid helium must have quite a different design from one that has to contain ice and steam.

The idea of defining a temperature scale with the aid of only one fixed point with an arbitrary choice of a *universal constant* for the temperature at this point was first suggested by Lord Kelvin in 1854, but it was not regarded as expedient at the time. The idea was revived in 1939 by W. F. Giauque, professor of chemistry at the University of California, and supported most vigorously by the physicists and chemists engaged in low-temperature research throughout the world.

In May, 1948, the Advisory Committee on Thermometry of the International Committee on Weights and Measures chose the value $\theta_i = 273.15°K$ for the ice point ($273.16°K$ for the triple point of water) for consideration by the International Union of Physicists. The Union, at its meeting in July, 1948, made the definite and positive recommendation that the Giauque proposal be adopted to replace the old scale. When the International Committee on Weights and Measures met in October, 1948, to consider this recommendation, it was felt that the advisory committee should study the matter further and report at the next meeting in 1954.

At the Tenth Conference on Weights and Measures in Paris during the summer of 1954, the Giauque proposal was passed. As we have seen, the single fixed point was chosen to be the triple point of water which was set arbitrarily at the value $273.16°K$.

1.13. Electric Resistance Thermometry. When the resistance thermometer is in the form of a long, fine wire, it is usually wound around a thin frame constructed so as to avoid excessive strains in the wire when the wire contracts upon cooling. In special circumstances the wire may be wound on or embedded in the material whose temperature is to be measured. In the very-low-temperature range, resistance thermometers often consist of small carbon composition radio resistors or a thin dab of colloidal carbon on an insulating surface. These may be bonded to the surface of the substance whose temperature is to be measured or placed in a hole drilled for that purpose.

It is customary to measure the resistance by maintaining a known constant current in the thermometer and measuring the potential difference across it with the aid of a very sensitive potentiometer. A typical circuit is shown in Fig. 1.9. The current is held constant by adjusting a

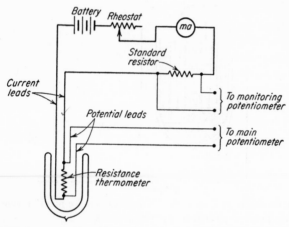

FIG. 1.9. Circuit for measuring the resistance of a resistance thermometer through which a constant current is maintained.

rheostat so that the pd across a standard resistor in series with the thermometer, as observed with a monitoring potentiometer, remains constant.

The platinum resistance thermometer may be used for very accurate work within the range of -200 to $1200°C$. It is rather slow, however, because of the mass of metal that must come to thermal equilibrium. The calibration of the instrument involves the measurement of R_{Pt} at various known temperatures and the representation of the results by an empiric formula. In a restricted range, the following quadratic equation is often used:

$$R_{Pt} = R_0(1 + At + Bt^2),$$

where R_0 is the resistance of the platinum wire when it is surrounded by melting ice and A and B are constants.

1.14. Thermocouple. The correct use of a thermocouple is shown in Fig. 1.10. The thermal emf is measured with a potentiometer, which, as a rule, must be placed at some distance from the system whose temperature is to be measured.   The reference junction, therefore, is placed near the test junction and consists of two connections with copper wire, maintained at the temperature of melting ice.   This arrangement allows the use of copper wires for connection to the potentiometer.   The binding posts of the potentiometer are usually made of brass, and therefore at the potentiometer there are two copper-brass thermocouples.   If the two binding posts are at the same temperature, these two copper-brass thermocouples introduce no error.

A thermocouple is calibrated by measuring the thermal emf at various known temperatures, the reference junction being kept at 0°C.   The

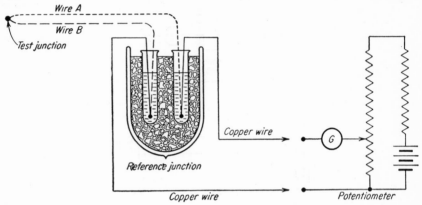

FIG. 1.10. Thermocouple of wires A and B with a reference junction consisting of two junctions with copper, connected to a potentiometer.

results of such measurements on most thermocouples can usually be represented by a cubic equation as follows:

$$\mathcal{E} = a + bt + ct^2 + dt^3,$$

where $\mathcal{E}$ is the thermal emf and the constants a, b, c, and d are different for each thermocouple.   Within a restricted range of temperature, a quadratic equation is often sufficient.   The range of a thermocouple depends upon the materials of which it is composed.   A platinum-platinum-rhodium couple has a range of 0 to 1600°C.   The advantage of a thermocouple is that it comes to thermal equilibrium with the system whose temperature is to be measured quite rapidly, because its mass is small.   It therefore follows temperature changes easily.

1.15. International Temperature Scale.   At the meeting of the Seventh General Conference of Weights and Measures in 1927, at which 31 nations were represented, an international temperature scale was adopted, not to replace the Celsius or ideal gas scales, but to provide a scale that could be easily and rapidly used to calibrate scientific and industrial instruments. Slight refinements were incorporated into the scale in a revision adopted in 1948. The international scale agrees with the Celsius scale at the basic fixed points listed in Table 1.2. At temperatures between these fixed points the departure from the Celsius scale is small enough to be neglected in most practical work. The temperature interval from the oxygen point to the gold point is divided into three main parts, as follows:

1. *From 0 to 660°C.* A platinum resistance thermometer with a platinum wire whose diameter must lie between the limits 0.05 and 0.20 mm is used, and the temperature is given by the formula

$$R_t = R_0(1 + At + Bt^2),$$

where the constants R_0, A, and B are determined by measurements at the ice point, steam point, and sulphur point.

2. *From −190 to 0°C.* The same platinum resistance thermometer is used and the temperature is given by the formula

$$R_t = R_0[1 + At + Bt^2 + C(t - 100)t^3].$$

R_0, A, and B are the same as before, and C is determined from one measurement at the oxygen point.

3. *From 660 to 1063°C.* A thermocouple, one wire of which is made of platinum, the other being an alloy of 90 per cent platinum and 10 per cent rhodium, is maintained with one junction at 0°C. The diameter of each wire must lie between 0.35 and 0.65 mm. The temperature is given by the formula

$$\mathcal{E} = a + bt + ct^2,$$

where a, b, and c, are determined from measurements at the antimony point, silver point, and gold point.

For temperatures higher than the gold point, an optical method is used. The intensity of the radiation of any convenient wavelength is compared with the intensity of radiation of the same wavelength emitted by a black body at the gold point. The temperature is then calculated with the aid of Planck's radiation law.

1.16. Fahrenheit Scale. The fixed points of the Fahrenheit scale were originally chosen to be the temperature of a freezing mixture of salt, ice, and salt solution at atmospheric pressure, 0°F, and the temperature of the human body, designated as 96°F. After a while the fixed points were changed to the ice point and the steam point, designated as 32°F and 212°F, respectively. Now that there is only one standard fixed point, the Fahrenheit scale is presumably defined by a relation between the so-called "absolute Fahrenheit" temperature or "Rankine" temperature θ_F and the ideal gas temperature θ.   Thus

$$\theta_F = \tfrac{9}{5}\theta.$$

The Fahrenheit temperature t_F, corresponding to the Celsius temperature, is presumably the difference between θ_F and some arbitrary constant which, at the present writing, has not yet been chosen.   In the past the relation that was used was

$$t_F = \theta_F - 459.69°.$$

PROBLEMS

1.1. The limiting value of the ratio of the pressures of a gas at the steam point and at the triple point of water when the gas is kept at constant volume is found to be 1.36605.   What is the ideal gas temperature of the steam point?

1.2. The resistance of a platinum wire is found to be 11.000 ohms at the ice point, 15.247 ohms at the steam point, and 28.887 ohms at the sulphur point.   Find the constants A and B in the equation

$$R = R_0(1 + At + Bt^2),$$

and plot R against t in the range from 0 to 660°C.

1.3. When the reference junction of a thermocouple is kept at the ice point and the test junction is at the Celsius temperature t, the emf $\mathcal{E}$ of the thermocouple is given by the equation

$$\mathcal{E} = \alpha t + \beta t^2$$

where $\alpha = 0.20$ mv/deg and $\beta = -5.0 \times 10^{-4}$ mv/deg².

(a) Compute the emf when $t = -100°C$, 200°C, 400°C, and 500°C, and draw a graph of $\mathcal{E}$ against t in this range.

(b) Suppose the emf $\mathcal{E}$ is taken as a thermometric property and that a temperature scale t^* is defined by the linear equation

$$t^* = a\mathcal{E} + b,$$

and that $t^* = 0$ at the ice point and $t^* = 100°$ at the steam point.   Find the numerical values of a and b, and draw a graph of $\mathcal{E}$ against t^*.

(c) Find the values of t^* when $t = -100°C$, 200°C, 400°C, and 500°C, and draw a graph of t^* against t.

(d) Compare the Celsius scale with the t^* scale.

1.4. It will be shown in Chap. 6 that, for the same number of moles of gas at the same temperature,

$$\lim_{P \to 0} (PV) = \text{a universal constant}$$

for all gases.   Show how this fact may be used to set up a temperature scale (a) using the triple point of water as the only fixed point; (b) using both the ice point and the steam point as fixed points.

1.5. When the ice point and the steam point are chosen as fixed points with 100 deg between them, the ideal gas temperature of the ice point may be written

$$\theta_i = \frac{100}{r_s - 1},$$

where $r_s = \lim (P_s/P_i)$ at const. V.

(*a*) Show that the fractional error in θ_i produced by an error in r_s is very nearly 3.73 times the fractional error in r_s, or

$$\frac{d\theta_i}{\theta_i} = 3.73\,\frac{dr_s}{r_s}.$$

Any ideal gas temperature may be written

$$\theta = \theta_i r,$$

where $r = \lim (P/P_i)$ at const. V.

(*b*) Show that the fractional error in θ is

$$\frac{d\theta}{\theta} = \frac{dr}{r} + 3.73\,\frac{dr_s}{r_s}.$$

(*c*) Now that there is only one fixed point at which the ideal gas temperature is a universal constant, show that the fractional error in θ is

$$\frac{d\theta}{\theta} = \frac{dr}{r},$$

where $r = \lim (P/P_3)$ at const. V.

2

Thermodynamic Systems

2.1. Thermodynamic Equilibrium. Suppose that experiments have been performed on a thermodynamic system and that the coordinates necessary and sufficient for a macroscopic description have been determined. When these coordinates change in any way whatsoever, either spontaneously or by virtue of outside influence, the system is said to undergo a *change of state.*† When a system is not influenced in any way by its surroundings, it is said to be isolated. In practical applications of thermodynamics, isolated systems are of little importance. We usually have to deal with a system that is influenced in some way by its surroundings. In general, the surroundings may exert forces on the system or provide contact between the system and a body at some definite temperature. When the state of a system changes, interactions usually take place between the system and its surroundings.

When there is no unbalanced force in the interior of a system and also none between a system and its surroundings, the system is said to be in a state of *mechanical equilibrium.* When these conditions are not satisfied, either the system alone or both the system and its surroundings will undergo a change of state, which will cease only when mechanical equilibrium is restored.

When a system in mechanical equilibrium does not tend to undergo a spontaneous change of internal structure, such as a chemical reaction, or a transfer of matter from one part of the system to another, such as diffusion or solution, however slow, then it is said to be in a state of *chemical equilibrium.* A system not in chemical equilibrium undergoes a change of state that, in some cases, is exceedingly slow. The change ceases when chemical equilibrium is reached.

Thermal equilibrium exists when there is no spontaneous change in the coordinates of a system in mechanical and chemical equilibrium when it

---

† This must not be confused with the terminology of elementary physics, where the expression "change of state" is often used to signify a transition from solid to liquid or liquid to gas, etc. Such a change in the language of thermodynamics is called a "change of phase."

is separated from its surroundings by a diathermic wall. In thermal equilibrium, all parts of a system are at the same temperature, and this temperature is the same as that of the surroundings. When these conditions are not satisfied, a change of state will take place until thermal equilibrium is reached.

When the conditions for all three types of equilibrium are satisfied, the system is said to be in a state of *thermodynamic equilibrium;* in this condition, it is apparent that there will be no tendency whatever for any change of state either of the system or of the surroundings to occur. *States of thermodynamic equilibrium can be described in terms of macroscopic coordinates that do not involve the time, i.e., in terms of thermodynamic coordinates.* Thermodynamics does not attempt to deal with any problem involving the rate at which a process takes place. The investigation of such problems is carried out in other branches of science, as in the kinetic theory of gases, hydrodynamics, and chemical kinetics.

When the conditions for any one of the three types of equilibrium that constitute thermodynamic equilibrium are not satisfied, the system is said to be in a *nonequilibrium state.* Thus, when there is an unbalanced force in the interior of a system or between a system and its surroundings, the following phenomena may take place: acceleration, turbulence, eddies, waves, etc. While such phenomena are in progress, a system passes through nonequilibrium states. If an attempt is made to give a macroscopic description of any one of these nonequilibrium states, it is found that the pressure varies from one part of a system to another. There is no single pressure that refers to the system as a whole. Similarly, in the case of a system at a different temperature from its surroundings a nonuniform temperature distribution is set up and there is no single temperature that refers to the system as a whole. We therefore conclude that, *when the conditions for mechanical and thermal equilibrium are not satisfied, the states traversed by a system cannot be described in terms of thermodynamic coordinates referring to the system as a whole.*

It must not be concluded, however, that we are entirely helpless in dealing with such nonequilibrium states. If we divide the system into a large number of small mass elements, then thermodynamic coordinates may be found in terms of which a macroscopic description of each mass element may be approximated. There are also special methods for dealing with systems in mechanical and thermal equilibrium but not in chemical equilibrium. All these special methods will be considered later. At present we shall deal exclusively with systems in thermodynamic equilibrium.

2.2. Equation of State. Imagine for the sake of simplicity a constant mass of gas in a vessel so equipped that the pressure, volume, and temperature may be easily measured. If we fix the volume at some arbitrary value and cause the temperature to assume an arbitrarily chosen value, then we shall not be able to vary the pressure at all. Once V and θ are chosen by us, the value of P at equilibrium is determined by nature. Similarly, if P and θ are chosen arbitrarily, then the value of V at equilibrium is fixed. That is, of the three thermodynamic coordinates P, V, and θ, only two are independent variables. This implies that there exists an equation of equilibrium which connects the thermodynamic coordinates and which robs one of them of its independence. Such an equation is called an *equation of state*. Every thermodynamic system has its own equation of state, although in some cases the relation may be so complicated that it cannot be expressed in terms of simple mathematical functions.

An equation of state expresses the individual peculiarities of one system in contradistinction to another and must therefore be determined either by experiment or by molecular theory. A general theory like thermodynamics, based on general laws of nature, is incapable of expressing the behavior of one material as opposed to another. An equation of state is therefore not a theoretical deduction from thermodynamics but is usually an experimental addition to thermodynamics. It expresses the results of experiments in which the thermodynamic coordinates of a system were measured as accurately as possible, within a limited range of values. An equation of state is therefore only as accurate as the experiments that led to its formulation and holds only within the range of values measured. As soon as this range is exceeded, a different form of equation of state may be valid.

For example, a system consisting of exactly 1 mole of gas (1 mole $= M$ gm, where M is the molecular weight), and at low pressure, has the equation of state

$$Pv = R\theta,$$

where R is a constant and the small v indicates molar volume. At higher pressures, its equation of state is more complicated, being fairly well represented by

$$\left(P + \frac{a}{v^2}\right)(v - b) = R\theta,$$

where a, b, and R are constants. As far as thermodynamics is concerned, the important thing is that an equation of state exists, not whether we can write it down mathematically.

It is obvious that no equation of state exists for the states traversed by a system which is not in mechanical and thermal equilibrium, since such states cannot be described in terms of thermodynamic coordinates referring to the system as a whole. For example, if a gas in a cylinder were to expand and to impart to a piston an accelerated motion, the gas might have, at any moment, a definite volume and temperature, but the corresponding pressure could not be calculated from an equation of state. The pressure would not be a thermodynamic coordinate because it would not only depend on the velocity and the acceleration of the piston but would also perhaps vary from point to point.

2.3. Chemical Systems.   Any system of constant mass that exerts on the surroundings a uniform hydrostatic pressure, in the absence of surface, gravitational, electric, and magnetic effects, we shall call a *chemical system*.   Chemical systems are divided into the following categories:

1. A *pure substance*, which is one chemical constituent in the form of a solid, a liquid, a gas, a mixture of any two, or a mixture of all three.

2. A *homogeneous mixture of different constituents*, such as a mixture of inert gases, a mixture of chemically active gases, a mixture of liquids, or a solution.

3. A *heterogeneous mixture*, such as a mixture of different gases in contact with a mixture of different liquids.

Experiment shows that the states of equilibrium† of a chemical system can be described with the aid of three coordinates, namely, the pressure P exerted by the system on the surroundings, the volume V, and the absolute temperature θ.   The pressure is measured in dynes per square centimeter and the volume in cubic centimeters; the most convenient scale of temperature is the ideal gas scale.   Other units of pressure, such as pounds per square inch, atmospheres, millimeters of mercury, and kilograms per square centimeter, are used in various applications of thermodynamics and will be used occasionally in this book.   In the absence, however, of any special remarks about units, it will be understood that cgs units are to be employed.

Every chemical system has an equation of state expressing a relation among the three coordinates P, V, and θ that is valid for states of equilibrium only.   If the system undergoes a small change of state whereby it passes from an initial state of equilibrium to another state of equilibrium very near the initial one, then all three coordinates, in general, undergo slight changes.   If the change of, say, V, is very small in comparison with V and very large in comparison with the space occupied by a few molecules, then this change of V may be written as a differential dV. If V were a geometrical quantity referring to the volume of *space*, then dV could be used to denote a portion of that space arbitrarily small. Since, however, V is a macroscopic coordinate denoting the volume of *matter*, then, for dV to have a meaning, it must be large enough to include enough molecules to warrant the use of the macroscopic point of view.

Similarly, if the change of P is very small in comparison with P and

† In the remainder of this book the word "equilibrium," unmodified by any adjective, will refer to thermodynamic equilibrium.

very large in comparison with molecular fluctuations, then it also may be represented by the differential dP. *Every infinitesimal in thermodynamics must satisfy the requirement that it represents a change in a quantity which is small with respect to the quantity itself and large in comparison with the effect produced by the behavior of a few molecules.* The reason for this is that thermodynamic coordinates such as volume, pressure, and temperature have no meaning when applied to a few molecules. This is another way of saying that thermodynamic coordinates are macroscopic coordinates.

We may imagine the equation of state solved for any coordinate in terms of the other two. Thus

$$V = \text{function of } (\theta, P).$$

An infinitesimal change from one state of equilibrium to another state of equilibrium involves a dV, a $d\theta$, and a dP, all of which we shall assume satisfy the condition laid down in the previous paragraph. A fundamental theorem in partial differential calculus enables us to write

$$dV = \left(\frac{\partial V}{\partial \theta}\right)_P d\theta + \left(\frac{\partial V}{\partial P}\right)_\theta dP,$$

where each partial derivative is itself a function of θ and P. Both the above partial derivatives have an important physical meaning. The student will remember from elementary physics a quantity called the average coefficient of volume expansion, or volume expansivity. This was defined as

$$\text{Av. vol. exp.} = \frac{\text{change of vol. per unit vol.}}{\text{change of temp.}}$$

and referred to conditions under which the pressure was constant. If the change of temperature is made smaller and smaller until it becomes infinitesimal, then the change in volume also becomes infinitesimal and we have what is known as the instantaneous volume expansivity, or just *volume expansivity*, which is denoted by β. Thus

$$\boxed{\beta = \frac{1}{V}\left(\frac{\partial V}{\partial \theta}\right)_P.}$$

Strictly speaking, β is a function of θ and P, but experiments to be described later show that there are many substances for which β is quite insensitive to a change in P and varies only slightly with θ. Consequently, within a small temperature range β may, as a rule, be regarded as a constant. It is clear that β is expressed in reciprocal degrees.

In many textbooks of elementary physics, a quantity called the average bulk modulus is introduced in the discussion of the velocity of a longitudinal wave.   It is defined thus:

$$\text{Av. bulk modulus} = -\frac{\text{change in pressure}}{\text{change in vol. per unit vol.}}.$$

Since a positive change (increase) of pressure produces a negative change (decrease) of volume, the minus sign is introduced to make the bulk modulus a positive number.   If the change of pressure is made infinitesimal, then the volume change is also infinitesimal and we have an instantaneous bulk modulus.   If we further require that the temperature be kept constant, the resulting quantity is called the *isothermal bulk modulus* and is denoted by B.   Thus

$$B = -V\left(\frac{\partial P}{\partial V}\right)_{\theta}.$$

It is clear that the isothermal bulk modulus has the same units as pressure, namely, dynes per square centimeter.   The reciprocal of the isothermal bulk modulus is called the *isothermal compressibility*, denoted by k. Thus

$$k = -\frac{1}{V}\left(\frac{\partial V}{\partial P}\right)_{\theta}.$$

To be exact, B and k are functions of θ and P; but experimentally they are found to vary but little, and they can therefore at times be regarded as practically constant.

If the equation of state is solved for P, then

$$P = \text{function of } (\theta, V)$$

and

$$dP = \left(\frac{\partial P}{\partial \theta}\right)_{V} d\theta + \left(\frac{\partial P}{\partial V}\right)_{\theta} dV.$$

Finally, if θ is imagined as a function of P and V,

$$d\theta = \left(\frac{\partial \theta}{\partial P}\right)_{V} dP + \left(\frac{\partial \theta}{\partial V}\right)_{P} dV.$$

In all the above equations the system was assumed to undergo an infinitesimal process from an initial state of equilibrium to another.   This enabled us to use an equation of equilibrium (equation of state) and to solve it for any coordinate in terms of the other two.   The differentials dP, dV, and $d\theta$ therefore are differentials of actual functions and are called *exact differentials*.   If dz is an exact differential of a function of, say, x and y, then dz may be written

$$dz = \left(\frac{\partial z}{\partial x}\right)_y dx + \left(\frac{\partial z}{\partial y}\right)_x dy.$$

An infinitesimal that is not the differential of an actual function is called an *inexact differential* and cannot be expressed by an equation of the above type. There are other distinctions between exact and inexact differentials that will be made clear later.

2.4. Mathematical Theorems. There are two simple theorems in partial differential calculus that are used very often in this subject. The proofs are as follows: Suppose there exists a relation among the three coordinates x, y, and z; thus

$$f(x, y, z) = 0.$$

Then x can be imagined as a function of y and z, and

$$dx = \left(\frac{\partial x}{\partial y}\right)_z dy + \left(\frac{\partial x}{\partial z}\right)_y dz.$$

Also, y can be imagined as a function of x and z, and

$$dy = \left(\frac{\partial y}{\partial x}\right)_z dx + \left(\frac{\partial y}{\partial z}\right)_x dz.$$

Substituting the second equation into the first, we have

$$dx = \left(\frac{\partial x}{\partial y}\right)_z \left[\left(\frac{\partial y}{\partial x}\right)_z dx + \left(\frac{\partial y}{\partial z}\right)_x dz \right] + \left(\frac{\partial x}{\partial z}\right)_y dz,$$

or $$dx = \left(\frac{\partial x}{\partial y}\right)_z \left(\frac{\partial y}{\partial x}\right)_z dx + \left[\left(\frac{\partial x}{\partial y}\right)_z \left(\frac{\partial y}{\partial z}\right)_x + \left(\frac{\partial x}{\partial z}\right)_y \right] dz.$$

Now, of the three coordinates, only two are independent. Choosing x and z as the independent coordinates, the above equation must be true for all sets of values of dx and dz. Thus, if $dz = 0$ and $dx \neq 0$, it follows that

$$\left(\frac{\partial x}{\partial y}\right)_z \left(\frac{\partial y}{\partial x}\right)_z = 1,$$

or $$\boxed{\left(\frac{\partial x}{\partial y}\right)_z = \frac{1}{(\partial y/\partial x)_z}.} \qquad (1)$$

If $dx = 0$ and $dz \neq 0$, it follows that

$$\left(\frac{\partial x}{\partial y}\right)_z \left(\frac{\partial y}{\partial z}\right)_x + \left(\frac{\partial x}{\partial z}\right)_y = 0,$$

$$\left(\frac{\partial x}{\partial y}\right)_z \left(\frac{\partial y}{\partial z}\right)_x = - \left(\frac{\partial x}{\partial z}\right)_y,$$

$$\left(\frac{\partial x}{\partial y}\right)_z \left(\frac{\partial y}{\partial z}\right)_x \left(\frac{\partial z}{\partial x}\right)_y = -1. \tag{2}$$

In the case of a chemical system, the second theorem yields the result

$$\left(\frac{\partial P}{\partial V}\right)_\theta \left(\frac{\partial V}{\partial \theta}\right)_P = - \left(\frac{\partial P}{\partial \theta}\right)_V.$$

The volume expansivity β and the isothermal bulk modulus B were defined as

$$\beta = \frac{1}{V}\left(\frac{\partial V}{\partial \theta}\right)_P,$$

$$B = -V\left(\frac{\partial P}{\partial V}\right)_\theta,$$

and therefore

$$\left(\frac{\partial P}{\partial \theta}\right)_V = \beta B.$$

An infinitesimal change in pressure may now be expressed in terms of these physical quantities. Thus

$$dP = \left(\frac{\partial P}{\partial \theta}\right)_V d\theta + \left(\frac{\partial P}{\partial V}\right)_\theta dV$$

$$= \beta B\, d\theta - \frac{B}{V}\, dV.$$

At constant volume,

$$dP = \beta B\, d\theta.$$

If we cause the temperature to change a finite amount from θ_i to θ_f at constant volume, the pressure will change from P_i to P_f, where the subscripts i and f denote the initial and final states, respectively. Upon integrating between these two states, we get

$$P_f - P_i = \int_{\theta_i}^{\theta_f} \beta B\, d\theta.$$

The right-hand member can be integrated if we know the way in which β and B vary with θ at constant volume. If the temperature range $\theta_f - \theta_i$ is small, very little error is introduced by assuming that both are constant. With these assumptions we get

$$P_f - P_i = \beta B(\theta_f - \theta_i),$$

from which the final pressure may be calculated. For example, consider the following problem: A mass of mercury at a pressure of 1 atm and a temperature of 0°C is kept at constant volume. If the temperature is raised to 10°C, what will be the final pressure? From tables of physical constants, β and B of mercury remain practically constant within the temperature range of 0 to 10°C and have the values

$$\beta = 181 \times 10^{-6} \text{ deg}^{-1}$$
$$B = 0.250 \times 10^{12} \text{ dynes/cm}^2,$$

whence

$$P_f - P_i = 181 \times 10^{-6} \text{ deg}^{-1} \times 0.250 \times 10^{12} \text{ dynes/cm}^2 \times 10 \text{ deg}$$
$$= 453 \times 10^6 \text{ dynes/cm}^2.$$

Since there are 1.01×10^6 dynes/cm^2 in 1 atm,

$$P_f - P_i = \frac{453 \times 10^6}{1.01 \times 10^6} \text{ atm}$$
$$= 449 \text{ atm},$$

and
$$P_f = 449 + 1 = 450 \text{ atm}.$$

2.5. Stretched Wire. Experiments on stretched wires are usually performed openly in the laboratory where the pressure remains constant at 1 atm and under conditions at which changes in volume are negligible. For most practical purposes, it is found unnecessary to include the pressure and the volume among the thermodynamic coordinates. A sufficiently complete thermodynamic description of a wire is given in terms of only three coordinates:

1. The tension in the wire $\mathscr{F}$ measured in dynes.
2. The length of the wire L measured in centimeters.
3. The ideal gas temperature θ.

The states of thermodynamic equilibrium are connected by an equation of state that as a rule cannot be expressed by a simple equation. For a wire at constant temperature within the limit of elasticity, Hooke's law holds, namely,

$$\mathscr{F} = \text{const. } (L - L_0),$$

where L_0 is the length at zero tension. If the tension is not balanced by an external force, the wire will describe some sort of accelerated motion such as a vibration and will pass through states that cannot be described in terms of thermodynamic coordinates referring to the wire as a whole.

If a wire undergoes an infinitesimal change from one state of equilibrium to another, then the infinitesimal change of length is an exact differential and can be written

$$dL = \left(\frac{\partial L}{\partial \theta}\right)_{\mathscr{F}} d\theta + \left(\frac{\partial L}{\partial \mathscr{F}}\right)_{\theta} d\mathscr{F},$$

where both partial derivatives are functions of θ and $\mathcal{F}$. These derivatives are connected with important physical quantities. In elementary
physics the average linear expansivity was defined as

$$\text{Av. lin. exp.} = \frac{\text{change of length per unit length}}{\text{change of temp.}},$$

the tension being considered constant. If the change of temperature
becomes infinitesimal, the *linear expansivity* α becomes

$$\alpha = \frac{1}{L}\left(\frac{\partial L}{\partial \theta}\right)_{\mathcal{F}}.$$

The experimental measurement of α will be considered later. Measurements of α show that it depends only slightly on $\mathcal{F}$ and varies mostly
with θ. In a small temperature range, however, it may be regarded as
practically constant. α is expressed in reciprocal degrees.

In elementary physics the average Young's modulus was defined as

$$\text{Av. Young's modulus} = \frac{\text{change of tension per unit area}}{\text{change of length per unit length}},$$

the temperature remaining constant. When the change of tension
becomes infinitesimal, we have what is known as the *isothermal Young's
modulus,* denoted by Y. Thus

$$Y = \frac{L}{A}\left(\frac{\partial \mathcal{F}}{\partial L}\right)_{\theta},$$

where A denotes the area of the wire. The isothermal Young's modulus
is found experimentally to depend but little on $\mathcal{F}$ and mostly on θ. For a
small temperature range, it may be regarded as practically constant.
The unit in which Y is expressed is dynes per square centimeter.

From the second theorem in Art. 2.4,

$$\left(\frac{\partial \mathcal{F}}{\partial \theta}\right)_{L} = -\left(\frac{\partial \mathcal{F}}{\partial L}\right)_{\theta}\left(\frac{\partial L}{\partial \theta}\right)_{\mathcal{F}},$$

whence
$$\left(\frac{\partial \mathcal{F}}{\partial \theta}\right)_{L} = -\alpha A Y.$$

2.6. Surface Film. The study of surface films is an interesting
branch of physical chemistry. There are three important examples of
such films:

1. The upper surface of a liquid in equilibrium with its vapor.

2. A soap bubble, or soap film, stretched across a wire framework,
consisting of two surface films with a small amount of liquid between.

3. A thin (sometimes monomolecular) oil film on the surface of water.

The student will recall from elementary physics that a surface film is like a stretched membrane. The surface on one side of any imaginary line pulls perpendicular to this line with a force equal and opposite to that exerted by the surface on the other side of the line. The force acting perpendicularly to a line of unit length is called the *surface tension*. An adequate thermodynamic description of a surface film is given by the specifying three coordinates:

1. The surface tension $\mathcal{S}$ in dynes per centimeter.
2. The area of the film A in square centimeters.
3. The ideal gas temperature θ.

In dealing with a surface film, the accompanying liquid must always be considered as part of the system. This may be done, however, without introducing the pressure and volume of the composite system because, as a rule, the pressure remains constant and volume changes are negligible. The surface of a pure liquid in equilibrium with its vapor has a particularly simple equation of state. Experiment shows that the surface tension of such a film does not depend on the area but is a function of the temperature only. For most pure liquids, the equation of state can be written

$$\mathcal{S} = \mathcal{S}_0 \left(1 - \frac{t}{t'}\right)^n,$$

where $\mathcal{S}_0$ is the surface tension at 0°C, t' is a temperature within a few degrees of the critical temperature, and n is a constant that lies between 1 and 2. It is clear from this equation that the surface tension decreases as t increases, becoming zero when $t = t'$.

The equation of state of a monomolecular oil film on water is particularly interesting. If $\mathcal{S}_W$ denotes the surface tension of a clean water surface and $\mathcal{S}$ the surface tension of the water covered by the monolayer, then, within a restricted range of values of A,

$$(\mathcal{S} - \mathcal{S}_W)A = \text{const. } \theta.$$

The difference $\mathcal{S} - \mathcal{S}_W$ is sometimes called the *surface pressure*. Such films can be compressed and expanded and, when deposited on glass, have interesting optical properties.

2.7. Reversible Cell. A reversible cell consists of two electrodes each immersed in a different electrolyte. The emf depends on the nature of the materials, the concentrations of the electrolytes, and the temperature. In Fig. 2.1 a schematic diagram of a reversible cell, the Daniell cell, is shown. A copper electrode immersed in a saturated $CuSO_4$ solution is separated by a porous wall from a zinc electrode immersed in a saturated solution of $ZnSO_4$. Experiment shows that the copper electrode is positive with respect to the zinc.

Suppose that the cell is connected to a potentiometer whose potential difference is slightly smaller than the emf of the cell. Under these conditions, the current that exists may be described conventionally as a transfer of positive electricity externally from the copper electrode to the zinc electrode. When this is the case, zinc goes into solution, zinc sulfate is formed, copper is deposited, and copper sulfate is used up. These changes are expressed by the chemical reaction

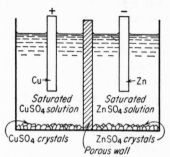

$$Zn + CuSO_4 \rightarrow Cu + ZnSO_4.$$

When positive electricity is transferred in the opposite direction, i.e., externally from zinc to copper, the reaction proceeds in the reverse direction (hence the name reversible cell); thus:

$$Cu + ZnSO_4 \rightarrow Zn + CuSO_4.$$

Fig. 2.1. The Daniell cell.

The important feature of a reversible cell is that the chemical changes accompanying the transfer of electricity in one direction take place to the same extent in the reverse direction when the same quantity of electricity is transferred in the reverse direction. Furthermore, according to one of Faraday's laws of electrolysis, the simultaneous disappearance of 1 mole of zinc and deposition of 1 mole of copper are accompanied by the transfer of exactly jF coulombs of electricity, where j is the valence and F is Faraday's constant, 96,500 coulombs. We may therefore define a quantity Z, called the *charge* of the cell, as a number whose absolute magnitude is of no consequence but whose change is numerically equal to the quantity of electricity that is transferred during the chemical reaction, the change being negative when positive electricity is transferred externally from the positive to the negative electrode. Thus, if Δn moles of zinc disappear and Δn moles of copper are deposited, the charge of the cell changes from Z_i to Z_f where

$$Z_f - Z_i = -\Delta njF.$$

Now, if we limit ourselves to reversible cells in which no gases are liberated and which operate at constant atmospheric pressure, we may ignore the pressure and the volume and describe the cell with the aid of three coordinates only:

1. The emf $\mathcal{E}$ in volts.
2. The charge Z in coulombs.
3. The ideal gas temperature θ.

When the cell is an open circuit, there is a tendency for diffusion to take place slowly and the cell is not in equilibrium. If the cell is connected, however, to a potentiometer and the circuit is adjusted until there is no current, then the emf of the cell is balanced and the cell is in mechanical and chemical equilibrium.   When thermal equilibrium is also satisfied, the cell is then in thermodynamic equilibrium.   The states of thermodynamic equilibrium of a reversible cell are connected by an equation of state among the coordinates $\mathcal{E}$, Z, and θ.   If the electrolytes are saturated solutions, a transfer of electricity accompanying the performance of the chemical reaction at constant temperature and pressure will not alter the concentrations of the electrolytes.   The emf will therefore remain constant.   Experiment shows that the emf of a saturated reversible cell at constant pressure is a function of the temperature only.   The equation of state is usually written

$$\mathcal{E} = \mathcal{E}_{20} + \alpha(t - 20°) + \beta(t - 20°)^2 + \gamma(t - 20°)^3,$$

where t is the Celsius temperature, $\mathcal{E}_{20}$ is the emf at 20°C, and α, β, and γ are constants depending on the materials.   We shall see later that, once the equation of state of a reversible cell is known, all the quantities of interest to a chemist which refer to the chemical reaction going on in the cell can be determined.

2.8. Paramagnetic Solid.   A paramagnetic substance in the absence of an external magnetic field is not a magnet.   Upon being introduced into a magnetic field it becomes slightly magnetized in the direction of the field.   Its permeability, however, is still very nearly unity, in contradistinction to a ferromagnetic substance like iron whose permeability may be very large.   The magnetized state of a paramagnetic substance may be described macroscopically by specifying the total magnetic moment of the substance, which we shall call the *magnetization*.   This quantity should not be confused with the intensity of magnetization, which is the magnetic moment per unit volume.   In thermodynamics it is not convenient to refer to the properties of a unit volume of material.   The magnetization of any substance may be measured in pole centimeters.

If a unit pole, placed in a magnetic field, is acted on by a force of 1 dyne, the *magnetic intensity* is said to be 1 oersted.   Most experiments on magnetic solids are performed at constant atmospheric pressure and involve only minute volume changes.   Consequently, we may ignore the pressure and the volume and describe a paramagnetic solid with the aid of only three thermodynamic coordinates:

1. The magnetic intensity $\mathcal{H}$ in oersteds (dynes per pole).
2. The magnetization I in pole centimeters.
3. The ideal gas temperature θ.

The states of thermodynamic equilibrium of a paramagnetic solid can be represented by an equation of state among these coordinates.   Experiment shows that the magnetization of many paramagnetic solids is a function of the ratio of the magnetic intensity to the temperature. For small values of this ratio the function reduces to a very simple form, namely,

$$I = C \frac{\mathscr{H}}{\theta},$$

which is known as *Curie's equation*, C being called the *Curie constant*. The Curie constant may be written

$$C = \frac{I}{\mathscr{H}} \theta = \frac{\mathscr{H} I}{\mathscr{H}^2} \theta.$$

It will be shown in the next chapter that, when $\mathscr{H}$ is measured in oersteds and I in pole centimeters, $\mathscr{H} I$ is measured in ergs and $\mathscr{H}^2$ in ergs per cubic centimeter. The unit in which the Curie constant is expressed is, therefore,

$$\text{Unit of } C = \frac{\text{erg}}{\text{erg/cm}^3} \text{ deg} = \text{cm}^3 \cdot \text{deg}.$$

Since the Curie constant depends upon the amount of material, its unit may be taken to be any one of the four listed in the accompanying table:

UNITS OF THE CURIE CONSTANT

Total	Per mole	Per gm	Per cm³
cm³ · deg	$\dfrac{\text{cm}^3 \cdot \text{deg}}{\text{mole}}$	$\dfrac{\text{cm}^3 \cdot \text{deg}}{\text{gm}}$	deg

At low temperatures, the behavior of some paramagnetic solids is represented more accurately by Weiss's equation, thus:

$$I = \frac{C\mathscr{H}}{\theta - N\rho C},$$

where C is Curie's constant, ρ is the density, and N is a constant. It can be seen that Weiss's equation reduces to Curie's equation when θ is large compared with $N\rho C$. Paramagnetic solids are of particular interest in thermodynamics. It will be seen later how they are used to obtain extremely low temperatures.

2.9. Intensive and Extensive Quantities. Imagine a system in equilibrium to be divided into two equal parts, each with equal mass. Those properties of each half of the system which remain the same are said to be *intensive*. Those which are halved are called *extensive*. The intensive coordinates of a system, such as temperature and pressure, are independent of the mass; the extensive coordinates are proportional to the mass. The thermodynamic coordinates that have been introduced in this chapter are listed in Table 2.1. The student should notice that four of the five intensive quantities listed in the table are denoted by script capital letters, whereas all the extensive quantities are represented by italic capital letters.

TABLE 2.1. INTENSIVE AND EXTENSIVE QUANTITIES

System	Intensive coordinate		Extensive coordinate	
Chemical system...............	Pressure	P	Volume	V
Stretched wire..................	Tension	$\mathscr{T}$	Length	L
Surface film....................	Surface tension	$\mathscr{S}$	Area	A
Electric cell....................	Emf	$\mathscr{E}$	Charge	Z
Paramagnetic solid.............	Magnetic intensity	$\mathscr{H}$	Magnetization	I

PROBLEMS

2.1. The equation of state of 1 mole of an ideal gas is $Pv = R\theta$, where R is the universal gas constant. Show that (a) $\beta = 1/\theta$; (b) $B = P$.

2.2. An approximate equation of state of 1 mole of a real gas at moderate pressures, devised to take into account the finite size of the molecules, is $P(v - b) = R\theta$, where b is a constant. Show that

$$(a)\ \beta = \frac{1}{\theta + (bP/R)}; \quad (b)\ B = P\left(1 + \frac{bP}{R\theta}\right).$$

Let P approach zero, and compare these results with those of Prob. 2.1.

2.3. An approximate equation of state of 1 mole of a real gas at moderate pressures is given by $Pv = R\theta(1 + B'P)$, where B' is a function of θ only. Show that

$$(a)\ \beta = \frac{1}{\theta} + \frac{P}{1 + B'P}\frac{dB'}{d\theta}; \quad (b)\ B = P(1 + B'P).$$

Let P approach zero, and compare with Prob. 2.1.

2.4. An approximate equation of state of 1 mole of a real gas at moderate pressures is given by $Pv = R\theta(1 + B''/v)$, where B'' is a function of θ only. Show that

$$(a)\ \beta = \frac{1}{\theta}\frac{1 + B''/v + (\theta/v)(dB''/d\theta)}{1 + 2B''/v}; \quad (b)\ B = P + \frac{B''R\theta}{v^2}.$$

Let v approach infinity, and compare with Prob. 2.1.

2.5. It will be proved in Chap. 6 that the speed of a longitudinal wave in any material is given by

$$\mathscr{V} = \sqrt{\frac{B_S}{\rho}},$$

where ρ is the density and B_S is the *adiabatic bulk modulus*, defined by the relation,

$$B_S = -V\left(\frac{\partial P}{\partial V}\right)_S,$$

where S is a property of matter called the *entropy*.

(a) Prove that

$$\gamma = \sqrt{\left(\frac{\partial P}{\partial \rho}\right)_S}.$$

(b) The entropy S of an ideal gas may be written

$$S = C_v \ln P + C_p \ln V + \text{const.},$$

where C_v and C_p are constants whose ratio C_p/C_v is designated by γ. Show that the adiabatic bulk modulus B_S of an ideal gas is equal to γP.

2.6. (a) A block of metal at a pressure of 1 atm and a temperature of 20°C is kept at constant volume. If the temperature is raised to 32°C what will be the final pressure? *Page 3!* $P_f - P_i = \frac{\beta}{k}(\theta_f - \theta_i)$ 891 atm.

(b) If the containing vessel has a negligibly small thermal expansivity and can withstand a maximum pressure of 1200 atm, what is the highest temperature to which the system may be raised? $36.146°C$

(Assume the volume expansivity and the isothermal bulk modulus to remain practically constant at the values 5.0×10^{-5} deg^{-1} and 1.5×10^{12} dynes/cm², respectively.)

2.7. A block of the same metal as in Prob. 2.6 at a pressure of 1 atm, a volume of 500 cm³, and a temperature of 20°C experiences a rise of temperature of 12 deg and an increase of volume of 0.05 cm³. Calculate the final pressure.

2.8. Express the volume expansivity and the isothermal compressibility in terms of the density ρ and its partial derivatives.

2.9. (a) Derive the equation

$$\frac{dV}{V} = \beta \, d\theta - k \, dP. \qquad Pg \, 28$$

(b) A hypothetical substance has the following volume expansivity and isothermal compressibility:

$$\beta = \frac{3a\theta^3}{V}, \qquad k = \frac{b}{V}, \qquad V = \tfrac{3}{4} a\theta^4 - bP$$

where a and b are constants. Find the equation of state.

2.10. The volume expansivity and the isothermal compressibility of a certain gas are

$$\beta = \frac{nR}{PV}, \qquad k = \frac{1}{P} + \frac{a}{V},$$

where n, R, and a are constants. Find the equation of state.

2.11. If a wire undergoes an infinitesimal change from an initial equilibrium state to a final equilibrium state, show that the change of tension is equal to

$$d\mathcal{F} = -\alpha A Y \, d\theta + \frac{A Y}{L} \, dL.$$

2.12. A metal wire of cross-sectional area 0.0085 cm² under a tension of 2×10^6 dynes and at a temperature of 20°C is stretched between two rigid supports 1.2 m apart. If the temperature is reduced to 8°C, what is the final tension? (Assume that α and Y remain constant at the values 1.5×10^{-5} deg^{-1} and 2.0×10^{12} dynes/cm², respectively.)

2.13. The fundamental frequency of vibration of a wire of length L, mass M, and tension $\mathcal{F}$ is given by

$$f_1 = \frac{1}{2L}\sqrt{\frac{\mathcal{F}L}{M}}.$$

With what frequency will the wire in Prob. 2.12 vibrate at 20°C; at 8°C?   (The density of the wire is 9.0 gm/cm³.)

2.14. If, in addition to the conditions mentioned in Prob. 2.12, the supports approach each other by 0.012 cm, what will be the final tension?   *same as 12*

2.15. The equation of state of an ideal elastic substance is

$$\mathcal{F} = K\theta\left(\frac{L}{L_0} - \frac{L_0^2}{L^2}\right),$$

where K is a constant and L_0 (the value of L at zero tension) is a function of the temperature only.

(a) Show that the isothermal Young's modulus is given by

$$Y = \frac{\mathcal{F}}{A} + \frac{3K\theta L_0^2}{AL^2}.$$

(b) Show that the isothermal Young's modulus at zero tension is given by

$$Y_0 = \frac{3K\theta}{A}.$$

(c) Show that the linear expansivity is given by

$$\alpha = \alpha_0 - \frac{\mathcal{F}}{AY\theta},$$

where α_0 is the value of the linear expansivity at zero tension, or

$$\alpha_0 = \frac{1}{L_0}\frac{dL_0}{d\theta}.$$

(d) Assume the following values for a certain sample of rubber: $\theta = 300°$K, $K = 1.333 \times 10^3$ dynes/deg, $A = 0.01$ cm², $\alpha_0 = 5 \times 10^{-4}$ deg⁻¹. Calculate $\mathcal{F}$, Y, and α for the following values of L/L_0: 0.5, 1.0, 1.5, 2.0. Show graphically how $\mathcal{F}$, Y, and α depend on the ratio L/L_0.

2.16. From the critical point, 5.2°K, down to the λ point, 2.19°K, the surface tension of liquid helium of mass number 4 (He⁴) is given approximately by

$$\mathscr{S} = 0.5\frac{\text{dynes}}{\text{cm}}\left(1 - \frac{\theta}{5.2°\text{K}}\right).$$

Plot $\mathscr{S}$ against θ in this temperature range.

It will be shown in Chap. 14 that the surface energy per unit area of a surface film is given by

$$\mathscr{S} - \theta\frac{d\mathscr{S}}{d\theta}.$$

Calculate this quantity and plot it against θ on the same graph as $\mathscr{S}$.

2.17. Solve Prob. 2.16 for liquid helium of mass number 3, He³ whose surface tension is given approximately by

$$\mathscr{S} = 0.23 \frac{\text{dynes}}{\text{cm}} \left(1 - \frac{\theta}{3.3°\text{K}} \right),$$

in the temperature range from 3.3 to 1.08°K.

2.18. It will be shown in Chap. 14 that the heat of reaction ΔH of the chemical reaction taking place in a reversible cell is given by the relation

$$\Delta H = -jF \left(\mathscr{E} - \theta \frac{d\mathscr{E}}{d\theta} \right).$$

Calculate the heat of reaction for a reversible cell whose emf varies with the temperature according to the equation

$$\mathscr{E} = a + b\theta + c\theta^2 + d\theta^3,$$

where a, b, c, and d are constants.

2.19. The equation of state of an ideal paramagnetic material valid for all values of the ratio $\mathscr{H}/\theta$ is given by Brillouin's equation, as follows:

$$I = \frac{Ng\mu_B}{2} \left[(2J + 1) \coth (2J + 1) \frac{g\mu_B\mathscr{H}}{2k\theta} - \coth \frac{g\mu_B\mathscr{H}}{2k\theta} \right]$$

where N, g, μ_B, J, and k are atomic constants.

(a) Find out how the hyperbolic cotangent of x behaves as x approaches zero.

(b) Show that Brillouin's equation reduces to Curie's equation when $\mathscr{H}/\theta$ approaches zero.

(c) Show that the Curie constant is given by

$$C = \frac{Ng^2J(J + 1)\mu_B^2}{3k}.$$

2.20. It will be shown in Chap. 16 that the entropy change ΔS_θ of a paramagnetic solid accompanying an *isothermal* increase of magnetic field from zero to $\mathscr{H}_1$ is given by

$$\Delta S_\theta = \int_0^{\mathscr{H}_1} \left(\frac{\partial I}{\partial \theta} \right)_\mathscr{H} d\mathscr{H},$$

where the integration takes place at constant θ.

(a) Assuming the validity of Curie's equation, evaluate the above integral.

(b) Show that, as θ approaches zero, ΔS_θ *does not* approach zero, in violation of the third law of thermodynamics. Curie's equation therefore cannot be valid at very low temperatures.

(c) (For students who have learned how to use hyperbolic functions.) Show that, when Brillouin's equation is used, ΔS_θ approaches zero as θ approaches zero in agreement with the third law of thermodynamics.

3
Work

3.1. Work. If a system undergoes a displacement under the action of a force, *work* is said to be done, the amount of work being equal to the product of the force and the component of the displacement parallel to the force. If a system as a *whole* exerts a force on its surroundings and a displacement takes place, the work that is done either by or on the system is called *external work*. Thus, a gas, confined in a cylinder and at uniform pressure, while expanding and imparting motion to a piston does external work on its surroundings. The work done, however, by part of a system on another part is called *internal work*. The interactions of molecules or electrons on one another constitute internal work.

Internal work has no place in thermodynamics. Only the work that involves an interaction between a system and its surroundings is significant. When a system does external work, the changes that take place can be described by means of macroscopic quantities referring to the system as a whole, in which case the changes may be imagined to accompany the raising or lowering of a suspended weight, the winding or unwinding of a spring, or, in general, the alternation of the position or configuration of some external mechanical device. This may be regarded as the ultimate criterion as to whether external work is done or not. It will often be found convenient throughout the remainder of this book to describe the performance of external work in terms of or in conjunction with the operation of a mechanical device such as a system of suspended weights. *Unless otheriwse indicated, the word work, unmodified by any adjective, will mean external work.*

A few examples will be found helpful. If an electric cell is on open circuit, changes that take place in the cell (such as diffusion) are not accompanied by the performance of work. If, however, the cell is connected to an external circuit through which electricity is transferred, the current may be imagined to produce rotation of the armature of a motor, thereby lifting a weight or winding a spring. Therefore, *for an electric cell to do work it must be connected to an external circuit.* As another example, consider a magnet far removed from any external electric

42

conductor. A change of magnetization within the magnet is not accompanied by the performance of work. If, however, the magnet undergoes a change of magnetization while it is surrounded by an electric conductor, eddy currents are set up in the conductor, constituting an external transfer of electricity. Hence, *for a magnetic system to do work it must interact with an electric conductor or with other magnets.*

It is the accepted convention of thermodynamics that work which is done by a system on its surroundings is positive, whereas work done on a system is negative.

3.2. Quasi-static Process. A system in thermodynamic equilibrium satisfies the following stringent requirements:

1. *Mechanical Equilibrium.* The force exerted by the system is uniform throughout the system and is balanced by the external forces.

2. *Thermal Equilibrium.* The temperature is uniform throughout the system and is the same as that of the surroundings.

3. *Chemical Equilibrium.* The internal structure and chemical composition remain constant.

Once a system is in thermodynamic equilibrium and the surroundings are kept unchanged, no motion will take place and no work will be done. If, however, the sum of the external forces is changed so that there is a finite unbalanced force acting on the system, then the condition for mechanical equilibrium is no longer satisfied and the following situations may arise:

1. Forces within the system may no longer be uniform throughout the system; and, as a result, turbulence, waves, etc., may be set up. Also, the system as a whole may execute some sort of accelerated motion.

2. As a result of this turbulence, acceleration, etc., a nonuniform temperature distribution may be brought about, as well as a finite difference of temperature between the system and its surroundings.

3. The sudden change in the forces and in the temperature may produce a state that does not correspond to chemical equilibrium, and a chemical change might proceed at a finite rate.

It is clear from the above considerations that a finite unbalanced force causes the system to pass through nonequilibrium states. If it is desired during a process to describe every state of a system by means of thermodynamic coordinates referring to the system as a whole, the process must *not* be brought about by a finite unbalanced force. We are led, therefore, to conceive of an ideal situation in which the external forces acting on a system are varied only slightly so that the unbalanced force is infinitesimal. A process performed in this ideal way is said to be *quasi-static. During a quasi-static process, the system is at all times infinitesimally near a state of thermodynamic equilibrium,* and all the states through which the system passes can be described by means of thermodynamic coordinates referring to the system as a whole.   An equation of state is valid, therefore, for all these states.   A quasi-static process is an idealization that is applicable to all thermodynamic systems, including electric and magnetic systems.   The conditions for such a process can never be rigorously satisfied in the laboratory, but they can be approached with almost any degree of accuracy.   In the next few articles it will be seen how approximately quasi-static processes may be performed by all the systems treated in Chap. 2.

3.3. Work in Changing the Volume of a Chemical System. Imagine any chemical system contained in a cylinder equipped with a movable piston on which the system and the surroundings may act. Suppose that the cylinder has a cross-sectional area A and that the pressure exerted by the system at the piston face is P.   The force on the piston is therefore PA.   If the piston moves out an infinitesimal distance dx, the system performs an infinitesimal amount of work dW (the differential sign with the line drawn through it will be explained later) equal to

$$dW = PA\ dx.$$

But
$$A\ dx = dV;$$

hence
$$\boxed{dW = P\ dV.}$$

Now suppose the piston is caused to move a finite amount so that the volume changes from V_i to V_f, and let the symbol P stand for the pressure at any moment on the piston face.   The amount of work W done by the system will evidently be

$$W = \int_{V_i}^{V_f} P\ dV.$$

If the motion of the piston is produced by a finite difference between the pressure exerted by the system and the external pressure, or, in other words, if the piston moves with accelerated motion, both P and V are functions of quantities involving the time.   The integration of the above equation therefore becomes a problem in hydrodynamics.   If, however, the change in volume is performed quasi-statically, P is at all times a thermodynamic coordinate and can be expressed as a function of θ and V by means of an equation of state.   The evaluation of the integral can then be accomplished once the behavior of θ is specified, because then P can be expressed as a function of V only.   If P is expressed as a function of V, the *path* of integration is defined.   Along a particular quasi-static path R, the work done by a system in going from a volume V_i to a larger volume V_f is

$$W_{if} = {}_R\!\int_{V_i}^{V_f} P\ dV,$$

whereas, from f to i, along the same path but in the opposite direction, the work absorbed by the system is

$$W_{fi} = {}_R\!\int_{V_f}^{V_i} P \, dV.$$

When the path R is quasi-static,

$$W_{if} = -W_{fi}.$$

Sufficient approximation to a quasi-static process may be achieved in practice by having the external pressure differ from that exerted by the system by only a small finite amount. In cgs units, P is measured in dynes per square centimeter and V in cubic centimeters, whence W is expressed in ergs. To express W in joules, divide by 10^7 ergs/joule. In engineering units, P is expressed in pounds per square inch (absolute pressure, not gauge pressure) and V in cubic feet; therefore, in order to express W in foot-pounds, it is necessary to multiply by 144 in.^{2}/ft^2.

3.4. P-V Diagram. As the volume of a chemical system changes by virtue of the motion of a piston in a cylinder, the position of the piston

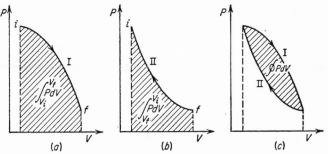

FIG. 3.1. P-V diagram. (a) Curve I, expansion; (b) curve II, compression; (c) curves I and II together constitute a cycle.

at any moment is proportional to the volume. A pen whose motion along the X axis of a diagram follows exactly the motion of the piston will trace out a line every point of which represents an instantaneous value of the volume. If, at the same time, this pen is given a motion along the Y axis such that the Y coordinate is proportional to the pressure, then the pressure and volume changes of the system during expansion or compression are indicated simultaneously on the same diagram. Such a device is called an *indicator*. The diagram in which pressure is plotted along the Y axis and volume along the X axis is called an *indicator diagram* or *P-V diagram*.

In Fig. 3.1(a), the pressure and volume changes of a gas during expansion are indicated by curve I. The $\int P \, dV$ for this process is evidently the shaded area under curve I. Similarly, for a compression, the work absorbed by the gas is represented by the shaded area under curve II in Fig. 3.1(*b*). In conformity with the sign convention for work, the area under I is regarded as positive, and that under II as negative. In Fig. 3.1(*c*), curves I and II are drawn together so that they constitute a series of processes whereby the gas is brought back to its initial state. Such a series of processes, represented by a closed figure, is called a *cycle*. The area within the closed figure is obviously the difference between the areas under curves I and II and therefore represents the *net* work done in the cycle. It should be noticed that the cycle is traversed in such a direction that the net work is positive. If the direction were reversed, the net work would be negative.

In engineering, indicator diagrams of the processes taking place in the cylinder of a steam engine or an internal-combustion engine are extremely valuable in providing information as to the work delivered at the piston face. The area within a closed curve is usually measured with a planimeter.

3.5. Work Depends on the Path. On the *P-V* diagram depicted in Fig. 3.2, an initial equilibrium state *i* (characterized by the coordinates P_i, V_i, θ_i) and a final equilibrium state *f* (coordinates P_f, V_f, θ_f) of a chemical system are represented by the two points *i* and *f*. There are many ways in which the system may be taken from *i* to *f*. For example, the pressure may be kept constant from *i* to *a* (*isobaric process*) and then the volume kept constant from *a* to *f* (*isochoric process*), in which case the work done is equal to the area under the line *ia*. Another possibility is the path *ibf*, in which case the work is the area under the line *bf*. The series of short isobarics and isochorics from *i* to *f* and the continuous curve from *i* to *f* represent other possibilities in each of which the work done is different. We can see, therefore, that the *work done by a system depends not only on the initial and final states but also on the intermediate states, i.e., on the path.* This is merely another way of saying that, for a quasi-static process, the expression

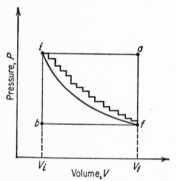

FIG. 3.2. Work depends on the path.

$$W = \int_{V_i}^{V_f} P \, dV$$

ntegrated until *P* is specified as a function of *V*.

ssion *P dV* is an infinitesimal amount of work and has been by the symbol d*W*. There is, however, an important dis-

tinction between an infinitesimal amount of work and the other infini-
tesimals we have considered up to now.   An infinitesimal amount of
work is an *inexact differential;* i.e., it is *not* the differential of an actual
function of the thermodynamic coordinates.   There is no function of the
thermodynamic coordinates representing the work in a body.   The
phrase "work in a body" has no meaning.   To indicate that an infinitesimal amount of work is *not* a mathematical differential of a function
W and to emphasize at all times that it is an inexact differential, a line
is drawn through the differential sign, thus: dW.

   3.6. Calculation of $\int P\,dV$ for Quasi-static Processes.   The preceding ideas will be clarified by the following examples:

   1. *Quasi-static Isothermal Expansion or Compression of an Ideal Gas.*

$$W = \int_{V_i}^{V_f} P\,dV,$$

but an ideal gas is one whose equation of state is

$$PV = nR\theta$$

where n and R are constants.   Substituting for P, we get

$$W = \int_{V_i}^{V_f} \frac{nR\theta}{V}\,dV$$

and, since θ is also constant,

$$W = nR\theta \int_{V_i}^{V_f} \frac{dV}{V}$$
$$= nR\theta \ln \frac{V_f}{V_i},$$

where the symbol ln denotes the natural, or Napierian, logarithm.   In
terms of the common logarithm, denoted by log,

$$W = 2.30 nR\theta \log \frac{V_f}{V_i}.$$

   If there are 2 moles of gas kept at a constant temperature of 0°C and
the gas is compressed from a volume of 4 liters to 1 liter, then,

$$n = 2 \text{ moles}$$
$$R = 8.31 \times 10^7 \text{ ergs/mole} \cdot \text{deg}$$
$$\theta = 273 \text{ deg (using three significant figures)}$$
$$V_i = 4 \text{ liters}$$
$$V_f = 1 \text{ liter}$$
$$W = 2.30 \times 2 \text{ mole} \times 8.31 \times 10^7 \frac{\text{ergs}}{\text{mole} \cdot \text{deg}} \times 273 \text{ deg} \times \log \tfrac{1}{4}$$
$$= 2.30 \times 2 \times 8.31 \times 10^7 \times 273 \times (-0.602) \text{ ergs}$$
$$= -6300 \times 10^7 \text{ ergs}$$
$$= -6300 \text{ joules}$$

the minus sign indicating that work was done on the gas.

2. *Quasi-static Isothermal Increase of Pressure on a Solid.* Suppose the pressure on 10 gm of solid copper is increased quasi-statically and isothermally at 0°C from zero to 1000 atm. The work is calculated as follows:

$$W = \int P \, dV.$$

$$dV = \left(\frac{\partial V}{\partial P}\right)_\theta dP + \left(\frac{\partial V}{\partial \theta}\right)_P d\theta.$$

Since the isothermal bulk modulus is

$$B = -V \left(\frac{\partial P}{\partial V}\right)_\theta,$$

we have, at constant temperature,

$$dV = -\frac{V}{B} dP.$$

Substituting for dV,

$$W = -\int_{P_i}^{P_f} \frac{V}{B} P \, dP.$$

Now the changes in V and B at constant temperature are so small that they may be neglected. Hence,

$$W = -\frac{V}{2B} (P_f^2 - P_i^2).$$

Since the volume is equal to the mass m divided by the density ρ,

$$W = -\frac{m}{2\rho B} (P_f^2 - P_i^2).$$

For copper at 0°C,

$\rho = 8.93$ gm/cm^3
$B = 1.31 \times 10^{12}$ dynes/cm^2
$m = 10$ gm
$P_i = 0$
$P_f = 1000$ atm $= 1.01 \times 10^9$ dynes/cm^2

Hence,

$$W = -\frac{10 \text{ gm} \times (1.01 \times 10^9)^2 (\text{dynes/cm}^2)^2}{2 \times 8.93 \text{ gm/cm}^3 \times 1.31 \times 10^{12} \text{ dynes/cm}^2}$$

$$= -\frac{10.2 \times 10^{18}}{23.4 \times 10^{12}} \text{ dyne} \cdot \text{cm}$$

$$= -0.0436 \times 10^7 \text{ ergs}$$

$$= -0.0436 \text{ joules},$$

where the minus sign indicates that work was done on the copper.

3.7. Work in Changing the Length of a Wire. If the length of a wire in which there is a tension $\mathcal{F}$ is changed from L to $L + dL$, the infinitesimal amount of work that is done is equal to

$$\bar{d}W = -\mathcal{F}\,dL.$$

The minus sign is used because a positive value of dL means an extension of the wire, for which work must be done on the wire, i.e., negative work. For a finite change of length from L_i to L_f,

$$W = -\int_{L_i}^{L_f}\mathcal{F}\,dL$$

where $\mathcal{F}$ indicates the instantaneous value of the tension at any moment during the process. If the wire is undergoing any kind of accelerated motion, the integral cannot be evaluated in terms of thermodynamic coordinates referring to the wire as a whole. If, however, the external force is maintained at all times only slightly different from the tension,

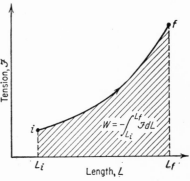

FIG. 3.3. $\mathcal{F}$-L diagram for a wire.

the process is sufficiently quasi-static to warrant the use of an equation of state, in which case the integration can be carried out once $\mathcal{F}$ is known as a function of L. When $\mathcal{F}$ is expressed in dynes and L in centimeters, W will be expressed in ergs. An extension or contraction of a wire may be represented on an $\mathcal{F}$-L diagram as shown in Fig. 3.3. The work done during an extension of the wire from the state i to the state f is represented by the area under the curve connecting i to f. This work depends, of course, upon the path.

3.8. Work in Changing the Area of a Surface Film. Consider a double surface film with liquid in between, stretched across a wire framework, one side of which is movable, as shown in Fig.

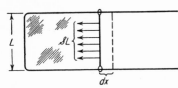

FIG. 3.4. Surface film stretched across a wire framework.

3.4. If the movable wire has a length L and the surface tension is $\mathcal{S}$, the force exerted by both films is $2\mathcal{S}L$. For an infinitesimal displacement dx, the work is

$$\bar{d}W = -2\mathcal{S}L\,dx.$$

But

$$2L\,dx = dA.$$

Hence

$$\bar{d}W = -\mathcal{S}\,dA.$$

(Why is the minus sign used?)   For a finite change from A_i to A_f,

$$W = - \int_{A_i}^{A_f} \mathscr{S} \, dA.$$

A quasi-static process may be approximated by maintaining the external force at all times only slightly different from that exerted by the film. During a quasi-static process, $\mathscr{S}$ is a function of thermodynamic coordinates only and the integral can be evaluated once the path is known.   It is obvious that the area under a curve on an $\mathscr{S}$-A diagram represents the work done on or by a surface film.   When $\mathscr{S}$ is expressed in dynes per centimeter and A in square centimeters, W will be in ergs.

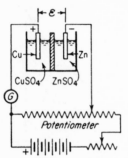

FIG. 3.5. Approximately quasi-static transfer of electricity in a reversible cell.

3.9. Work in Varying the Charge of a Reversible Cell.   The conventional description of an electric current is that it is the motion of positive electricity from a region of higher to a region of lower potential.   Although this is opposite to the direction of electron drift, the convention is still used, and it is still convenient to adopt it in thermodynamics.   Imagine a reversible cell of emf $\mathscr{E}$ to be connected to a potentiometer so that an almost continuous variation of potential difference may be obtained with a sliding contactor.   The circuit is shown in Fig. 3.5.   The external potential difference may be made equal to, slightly less, or slightly more than $\mathscr{E}$ by sliding the contactor.

If the external potential difference is made infinitesimally smaller than $\mathscr{E}$, then, during the short time this difference exists, there is a transfer of a quantity of electricity dZ through the external circuit in a direction from the positive to the negative electrode.   In this case, work is done by the cell on the outside.   If the external potential difference is made slightly larger than $\mathscr{E}$, electricity is transferred in the opposite direction and work is done on the cell.   In either case, the amount of work is

$$\boxed{dW = -\mathscr{E} \, dZ.}$$

When the cell is discharging through the external circuit, dZ is negative, i.e., there is a quantity Z connected with the "state of charge" of the cell which decreases by an amount dZ, where dZ is the actual quantity of electricity transferred.   Charging the cell involves an increase in Z or a positive dZ.

If Z changes by a finite amount,

$$W = - \int_{Z_i}^{Z_f} \mathscr{E} \, dZ.$$

If the current is i, then in time $d\tau$, $dZ = i\,d\tau$, and

$$W = -\int_i^f \mathcal{E}\,i\,d\tau.$$

With $\mathcal{E}$ in volts and the charge in coulombs, the work will be expressed in joules.

3.10. Work in Changing the Magnetization of a Magnetic Solid.
Consider a sample of magnetic material in the form of a ring of cross-sectional area A and of mean circumference L. Suppose an insulated wire is wound on top of the sample, forming a toroidal winding of N closely spaced turns, as shown in Fig. 3.6. A current may be maintained in the winding by a battery and, by moving the sliding contactor of a rheostat, this current may be changed.

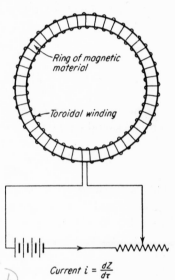

Ring of magnetic material

Toroidal winding

Current $i = \frac{dZ}{d\tau}$

Fig. 3.6. Changing the magnetization of a magnetic solid.

The effect of a current in the winding is to set up a magnetic field with magnetic induction $\mathcal{B}$. Suppose the current is changed and, in time $d\tau$, the magnetic induction changes by an amount $d\mathcal{B}$. Then, by Faraday's principle of electromagnetic induction, there is induced in the winding a back emf $\mathcal{E}$, where

$$\mathcal{E} = -NA\frac{d\mathcal{B}}{d\tau}.$$

During the time interval $d\tau$, a quantity of electricity dZ is transferred in the circuit, and the work done by the system to maintain the current is

$$dW = \mathcal{E}\,dZ$$
$$= -NA\frac{d\mathcal{B}}{d\tau}\,dZ$$
$$= -NA\frac{dZ}{d\tau}\cdot d\mathcal{B}$$
$$= -NAi\,d\mathcal{B},$$

where i, equal to $dZ/d\tau$, is the momentary value of the current.

The magnetic intensity $\mathcal{H}$ due to a current i in a toroidal winding is given by

$$\mathcal{H} = \frac{4\pi Ni}{L} = \frac{4\pi NAi}{AL}$$
$$= \frac{4\pi NAi}{V},$$

where V is the volume of magnetic material. Therefore

$$NAi = \frac{V}{4\pi} \mathcal{H},$$

and

$$dW = -\frac{V}{4\pi} \mathcal{H} \, d\mathcal{B}.$$

It is shown in textbooks on magnetism that, in the case of a ring where there are no magnetic poles,

$$\mathcal{B} = \mathcal{H} + 4\pi \frac{I}{V},$$

and therefore

$$dW = -\frac{V}{4\pi} \mathcal{H} \, d\mathcal{H} - \mathcal{H} \, dI.$$

If no material were present within the toroidal winding, I would be zero, $\mathcal{B}$ would equal $\mathcal{H}$, and

$$dW = -\frac{V}{4\pi} \mathcal{H} \, d\mathcal{H} \qquad \text{(vacuum only).}$$

This is the work necessary to increase the magnetic field in a volume V *of empty space* by an amount $d\mathcal{H}$. The second term, $-\mathcal{H} \, dI$ is the work done in increasing the magnetization of the material by an amount dI. We shall be concerned in this book with changes of temperature, energy, etc., of the material only, brought about by work done on or by the material. Consequently, for the purpose of this book,

$$\boxed{dW = -\mathcal{H} \, dI.}$$

The minus sign merely provides that an increase of magnetization (positive dI) involves negative work. If $\mathcal{H}$ is measured in oersteds (dynes per unit pole) and I in pole centimeters, then the work will be expressed in ergs. If the magnetization is caused to change a finite amount from I_i to I_f, the work will be

$$W = -\int_{I_i}^{I_f} \mathcal{H} \, dI.$$

Modern experiments on paramagnetic materials are usually performed on samples in the form of cylinders or ellipsoids, not toroids. In these cases, the $\mathcal{H}$ field inside the material is somewhat smaller than the $\mathcal{H}$ field generated by the electric current in the surrounding winding because of the reverse field (demagnetizing field) set up by magnetic poles which form on the surfaces of the samples. In longitudinal magnetic fields, the demagnetizing effect may be either rendered negligible by using cylinders whose length is much larger than the diameter, or corrected for in a simple way. In transverse magnetic fields, a correction factor must be applied. We shall limit ourselves to toroids or to long thin cylinders in longitudinal fields where the internal and external $\mathcal{H}$ fields are the same.

In any actual case, a change of magnetization is accomplished very nearly quasi-statically, and therefore an equation of state may be used in the integration of the expression denoting the work. A process involving a change of magnetization may be plotted on an $\mathcal{H}$-I diagram, in which case the area under a curve represents the work done.

3.11. Summary and Notation. The results of this chapter are summarized in Table 3.1. It will be noticed that each expression for work is the product of an intensive and an extensive quantity.

TABLE 3.1. WORK

System	Intensive quantity (generalized force)	Extensive quantity (generalized displacement)	Work
Chemical system...	$\begin{cases} P \text{ in dynes/cm}^2 \\ P \text{ in lb/in.}^2 \end{cases}$	V in cm^3 V in ft^3	$\int P \, dV$ in ergs $144\int P \, dV$ in ft-lb
Wire..............	$\mathcal{F}$ in dynes	L in cm	$-\int \mathcal{F} \, dL$ in ergs
Surface film........	$\mathcal{A}$ in dynes/cm	A in cm^2	$-\int \mathcal{A} \, dA$ in ergs
Reversible cell......	$\mathcal{E}$ in volts	Z in coulombs	$-\int \mathcal{E} \, dZ$ in joules
Paramagnetic solid.	$\mathcal{H}$ in oersteds	I in pole cm	$-\int \mathcal{H} \, dI$ in ergs

Consequently, work is an extensive quantity. In the case of extensive quantities, the following notation will be adopted:

1. When the mass of the system is not specified and may be regarded as any constant value, capitals will be used; thus, V, L, A, Z, I, U, W, Q.

2. When the mass of the system is exactly 1 gm, 1 lb, or 1 mole, lower-case letters will be used; thus, v, l, a, z, i, u, w, q. A quantity that refers to unit mass, i.e., to 1 gm or 1 lb, is called a *specific* quantity; thus "specific volume," "specific magnetization," "specific internal energy," etc. One that refers to a mole of material is called a *molar* quantity; thus, "molar volume," "molar heat," etc. When lower-case letters are used, one must have recourse to the context to determine whether they are specific or molar. Usually, there are other quantities in an equation that serve to settle this point. If not, the equation will hold equally well in either case.

We have seen that a work diagram is obtained if any one of the intensive coordinates is plotted against its corresponding extensive coordinates. There are therefore as many work diagrams as there are systems. It is desirable at times, for the sake of argument, to refer to a work diagram that does not refer to one system in particular, but represents the behavior of any system. If we designate the intensive quantities $P, \mathcal{F}, \mathcal{A}, \mathcal{E}$, and $\mathscr{H}$ as *generalized forces*, and their corresponding extensive quantities $V, L, A, Z,$ and I as *generalized displacements*, we may represent the work done by any system on a *generalized work diagram* by plotting the generalized force $\mathscr{Y}$ against the generalized displacement X. Conclusions based upon such a diagram will hold for any system.

PROBLEMS

3.1. (a) Steam is admitted to the cylinder of a steam engine at a constant pressure of 300 lb/in.² The bore of the cylinder is 8 in. and the stroke of the piston is 12 in. How much work is done per stroke?

(b) If 10 lb of water is evaporated at atmospheric pressure until a volume of 288.5 ft³ is occupied, how much work is done?

3.2. A thin-walled metal bomb of volume V_B contains n moles of gas at high pressure. Connected to the bomb is a capillary tube and stopcock. When the stopcock is opened slightly, the gas leaks slowly into a cylinder equipped with a nonleaking, frictionless piston where the pressure remains constant at the atmospheric value P_0.

(a) Show that, after as much gas as possible has leaked out, an amount of work

$$W = P_0(nv_0 - V_B)$$

has been done, where v_0 is the molar volume of the gas at atmospheric pressure and temperature.

(b) How much work would be done if the gas leaked directly into the atmosphere?

3.3. Calculate the work done by 1 mole of a gas during a quasi-static, isothermal expansion from an initial volume v_i to a final volume v_f when the equation of state is

(a) $P(v - b) = R\theta.$

(b) $Pv = R\theta(1 + B'P).$

(c) $Pv = R\theta\left(1 + \dfrac{B''}{v}\right).$

3.4. During a quasi-static adiabatic expansion of an ideal gas, the pressure at any moment is given by the equation

$$PV^\gamma = K,$$

where γ and K are constants. Show that the work done in expanding from a state (P_i, V_i) to a state (P_f, V_f) is

$$W = \frac{P_iV_i - P_fV_f}{\gamma - 1}.$$

If the initial pressure and volume are, respectively, 10 atm and 1 liter and the final values 2 atm and 3.16 liters, how many joules of work are done by a gas whose $\gamma = 1.4$?

3.5. A stationary vertical cylinder, closed at the top, contains a gas whose volume may be changed with the aid of a heavy, frictionless, nonleaking piston of weight w.

(a) How much work is done by an outside agent in compressing the gas an amount dV by raising the piston a distance dy.

(b) If this device is used as part of an engine, what expression for work is appropriate to calculate the net work delivered to or absorbed from the outside agent?

(c) If this device is used only to produce temperature changes of the gas, what expression for work would be appropriate?

(d) Compare this situation with that involved in increasing the magnetic induction of a ring of magnetic material.

3.6. The pressure on 100 gm of metal is increased quasi-statically and isothermally from zero to 1000 atm. Assuming the density and the isothermal bulk modulus to remain constant at the values 10.0 gm/cm^3 and 1.50 × 10^{12} dynes/cm^2, respectively, calculate the work in joules.

3.7. (*a*) The tension in a wire is increased quasi-statically and isothermally from $\mathscr{F}_i$ to $\mathscr{F}_f$. If the length, cross-sectional area, and isothermal Young's modulus of the wire remain practically constant, show that the work done is

$$W = -\frac{L}{2AY}(\mathscr{F}_f^2 - \mathscr{F}_i^2).$$

(*b*) The tension in a metal wire 1 meter long and 0.001 cm^2 in area is increased quasi-statically and isothermally at 0°C from 10^6 to 10^7 dynes. How many joules of work are done? (Isothermal Young's modulus at 0°C is 2.50 × 10^{12} dynes/cm^2.)

3.8. The equation of state of an ideal elastic substance is

$$\mathscr{F} = K\theta\left(\frac{L}{L_0} - \frac{L_0^2}{L^2}\right),$$

where K is a constant and L_0 (the value of L at zero tension) is a function of temperature only. Calculate the work necessary to compress the substance from $L = L_0$ to $L = L_0/2$ quasi-statically and isothermally.

3.9. Prove that the work done during a quasi-static isothermal change of state of a paramagnetic substance obeying Curie's equation is given by

$$W = \frac{\theta}{2C}(I_i^2 - I_f^2)$$

$$= \frac{C}{2\theta}(\mathscr{H}_i^2 - \mathscr{H}_f^2).$$

3.10. Show that the magnetic energy per unit volume in empty space is $\mathscr{H}^2/8\pi$.

3.11. Two hundred cubic centimeters of a paramagnetic substance is maintained at constant temperature. A magnetic field is increased quasi-statically and isothermally from zero to 15,000 oersteds. Assuming Curie's equation to hold, and the Curie constant per unit volume to be 0.15 deg,

(*a*) How much work would have to be done if no material were present?

(*b*) How much work is done to change the magnetization of the material when the temperature is 300°K, and when it is 1°K?

(*c*) How much work is done by the agent supplying the magnetic field at both temperatures?

3.12. A superconducting cylinder is placed in a longitudinal magnetic field, and the field is increased isothermally starting from zero. From $\mathscr{H} = 0$ to $\mathscr{H} = \mathscr{H}_T$, the material remains superconducting with $\mathscr{B} = 0$ and $I = -V\mathscr{H}/4\pi$. At $\mathscr{H} = \mathscr{H}_T$, the material quickly becomes normal, $\mathscr{B}$ suddenly rising to the value $\mathscr{H}_T$, and I suddenly changing to the value zero.

(*a*) Calculate the total work during the entire process.

(*b*) Calculate the work done on the material only during the entire process.

4

The First Law of Thermodynamics

4.1. Work and Heat. It was shown in Chap. 3 how a system could be transferred from an initial to a final state by means of a quasi-static process and how the work done during the process could be calculated. There are other means, however, of changing the state of a system that do not necessarily involve the performance of a quasi-static process. Consider, for example, the four situations depicted in Fig. 4.1. In (*a*) the system is a composite one consisting of some water and a paddle wheel, which is caused to rotate and churn the water by means of a falling weight. In (*b*) both the water and the resistor constitute the system, the electric current in the resistor being maintained by a generator turned by means of a falling weight. In both cases the state of the system is caused to change; and since the agency for changing the state of the system is a falling weight, both processes involve the performance of work.

In (*c*) and (*d*), however, the situation is quite different. The system in both cases is some water in a diathermic container. In (*c*) the system is in contact with the burning gases from a bunsen burner, i.e., with another body at a higher temperature, whereas in (*d*) the system is near but not in contact with an electric lamp whose temperature is much higher than that of the water. In both cases the state of the system is caused to change, but in neither case can the agency for the change be described by mechanical means.

What happens when two systems at different temperatures are placed together is one of the most familiar experiences of mankind. It is well known that the final temperature reached by both systems is intermediate between the two starting temperatures. Up to the beginning of the nineteenth century, such phenomena, which comprise the subject of *calorimetry*, were explained by postulating the existence of a substance, caloric, or heat, in every body. It was believed that a body at a high temperature contained much caloric and one at a low temperature only a little. When the two bodies were put together, the body rich in caloric lost some to the other, and thus the final temperature was intermediate. Although today we know that heat is not a substance whose total amount

56

remains constant, nevertheless we ascribe the changes that take place
in Fig. 4.1(c) and (d) to the transfer of "something" from the body at
the higher temperature to the one at the lower, and this "something"
we call heat. We therefore adopt as a *calorimetric* definition of heat
*that which is transferred between a system and its surroundings by virtue
of a temperature difference only.* Whether heat is a substance or a form
of energy cannot be decided yet, but it will appear later that it is a

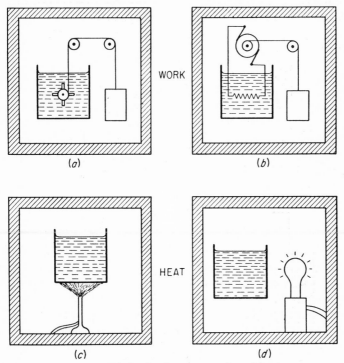

FIG. 4.1. Distinction between work and heat.

form of energy. It is obvious that an adiabatic wall is one which is
impervious to heat (heat insulator) and that a diathermic wall is a heat
conductor.

It is important to observe that the decision as to whether a particular
change of state involves the performance of work or the transfer of heat
requires first an unequivocal answer to the questions "What is the system, and what are the surroundings?" For example, in Fig. 4.1(b), if
the resistor is regarded as the system and the water as the surroundings,
then there is a transfer of heat from the resistor by virtue of the temperature difference between the resistor and the water. Also, if a small part
of the water is regarded as the system, the rest of the water being the

surroundings, then again there is a transfer of heat. Regarding, however, the composite system composed of both the water and the resistor, the surroundings do not contain any object whose temperature differs from that of the system, and hence no heat is transferred between *this composite system* and its surroundings.

4.2. Adiabatic Work. When a system is completely surrounded by an adiabatic envelope, it may still be coupled to the outside so that work may be done. Four examples of *adiabatic work* are shown in Fig. 4.2. It is an important fact of experience that the state of a system may be caused to change from a given initial state to a suitable final state by

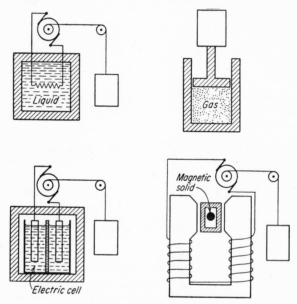

FIG. 4.2. Adiabatic work.

the performance of adiabatic work *only*. Consider for the sake of simplicity the two states i and f of a composite system composed of water in which is embedded a resistor, shown on the P-t diagram of Fig. 4.3. The initial state i is characterized by the coordinates $P_i = 1$ atm, $t_i = 14.5°$C; and the final state f by $P_f = 1$ atm, $t_f = 15.5°$C. To cause the system to proceed from i to f along path I by the performance of adiabatic work only, it would be necessary merely to surround the water with an adiabatic envelope, keep the water at atmospheric pressure, and maintain a current in the resistor for a suitable interval of time.

But path I is not the only path by which the system may be changed from i to f by the performance of adiabatic work only. We might compress the water adiabatically from i to j, then use a current in the resistor from j to k, and then expand from k to f, the whole series of processes being designated by path II. Or we might make use of a similar adiabatic path III.   There are an infinite number of paths by which a system may be transferred from an initial state to a final state by the performance of adiabatic work only. Although accurate measurements of adiabatic work along different paths between the same two states have never been made, nevertheless, indirect experiments indicate that the adiabatic work is the same along all such paths.   The generalization of this result is known as the *first law of thermodynamics*, namely:

If a system is caused to change from an initial state to a final state by adiabatic means only, the work done is the same for all adiabatic paths connecting the two states.

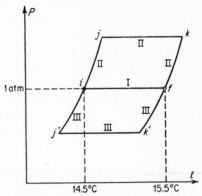

Whenever a quantity is found to depend only on the initial and final states and not on the path connecting them, an important conclusion can be drawn. The student will recall from mechanics that, in moving an object from a point i in a gravitational field to another point f, in the absence of friction the work done depends only on the positions of the two points and not on the path through which the body was moved. It was concluded from this that there exists a function of the space coordinates of the body

FIG. 4.3. Changing the state of a system from i to f along three different adiabatic paths.

whose final value minus its initial value is equal to the work done. This function was called the potential-energy function. Similarly, the work done in moving a quantity of electricity from one point in an electric field to another is also independent of the path and is therefore also expressible as the value of a function (the electric potential function) at the final state minus its value at the initial state.   It therefore follows from the first law of thermodynamics that there exists a function of the coordinates of a thermodynamic system whose value at the final state minus its value at the initial state is equal to the adiabatic work in going from one state to the other.   This function is known as the *internal-energy function.*

Denoting the internal-energy function by U, we have

$$-W_{i \rightarrow f} \text{ (adiabatic)} = U_f - U_i$$

where the minus sign is introduced so that, when work is done *on* a system, U_f will be greater than U_i. It is found by experiment that it is not always possible to take a system from an initial state i to *any* state f by the performance of adiabatic work alone. It will be shown later, however, when entropy is discussed, that if f cannot be reached in this way, it is always possible to go from f to i by adiabatic means, in which case the change in internal energy from i to f, instead of being $-W_{i \to f}$, is $+W_{f \to i}$.

4.3. Internal-energy Function. The physical interpretation of the difference $U_f - U_i$ is the increase in energy of the system. The equality, therefore, of the increase of energy and the adiabatic work expresses the principle of the conservation of energy. It should be emphasized, however, that the equation expresses more than the principle of the conservation of energy. It states that there exists an energy function, the difference between two values of which is the energy change of the system.

The internal energy is a function of as many thermodynamic coordinates as are necessary to specify the state of a system. The equilibrium states of a chemical system, for example, describable by means of three thermodynamic coordinates P, V, and θ, are completely determined by only two, since the third is fixed by the equation of state. Therefore, the internal energy may be thought of as a function of only two (any two) of the thermodynamic coordinates. This is true for each of the simple systems described in Chap. 2. It is not always possible to write this function in simple mathematical form. Very often the exact form of the function is unknown. It must be understood, however, that it is not necessary to know actually what the internal-energy function is, so long as we can be sure that such a function exists.

If the coordinates characterizing the two states differ from each other only infinitesimally, the change of internal energy is dU, where dU is an exact differential, since it is the differential of an actual function. In the case of a chemical system, if U is regarded as a function of θ and V, then

$$dU = \left(\frac{\partial U}{\partial \theta}\right)_V d\theta + \left(\frac{\partial U}{\partial V}\right)_\theta dV,$$

or, regarding U as a function of θ and P,

$$dU = \left(\frac{\partial U}{\partial \theta}\right)_P d\theta + \left(\frac{\partial U}{\partial P}\right)_\theta dP.$$

The student should realize that the two partial derivatives $(\partial U/\partial \theta)_V$ and $(\partial U/\partial \theta)_P$ are not equal. The first is a function of θ and V, and the second a function of θ and P. They are different mathematically and also have a different physical meaning.

4.4. Mathematical Formulation of the First Law. We have been considering up to now processes wherein a system undergoes a change of state through the performance of adiabatic work only.   Such experiments must be performed in order to measure the change in the energy function of a system, but they are not the usual processes that are carried out in the laboratory.   In Fig. 4.4 there are depicted two examples of processes involving changes of state that take place nonadiabatically.   In (a) a gas is in contact with a bunsen flame whose temperature is higher than that of the gas and at the same time is allowed to expand.   In (b) the magnetization of a paramagnetic solid is increased while it is in contact with liquid helium, the temperature of which is lower than that of the solid.   As a matter of fact, some of the helium boils away during the magnetization.

Let us now imagine two different experiments performed on the same system.   In one we measure the adiabatic work necessary to change the state of the system from i to f. This is $U_f - U_i$. In the other we cause the system to undergo the *same* change of state, but nonadiabatically, and measure the work done.   The result of all such experiments is that *the nonadiabatic work is* **not** *equal to* $U_f - U_i$.   In order that this result shall be consistent with the principle of the conservation of energy, we are forced to conclude that energy has been transferred by means *other than* the performance of work.   This energy, whose transfer between the

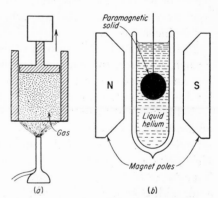

FIG. 4.4. Nonadiabatic processes.

system and its surroundings is required by the principle of the conservation of energy and which has taken place only by virtue of the temperature difference between the system and its surroundings, is what we have previously called heat.   We therefore give the following as our *thermodynamic* definition of heat: *When a system whose surroundings are at a different temperature and on which work may be done undergoes a process, the energy transferred by nonmechanical means, equal to the difference between the internal-energy change and the work done, is called heat.*   Denoting this difference by Q, we have

$$Q = U_f - U_i - (-W)$$

or

$$\boxed{Q = U_f - U_i + W,}$$

where the convention has been adopted that Q is positive when it enters a system and negative when it leaves (just the opposite of the sign convention for W). The preceding equation is known as the *mathematical formulation of the first law*.

It should be emphasized that the mathematical formulation of the first law contains three related ideas: (1) the existence of an internal-energy function; (2) the principle of the conservation of energy; (3) the definition of heat as *energy* in transit.

It was many years before it was understood that heat is energy. The first really conclusive evidence that heat could not be a substance was given by Benjamin Thompson, an American from Woburn, Mass., who later became Count Rumford of Bavaria. Rumford, in 1798, observed the temperature rise of the brass chips produced during the boring of cannon and concluded that the work of boring was responsible for the flow of heat. One year later, Sir Humphry Davy tried to show that two pieces of ice could be melted by rubbing them together. His idea was to show that heat is a manifestation of energy, but his experiment was highly inconclusive.

The idea that heat is a form of energy was put forward by Séguin, a French engineer, in 1839 and by Mayer, a German physician, in 1842, but no conclusive experiments were performed by either. It remained for Joule, an independent investigator with a private laboratory, in the period from 1840 to 1849, to clinch the matter by performing a series of admirable experiments on the relation between heat and work and to establish once and for all the equivalence of these two quantities. Von Helmholtz, a surgeon in the Prussian army, recognized the epoch-making importance of Joule's work and wrote a brilliant paper in 1847, applying Joule's ideas to the sciences of physical chemistry and physiology.

4.5. Concept of Heat. Heat is energy in transit. It flows from one point to another. When the flow has ceased, there is no longer any occasion to use the word heat. It would be just as incorrect to refer to the "heat in a body" as it would be to speak about the "work in a body." The performance of work and the flow of heat are methods whereby the internal energy of a system is changed. It is impossible to separate or divide the internal energy into a mechanical and a thermal part.

We have seen that, in general, the work done on or by a system is not a function of the coordinates of the system but depends on the path by which the system was brought from the initial to the final state. Exactly the same is true of the heat transferred to or from a system. Q is not a function of the thermodynamic coordinates but depends on the path. An infinitesimal amount of heat, therefore, is an inexact differential and is represented by the symbol đQ.

To quote from Slater's "Introduction to Chemical Physics":

At first sight, it seems too bad that $\int dQ$ is not independent of the path, for some such quantity would be useful. It would be pleasant to be able to say, in a given state of the system, that the system had so and so much heat energy. Starting from the absolute zero of temperature, where we could say that the heat energy was zero, we could heat the body up to the state we were interested in, find $\int dQ$ from absolute zero up to this state, and call that the heat energy. But the stubborn fact remains that we should get different answers if we heated it up in different ways. For instance, we might heat it at an arbitrary constant pressure until we reached the desired temperature, then adjust the pressure at constant temperature to the desired value; or we might raise it first to the desired pressure, then heat it at that pressure to the final temperature; or many other equally simple processes. Each would give a different answer, as we can easily verify. There is nothing to do about it.

Imagine a system A in thermal contact with a system B, the two systems being surrounded by adiabatic walls. For system A alone

$$Q = U_f - U_i + W,$$

and for system B alone

$$Q' = U_f' - U_i' + W'.$$

Adding, we get

$$Q + Q' = (U_f + U_f') - (U_i + U_i') + W + W'.$$

Since $(U_f + U_f') - (U_i + U_i')$ is the change in energy of the composite system and $W + W'$ is the work done by the composite system, it follows that $Q + Q'$ is the heat transferred by the composite system. Since the composite system is surrounded by adiabatic walls,

$$Q + Q' = 0,$$

and

$$Q = -Q'.$$

In other words, *under adiabatic conditions, the heat lost (or gained) by system A is equal to the heat gained (or lost) by system B.*

4.6. Differential Form of the First Law. A process involving only infinitesimal changes in the thermodynamic coordinates of a system is known as an infinitesimal process. For such a process the first law becomes

$$\boxed{dQ = dU + dW.}$$

If the infinitesimal process is quasi-static, then dU and dW can be expressed in terms of thermodynamic coordinates only. An infinitesimal quasi-static process is one in which the system passes from an initial equilibrium state to a neighboring equilibrium state

For an infinitesimal quasi-static process of a chemical system, the first law becomes

$$dQ = dU + P\,dV,$$

where U is a function of any two of the three thermodynamic coordinates and P is, of course, a function of V and θ. A similar equation may be written for each of the other simple systems as shown in Table 4.1.

TABLE 4.1. THE FIRST LAW FOR SIMPLE SYSTEMS

System	First law	U is a function of *any two* of
Chemical system............	$dQ = dU + P\,dV$	P, V, θ
Wire......................	$dQ = dU - \mathscr{F}\,dL$	$\mathscr{F}, L, \theta$
Surface film...............	$dQ = dU - \mathscr{S}\,dA$	$\mathscr{S}, A, \theta$
Electric cell...............	$dQ = dU - \mathscr{E}\,dZ$	$\mathscr{E}, Z, \theta$
Paramagnetic solid.........	$dQ = dU - \mathscr{H}\,dI$	$\mathscr{H}, I, \theta$

In the case of more complicated systems, it is merely necessary to replace dW in the first law by two or more expressions. For example, the operation of a reversible cell in which gases are liberated may involve work in changing not only its charge but also its volume. Hence

$$dQ = dU + P\,dV - \mathscr{E}\,dZ,$$

and U is a function of three of $P, V, \theta, \mathscr{E}, Z$. In the case of a paramagnetic gas,

$$dQ = dU + P\,dV - \mathscr{H}\,dI,$$

and U is a function of three of $P, V, \theta, \mathscr{H}, I$. In the case of a liquid and its surface,

$$dQ = dU + P\,dV - \mathscr{S}\,dA,$$

and U is a function of three of $P, V, \theta, \mathscr{S}, A$.

4.7. Mechanical Equivalent of Heat. Joule's Measurements. In general, when heat enters a system, a change of state occurs involving a change in some or all of the thermodynamic coordinates. A definite change under specified conditions in any one convenient coordinate of any easily reproduced system may serve to indicate the absorption of a standard amount of heat. Thus, a *calorie* of heat is defined as that amount of heat whose absorption by 1 gm of water at constant atmospheric pressure is accompanied by a temperature rise from 14.5 to 15.5°C. The same change in m gm of water under the same conditions indicates the absorption of m cal of heat. Similarly, in engineering, a Btu (British thermal unit) is that quantity of heat which produces a rise in tem-

perature from 63 to 64°F in 1 lb of water.   One Btu is equal to 252 cal.
The branch of experimental physics or physical chemistry dealing with
direct or indirect measurements of heat is known as *calorimetry*.   A container or system of vessels in which either a heat transfer takes place or
effects are produced that are equivalent to a flow of heat is called a *calorimeter*.   Each experimental problem requires a calorimeter of a special
design.   Various calorimeters will be described throughout this chapter.

Suppose that the absorption of an amount of heat Q by a system is
accompanied by a change of internal energy $U_f - U_i$ and the performance of an amount of work W'.   Then, from the first law,

$$Q = U_f - U_i + W',$$

where both sides of the equation are expressed in joules.   If, instead, it
is desired to express Q in calories and, at the same time, both $U_f - U_i$
and W' in joules, a conversion factor J must be introduced explicitly,
thus:

$$JQ = U_f - U_i + W',$$

where J is called the *mechanical equivalent of heat*.

Now suppose that the system is shielded so that no heat may be transferred and that the same changes are caused to take place by the performance of work W *on* the system.   Then, applying the first law, we get

$$0 = U_f - U_i + W' - W,$$

where all quantities are expressed in joules.   It follows that $JQ = W$, or

$$J = \frac{W}{Q} = \left\{ \begin{array}{l} \text{a dimensionless conversion factor whose numerical value is} \\ \text{equal to the number of joules of work necessary to pro-} \\ \text{duce the same change of state in a system as that pro-} \\ \text{duced by the absorption of 1 cal of heat.} \end{array} \right.$$

If we choose as our system 1 gm of water and as our change of state the
change from 14.5 to 15.5°C at constant atmospheric pressure, the mechanical equivalent of heat becomes numerically equal to the number of joules
of work necessary to produce a change of temperature from 14.5 to 15.5°C
in 1 gm of water at atmospheric pressure.

The mechanical equivalent of heat was measured by Joule first in
1840 and many times later in the following years.   In his first method,
an electric generator was rotated by a known amount of mechanical
energy, and the resulting electrical energy was supplied to a known mass
of water, giving rise to a measured rise of temperature.   This method
was then replaced by the method most often associated with his name,
namely, that in which a mass of water is churned by paddle wheels set
in rotation by a series of falling weights.   A short while after the British

Association set up the practical electric units, Joule redetermined the mechanical equivalent of heat by measuring the temperature rise of water surrounding an electric resistor through which a known current was flowing. His result differed so much from his previous, purely mechanical measurement that he was led to repeat with greater accuracy the experiment with the paddle wheels. Confirming his previous measurement, he concluded that the British Association standard of resistance was at fault.

The best value obtained by Joule in all these experiments was 772.5 ft · lb/Btu, or 4.155 joules/cal. In evaluating his work, it is important to bear in mind that Joule did not have at his disposal the accurately standardized thermometers which exist today; nor was he able to make such reliable corrections for heat losses as are possible now. In spite of this, his final result differs from the present accepted value by less than 1 per cent. The work of Joule must be regarded as one of the most remarkable series of pioneer experiments, in respect not only to the skill and care exercised but to the influence these experiments had in convincing scientists throughout the world of the correctness of the mechanical theory of heat.

4.8. Later Measurements of _J_. Of all the measurements made in the period after Joule up to about 1930, four stand out for their refinement and precision:

1. *Experiments of Rowland, 1879.* While professor of physics at Johns Hopkins University in Baltimore, Rowland engaged in an elaborate and painstaking research on the determination of J that, to this day, remains a model of careful and accurate experimentation. Rowland suspended a large calorimeter on a wire and caused the water in the calorimeter to be churned by a series of perforated paddle wheels set in rotation by a steam engine. A counter torque was applied to the calorimeter to keep it from rotating; by multiplying this torque by the angle of rotation of the paddle wheels, the work delivered to the water was obtained. The temperature of the water was measured at regular intervals with the aid of mercury thermometers calibrated with reference to an air thermometer. In this way, Rowland was able to measure the work corresponding to a 1° temperature rise not only at 15°C but also at a number of other temperatures. His value of J was 4.189 joules/cal.

So confident was Rowland of the accuracy of his results that he wrote, "Between the limits of 15°C and 25°C, I feel almost certain that no subsequent experiments will change my values so much as 2 parts in 1000." Twenty years later, when the constant-volume hydrogen thermometer was adopted as a world standard, Day, with Rowland's permission and advice, compared Rowland's mercury thermometers with the hydrogen standard and recomputed J, which became 4.188 joules/cal.

That Rowland's statement was no idle boast is substantiated by the fact that his value differs from the accepted value today by only 2 parts in 4000! Commenting on the agreement between Rowland's value of J and their own value of 4.186 (see Art. 4.9) made at the National Bureau of Standards in 1939, Osborne, Stimson, and Ginnings stated, "It is possible that Rowland's remarkable agreement with N.B.S. 1939 is accidental, but it is more likely to be due to the extreme care that Rowland exercised."

2. *Experiments of Callendar and Barnes, 1899.* These physicists employed what is known as a *continuous-flow method.* An electric current was maintained in a resistance wire placed along the axis of a narrow glass tube through which a constant stream of water was caused to flow. The inlet and outlet temperatures of the water were measured with platinum resistance thermometers, and fairly good thermal insulation was achieved by evacuating the space around the central tube. The flow of water and the strength of the electric current were chosen so that the rise of temperature of the water was only a few degrees. To make a correction for the small loss of energy due to the flow of heat from the water to its cooler surroundings, two separate experiments were performed, each with a different flow of water and a different electric current, but with the same change in temperature. In both experiments the heat loss was the same and could be eliminated from the equations.

The potential difference $\mathcal{E}$ in volts and the electric current i in amperes were measured, the product $\mathcal{E}i$ representing the number of joules of electrical energy supplied per second. If m gm of water flows through the calorimeter in τ sec, then

$$\text{Energy supplied to 1 gm of water} = \frac{\mathcal{E}i\tau}{m}.$$

This quantity was determined for various temperature intervals starting at a number of different initial temperatures. The value of the above ratio corresponding to a rise of temperature from 14.5 to 15.5°C, corrected for heat loss, gave the desired mechanical equivalent of heat. The value found was 4.182 joules/cal. The advantage of this method lies in the fact that, once a steady state is reached, no change of temperature occurs in any part of the apparatus and therefore no correction need be made to allow for the energy supplied to the glass tube, to the resistance wire, etc. It is also not necessary to allow for a lag in the reading of the thermometers.

3. *Experiments of Jaeger and Steinwehr, 1921.* In the experiments of Jaeger and Steinwehr, an electric current was maintained in a coil of wire surrounded by m gm of water, and the rise of temperature of the water was noted. If the potential difference across the coil is $\mathcal{E}$, the

current is i, and the time necessary for a rise of temperature from 14.5 to 15.5°C is τ, then, aside from corrections, the mechanical equivalent of heat is

$$J = \frac{\mathscr{E}i\tau}{m}.$$

A very large mass of water was used. The fraction of the total electrical energy that was transformed into internal energy of the calorimeter, the resistance coil, etc., was therefore very small. At no time was the temperature of the system more than a few degrees above the surroundings, and hence the rate of flow of heat to the surroundings could be calculated accurately. The large mass of water was very efficiently stirred. The final result was 4.1850 joules/cal.

4. *Experiments of Laby and Hercus, 1927.* Laby and Hercus made use of the principle of the electromagnetic brake. A stationary calorimeter consisting of 14 copper tubes through which a flow of water was maintained was placed between the poles of an electromagnet which was mounted on bearings so as to rotate around the calorimeter. Eddy currents were induced in the calorimeter, thus supplying electrical energy to the calorimeter and the water, which caused a difference between the inlet and outlet temperatures of the water. The amount of electrical energy was not measured electrically; instead, the power expended in rotating the electromagnet was calculated by measuring the torque and the angular speed. The product of the torque and the angular speed minus the power expended to overcome friction in the bearings (which could easily be measured) represented the energy supplied per second by the eddy currents. Heat loss from the copper tubes to the surrounding air was minimized by placing the tubes in a vacuum flask. Since this was a continuous-flow method, no corrections had to be made for the absorption of energy by parts of the apparatus. The final value, after a reappraisal in 1935, was 4.1852 joules/cal.

4.9. Latest Determination of *J*. In the 12-year interval between 1927 and 1939, important refinements were made in the fundamental thermometric and electric standards that made it advisable to undertake a redetermination of the mechanical equivalent of heat. First, the international temperature scale was developed and adopted, thus ensuring that the readings of a platinum resistance thermometer were in agreement with those of the ideal gas scale; second, by means of very accurate dynamical measurements on electric circuits it was possible to convert *international joules* (based upon the Weston cell standard of emf and the manganin-resistance standard) to *absolute joules* (based upon the standard meter, kilogram, and second) with the result that

1 international joule = 1.000165 abs. joules.

TABLE 4.2. MEASUREMENTS BY OSBORNE,
STIMSON, AND GINNINGS, NATIONAL BUREAU OF
STANDARDS, 1939

Temp., °C	Abs. joules / gm · deg C	Temp., °C	Abs. joules / gm · deg C
0	4.2177	50	4.1807
5	4.2022	55	4.1824
10	4.1922	60	4.1844
15	**4.1858**	65	4.1868
20	4.1819	70	4.1896
25	4.1796	75	4.1928
30	4.1785	80	4.1964
35	4.1782	85	4.2005
40	4.1786	90	4.2051
45	4.1795	95	4.2103
50	4.1807	100	4.2160

Therefore, with all the tremendous resources of the National Bureau of Standards at their disposal, Osborne, Stimson, and Ginnings undertook in 1939 to determine the amount of work needed to increase the temperature of 1 gm of water 1°C at temperatures over the entire range of 0 to 100°C. They used the simple electrical method of supplying energy electrically and noting the accompanying rise of temperature of a large mass of water. Measurements of pd and current were referred directly to N.B.S. standards, temperature was measured on the international scale, and particular attention was paid to the shielding of the apparatus. Their results are shown in Table 4.2 and are compared with other determinations in Fig. 4.5. We may therefore write, for the most accurate value of J up to the present time,

$$J = 4.1858 \text{ joules/cal.}$$

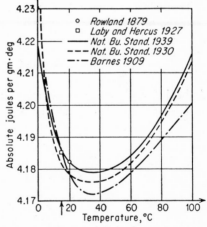

FIG. 4.5. Amount of work necessary to increase the temperature of 1 gm of water 1 degree on the Celsius scale. The value at 15°C is the mechanical equivalent of heat.

Besides the 15° calorie, which is the standard thermal unit throughout the world, there is another calorie that is used in international steam tables known as the *international steam table calorie* (IT cal) and defined as

$$1 \text{ IT cal} = \frac{1}{860} \text{ international watt} \cdot \text{hour}$$
$$= 4.1860 \text{ international joules}$$
$$= 4.1868 \text{ abs. joules.}$$

From the recent N.B.S. measurements just described, the IT calorie corresponds to about a 14° calorie.

A chronological list of the values of the mechanical equivalent of heat is given in Table 4.3.

TABLE 4.3. VALUES OF THE MECHANICAL EQUIVALENT OF HEAT

Experimenters	Date	J, joules/cal
Joule.....................................	1850	4.155
Rowland.................................	1879	4.188
Calendar and Barnes.......................	1899	4.182
Jaeger and Steinwehr......................	1921	4.185
Laby and Hercus..........................	1927	4.185
Osborne, Stimson, and Ginnings.............	1939	4.1858

4.10. Heat Capacity.   When heat is absorbed by a system, a change of temperature may or may not take place, depending on the process. If a system undergoes a change of temperature from θ_i to θ_f during the transfer of Q units of heat, the *average heat capacity* of the system is defined as the ratio

$$\text{Average heat capacity} = \frac{Q}{\theta_f - \theta_i}.$$

As both Q and $\theta_f - \theta_i$ get smaller, this ratio approaches the *instantaneous heat capacity*, or heat capacity, C, thus:

$$C = \lim_{\theta_f \to \theta_i} \frac{Q}{\theta_f - \theta_i}$$

$$\boxed{C = \frac{dQ}{d\theta}.}$$

The heat capacity of a system per unit mass is called the specific heat capacity or *specific heat* and is written

$$c = \frac{1}{m}\frac{dQ}{d\theta} = \frac{dQ/m}{d\theta} = \frac{dq}{d\theta},$$

being measured in calories per gram degree centigrade or Btu per pound degree Fahrenheit.   The molar heat capacity is also written in lower-case letters but has the units calories per mole degree.

The heat capacity may be negative, zero, positive, or infinite, depending on the process the system undergoes during the heat transfer. It has a definite value only for a definite process. In the case of a chemical system, the ratio $dQ/d\theta$ has a unique value when the pressure is kept constant. Under these conditions, C is called the *heat capacity at constant pressure* and is denoted by the symbol C_P, where

$$C_P = \left(\frac{dQ}{d\theta}\right)_P.$$

In general, C_P is a function of P and θ. Similarly, the heat capacity at constant volume is

$$C_V = \left(\frac{dQ}{d\theta}\right)_V$$

and depends on both V and θ. In general, C_P and C_V are different. Both will be discussed thoroughly throughout the book. Each system has its own heat capacities as shown in Table 4.4.

TABLE 4.4

System	Heat capacities	Symbol
Chemical system	Heat capacity at constant pressure Heat capacity at constant volume	C_P C_V
Linear system	Heat capacity at constant tension Heat capacity at constant length	$C_{\mathscr{F}}$ C_L
Surface system	Heat capacity at constant surface tension Heat capacity at constant area	$C_{\mathscr{A}}$ C_A
Electric system	Heat capacity at constant emf Heat capacity at constant charge	$C_{\mathscr{E}}$ C_Z
Magnetic system	Heat capacity at constant field Heat capacity at constant magnetization	$C_{\mathscr{H}}$ C_I

Each heat capacity is a function of two variables. Within a small range of variation of these coordinates, however, the heat capacity may be regarded as practically constant. Very often, one heat capacity can be set equal to another without much error. Thus, the $C_{\mathscr{H}}$ of a paramagnetic solid is at times very nearly equal to C_P.

The measurement made by Osborne, Stimson, and Ginnings of the energy necessary to raise the temperature of 1 gm of water 1°C at various temperatures is essentially a measurement of the specific heat at constant pressure in joules per gram degree. If the numbers in Table 4.2 are divided by 4.1858 joules/cal, they may be converted into calories per gram degree. The variation of c_P of water with temperature is slight, and consequently it may be neglected in all practical problems.

4.11. Measurement of Heat Capacity. Most modern measurements of heat capacity involve the electrical method in which electrical energy is supplied to the system and the equivalent heat is calculated. The shape, size, and construction of the calorimeter, heating coils, thermometers, etc., depend on the nature of the material to be studied and the temperature range desired. It is impossible to describe one calorimeter that is sufficient for all purposes. In general, the measurement of any heat capacity is a research problem requiring all the ability of a trained physicist or physical chemist, the facilities of a good shop, and the skill of a good glass blower. The method of mixtures, described in textbooks of college physics, is of value only in providing a rough measurement of the average C_P in the neighborhood of room temperature. Modern physics, however, requires the accurate determination of the temperature variation of C_P over a wide temperature range, starting as low as possible.

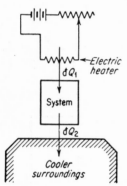

The accurate measurement of the C_V of a solid is almost impossible. In order to find C_V, one first measures C_P and then uses a theoretical formula relating C_P to C_V (see Chap. 13).

FIG. 4.6. System gaining energy from an electric heater and simultaneously losing energy to the cooler surroundings.

The theory underlying the modern methods of measuring C_p may be understood from Fig. 4.6, which shows schematically a system whose heat capacity is to be measured undergoing two energy transfers simultaneously: a gain of energy from an electric heater and a loss of energy to the cooler surroundings. In an infinitesimal time interval $d\tau$, the net heat transferred to the system dQ is

$$dQ = dQ_1 - dQ_2 = C_P \, d\theta.$$

If the potential difference across the electric heater is $\mathcal{E}$ and the current is i, $dQ_1 = \mathcal{E}i \, d\tau/J$, and

$$\boxed{\frac{\mathcal{E}i}{J} \, d\tau - dQ_2 = C_P \, d\theta.}$$

1. *Heating-curve Method.* If energy is supplied to the system *at a constant rate*, and furthermore if the system is shielded so that *no energy is lost to the surroundings*, then $\mathcal{E}i/J = $ const. and $dQ_2 = 0$. Then

$$\frac{\mathscr{E}i}{J} = C_P \frac{d\theta}{d\tau}.$$

The temperature is measured as a function of the time and a *heating curve* (θ vs. τ) is drawn. The slope of the heating curve, $d\theta/d\tau$, in conjunction with the known value of $\mathscr{E}i/J$ is all that is needed to determine C_p.

The construction of a calorimeter that has proved useful in measurements of the C_p of solids at low temperatures (which is the region of most interest to physicists and chemists) is shown in Fig. 4.7. It is known as an *adiabatic vacuum calorimeter* and is a modification by Simon and Lange of a calorimeter designed by Nernst. The sub-

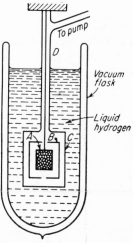

FIG. 4.7. Adiabatic vacuum calorimeter for low-temperature work.

stance to be investigated is placed in a thin-walled copper vessel A. Inside A are also a heating coil and a resistance thermometer (not shown). Surrounding A is a thermostat of brass B equipped with a separate heating coil. One junction of a thermocouple touches the outside of A, and the other junction of the same thermocouple touches the inside of B. By regulating the currents in the heating coils of A and B independently so as to make the thermocouple read zero, it is possible to keep the temperatures of A and B equal and therefore to prevent any heat loss. Surrounding B is a copper vessel C, which is evacuated to a high vacuum through the tube D. The connecting wires to the thermocouple, heating coils, and resistance thermometer are also brought out through the tube D. For low-temperature work, the whole apparatus is immersed in liquid hydrogen contained in a Dewar flask.

2. *Cooling-curve Method.* If the system loses energy to the surroundings while it gains energy from an electric heater, the power input $\mathscr{E}i/J$ is set at an arbitrary value and the temperature is allowed to rise until equilibrium is reached, at which the temperature θ remains constant. These values of power input and equilibrium temperature are then measured and, when plotted, give one point on the curve shown in Fig. 4.8(a). The power input is then increased, and again the temperature is allowed to achieve a new equilibrium value. The new values of $\mathscr{E}i/J$ and θ determine a second point on the curve of Fig. 4.8(a). In this way a *power input curve* is obtained. At any point, $d\theta = 0$ and

$$\frac{dQ_2}{d\tau} = \frac{\mathscr{E}i}{J}. \tag{1}$$

When the system is at its highest temperature, the power supply is cut off and the system is allowed to cool, during which process the temperature is measured as a function of the time. A *cooling curve* (θ vs. τ) is plotted, as shown in Fig. 4.8(b). At any point on the cooling curve, $\mathscr{E}i/J = 0$ and

$$\frac{\text{d}Q_2}{\text{d}\tau} = -C_P \frac{d\theta}{d\tau}. \tag{2}$$

Combining Eqs. (1) and (2), we have

$$C_P \left(-\frac{d\theta}{d\tau} \right) = \frac{\mathscr{E}i}{J},$$

where the slope of the cooling curve at any desired θ and the corresponding power input may be determined from the two curves in Fig. 4.8(a) and (b).

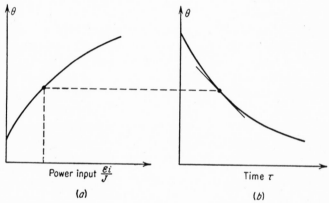

Fig. 4.8. Curves for the determination of heat capacity by the cooling-curve method.

4.12. Quasi-static Flow of Heat. Heat Reservoir.

It was shown in Chap. 3 that a process caused by a finite unbalanced force is attended by phenomena such as turbulence and acceleration that cannot be handled by means of thermodynamic coordinates that refer to the system as a whole. A similar situation exists when there is a finite difference between the temperature of a system and that of its surroundings. A nonuniform temperature distribution is set up in the system, and the calculation of this distribution and its variation with time is in most cases an elaborate mathematical problem. During a quasi-static process, however, the difference between the temperature of a system and that of its surroundings is infinitesimal. As a result, the temperature of the system is at any moment uniform throughout, and its changes are infinitely slow. The flow of heat is also infinitely slow and may be calculated in a simple manner in terms of thermodynamic coordinates referring to the system as a whole.

Suppose that a system is in good thermal contact with a body of extremely large mass and that a quasi-static process is performed. A finite amount of heat that flows during this process will not bring about an appreciable change in the temperature of the surrounding body if the mass is large enough. For example, a cake of ice of ordinary size, thrown into the ocean, will not produce a drop in temperature of the ocean. No ordinary flow of heat into the outside air will produce a rise of temperature of the air. The ocean and the outside air are approximate examples of an ideal body called a *heat reservoir*. *A heat reservoir is a body of such a large mass that it may absorb or reject an unlimited quantity of heat without suffering an appreciable change in temperature or in any other thermodynamic coordinate.* It is not to be understood that there is no change in the thermodynamic coordinates of a heat reservoir when a finite amount of heat flows in or out. There is a change, but an extremely small one, too small to be measured.

Any quasi-static process of a system in contact with a heat reservoir is bound to be isothermal. To describe a quasi-static flow of heat involving a change of temperature, one could conceive of a system placed in contact successively with a series of reservoirs. Thus, if we imagine a series of reservoirs ranging in temperature from θ_i to θ_f placed successively in contact with a system at constant pressure of heat capacity C_P, in such a way that the difference in temperature between the system and the reservoir with which it is in contact is infinitesimal, the flow of heat will be quasi-static and can be calculated as follows: By definition,

$$C_P = \left(\frac{dQ}{d\theta}\right)_P,$$

and therefore

$$Q = \int_{\theta_i}^{\theta_f} C_P \, d\theta.$$

For example, the heat that is absorbed by m gm of water from a series of reservoirs varying in temperature from θ_i to θ_f during a quasi-static isobaric process is

$$Q = \int_{\theta_i}^{\theta_f} C_P \, d\theta$$

$$= m \int_{\theta_i}^{\theta_f} c_P \, d\theta;$$

and if the specific heat c_P is assumed to remain practically constant,

$$Q = mc_P(\theta_f - \theta_i).$$

For a quasi-static isochoric process,

$$Q = \int_{\theta_i}^{\theta_f} C_V \, d\theta.$$

Similar considerations hold for other systems and other quasi-static processes.

PROBLEMS

4.1. A combustion experiment is performed by burning a mixture of fuel and oxygen in a constant-volume "bomb" surrounded by a water bath. During the experiment the temperature of the water is observed to rise. Regarding the mixture of fuel and oxygen as the system,

    (*a*) Has heat been transferred? *yes*

    (*b*) Has work been done? *no*

    (*c*) What is the sign of ΔU? (−)

4.2. A liquid is irregularly stirred in a well-insulated container and thereby undergoes a rise in temperature. Regarding the liquid as the system,

    (*a*) Has heat been transferred? *no*

    (*b*) Has work been done? *yes*

    (*c*) What is the sign of ΔU? (+)

4.3. A vessel with rigid walls and covered with asbestos is divided into two parts by a partition. One part contains a gas, and the other is evacuated. If the partition is suddenly broken, show that the initial and final internal energies of the gas are equal. $dQ = 0 \quad dW = 0 \quad \therefore dU = 0$

4.4. A vessel with rigid walls and covered with asbestos is divided into two parts by an insulating partition. One part contains a gas at temperature T and pressure P. The other part contains a gas at temperature T' and pressure P'. The partition is removed. What conclusion may be drawn by applying the first law of thermodynamics?

4.5. A mixture of hydrogen and oxygen is enclosed in a rigid insulating container and exploded by a spark. The temperature and pressure both increase considerably. Neglecting the small amount of energy provided by the spark itself, what conclusion may be drawn by applying the first law of thermodynamics? $dQ = dU$

4.6. When a system is taken from state *a* to state *b*, in Fig. 4.9, along the path *acb*, 80 Btu of heat flow into the system, and the system does 30 Btu of work.

$dQ = 80\,Btu \qquad dW = 30\,Btu \qquad \therefore dU$

non adiabatic

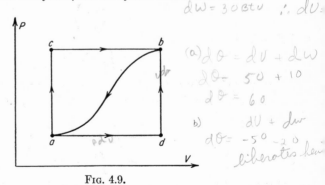

Fig. 4.9.

(a) $dQ = dU + dW$
$dQ = 50 + 10$
$dQ = 60$

(b) $dU + dW$
$dQ = -50 - 20$
liberates heat

    (*a*) How much heat flows into the system along path *adb*, if the work done is 10 Btu?

    (*b*) When the system is returned from *b* to *a* along the curved path, the work done on the system is 20 Btu. Does the system absorb or liberate heat and how much?

    (*c*) If $U_a = 0$ and $U_d = 40$ Btu, find the heat absorbed in the processes *ad* and *db*.

$U_{a \to b} = 50$
$U_{a \to d} = 40$
$\therefore U_{d \to b} = 10$

4.7. A cylindrical tube with rigid walls and covered with asbestos is divided into two parts by a rigid insulating wall with a small hole in it. A frictionless insulating piston is held against the perforated partition, thus preventing the gas that is on the other side from seeping through the hole. The gas is maintained at a pressure P_i by another frictionless insulating piston. Imagine both pistons to move simultaneously in such a way that, as the gas streams through the hole, the pressure remains at the constant value P_i on one side of the dividing wall and at a constant lower value P_f on the other side, until all the gas is forced through the hole. Prove that

$$U_i + P_iV_i = U_f + P_fV_f.$$

4.8. An exhausted chamber with nonconducting walls is connected through a valve to the atmosphere, where the pressure is P_0. The valve is opened and air flows into the chamber until the pressure within the chamber is P_0. Prove that $u_0 + P_0v_0 = u_f$, where u_0 and v_0 are the molar energy and molar volume of the air at the temperature and pressure of the atmosphere and u_f is the molar energy of the air in the chamber. (HINT: Connect to the chamber a cylinder equipped with a frictionless nonleaking piston. Suppose the cylinder to contain exactly the amount of air that will enter the chamber when the valve is opened. As soon as the first small quantity of air enters the chamber, the pressure in the cylinder is reduced a small amount below atmospheric pressure, and the outside air forces the piston in.)

4.9. A bomb of volume V_B contains n moles of gas at high pressure. Connected to the bomb is a capillary tube through which the gas may slowly leak out into the atmosphere, where the pressure is P_0. Surrounding the bomb and capillary is a water bath, in which is immsersed an electrical resistor. The gas is allowed to leak slowly through the capillary into the atmosphere while, at the same time, electrical energy is dissipated in the resistor at such a rate that the temperature of the gas, the bomb, the capillary, and the water is kept equal to that of the outside air. Show that, after as much gas as possible has leaked out during time τ, the change of internal energy is

$$\Delta U = \mathcal{E}i\tau - P_0(nv_0 - V_B),$$

where v_0 is the molar volume of the gas at atmospheric pressure, $\mathcal{E}$ is the pd across the resistor, and i is the current in the resistor.

4.10. A thick-walled insulated metal chamber contains n_i moles of helium at high pressure P_i. It is connected through a valve with a large almost empty gasholder in which the pressure is maintained at a constant value P_0, very nearly atmospheric. The valve is opened slightly and the helium flows slowly and adiabatically into the gasholder until the pressures on the two sides of the valve are equalized. Prove that

$$u_i - \frac{n_f}{n_i}u_f = \left(1 - \frac{n_f}{n_i}\right)h'$$

where n_f = number of moles of helium left in the chamber
u_i = initial molar energy of helium in the chamber
u_f = final molar energy of helium in the chamber
$h' = u' + P_0v'$ (where u' = molar energy of helium in the gasholder; v' = molar volume of helium in the gasholder)

4.11. Derive the equations listed in the accompanying table.

System	Heat capacity at constant extensive variable	Heat capacity at constant intensive variable
Chemical system.................	$C_V = \left(\dfrac{\partial U}{\partial \theta}\right)_V$	$C_P = \left(\dfrac{\partial U}{\partial \theta}\right)_P + PV\beta$
Stretched wire..................	$C_L = \left(\dfrac{\partial U}{\partial \theta}\right)_L$	$C_{\mathscr{F}} = \left(\dfrac{\partial U}{\partial \theta}\right)_{\mathscr{F}} - \mathscr{F}L\alpha$
Paramagnetic solid obeying Curie's equation	$C_I = \left(\dfrac{\partial U}{\partial \theta}\right)_I$	$C_{\mathscr{H}} = \left(\dfrac{\partial U}{\partial \theta}\right)_{\mathscr{H}} + \dfrac{I^2}{C}$

4.12. A certain solid obeys the equation of state

$$V = V_0 - AP + B\theta,$$

and its internal energy is given by

$$U = C\theta + \frac{(V - V_0)^2}{2A}$$

where A, B, C, and V_0 are constants. Calculate the heat capacities C_v and C_p.

4.13. One mole of a gas obeys the equation of state

$$\left(P + \frac{a}{v^2}\right)(v - b) = R\theta,$$

and its internal energy is given by

$$u = c\theta - \frac{a}{v},$$

where a, b, c, and R are constants. Calculate the heat capacities C_v and C_p.

4.14. The equation of state of a monatomic solid is

$$Pv + G = \Gamma u,$$

where v is the molar volume, G is a function of v only, and Γ is a constant. Prove that

$$\Gamma = \frac{\beta v}{c_v k},$$

where k is the isothermal compressibility. This relation, first derived by Grüneisen, is of fundamental importance in the theory of the solid state.

4.15. Starting with the first law for a chemical system, derive the equations:

(a) $dQ = C_V\, d\theta + \left[\left(\dfrac{\partial U}{\partial V}\right)_\theta + P\right] dV,$

(b) $C_P = C_V + \left[\left(\dfrac{\partial U}{\partial V}\right)_\theta + P\right] V\beta,$

(c) $dQ = C_V\, d\theta + \dfrac{C_P - C_V}{V\beta}\, dV.$

4.16. (a) Energy is supplied electrically at a constant rate to a thermally insulated substance. The heating curve has the form shown in Fig. 4.10. Draw a rough graph showing the dependence of heat capacity on temperature. (b) Repeat for a heating curve of the form shown in Fig. 4.11.

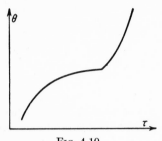

Fig. 4.10.

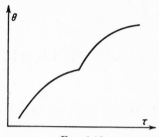

Fig. 4.11.

4.17. A carbon cylinder of mass 338 gm is raised to a temperature of 500°C and then allowed to cool. Temperature readings are taken at 2-min intervals according to the following table:

Time, min.............	2	4	6	8	10	12	14	16	18	20	22
Temp., °C..............	435	365	310	265	230	200	180	160	140	125	115

Electrical power is now supplied and slowly varied, the equilibrium temperature being measured at each value of the power, thus:

Power input, watts.......	0	50	100	150	200	250	300	350	400	450	500
Equil. temp., °C.........	25	150	215	265	305	340	375	400	430	450	470

Calculate the specific heat of carbon at the following Celsius temperatures: 125, 200, 300, 400°.

4.18. The molar heat capacity at constant pressure of a gas varies with the temperature according to the equation

$$C_p = a + b\theta - \frac{c}{\theta^2},$$

where a, b, and c are constants. How much heat is transferred during an isobaric process in which n moles of gas undergo a temperature rise from θ_i to θ_f?

4.19. The molar heat capacity at constant magnetic field of a paramagnetic solid at low temperatures varies with temperature and field according to the relation

$$C_{\mathcal{H}} = \frac{b + C\mathcal{H}^2}{\theta^2} + D\theta^3,$$

where b, C, and D are constants. How much heat is transferred during a process in which $\mathcal{H}$ remains constant at the value $\mathcal{H}_0$ and the temperature of n moles of material changes from θ_i to θ_f?

5

Transfer of Heat

5.1. Heat Conduction. When two parts of a material substance are maintained at different temperatures and the temperature of each small volume element of the intervening substance is measured, experiment shows a continuous distribution of temperature. The transport of energy between neighboring volume elements by virtue of the temperature difference between them is known as *heat conduction*. The fundamental law of heat conduction is a generalization of the results of experiments on the linear flow of heat through a slab perpendicular to the faces. A piece of material is made in the form of a slab of thickness Δx and of area A. One face is maintained at the temperature θ and the other at $\theta + \Delta\theta$. The heat Q that flows perpendicular to the faces for a time τ is measured. The experiment is repeated with other slabs of the same material but with different values of Δx and A. The results of such experiments show that, for a given value of $\Delta\theta$, Q is proportional to the time and to the area. Also, for a given time and area, Q is proportional to the ratio $\Delta\theta/\Delta x$, provided that both $\Delta\theta$ and Δx are small. These results may be written

$$\frac{Q}{\tau} \propto A \frac{\Delta\theta}{\Delta x},$$

which is only approximately true when $\Delta\theta$ and Δx are finite but which is rigorously true in the limit as $\Delta\theta$ and Δx approach zero. If we generalize this result for an infinitesimal slab of thickness dx, across which there is a temperature difference $d\theta$, and introduce a constant of proportionality k, the fundamental law of heat conduction becomes

$$\dot{Q} = \frac{dQ}{d\tau} = -kA \frac{d\theta}{dx}.$$

The derivative $d\theta/dx$ is called the *temperature gradient*. The minus sign is introduced in order that the positive direction of the flow of heat should coincide with the positive direction of x. For heat to flow in the positive direction of x, this must be the direction in which θ decreases.

80

k is called the *thermal conductivity*. A substance with a large thermal conductivity is known as a *thermal conductor* and one with a small value of k as a *thermal insulator*. It will be shown in the next article that the numerical value of k depends upon a number of factors, one of which is the temperature. Volume elements of a conducting material may therefore differ in thermal conductivity. If the temperature difference, however, between parts of a substance is small, k can be considered practically constant throughout the substance. This simplification is usually made in practical problems involving the calculation of the temperature at some point in a body at a given time.

To handle general problems in the conduction of heat it is necessary to transform the general equation into the form of a second-order partial differential equation. The solution of this equation subject to given boundary conditions involves, as a rule, the use of functions and series beyond the scope of collegiate mathematics. There are three simple cases, however, that can be handled in an elementary way. In all cases we shall assume that k is constant throughout the conducting substance.

1. *Linear Flow of Heat Perpendicular to the Faces of a Slab.* If the temperature difference $\theta_1 - \theta_2$ and the thickness x are small, it is obvious that

$$\dot{Q} = kA \frac{\theta_1 - \theta_2}{x}.$$

2. *Radial Flow of Heat between Two Coaxial Cylinders.* Suppose the conducting material lies between an inner cylinder of radius r_1 and an outer cylinder of radius r_2, both of length L. If the inner cylinder is maintained at the constant temperature θ_1 and the outer at θ_2, there will be a steady radial flow of heat at the constant rate of $\dot{Q}$. Consider the flow of this amount of heat across a cylindrical shell of material bounded by the cylinders at r and $r + dr$ (see

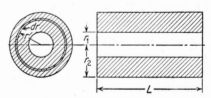

FIG. 5.1. Radial flow of heat in a cylinder.

Fig. 5.1). Let θ be the temperature at r and $\theta + d\theta$ be the temperature at $r + dr$. The area of the shell is

$$A = 2\pi rL$$

and the temperature gradient is $d\theta/dr$. Hence,

$$\dot{Q} = -k2\pi rL \frac{d\theta}{dr},$$

and

$$d\theta = -\frac{\dot{Q}}{2\pi Lk} \frac{dr}{r}.$$

Integrating between r_1 and r_2, we get

$$\theta_1 - \theta_2 = \frac{\dot{Q}}{2\pi L k} \ln \frac{r_2}{r_1}.$$

3. *Radial Flow of Heat between Two Concentric Spheres.* If the conducting material lies between an inner sphere of radius r_1 held at constant temperature θ_1 and an outer sphere of radius r_2 held at constant temperature θ_2, there will be a steady radial flow of heat at the *constant* rate of $\dot{Q}$. Considering this flow across the spherical shell bounded by the spheres at r and $r + dr$, we have

$$\dot{Q} = -kA\frac{d\theta}{dr}$$

$$= -k4\pi r^2 \frac{d\theta}{dr},$$

and

$$d\theta = -\frac{\dot{Q}}{4\pi k}\frac{dr}{r^2}.$$

Integrating between r_1 and r_2, we get

$$\theta_1 - \theta_2 = \frac{\dot{Q}}{4\pi k}\left(\frac{1}{r_1} - \frac{1}{r_2}\right).$$

5.2. Measurement of Thermal Conductivity. When the substance to be investigated is a metal, it is made into the form of a bar, and one end is heated electrically while the other end is cooled with a stream of water. The surface of the bar is thermally insulated, and the heat lost through the insulation is calculated by subtracting the rate at which heat enters the water from the rate at which electrical energy is supplied. In the case of most metals, the heat lost from the surface is very small in comparison with that which flows through the bar. The temperature is measured with suitable thermocouples at two places L cm apart, and the equation

$$k = \frac{L}{A(\theta_1 - \theta_2)}\dot{Q}$$

is used to determine the average thermal conductivity within the given temperature range. If $\theta_1 - \theta_2$ is small, k is practically equal to the thermal conductivity at the mean temperature.

When the substance to be investigated is a nonmetal, it is made into the form of a thin disk, or plate, and the same general method is used. The substance is contained between two copper blocks, one of which is heated electrically, the other being cooled by running water. The thermal contact between the copper blocks and the substance is improved by smearing them with glycerin. In most cases, the rate at which heat is supplied is almost equal to the rate at which heat enters the water,

showing that there is little loss of heat from the edges.   A modification
of this apparatus that almost completely eliminates the error due to
loss of heat from the edges is depicted in Fig. 5.2.   A hot plate A in the
form of a square and another independently heated hot plate B in the
form of a square ring are completely surrounded by the material to be
studied.   The "guard ring" B is maintained at the same temperature
as A and therefore causes the same temperature gradient in the material
near it as there is in the material near A.   Under these conditions the
heat flows away from A perpendicular to the surface.

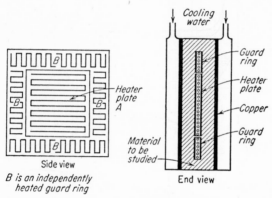

FIG. 5.2. Measurement of the thermal conductivity of a slab of nonmetal.

In pure science, the thermal conductivity is expressed in calories per
second centimeter degree Celsius, whereas, in practical work, it is more
convenient to use the unit Btu per hour foot degree Fahrenheit.
The conversion factor is

$$1 \frac{\text{cal}}{\text{sec} \cdot \text{cm} \cdot \text{deg C}} = 242 \frac{\text{Btu}}{\text{hr} \cdot \text{ft} \cdot \text{deg F}}.$$

Experiments show that the thermal conductivity of a metal is extraor-
dinarily sensitive to impurities.   The slightest trace of arsenic in copper
reduces the thermal conductivity from 0.93 to 0.34 cal/sec · cm · deg.   A
change in internal structure brought about by continued heating or a
large increase in pressure also affects the value of k.   No appreciable
change in the k of solids and liquids takes place, however, under moderate
changes of pressure.   Liquefaction always produces a decrease in the
thermal conductivity, for example, from 0.065 to 0.022 in the case of
mercury at $-39°C$ and from 0.0040 to 0.00132 in the case of ice at 0°C,
as shown in Fig. 5.3.
   1. *Liquids.*   The thermal conductivity of a liquid usually increases
as the temperature is raised.   In the case of some liquids, however, the

thermal conductivity first rises and then decreases, as shown in Fig. 5.4 in the case of water.

2. *Nonmetallic Solids.* Nonmetallic solids behave in a manner similar to that of liquids. At ordinary temperatures they are poor conductors of heat; in general, the thermal conductivity increases as the temperature is raised. In the region of low temperatures, however, the behavior is

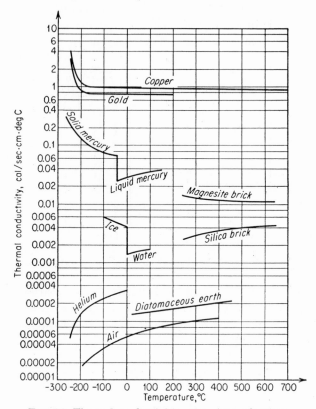

FIG. 5.3. Thermal conductivities of various substances.

quite different, as shown in Fig. 5.5 where it may be seen that the thermal conductivity of quartz rises to a maximum of 4 cal/sec · cm · deg (four times the conductivity of silver at room temperature) at a temperature of 10°K.

3. *Metals.* The thermal conductivity of some metals remains quite constant over a wide temperature range. Thus, silver, copper, and gold have thermal conductivities that remain practically constant at the values 1.0, 0.9, and 0.7 cal/sec · cm · deg, respectively, in the temperature range from −160 to 700°C.

As a general rule, the thermal conductivity of metals increases as the temperature is lowered until a maximum is reached. Further reduction of temperature causes a decrease toward zero, as shown in the case of

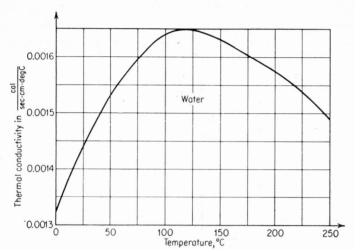

Fɪɢ. 5.4. Thermal conductivity of water.

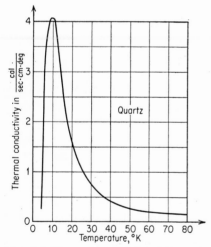

Fɪɢ. 5.5. Thermal conductivity of quartz at low temperatures.

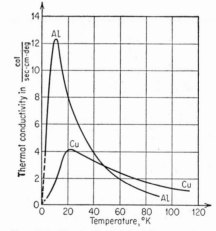

Fɪɢ. 5.6. Thermal conductivity of aluminum and of copper at low temperatures.

copper and aluminum in Fig. 5.6. It is interesting to note that, at room temperature, copper is a much better heat conductor than aluminum, but at about $7°K$, the conductivity of aluminum is eleven times that of copper.

Thermal and electric conductivity of metals go together. This important fact was first stated by Wiedemann and Franz, who showed that the ratio of the thermal to the electric conductivity was approximately the same for most metals at the same temperature. Lorentz later showed that this ratio was not only the same for all metals at the same temperature, but varied directly with the absolute temperature. If σ denotes the electric conductivity in $\text{ohm}^{-1}\ \text{cm}^{-1}$ (reciprocal of resistivity), Lorentz's law can be written

$$\frac{k}{\sigma\theta} = \text{const.} = 3\left(\frac{R}{F}\right)^2 = 2.23 \times 10^{-8}\ \frac{\text{volt}^2}{\text{deg}^2}.$$

The approximate validity of this law in the temperature range from -170 to $100°C$ is shown in Table 5.1.

TABLE 5.1. VALUES OF $\dfrac{Jk}{\sigma\theta}$ IN $10^{-8}\ \dfrac{\text{volts}^2}{\text{deg}^2}$

Metal	$-170°C$	$-100°C$	$0°C$	$18°C$	$100°C$
Copper.............	1.85	2.17	2.30	2.32	2.32
Silver...............	2.04	2.29	2.33	2.33	2.37
Zinc................	2.20	2.39	2.45	2.43	2.33
Cadmium............	2.39	2.43	2.40	2.39	2.44
Tin................	2.48	2.51	2.49	2.47	2.49
Lead...............	2.55	2.54	2.53	2.51	2.51

4. *Gases.* Gases are by far the poorest heat conductors. At pressures above a certain value depending on the nature of the gas and the dimensions of the containing vessel, the thermal conductivity is independent of the pressure. Under the usual laboratory conditions, this limiting pressure is considerably below 1 atm. The thermal conductivity of a gas always increases as the temperature is raised, as is evident in Fig. 5.3.

5.3. Laminar Flow. Poiseuille's Equation. When a fluid (either a gas or a liquid) flows between two plates or in a cylindrical tube, one layer may slide past another. If a friction force exists along the surface of contact between any two layers, the fluid is said to be *viscous* and the internal friction force is called a *viscous force*. In general, each layer of fluid moves with a different velocity, the layer closest to a stationary wall having zero velocity.

Suppose a fluid is flowing in the positive x direction and we consider two thin layers shown in Fig. 5.7. Let the upper layer move with a speed greater than that of the lower. Then the lower layer exerts a friction force f on the upper which is directed toward the left and is distributed over the entire area of contact A. Conversely, the upper exerts a friction force on the lower equal in magnitude but directed toward the right. The fundamental law of viscosity is that the magnitude of the viscous force f is proportional to the area A and to the *velocity gradient* $d\mathscr{V}/dy$ that exists where the contact area is located. Thus

$$f = \eta A \frac{d\mathscr{V}}{dy},$$

where η (Greek, eta) is called the *coefficient of viscosity* or just the *viscosity*. Since

$$\eta = \frac{\frac{f}{A}}{\frac{d\mathscr{V}}{dy}},$$

the viscosity has the units

$$\frac{\dfrac{\text{dyne}}{\text{cm}^2}}{\dfrac{\text{cm}}{\text{sec} \cdot \text{cm}}} = \frac{\dfrac{\text{gm} \cdot \text{cm}}{\text{sec}^2 \cdot \text{cm}^2}}{\dfrac{1}{\text{sec}}} = \frac{\text{gm}}{\text{sec} \cdot \text{cm}},$$

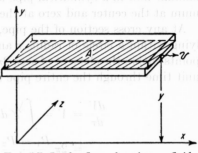

FIG. 5.7. In the flow of a viscous fluid, one layer slides over another. The force of friction is $\eta A(d\mathscr{V}/dy)$.

and 1 gm/sec · cm is called 1 *poise*, after Poiseuille, who was one of the first to study viscosity.

Consider the flow of a viscous fluid through the cylindrical pipe of diameter D, shown in Fig. 5.8. If the pressure P is a function of x only, and velocity $\mathscr{V}$ is a function of r only, becoming zero when $r = D/2$, the flow is said to be *laminar*. (Laminar flow is often referred to as streamline flow.) At any moment, any cylinder of fluid such as that shown with radius r and length L is in equilibrium, since the velocity of every

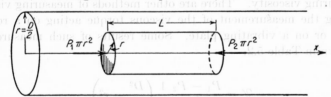

FIG. 5.8. Laminar flow of a viscous fluid in a cylindrical pipe. Velocity depends only on r, while pressure depends only on x. The indicated cylinder is in equilibrium.

layer is constant. The remainder of the fluid exerts a viscous force over the area $2\pi rL$, at every point of which the velocity gradient is $d\mathscr{V}/dr$. Since $d\mathscr{V}/dr$ is negative, the viscous force is $+\eta 2\pi rL\, d\mathscr{V}/dr$. Summing the forces in the x direction, we get

$$\Sigma F_x = P_1 \pi r^2 - P_2 \pi r^2 + \eta 2\pi rL \frac{d\mathscr{V}}{dr} = 0.$$

Therefore

$$-d\mathscr{V} = \frac{P_1 - P_2}{L} \frac{1}{2\eta} r\, dr,$$

and

$$-\int_{\mathscr{V}}^{0} d\mathscr{V} = \frac{P_1 - P_2}{L} \frac{1}{2\eta} \int_{r}^{D/2} r\, dr.$$

This becomes

$$\mathcal{V} = \frac{P_1 - P_2}{L} \frac{1}{4\eta} \left(\frac{D^2}{4} - r^2 \right),$$

which shows that the velocity distribution of a viscous fluid executing laminar flow in a cylindrical pipe is parabolic, the velocity being a maximum at the center and zero at the walls.

At any cross section of the pipe, the velocity is the same at all points lying within a circle of radius r and one of radius $r + dr$, that is, at all points within the element of area $2\pi r \, dr$. The volume of fluid flowing per unit time through the entire pipe is

$$\frac{dV}{d\tau} = \dot{V} = \int \mathcal{V} \, dA = \int_0^{D/2} \mathcal{V} 2\pi r \, dr,$$

$$= 2\pi \frac{P_1 - P_2}{4\eta L} \int_0^{D/2} \left(\frac{D^2}{4} - r^2 \right) r \, dr,$$

and finally

$$\boxed{\dot{V} = \frac{\pi D^4}{128\eta} \frac{P_1 - P_2}{L},}$$

which is known as *Poiseuille's equation*. By measuring the pressure gradient $(P_1 - P_2)/L$, the diameter D, and the volume flow $\dot{V}$ of a fluid undergoing laminar flow, and using Poiseuille's equation, the viscosity may be obtained. This is a convenient and often-used method of measuring viscosity. There are other methods of measuring viscosity involving the measurement of the viscous torque acting on a rotating cylinder or on a vibrating plate. Some results of such measurements are shown in Table 5.2.

Since

$$\mathcal{V} = \frac{P_1 - P_2}{L} \frac{1}{4\eta} \left(\frac{D^2}{4} - r^2 \right),$$

TABLE 5.2. TYPICAL VALUES OF VISCOSITY

Temp., °C	Viscosity of castor oil, poise	Viscosity of water, cp[†]	Viscosity of air, μp[†]
0	53	1.792	171
20	9.86	1.005	181
40	2.31	0.656	190
60	0.80	0.469	200
80	0.30	0.357	209
100	0.17	0.284	218

† 1 cp = 10^{-2} poise; 1μp = 10^{-6} poise.

the maximum velocity $\mathscr{V}_{max}$ is the value of $\mathscr{V}$ at $r = 0$, or

$$\mathscr{V}_{max} = \frac{D^2}{16\eta} \frac{P_1 - P_2}{L}.$$

Hence Poiseuille's equation may be written

$$\dot{V} = \frac{\pi D^2}{4} \frac{\mathscr{V}_{max}}{2}.$$

The average velocity $\bar{\mathscr{V}}$, defined as the total volume of fluid flowing per unit of time, $\dot{V}$, divided by the cross-sectional area of the pipe, $\pi D^2/4$, is therefore

$$\boxed{\bar{\mathscr{V}} = \frac{\mathscr{V}_{max}}{2}} \qquad \text{(laminar flow)}.$$

Laminar flow of a viscous fluid in a cylindrical pipe may therefore be characterized by the fact that the average velocity is one-half the maximum velocity.

5.4. Turbulent Flow. Reynolds Number. Experiment indicates that there is a combination of four factors that determines whether or not the flow of a fluid through a pipe is laminar. The combination is known as *Reynolds number*, N_{Re}, and is defined as

$$N_{Re} = \frac{\rho \bar{\mathscr{V}} D}{\eta},$$

where ρ = density in gm/cm^3
$\bar{\mathscr{V}}$ = average velocity in cm/sec
η = viscosity in gm/sec · cm (poise)
D = diameter of pipe in cm
It is easily seen that Reynolds number is dimensionless, since

$$\frac{\rho \bar{\mathscr{V}} D}{\eta} \text{ has the units } \frac{\dfrac{gm}{cm^3} \dfrac{cm}{sec} cm}{\dfrac{gm}{sec \cdot cm}} = 1.$$

The character of flow of a fluid is brought to light in a striking way by plotting the measured value of the ratio $\bar{\mathscr{V}}/\mathscr{V}_{max}$ against N_{Re}, as shown in Fig. 5.9. It is seen that, for values of the Reynolds number up to about 2000, the ratio $\bar{\mathscr{V}}/\mathscr{V}_{max}$ is exactly 0.5, characteristic of laminar flow. For values of the Reynolds number above about 3000, the flow is said to be *turbulent*, because of the violent, disordered eddying and whirling of the fluid. The ascending smoke of a cigarette burning in the still air of a room illustrates both types of flow. Near the cigarette the

smoke rises in a straight, unbroken line. This is laminar flow. A foot
or more above the cigarette the smoke stream breaks up into a disordered
series of eddies which are characteristic of turbulent flow.

5.5. Heat Convection. A current of liquid or gas that absorbs heat
at one place and then moves to another place, where it mixes with a
cooler portion of the fluid and rejects heat, is called a *convection current*.
If the motion of the fluid is caused by a difference in density that accom-
panies a temperature difference, the phenomenon is called *natural convection*. If the fluid is made to move by the action of a pump or a fan, it is
called *forced convection*.

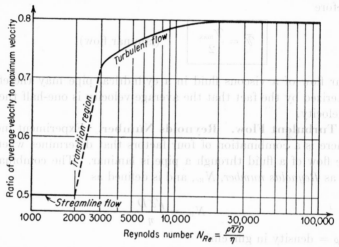

FIG. 5.9. Ratio of average to maximum velocity for isothermal flow in smooth pipes.

Consider a fluid in contact with a flat or curved wall whose temperature is higher than that of the main body of the fluid. Although the
fluid may be in motion, there is a relatively thin film of stagnant fluid
next to the wall, the thickness of the film depending upon the character
of the motion of the main body of fluid. The more turbulent the motion,
the thinner the film. Heat is transferred from the wall to the fluid by a
combination of conduction through the film and convection in the fluid.
Neglecting the transfer of heat by radiation (which must be taken into
account separately), we may define a convection coefficient h that includes
the combined effect of conduction through the film and convection in the
fluid. Thus,

$$\dot{Q} = hA\,\Delta\theta,$$

where $\dot{Q}$ is the rate of heat transfer by convection, A is the area of the
wall, and $\Delta\theta$ or Δt is the temperature difference between the surface of

the wall and the main body of the fluid. The fundamental problem of heat convection is to find the value of h that is appropriate to a particular piece of equipment.

Experiment shows that the convection coefficient depends on the following factors:

1. Whether the wall is flat or curved.
2. Whether the wall is horizontal or vertical.
3. Whether the fluid in contact with the wall is a gas or a liquid.
4. The density, viscosity, specific heat, and thermal conductivity of the fluid.
5. Whether the velocity of the fluid is small enough to give rise to laminar flow or large enough to cause turbulent flow.
6. Whether evaporation, condensation, or formation of scale takes place.

Since the physical properties of the fluid depend upon temperature and pressure, it is clear that the rigorous calculation of a convection coefficient appropriate to a given wall and fluid is an enormously complicated problem. It is only in recent years that solutions of the problem, good enough for practical purposes, have been achieved with the aid of dimensional analysis. Such analysis yields an expression for h containing the physical properties and velocity of the fluid and unknown constants and exponents. The constants and exponents are then obtained by experiment.

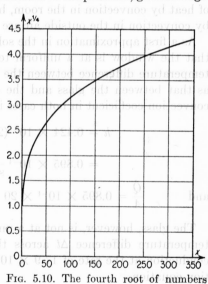

FIG. 5.10. The fourth root of numbers from 0 to 350.

5.6. Natural Convection. A case of particular interest is that of natural convection from a wall or a pipe at a constant temperature surrounded by air at atmospheric pressure and differing in temperature by an amount Δt. Combining the results of dimensional analysis and of experiment, it can be shown that the convection coefficient which is appropriate to this situation is given in Table 5.3 (see page 92).

To facilitate the computation of these convection coefficients, a graph of the fourth root of numbers up to 350 is given in Fig. 5.10.

As an example of a problem involving natural convection, consider the following: The air in a room is at a temperature of 25°C, and the outside air is at −15°C. How much heat is transferred through unit area of a

TABLE 5.3. COEFFICIENTS OF NATURAL CONVECTION IN AIR
AT ATMOSPHERIC PRESSURE

Equipment	Convection coefficient, $\dfrac{\text{cal}}{\text{sec} \cdot \text{cm}^2 \cdot \text{deg}}$
Horizontal plate, facing upward..........	$0.596 \times 10^{-4}(\Delta t)^{\frac{1}{4}}$
Horizontal plate, facing downward........	$0.314 \times 10^{-4}(\Delta t)^{\frac{1}{4}}$
Vertical plate..........................	$0.424 \times 10^{-4}(\Delta t)^{\frac{1}{4}}$
Horizontal or vertical pipe..............	$1.00 \ \times 10^{-4}\left(\dfrac{\Delta t}{D}\right)^{\frac{1}{4}}$

glass windowpane of thermal conductivity 2.5×10^{-3} cal/sec $\cdot$ cm $\cdot$ deg C and of thickness 2 mm? To assume that the inner surface of the glass is at 25°C and the outer surface is at -15°C is entirely erroneous, as anyone can verify by touching the inner surface of a glass windowpane on a cold day. One must expect a much smaller temperature difference across the windowpane so that, in the steady state, the rates of transfer of heat by convection in the room, by conduction through the glass, and by convection in the outside air are all equal.

As a first approximation in the solution of this problem, let us assume that the window is at a uniform temperature t. If $t = 5$°C, then the temperature difference between the inside air and the glass is the same as that between the glass and the outside air, or 20 deg. Hence, the convection coefficient in both cases is

$$h = 0.424 \times 10^{-4}(20)^{\frac{1}{4}} \frac{\text{cal}}{\text{sec} \cdot \text{cm}^2 \cdot \text{deg}},$$

$$= 0.895 \times 10^{-4} \frac{\text{cal}}{\text{sec} \cdot \text{cm}^2 \cdot \text{deg}},$$

and $\dfrac{\dot{Q}}{A} = 0.895 \times 10^{-4} \times 20 = 17.9 \times 10^{-4} \dfrac{\text{cal}}{\text{sec} \cdot \text{cm}^2}.$

The glass, however, is not at a uniform temperature; there must be a temperature difference Δt across the glass sufficient to provide heat conduction at the rate of 17.9×10^{-4} cal/sec $\cdot$ cm^2. Using the conduction equation,

$$\Delta t = \frac{x}{k} \frac{\dot{Q}}{A}$$

$$= \frac{0.2}{2.5 \times 10^{-3}} \times 17.9 \times 10^{-4} \text{ deg}$$

$$= 0.14 \text{ deg}.$$

With sufficient accuracy we may therefore say that the inner surface is at 5.07°C and the outer surface at 4.93°C.

An arrangement encountered often in practice consists of a wall maintained at a constant temperature t_W, coated with a layer of insulating material of thickness x and of thermal conductivity k. The outside of the insulation is in contact with the air at atmospheric pressure and at temperature t_A. Heat is transferred by conduction through the insulation and by natural convection through the air. In the steady state, the rate at which heat is conducted through unit area of the insulating material is equal to the rate at which it is supplied to the air by convection, or

$$\frac{\dot{Q}}{A} = \frac{k}{x}(t_W - t) = h(t - t_A),$$

where t is the temperature of the outside surface of insulation. Besides k and x, t_W and t_A are known. Since h varies as the fourth root of $t - t_A$, the simplest way to solve for t is by trial and error. Thus, assuming t to be any arbitrary value, h is calculated and then multiplied by $t - t_A$. The value of $(k/x)(t_W - t)$ is then calculated and compared with $h(t - t_A)$. If these quantities are not equal, another value of t is chosen, and so on, until the equation

$$\frac{k}{x}(t_W - t) = h(t - t_A)$$

is satisfied.

The conduction and convection equations, respectively, may be written

$$\frac{x}{k}\frac{\dot{Q}}{A} = t_W - t,$$

$$\frac{1}{h}\frac{\dot{Q}}{A} = t - t_A.$$

Adding these equations, we get

$$\left(\frac{x}{k} + \frac{1}{h}\right)\frac{\dot{Q}}{A} = t_W - t_A.$$

We define an *over-all coefficient of heat transfer* $\bar{U}$ by the equation

$$\frac{1}{A}\frac{dQ}{d\tau} = \bar{U}(t_W - t_A),$$

and hence

$$\boxed{\frac{1}{\bar{U}} = \frac{x}{k} + \frac{1}{h}.}$$

5.7. Forced Convection. Experiments on forced convection through circular pipes, combined with dimensional analysis, show that for turbulent flow the following equation holds:

$$\frac{hD}{k} = 0.023\left(\frac{\rho \mathcal{V} D}{\eta}\right)^{0.8}\left(\frac{c_P \eta}{k}\right)^{0.4}.$$

This equation is written in terms of dimensionless ratios. The left-hand member is called the Nusselt number. On the right-hand side, the first term in parentheses will be recognized as the Reynolds number. The second term in parentheses is called the Prandtl number.

Experiments on many gases and vapors show that, over a moderate temperature and pressure range, the ratio of viscosity to thermal conductivity remains approximately constant. It can be seen from Fig. 5.11 that the temperature variation of the thermal conductivity of helium is very similar to that of the viscosity. The specific heat at constant pressure of helium is quite constant, so that the Prandtl number, calculated and listed in Table 5.4, is approximately constant. It is customary to take as an acceptable average *for all gases and vapors* the value

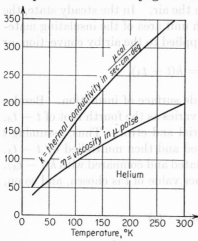

FIG. 5.11. Thermal conductivity and viscosity of helium.

$$N_{\mathrm{Pr}} = \frac{c_P \eta}{k} = 0.78 \quad \text{(approx.)}.$$

Introducing this value and solving for h, we get

$$h = 0.027 c_P (\rho \mathscr{V})^{0.8} \left(\frac{\eta}{D} \right)^{0.2}.$$

Inasmuch as we shall consider forced convection only in pipes, it is convenient at this point to define a *convection coefficient per unit length* h_L, instead of the usual coefficient per unit area h. For a pipe of length L

TABLE 5.4. PRANDTL NUMBER FOR HELIUM AT
LOW PRESSURE

θ, °K	c_P, $\dfrac{\text{cal}}{\text{gm} \cdot \text{deg}}$	η, μp	k, $\dfrac{\mu\text{cal}}{\text{sec} \cdot \text{cm} \cdot \text{deg}}$	Prandtl No., $\dfrac{c_P \eta}{k}$ (no units)
20	1.25	35	50	0.88
60	1.25	70	114	0.77
100	1.25	98	167	0.74
140	1.25	122	216	0.71
180	1.25	144	258	0.70
220	1.25	165	297	0.70
260	1.25	184	332	0.69
300	1.25	202	364	0.69

and surface area A, the fundamental equation of convection

$$\dot{Q} = hA \, \Delta t$$

may be written

$$\dot{Q} = h_L L \, \Delta t.$$

Therefore $hA = h_L L$, and since $A = \pi DL$,

$$h = \frac{h_L}{\pi D}.$$

Another change is also worthwhile. The rate of flow of mass $\dot{m}$ in grams per second is given by

$$\dot{m} = \rho \, \frac{\pi D^2}{4} \, \mathcal{V},$$

and therefore $\rho \mathcal{V} = \dfrac{4\dot{m}}{\pi D^2}.$

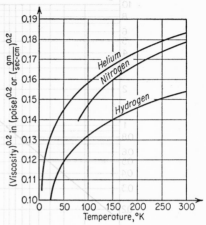

FIG. 5.12. Values of viscosity raised to the 0.2 power, for hydrogen, nitrogen, and helium.

Making these substitutions, we get finally, with sufficient accuracy,

$$h_L = 0.10 c_P \eta^{0.2} \left(\frac{\dot{m}}{D}\right)^{0.8},$$

where h_L = convection coefficient per unit length, cal/sec · cm · deg

c_P = specific heat at constant pressure, cal/gm · deg

η = viscosity, gm/sec · cm (poise)

$\dot{m}$ = rate of flow of mass, gm/sec

D = diameter of pipe, cm

As an aid to the student in evaluating forced convection coefficients, values of the viscosity raised to the 0.2 power are plotted for helium. nitrogen, and hydrogen in Fig. 5.12, and a logarithmic graph of $(\dot{m}/D)^{0.8}$ is given in Fig. 5.13. Consider the following example:

Helium gas is forced at the rate of 0.4 gm/sec through a pipe of 2 mm diameter. The average temperature of the helium is 300°K. (a) Is the flow turbulent? (b) If so, what is the convection coefficient?

(a) Since

$$\dot{m} = \rho \, \frac{\pi D^2}{4} \, \mathcal{V},$$

$$\rho \mathcal{V} D = \frac{4\dot{m}}{\pi D}$$

$$= \frac{4 \times 0.4 \text{ gm/sec}}{3.14 \times 0.2 \text{ cm}}$$

$$= 2.55 \, \frac{\text{gm}}{\text{sec} \cdot \text{cm}}$$

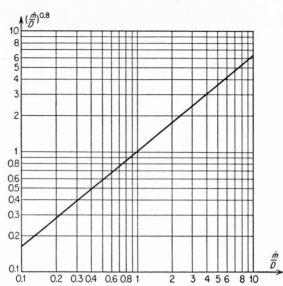

FIG. 5.13. Logarithmic graph for obtaining $(\dot{m}/D)^{0.8}$.

From Table 5.4,

$$\eta = 202 \times 10^{-6} \frac{\text{gm}}{\text{sec} \cdot \text{cm}}.$$

Therefore

$$N_{\text{Re}} = \frac{\rho \mathscr{V} D}{\eta} = \frac{2.55}{2.02} \times 10^4$$

$$= 12{,}600,$$

and the motion is turbulent.

(b)

$$h_L = 0.10 c_P \eta^{0.2} \left(\frac{\dot{m}}{D}\right)^{0.8}$$

$$= 0.10 \times 1.25 \frac{\text{cal}}{\text{gm} \cdot \text{deg}} \times 0.183 \left(\frac{\text{gm}}{\text{sec} \cdot \text{cm}}\right)^{0.2} \times 1.75 \left(\frac{\text{gm}}{\text{sec} \cdot \text{cm}}\right)^{0.8}$$

$$= 0.040 \frac{\text{cal}}{\text{sec} \cdot \text{cm} \cdot \text{deg}}.$$

5.8. Single-current Heat Exchanger. There are many experimental problems that require the design of apparatus for heating or cooling a fluid flowing through a pipe when the pipe is immersed in a liquid bath that maintains the outer wall of the pipe at a constant temperature. As a rule, the thickness of the pipe is so small and its thermal conductivity so large that very little error is introduced by neglecting the temperature gradient across the pipe wall.

Suppose, for the sake of definiteness, that the gas is to be cooled from a temperature t_H to a temperature t_C by running through a pipe of diameter D and length L immersed in a bath of temperature t_B, as shown schematically in Fig. 5.14.   If the rate of flow of mass $\dot{m}$, the average specific heat c_P, and the convection coefficient h_L at the average temperature of the gas are assumed constant at all points along the pipe, how long must the pipe be?

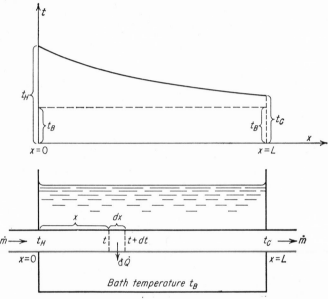

FIG. 5.14. Single-current heat exchanger.

Consider an infinitesimal portion of the pipe between the planes at x and $x + dx$.   At these two places the temperatures are t and $t + dt$, respectively.   The heat rejected by the gas in this region per unit of time is

$$\mathrm{d}\dot{Q} = -\dot{m}c_P\, dt.$$

Since we have assumed $\dot{m}$ and c_P to be constant, this equation may be integrated to give the total rate of loss of heat from the entire pipe. Thus

$$\dot{Q} = \dot{m}c_P(t_H - t_C),$$

and

$$-\frac{dt}{\mathrm{d}\dot{Q}} = \frac{t_H - t_C}{\dot{Q}}.$$

The rate $\mathrm{d}\dot{Q}$ at which heat is lost from the infinitesimal section of length dx and temperature t must be equal to the rate of transfer of heat by convection to the pipe wall, or

$$\mathrm{d}\dot{Q} = h_L\, dx(t - t_B).$$

Introducing this value of $d\dot{Q}$ into the previous equation, we get

$$-\frac{dt}{t - t_B} = \frac{h_L}{\dot{Q}} (t_H - t_C) \, dx.$$

Assuming h_L to be approximately constant along the pipe, we integrate as follows:

$$-\int_{t_H}^{t_C} \frac{dt}{t - t_B} = \frac{h_L}{\dot{Q}} (t_H - t_C) \int_0^L dx,$$

$$\ln \frac{t_H - t_B}{t_C - t_B} = \frac{h_L L}{\dot{Q}} (t_H - t_C),$$

$$= \frac{h_L L}{\dot{Q}} [(t_H - t_B) - (t_C - t_B)],$$

or
$$\frac{\dot{Q}}{h_L L} = \frac{(t_H - t_B) - (t_C - t_B)}{\ln [(t_H - t_B)/(t_C - t_B)]}.$$

The fraction on the right plays a major role in calculations on heat exchangers. It is called the *log mean temperature difference* and we shall designate it by means of capital Greek lambda, Λ. Thus

$$\Lambda = \frac{t_H - t_B - (t_C - t_B)}{\ln [(t_H - t_B)/(t_C - t_B)]},$$

and it is seen that the nearer t_C is to t_B, the smaller Λ is. The total length of the heat exchanger L may be written very simply in terms of the log mean temperature difference, thus:

$$L = \frac{\dot{Q}}{h_L \Lambda}.$$

If the flow is turbulent, h_L is calculated at the average temperature of the fluid by means of the equation of the preceding article. Usually the pipe is coiled in order to take up as little space as possible. This alters the convection coefficient by a few per cent, and if necessary a rough correction factor may be applied to take account of it.

EXAMPLE. Helium gas flows at the rate of 0.4 gm/sec through a pipe of diameter 2 mm immersed in a bath of liquid nitrogen at a temperature of 78°K. The gas enters at 300°K, and if the gas is to leave at 84°K, how long must the pipe be? We have

$$\dot{Q} = \dot{m} c_P (t_H - t_C),$$

$$= 0.4 \, \frac{\text{gm}}{\text{sec}} \times 1.25 \, \frac{\text{cal}}{\text{gm} \cdot \text{deg}} \times 216 \text{ deg},$$

$$= 108 \, \frac{\text{cal}}{\text{sec}}.$$

The average temperature of the helium is 192°K, at which

$$\eta^{0.2} = 0.1725 \left(\frac{gm}{sec \cdot cm} \right)^{0.2},$$

and

$$\left(\frac{\dot{m}}{D} \right)^{0.8} = \left(\frac{0.4}{0.2} \right)^{0.8} \left(\frac{gm}{sec \cdot cm} \right)^{0.8}.$$

Hence,

$$h_L = 0.10 \times 1.25 \frac{cal}{gm \cdot deg} \times 0.1725 \left(\frac{gm}{sec \cdot cm} \right)^{0.2} \times 1.75 \left(\frac{gm}{sec \cdot cm} \right)^{0.8},$$

$$= 0.0378 \frac{cal}{sec \cdot cm \cdot deg}.$$

The log mean temperature difference is

$$\Lambda = \frac{222 \text{ deg} - 6 \text{ deg}}{2.30 \times \log 22\frac{2}{6}} = 60.0 \text{ deg.}$$

Therefore,

$$L = \frac{\dot{Q}}{h_L \Lambda},$$

$$= \frac{108 \text{ cal/sec}}{0.0378 \text{ cal/sec} \cdot cm \cdot deg \times 60 \text{ deg}},$$

$$= 47.6 \text{ cm.}$$

If the helium were required to emerge at a temperature nearer that of the liquid nitrogen bath, the exchanger would have to be longer.

5.9. Countercurrent Heat Exchanger. There are many important pieces of equipment in which it is necessary to have efficient heat transfer between two opposing fluid streams. The apparatus for this purpose is called a *countercurrent heat exchanger* and is usually constructed in the form of a double pipe, that is, a pipe within a pipe. One stream flows in one direction through the central circular space, and the other stream flows in the opposite direction in the surrounding annular space. Copper is often used, and the heat conduction through the copper wall is so good that it is often possible to ignore the slight temperature gradient across the wall.

If t is the average temperature of a length dx of one stream, t' the temperature of the same part of the other stream, and t_W the temperature of the wall between the streams, then the magnitude of the rate at which heat is transferred by convection to the wall in one stream is

$$d\dot{Q} = h_L \, dx(t - t_W),$$

and in the other

$$d\dot{Q} = h'_L \, dx(t_W - t').$$

It follows therefore that

$$\left(\frac{1}{h_L} + \frac{1}{h'_L}\right) \mathrm{d}\dot{Q} = dx(t - t').$$

Defining the *over-all coefficient of heat transfer per unit length* $\bar{U}_L$ by means of the equation

$$\mathrm{d}\dot{Q} = \bar{U}_L\, dx(t - t'),$$

we get

$$\frac{1}{\bar{U}_L} = \frac{1}{h_L} + \frac{1}{h'_L}.$$

Consider the schematic representation of a countercurrent heat exchanger, shown in Fig. 5.15. Let $\mathrm{d}\dot{Q}$ be the magnitude of the rate

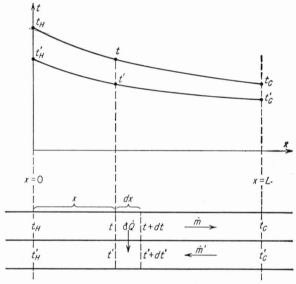

Fig. 5.15. Countercurrent heat exchanger.

of heat transfer between the two opposing streams in the infinitesimal portion of the exchanger between x and $x + dx$. The transfer of this heat causes a temperature change dt in one stream and dt' in the other. In one stream, $\mathrm{d}\dot{Q} = -\dot{m}c_P\, dt$, and assuming $\dot{m}$ and c_P to be constant along the pipe, $\dot{Q} = \dot{m}c_P(t_H - t_C)$, whence

$$-\frac{dt}{\mathrm{d}\dot{Q}} = \frac{t_H - t_C}{\dot{Q}}. \tag{1}$$

In the other stream, $\mathrm{d}\dot{Q} = -\dot{m}'c'_P\, dt'$ and, with constant $\dot{m}'$ and c'_P, $\dot{Q} = \dot{m}'c'_P(t'_H - t'_C)$. Therefore

$$-\frac{dt'}{d\dot{Q}} = \frac{t'_H - t'_C}{\dot{Q}}. \tag{1'}$$

Subtracting Eq. (1') from Eq. (1), we get

$$-\frac{d(t - t')}{d\dot{Q}} = \frac{t_H - t'_H - (t_C - t'_C)}{\dot{Q}}.$$

Now, using the definition of the over-all coefficient of heat transfer per unit length,

$$d\dot{Q} = \bar{U}_L \, dx(t - t'),$$

and substituting this into the previous equation, we get

$$-\frac{1}{\bar{U}_L}\frac{d(t - t')}{t - t'} = \frac{t_H - t'_H - (t_C - t'_C)}{\dot{Q}} \, dx.$$

Integrating along the pipe, assuming $\bar{U}_L$ to be constant,

$$-\frac{1}{\bar{U}_L}\int_{t_H - t_{H'}}^{t_C - t_{C'}}\frac{d(t - t')}{t - t'} = \frac{t_H - t'_H - (t_C - t'_C)}{\dot{Q}}\int_0^L dx,$$

and

$$\frac{1}{\bar{U}_L}\ln\frac{t_H - t'_H}{t_C - t'_C} = \frac{L}{\dot{Q}}[t_H - t'_H - (t_C - t'_C)],$$

or

$$\frac{\dot{Q}}{\bar{U}_L L} = \frac{t_H - t'_H - (t_C - t'_C)}{\ln\dfrac{t_H - t'_H}{t_C - t'_C}}.$$

The right-hand fraction will be recognized to be the log mean temperature difference Λ, whence, finally

$$\boxed{L = \frac{\dot{Q}}{\bar{U}_L \Lambda},}$$

which is of the same form as the equation for the length of a single-current heat exchanger.

5.10. Thermal Radiation. Black Body. A substance may be stimulated to emit electromagnetic radiation in a number of ways:

1. An electric conductor carrying a high-frequency alternating current emits radio waves.

2. A hot solid or liquid emits thermal radiation.

3. A gas carrying an electric discharge may emit visible or ultraviolet radiation.

4. A metal plate bombarded by high-speed electrons emits X rays.

5. A substance the atoms of which are radioactive may emit γ rays.

6. A substance exposed to radiation from an external source may emit fluorescent radiation.

All these radiations are electromagnetic waves, differing only in wavelength. We shall be concerned in this article only with thermal radiation, i.e., the radiation emitted by a solid or a liquid by virtue of its temperature. The radiation characteristics of gases require a special treatment. In the following pages we shall assume that gases are transparent to thermal radiation. When thermal radiation is dispersed by a suitable prism, a continuous spectrum is obtained. The distribution of energy among the various wavelengths is such that, at temperatures below about 500°C, most of the energy is associated with infrared waves, whereas, at higher temperatures, some visible radiation is emitted. In general, the higher the temperature of a body, the greater is the total energy emitted.

The loss of energy due to the emission of thermal radiation may be compensated in a variety of ways. The emitting body may be a source of energy itself, such as the sun; or there may be a constant supply of electrical energy from the outside, as in the case of the filament of an electric light. Energy may be supplied also by heat conduction or by the performance of work on the emitting body. In the absence of these sources of supply, the only other way in which a body may receive energy is by the absorption of radiation from surrounding bodies. In the case of a body that is surrounded by other bodies, the internal energy of the body will remain constant when the rate at which radiant energy is emitted is equal to that at which it is absorbed.

Experiment shows that the rate at which a body emits thermal radiation depends on the temperature and on the nature of the surface. The total radiant energy emitted per second per unit area is called the *radiant emittance* of the body. For example, the radiant emittance of tungsten at 2177°C is 50 joules/sec · cm², or 50 watts/cm². When thermal radiation is incident upon a body equally from all directions, the radiation is said to be *isotropic*. Some of the radiation may be absorbed, some reflected, and some transmitted. In general, the fraction of the incident isotropic radiation of all wavelengths that is absorbed depends on the temperature and the nature of the surface of the absorbing body. This fraction is called the *absorptivity*. At 2477°C the absorptivity of tungsten is approximately 0.25. To summarize:

$$\text{Radiant emittance} = \mathcal{R} = \begin{cases} \text{total radiant energy emitted per sec per} \\ \text{cm}^2. \end{cases}$$

$$\text{Absorptivity} = \alpha = \begin{cases} \text{fraction of the total energy of isotropic} \\ \text{radiation that is absorbed.} \end{cases}$$

There are some substances, such as lampblack, whose absorptivity is very nearly unity. For theoretical purposes it is useful to conceive of an ideal substance capable of absorbing all the thermal radiation falling on it. Such a body is called a *black body*. If a black body is indicated by the subscript B, we have

$$\alpha_B = 1.$$

A very good experimental approximation to a black body is provided by a cavity the interior walls of which are maintained at a uniform temperature and which communicates with the outside by means of a hole having a diameter small in comparison with the dimensions of the cavity. Any radiation entering the hole is partly absorbed and partly diffusely reflected a large number of times at the interior walls, only a negligible fraction eventually finding its way out of the hole. *This is true regardless of the materials of which the interior walls are composed.*

The radiation emitted by the interior walls is similarly absorbed and diffusely reflected a large number of times, so that the cavity is filled with isotropic radiation. Let us define as the *irradiance* within the cavity the radiant energy falling in unit time upon unit area of any surface within the cavity. Suppose a black body whose temperature is the same as that of the walls is introduced into the cavity. Then, denoting the irradiance by H,

Radiant energy absorbed per sec per cm^2 = $\alpha_B H = H$

and   Radiant energy emitted per sec per cm^2 = $\mathcal{R}_B$.

Since the temperature of the black body remains constant, the rate at which the energy is absorbed must equal the rate at which it is emitted, whence

$$H = \mathcal{R}_B,$$

or *the irradiance within a cavity whose walls are at the temperature θ is equal to the radiant emittance of a black body at the same temperature.* For this reason, the radiation within a cavity is called *black-body radiation*. Such radiation is studied by allowing a small amount to escape from a small hole leading to the cavity. Since H is independent of the materials of which the interior walls are composed, it follows that *the radiant emittance of a black body is a function of the temperature only.*

5.11. Kirchhoff's Law. Radiated Heat. The radiant emittance of a non-black body depends as well on the nature of the surface as on the temperature, according to a simple law that we may derive as follows: Suppose that a non-black body at the temperature θ, with radiant emittance $\mathcal{R}$ and absorptivity α, is introduced into a cavity whose interior walls are at the same temperature and where the irradiance is H. Then,

Radiant energy absorbed per sec per cm^2 = αH.

and   Radiant energy emitted per sec per cm^2 = $\mathcal{R}$.

Since the non-black body is in equilibrium,

$$\mathcal{R} = \alpha H,$$

but, from Art. 5.10, $H = \mathcal{R}_B$. Hence,

$$\boxed{\mathcal{R} = \alpha \mathcal{R}_B,}$$

or *the radiant emittance of any body at any temperature is equal to a fraction of the radiant emittance of a black body at that temperature, the fraction being the absorptivity at that temperature.*

This equation, known as *Kirchhoff's law*, shows that the absorptivity of a body may be determined experimentally by measuring the radiant emittance of the body and dividing it by that of a black body at the same temperature. Values of the absorptivity of various surfaces, measured in this way, are given in Table 5.5. It should be emphasized that the tabulated values of absorptivity refer to the thermal radiation appropriate to the temperature listed in column 1. Thus, the absorptivity of ice is 0.97 not for visible radiation but for the long infrared waves associated with matter at 0°C.

TABLE 5.5. APPROXIMATE ABSORPTIVITIES OF VARIOUS
SURFACES, AS COMPILED BY HOTTEL
Values at intermediate temperatures may be obtained by
linear interpolation

Material	Temperature range, °C	Absorptivity
Polished metals:		
Aluminum.............	250– 600	0.039–0.057
Brass................	250– 400	0.033–0.037
Chromium............	50– 550	0.08 –0.26
Copper..............	100	0.018
Iron.................	150–1000	0.05 –0.37
Nickel..............	20– 350	0.045–0.087
Zinc................	250– 350	0.045–0.053
Filaments:		
Molybdenum.........	750–2600	0.096–0.29
Platinum............	30–1200	0.036–0.19
Tantalum............	1300–3000	0.19 –0.31
Tungsten............	30–3300	0.032–0.35
Other materials:		
Asbestos............	40– 350	0.93 –0.95
Ice (wet)............	0	0.97
Lampblack...........	20– 350	0.95
Rubber (gray)........	25	0.86

It should be noticed that the word "heat" has not appeared as yet. If there is a temperature difference between a body and its surroundings, then, in a given interval of time, the body loses an amount of internal energy equal to the energy radiated minus the energy absorbed, whereas the surroundings gain an amount of internal energy equal to the energy absorbed minus the energy radiated. The gain of one equals the loss of the other. *The gain or loss of internal energy, equal to the difference between the energy of the thermal radiation which is absorbed and that which is radiated, is called heat.* This statement is in agreement with the original definition of heat, since a gain or loss of energy by radiation and absorption will take place only if there is a difference in temperature between a body and its surroundings. If the two temperatures are the same, there is no net gain or loss of internal energy of either the body or its surroundings, and there is therefore no transfer of heat.

Imagine a cavity whose interior walls are maintained at a constant temperature θ_W. Suppose that a non-black body at a temperature θ different from that of the walls is placed in the cavity. If the body is small compared with the size of the cavity, then the character of the radiation in the cavity will not be appreciably affected by its introduction. Let H, as before, denote the irradiance within the cavity, and $\mathcal{R}$ and α the radiant emittance and absorptivity, respectively, of the body. Then, as before,

$$\text{Radiant energy absorbed per sec per cm}^2 = \alpha H$$

and   Radiant energy emitted per sec per cm$^2 = \mathcal{R}$,

but now *these two rates are not equal.* The difference between them is the heat transferred by radiation per second per square centimeter. If dQ is the heat transferred in time $d\tau$ to the whole body whose area is A, then

$$\dot{Q} = \frac{dQ}{d\tau} = A(\alpha H - \mathcal{R}),$$

where, it must be remembered, α and $\mathcal{R}$ refer to the temperature θ and H to the temperature θ_W. Now

$$H = \mathcal{R}_B(\theta_W)$$

and $\mathcal{R} = \alpha \mathcal{R}_B(\theta)$.

Hence, $\dot{Q} = A\alpha[\mathcal{R}_B(\theta_W) - \mathcal{R}_B(\theta)]$,

or the rate at which heat is transferred by radiation is proportional to the difference between the radiant emittances of a black body at the two temperatures in question.

5.12. Stefan-Boltzmann Law. The first measurements of the heat transferred by radiation between a body and its surroundings were made by Tyndall. On the basis of these experiments, it was concluded by

Stefan in 1879 that the heat radiated was proportional to the difference of the fourth powers of the absolute temperatures. This purely experimental result was later derived thermodynamically by Boltzmann, who showed that the radiant emittance of a black body at any temperature θ is equal to

$$\mathcal{R}_B(\theta) = \sigma\theta^4.$$

This law is now known as the *Stefan-Boltzmann law*, and σ is called the Stefan-Boltzmann constant.

Referring to Art. 5.11, we have for the heat transferred by radiation between a body at the temperature θ and walls at θ_W,

$$\dot{Q} = A\alpha\sigma(\theta_W^4 - \theta^4),$$

where α refers to the temperature θ.

Two simple methods may be employed for the determination of the Stefan-Boltzmann constant.

1. *Nonequilibrium Method.* A blackened silver disk is placed in the center of a large blackened copper hemisphere. The silver disk is covered and shielded from radiation until the copper hemisphere achieves the temperature of condensing steam; this temperature is measured with a thermocouple. Then the disk is uncovered, and its temperature is measured as a function of the time. From the resulting heating curve the slope $d\theta/d\tau$ is obtained. Assuming the silver disk to be a black body, and putting $dQ = C_P\, d\theta$ where C_P is the heat capacity at constant pressure, we have

$$\frac{C_p\, d\theta}{d\tau} = A\sigma(\theta_W^4 - \theta^4),$$

whence

$$\sigma = \frac{C_p}{A(\theta_W^4 - \theta^4)}\frac{d\theta}{d\tau}.$$

2. *Equilibrium Method.* A hollow blackened copper sphere is provided with an electric heater and a thermocouple and is suspended inside a vessel whose walls are maintained at a constant temperature θ_W. Electrical energy is supplied at a constant rate $\mathcal{E}i$ until the sphere achieves an equilibrium temperature θ at which the rate of supply of energy is equal to the rate of emission of radiation. Assuming the sphere to be a black body, we have at equilibrium

$$\frac{\mathcal{E}i}{J} = A\sigma(\theta^4 - \theta_W^4),$$

whence

$$\sigma = \frac{\mathcal{E}i}{4\pi r^2 J(\theta^4 - \theta_W^4)},$$

where r is the radius of the sphere. The best measurements, to date, have yielded the value

$$\sigma = 5.672 \times 10^{-5} \frac{\text{erg}}{\text{sec} \cdot \text{cm}^2 \cdot \text{deg}^4}.$$

PROBLEMS

5.1. A number n of slabs of different materials and thicknesses are placed in contact, side by side. If the temperature of the exposed face of the first slab is θ_1 and that of the exposed face of the nth slab is θ_{n+1}, show that, in the steady state, the heat conducted per unit time per unit area is

$$\frac{\dot{Q}}{A} = \bar{U}(\theta_1 - \theta_{n+1})$$

where the over-all coefficient of heat transfer $\bar{U}$ is given by

$$\frac{1}{\bar{U}} = \frac{x_1}{k_1} + \frac{x_2}{k_2} + \cdots + \frac{x_n}{k_n},$$

where $x_1, x_2, \ldots, x_n$ are the respective thicknesses and $k_1, k_2, \ldots, k_n$ are the respective thermal conductivities.

5.2. A furnace wall is constructed of two layers, where x_1 and x_2 are 10 and 20 cm, respectively; k_1 and k_2 are 0.002 and 0.004 cal/sec $\cdot$ cm $\cdot$ deg, respectively. The inner surface is maintained at a temperature of 600°C and the outer surface at a temperature of 460°C. Calculate (a) the heat current per unit area; (b) the temperature at the interface.

5.3. Heat flows radially outward through a cylindrical insulator of outside radius r_2 surrounding a steam pipe of outside radius r_1. The temperature of the inner surface of the insulator is θ_1, that of the outer surface is θ_2. At what radial distance from the center of the pipe is the temperature just halfway between θ_1 and θ_2?

5.4. A number n of concentric cylindrical shells of different materials and thicknesses are used to cover a pipe whose temperature and radius are θ_1 and r_1, respectively. If the temperature of the outer surface of the nth covering is θ_{n+1}, show that the heat conducted per unit time per unit length is

$$\frac{\dot{Q}}{L} = \bar{U}_L(\theta_1 - \theta_{n+1})$$

where the over-all coefficient of heat transfer $\bar{U}_L$ is given by

$$\frac{1}{\bar{U}_L} = \frac{1}{2\pi}\left(\frac{1}{k_1}\ln\frac{r_2}{r_1} + \frac{1}{k_2}\ln\frac{r_3}{r_2} + \cdots + \frac{1}{k_n}\ln\frac{r_{n+1}}{r_n} \right),$$

and the k's and r's are the respective thermal conductivities and radii.

5.5. The thermal conductivity of a metal at low temperatures varies with the temperature according to the equation

$$\frac{1}{k} = a\theta^2 + \frac{b}{\theta}.$$

Consider a slab of metal with a constant heat current $\dot{Q}$ perpendicular to its faces of area A. If $\theta = \theta_0$ when $x = 0$, calculate θ as a function of x when (a) θ is so small that $a\theta^3 \ll b$; (b) θ is large enough to consider $a\theta^3 \gg b$.

5.6. The temperature distribution in the air on both sides of a wall and in the wall itself is shown in Fig. 5.16. If the wall has a thickness x and a thermal conductivity k, and if the convection coefficients on both sides of the wall are h_2 and h_3, respectively, show that

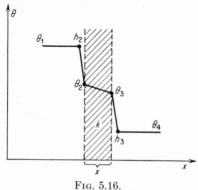

$$\frac{\dot{Q}}{A} = \bar{U}(\theta_1 - \theta_4)$$

where

$$\frac{1}{\bar{U}} = \frac{1}{h_2} + \frac{x}{k} + \frac{1}{h_3}.$$

FIG. 5.16.

5.7. A brick wall 20 cm thick of thermal conductivity 0.0141 cal/sec · cm · deg separates a room where the air has a temperature of 20°C from the outside where the air is at −18°C. If the convection coefficient on the inside is 10^{-4} cal/sec · cm^2 · deg and twice as large on the outside, find (a) the heat current per unit area through the wall; (b) the temperature of the inside surface; (c) the temperature of the outside surface; (d) the over-all heat-transfer coefficient.

5.8. Derive a general expression for the over-all heat-transfer coefficient for radial heat transfer (a) by conduction through a substance lying between coaxial cylinders and by convection in the surrounding air; (b) by conduction through a substance lying between concentric spheres and by convection in the surrounding air.

5.9. A vertical wall 10 m^2 is kept at a constant temperature of 300°C. A layer of insulating material of thermal conductivity 0.00050 cal/sec · cm · deg and of thickness 5 cm covers the wall. The surrounding air is at atmospheric pressure and at 20°C. Calculate (a) the heat lost per minute by conduction and natural convection; (b) the temperature of the outer surface of the insulation.

5.10. An electric transformer is in a cylindrical tank 60 cm in diameter and 1 m high, with flat top and bottom. If the tank transfers heat to the air only by natural convection, and the electrical losses are to be dissipated at the rate of 1 kw, how many degrees will the tank surface rise above room temperature?

5.11. The air above the surface of a fresh-water lake is at a temperature θ_A, while the water is at its freezing point θ_i. ($\theta_A < \theta_i$.) After a time τ has elapsed, ice of thickness y has formed. Assuming that the heat which is liberated when the water freezes flows up through the ice by conduction and thence into the air by natural convection,

(a) Prove that

$$\frac{y}{h} + \frac{y^2}{2k} = \frac{\theta_i - \theta_A}{\rho l}\,\tau,$$

where h is the convection coefficient per unit area and is assumed constant while the ice forms, k is the thermal conductivity of ice, l is the heat of fusion of ice, and ρ is the density of ice. (HINT: The temperature of the upper surface of the ice, θ, is variable. Assume the ice to have a thickness y, and imagine an infinitesimal thickness dy to form in time $d\tau$.)

Assuming the following numbers:

$$h = 10^{-3} \frac{\text{cal}}{\text{sec} \cdot \text{cm}^2 \cdot \text{deg}}, \qquad k = 5 \times 10^{-3} \frac{\text{cal}}{\text{sec} \cdot \text{cm} \cdot \text{deg}},$$

$$l = 80 \frac{\text{cal}}{\text{gm}}, \rho = 0.90 \frac{\text{gm}}{\text{cm}^3}, \quad \theta_i = 273°\text{K}, \theta_A = 253°\text{K},$$

(b) Calculate the time for 2 cm of ice to form.

(c) Calculate the temperature of the top surface of the ice at this moment.

(d) Calculate the over-all coefficient of heat transfer at this moment.

5.12. Hydrogen gas at 150°K flows through a pipe 5 mm in diameter at the rate of 0.2 gm/sec.

(a) What is the Reynolds number?

(b) Calculate the convection coefficient per unit length. ($c_P = 3.5$ cal/gm · deg.)

5.13. A convenient numerical measure of the efficacy of a single-current heat exchanger is provided by the following quantity E called the "efficiency":

$$E = \frac{t_H - t_C}{t_H - t_B}.$$

(a) Show that

$$E = 1 - e^{-h_L L / \dot{m} c_P}$$

(b) Calculate the efficiency of the single-current heat exchanger in the example of Art. 5.8.

5.14. Helium gas flows at the rate of 0.5 gm/sec through a thin metal pipe of diameter 2.5 mm immersed in a bath of liquid hydrogen at 20°K. The helium enters at 80°K. If the efficiency of this exchanger is to be 95 per cent,

(a) At what temperature will the helium emerge?

(b) What is the length of the exchanger?

5.15. Hydrogen gas at a temperature of 80°K flows through a thin metal pipe of diameter 4 mm immersed in a bath of liquid helium whose temperature is 4°K. The Reynolds number is 5000, $c_P = 3.5$ cal/gm · deg, and the average viscosity is 20×10^{-6} poise.

(a) What is the rate of flow in grams per second?

(b) What is the convection coefficient per unit length?

(c) How long must the pipe be in order for the hydrogen to emerge at 20°K?

(d) What is the efficiency?

5.16. Helium flows at the rate of 0.4 gm/sec through the central tube of a countercurrent heat exchanger whose diameter is 0.2 cm. It enters at 300°K and leaves at 84°K and has a heat capacity of 1.25 cal/gm · deg. Nitrogen flows in the opposite direction in the outer annular space at the rate of 3 gm/sec. This space is equivalent in all respects to a pipe of diameter 1 cm. The heat capacity of nitrogen is 0.25 cal/gm · deg, and it enters at a temperature of 78°K.

(a) What is the total heat current from the helium to the nitrogen?

(b) At what temperature does the nitrogen emerge?

(c) What is the log mean temperature difference?

(d) What is the over-all heat-transfer coefficient per unit length?

(e) How long is the exchanger?

5.17. The efficiency of a countercurrent heat exchanger is defined to be

$$E = \frac{t'_H - t'_C}{t_H - t'_C}$$

where the symbols refer to Fig. 5.15. Calculate the efficiency of the heat exchanger of Prob. 5.16.

5.18. Hydrogen gas flows through the outer annular space of a countercurrent heat exchanger at the rate of 0.142 gm/sec. Its entering temperature is 300°K, and its average specific heat is 3.5 cal/gm · deg. Helium gas flows in the opposite direction through the central portion of the exchanger at the rate of 0.4 gm/sec. Its entering temperature is 5°K and its average specific heat is 1.25 cal/gm · deg. Assuming the average over-all heat-transfer coefficient per unit length to be 0.05 cal/sec · cm · deg, and the efficiency to be 94 per cent,

     (a) At what temperature does the helium emerge?

     (b) What is the total heat current from the hydrogen to the helium?

     (c) At what temperature does the hydrogen emerge?

     (d) What is the log mean temperature difference?

     (e) What is the length of the exchanger?

5.19. An uninsulated steam pipe of diameter 8 cm and absorptivity 0.8 passes vertically through a room in which the air and all solid surfaces are at the average temperature of 27°C. If the surface temperature of the steam pipe is 97°C, compare the rate of heat loss per meter of pipe by radiation with that by natural convection.

5.20. A solid cylindrical aluminum rod 15 cm long has one end maintained at a temperature of 60.00°K with the aid of solid nitrogen. The other end is blackened and exposed to thermal radiation from a body at 500°K, no energy being lost or gained elsewhere. When equilibrium is reached, what is the temperature of the blackened end? (NOTE: Refer to Fig. 5.6.)

5.21. A spherical metal can 2 cm in radius with a surface absorptivity of 0.2 contains liquid helium at its normal boiling point 4.2°K at which its heat of vaporization is 5 cal/gm. The can is in a large cavity whose interior walls are maintained at the temperature of liquid nitrogen, 78°K, the intervening space being evacuated. How much helium is lost per hour?

5.22. The operating temperature of a tungsten filament in an incandescent lamp is 2460°K, and its absorptivity is 0.35. Find the surface area of the filament of a 60-watt lamp.

5.23. A nickel wire of length 130.2 cm and diameter 0.0326 cm is blackened and placed along the axis of an evacuated glass tube. The wire is connected to a d-c source, a rheostat, an ammeter, and a voltmeter, and the current is increased until, at the moment the wire is about to melt, the ammeter reads 20.0 amp and the voltmeter 33.9 volts. Assuming that all the energy supplied was radiated and that the radiation of the glass tube is negligible, calculate the melting temperature of nickel.

5.24. (a) A small body with temperature θ and absorptivity α is placed in a large evacuated cavity whose interior walls are at a temperature θ_W. When $\theta_W - \theta$ is small, show that the rate of heat transfer by radiation is

$$\dot{Q} = 4\theta_W^3 A\alpha\sigma(\theta_W - \theta).$$

(b) If the body remains at constant pressure, show that the time for the temperature of the body to change from θ_1 to θ_2 is given by

$$\tau = \frac{C_p}{4\theta_W^3 A\alpha\sigma} \ln \frac{\theta_W - \theta_1}{\theta_W - \theta_2}.$$

(c) Two small blackened spheres of identical size, one of copper, the other of aluminum, are suspended by silk threads within a large hole in a block of melting ice. It is found that it takes 10 min for the temperature of the aluminum to drop from 3 to 1°C, and 14.2 min for the copper to undergo the same temperature change. What is the ratio of specific heats of aluminum and copper? (Densities of Al and Cu are 2.7 and 8.9 gm/cm³, respectively.)

of a power series (or *virial expansion*) of the form

$$Pv = R\theta(1 + B'P + C'P^2 + D'P^3 + \cdots),$$

where B', C', etc., are called *virial coefficients* (A the first virial coefficient B' the second, etc.), and depend on the temperature and on the nature of the gas. It should be noticed in Fig. 6.1 that, in the pressure range from 0 to about 10 atm, the relation between Pv and P is practically

6

Ideal Gases

6.1. Equation of State of a Gas. It was emphasized in Chap. 1 that a gas is the best-behaved thermometric substance because of the fact that the ratio of the pressure P of a gas at any temperature to the pressure P_3 of the same gas at the triple point, as both P and P_3 approach zero, approaches a value independent of the nature of the gas. The limiting value of this ratio, multiplied by 273.16°, was defined to be the ideal gas temperature θ of the system at whose temperature the gas exerts the pressure P. The reason for this regular behavior may be found by investigating the way in which the product PV of a gas depends on P.

TABLE 6.1. VIRIAL COEFFICIENTS FOR NITROGEN
$$Pv/R\theta = 1 + B'P + C'P^2 + D'P^3$$

θ, °K	B', 10^{-3} atm^{-1}	C', 10^{-6} atm^{-2}	D', 10^{-9} atm^{-3}
100	-17.951	-348.7	$-21,6630.$
200	-2.125	-0.0801	$+57.27$
300	-0.183	$+2.08$	$+2.98$
400	$+0.279$	$+1.14$	-0.97
500	$+0.408$	$+0.623$	-0.89

Suppose that the pressure P and the volume V of n moles of gas held at any constant temperature is measured over a wide range of values of the pressure and the product Pv, where $v = V/n$, is plotted as a function of P. Experiments of this sort were first performed by Amagat in France in 1870 and later by Holborn and Otto in Berlin and by Kamerlingh-Onnes and Keesom in Leiden. Nowadays, such measurements are made at many bureaus of standards and universities. A typical set of isotherms of nitrogen, obtained by Friedman, is shown in Fig. 6.1. The relation between Pv and P may be expressed by means of a power series (or *virial* expansion) of the form

$$Pv = A(1 + B'P + C'P^2 + \cdots),$$

where A, B', C', etc., are called *virial coefficients* (A the first virial coefficient, B' the second, etc.), and depend on the temperature and on the nature of the gas. It should be noticed in Fig. 6.1 that, in the pressure range from 0 to about 40 atm, the relation between Pv and P is practically

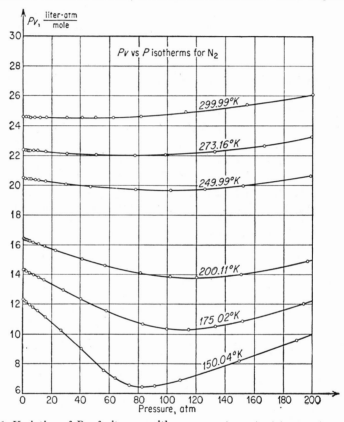

FIG. 6.1. Variation of Pv of nitrogen with pressure at constant temperature. (*A. S. Friedman,* 1950.)

linear, so that only the first two terms in the expansion are significant. In general, the greater the pressure range, the larger the number of terms in the virial expansion.

The virial coefficients play an important role not only in practical thermodynamics but also in theoretical physics where they are related to molecular properties. Except at very low temperatures, the virial coefficients are quite small, as shown in Table 6.1 where they are given for nitrogen at five different temperatures.

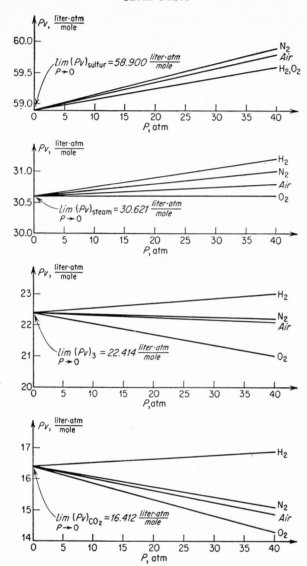

FIG. 6.2. The fundamental property of gases is that $\lim_{P\to 0} (Pv)_\theta$ is independent of the nature of the gas and depends only on θ.

The remarkable property of gases that makes them so valuable in thermometry is displayed in Fig. 6.2 where the product Pv is plotted against P for four different gases, all at the temperature of boiling sulfur in the top graph, all at the temperature of boiling water in the one beneath, all at the triple point of water in the next lower graph, and all at the temperature of solid CO_2 in the lowest. In each case it is seen that, as the pressure approaches zero, the product Pv approaches the same value for all gases at the same temperature. It follows from this that the *first virial coefficient A is independent of the nature of the gas and depends only on temperature.* Thus

$$\lim_{P \to 0} (Pv) = A = \begin{cases} \text{function of temp. only,} \\ \text{independent of gas.} \end{cases}$$

Now consider the limiting values of the two ratios:

$$\left. \begin{aligned} \lim \frac{P}{P_3} \text{ (const. } V) &= \lim \frac{PV/n}{P_3V/n} = \frac{\lim (Pv)}{\lim (Pv)_3} \\ \lim \frac{V}{V_3} \text{ (const. } P) &= \lim \frac{PV/n}{PV_3/n} = \frac{\lim (Pv)}{\lim (Pv)_3} \end{aligned} \right\} = \frac{A}{A_3}.$$

It follows that

$$\theta = 273.16° \frac{\lim (Pv)}{\lim (Pv)_3},$$

and

$$\lim (Pv) = \left[\frac{\lim (Pv)_3}{273.16°} \right] \theta.$$

The bracket is called the *universal gas constant* and is denoted by R. Thus

$$R = \frac{\lim (Pv)_3}{273.16°}.$$

The best value obtained so far for $\lim (Pv)_3$ is 22.4216 liter · atm/mole, or 2271.87 joule/mole. Hence

$$R = \frac{22.4216 \text{ liter} \cdot \text{atm/mole}}{273.16 \text{ deg}} = \frac{2271.87 \text{ joule/mole}}{273.16 \text{ deg}},$$

$$R = \begin{cases} 0.08208 \text{ liter} \cdot \text{atm/mole} \cdot \text{deg,} \\ 8.317 \times 10^7 \text{ ergs/mole} \cdot \text{deg,} \\ 8.317 \text{ joules/mole} \cdot \text{deg,} \\ 1.987 \text{ cal/mole} \cdot \text{deg.} \end{cases}$$

Finally, substituting for v its value V/n, we may write the equation of state of a gas in the limit of low pressures in the form

$$\boxed{\lim (PV) = nR\theta.}$$

6.2. Compressibility Factor. We have seen that for any gas

$$\lim_{p \to 0} (Pv) = A = R\theta.$$

The virial expansion may therefore be written

$$\frac{Pv}{R\theta} = 1 + B'P + C'P^2 + \cdots.$$

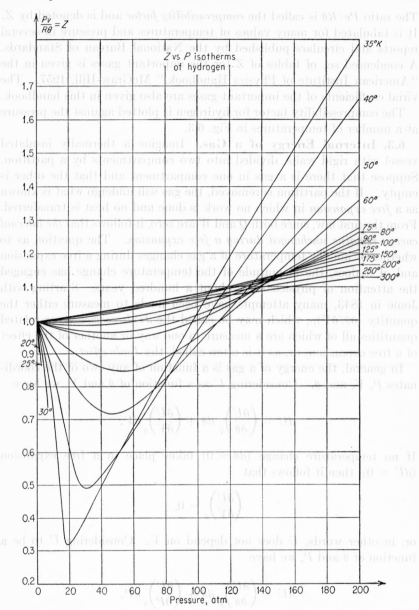

Fig. 6.3. Variation of Z of hydrogen with pressure at constant temperature.   (*A. S. Friedman*, 1950.)

The ratio $Pv/R\theta$ is called the *compressibility factor* and is denoted by Z. It is tabulated for many values of temperatures and pressure in several reports and circulars published by the National Bureau of Standards. A condensed set of tables of Z for the important gases is given in the "American Institute of Physics Handbook," McGraw-Hill, 1957. The virial coefficients of the important gases are also given in this handbook.

The compressibility factor for hydrogen is plotted against the pressure at a number of temperatures in Fig. 6.3.

6.3. Internal Energy of a Gas. Imagine a thermally insulated vessel with rigid walls, divided into two compartments by a partition. Suppose that there is a gas in one compartment and that the other is empty. If the partition is removed, the gas will undergo what is known as a *free expansion* in which no work is done and no heat is transferred. From the first law, since both Q and W are zero, it follows that *the internal energy remains unchanged during a free expansion*. The question as to whether or not the temperature of a gas changes during a free expansion and, if it does, the magnitude of the temperature change has engaged the attention of physicists for about a hundred years. Starting with Joule in 1843, many attempts have been made to measure either the quantity $(\partial\theta/\partial V)_U$, which may be called the *Joule coefficient*, or related quantities all of which are a measure in one way or another of the effect of a free expansion, or, as it is often called, the *Joule effect*.

In general, the energy of a gas is a function of any two of the coordinates P, V, and θ. Considering U as a function of θ and V, we have

$$dU = \left(\frac{\partial U}{\partial \theta}\right)_V d\theta + \left(\frac{\partial U}{\partial V}\right)_\theta dV.$$

If no temperature change $(d\theta = 0)$ takes place in a free expansion $(dU = 0)$, then it follows that

$$\left(\frac{\partial U}{\partial V}\right)_\theta = 0,$$

or, in other words, U does not depend on V. Considering U to be a function of θ and P, we have

$$dU = \left(\frac{\partial U}{\partial \theta}\right)_P d\theta + \left(\frac{\partial U}{\partial P}\right)_\theta dP.$$

If no temperature change $(d\theta = 0)$ takes place in a free expansion $(dU = 0)$, then it follows that

$$\left(\frac{\partial U}{\partial P}\right)_\theta = 0,$$

or, in other words, U does not depend on P. It is apparent then that, if no temperature change takes place in a free expansion, U is independent of V and of P, and therefore U *is a function of θ only.*

Two methods of studying the Joule effect have been employed. In the original method of Joule, two vessels connected by a short tube and stopcock were immersed in a water bath. One vessel contained air at high pressure, and the other was evacuated. The temperature of the water was measured before and after the expansion, the idea being to infer the temperature change of the gas from the temperature change of the water. Since the heat capacity of the vessels and the water was approximately one thousand times as large as the heat capacity of the air, Joule was unable to detect any temperature change of the water, although, in the light of our present knowledge, the air must have suffered a temperature change of several degrees.

The second method of studying the Joule coefficient consists of an attempt to measure the temperature of the gas almost immediately after the free expansion, before the gas has had a chance to exchange heat with its surroundings, by using the gas itself as its own thermometer. In the experiments of Hirn in 1865, a vessel was divided into two equal compartments by a thin partition, which could be broken with the aid of a metal ball. Originally, both compartments contained air at atmospheric pressure. The air from one compartment was then pumped into the other compartment, and the temperature of the compressed gas was allowed to come to its original value. The partition was then broken, and soon afterward the pressure was measured with the aid of a U-tube manometer containing a light liquid and found to be the value that existed when the gas originally occupied the whole vessel. It was therefore concluded that no temperature change took place. Cazin repeated this experiment in 1870 with similar apparatus.

The results of this method are doubtful because of the oscillations of the liquid in the manometer tube. If sufficient time elapses in order to allow the oscillations of the manometric liquid to subside, then, during this time, there is a transfer of heat between the gas and the walls of the vessel, which vitiates the results. Further complications arise from the conduction of heat through metal valve connections due to a temperature difference created by the rapidly streaming gas. In the experiments of Keyes and Sears in 1924, the gas was not used as its own thermometer, but, instead, a platinum resistance thermometer was employed to measure the temperature immediately after expansion. Temperature changes of approximately the right order were measured, but only a few rough measurements were made.

A direct measurement of the temperature change associated with a free expansion is so difficult that it seems necessary to give up the idea of a precise measurement of the Joule coefficient. Modern methods of attacking the problem of the internal energy of a gas involve the measurement of the quantity $(\partial u/\partial P)_\theta$ by having the gas undergo an isothermal expansion in which heat is transferred and also work is done. The most extensive series of measurements of this kind was performed by Rossini and Frandsen in 1932 at the National Bureau of Standards by a method elaborated by Washburn. The apparatus is shown in Fig. 6.4. A bomb B contains n moles of gas at a pressure P and communicates with the atmosphere through a long coil wrapped around the bomb. The whole apparatus is immersed in a water bath the temperature of which may be maintained constant at exactly the same value as that of the surrounding atmosphere.

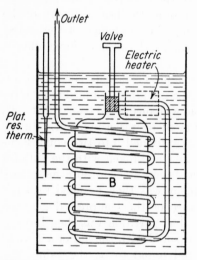

Fig. 6.4. Apparatus of Rossini and Frandsen for measuring $(\partial u/\partial P)_\theta$ of a gas.

The experiment is performed as follows: When the stopcock is opened slightly, the gas flows slowly through the long coil and out into the air. At the same time, the temperature of the gas, the bomb, the coils, and the water is maintained constant by an electric heating coil immersed in the water. The electrical energy supplied to the water is therefore the heat Q absorbed by the gas during the expansion. The work done by the gas is evidently

$$W = P_0(nv_0 - V_B),$$

where P_0 is atmospheric pressure, v_0 is the molar volume at atmospheric temperature and pressure, and V_B is the volume of the bomb.

If $u(P, \theta)$ is the molar energy at pressure P and temperature θ and $u(P_0, \theta)$ is the molar energy at atmospheric pressure and the same temperature, then, from the first law,

$$u(P, \theta) - u(P_0, \theta) = \frac{W - Q}{n},$$

provided that corrections have been made to take account of the energy changes due to the contraction of the walls of the bomb. In this way, the energy change was measured for various values of the initial pressure and was plotted against the pressure, as shown in Fig. 6.5. Since $u(P_0, \theta)$ is constant, it follows that the slope of the resulting curve at any value of P is equal to $(\partial u/\partial P)_\theta$. Within the pressure range of 1 to 40 atm, it is seen that $(\partial u/\partial P)_\theta$ *is independent of the pressure,* depending only on the temperature.   Thus

$$\left(\frac{\partial u}{\partial P}\right)_\theta = f(\theta)$$

and
$$u = f(\theta)P + F(\theta)$$

where $F(\theta)$ is another function of the temperature only.

Rossini and Frandsen's experiments with air, oxygen, and mixtures of oxygen and carbon dioxide lead to the conclusion that the internal energy of a gas is a function of both temperature and pressure.   They found no pressure or temperature range in which the quantity $(\partial u/\partial P)_\theta$ was equal to zero.

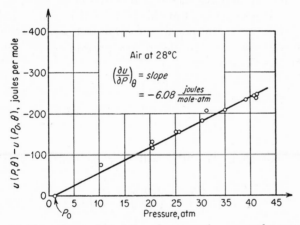

FIG. 6.5. Dependence of the internal energy of a gas on the pressure.

Washburn's method has somewhat the same disadvantage as Joule's original method in that the heat capacity of the gas is much smaller than that of the calorimeter and water bath.   To keep the temperature of the gas constant within reasonable limits, the temperature of the water must be kept constant to less than a thousandth of a degree.   In Rossini and Frandsen's measurements the final precision was estimated to be $2\frac{1}{2}$ per cent.

Another determination of the average value of $(\partial u/\partial P)_\theta$ of air in a pressure range of over 50 atm was made by Baker in 1938 by a somewhat different method capable of an accuracy of 0.1 per cent.   In Baker's experiment, the air expanded from a thin spherical metal bomb into the space between it and an outer concentric thin spherical shell.   The temperature of the outer shell was measured at small time intervals starting from the moment after the expansion until the temperature returned to its original value; during this time, heat flowed into the gas at a rate that was a known function of the temperature difference between the outer shell and its surroundings, which were held at a constant temperature. By making the two shells very thin, the ratio of the heat capacity of the shells to that of the gas was very much smaller than in any previous work. The heat transferred to the gas could be calculated with great accuracy, and many corrections were applied with extreme care. The few measurements that have been made with this apparatus up to the present time have substantiated the results of Rossini and Frandsen.

6.4. The Concept of an Ideal Gas. We have seen that, in the case of a real gas, only in the limit as the pressure approaches zero does the equation of state assume the simple form $PV = nR\theta$. Furthermore, the internal energy of a real gas is a function of pressure as well as of temperature. It is convenient at this point to define an ideal gas whose properties, while not corresponding to those of any existing gas, are approximately those of a real gas at low pressures. By definition, an ideal gas satisfies the equations

$$\boxed{\begin{array}{l} PV = nR\theta \\ \left(\dfrac{\partial U}{\partial P}\right)_\theta = 0 \end{array}}$$ (ideal gas).

The requirement that $(\partial U/\partial P)_\theta = 0$ may be written in other ways. Thus

$$\left(\frac{\partial U}{\partial V}\right)_\theta = \left(\frac{\partial U}{\partial P}\right)_\theta \left(\frac{\partial P}{\partial V}\right)_\theta ,$$

and since $(\partial P/\partial V)_\theta = -nR\theta/V^2 = -P/V$, and therefore is not zero, whereas $(\partial U/\partial P)_\theta$ is zero, it follows that, for an ideal gas

$$\boxed{\left(\frac{\partial U}{\partial V}\right)_\theta = 0}$$ (ideal gas).

Finally, since both $(\partial U/\partial P)_\theta$ and $(\partial U/\partial V)_\theta$ are zero,

$$\boxed{U = f(\theta) \text{ only}}$$ (ideal gas).

Whether an actual gas may be treated as an ideal gas depends upon the error that may be tolerated in a given calculation. An actual gas at pressures below about two atmospheres may be treated as an ideal gas without introducing an error greater than a few per cent. Even in the case of a saturated vapor in equilibrium with its liquid, the ideal gas equation of state may be used with only a small error if the vapor pressure is low. From a molecular point of view, it can be shown that the properties of an ideal gas are possessed by an assembly of a large number of molecules among which there are no attractive or repulsive forces.

6.5. Thermodynamic Equations. In a previous chapter it was shown that, for an infinitesimal quasi-static process for any chemical system, the first law becomes

$$dQ = dU + P \, dV$$

and the heat capacity at constant volume is given by

$$C_V = \left(\frac{\partial U}{\partial \theta}\right)_V .$$

In the special case of an ideal gas, U is a function of θ only, and therefore the partial derivative with respect to θ is the same as the total derivative. Consequently,

$$C_V = \frac{dU}{d\theta},$$

and

$$\boxed{dQ = C_V \, d\theta + P \, dV.} \tag{1}$$

Now, all equilibrium states are represented by the ideal gas equation

$$PV = nR\theta,$$

and, for an infinitesimal quasi-static process,

$$P \, dV + V \, dP = nR \, d\theta.$$

Substituting the above in Eq. (1), we get

$$dQ = (C_V + nR) \, d\theta - V \, dP,$$

and, dividing by $d\theta$,

$$\frac{dQ}{d\theta} = C_V + nR - V \frac{dP}{d\theta}.$$

At constant pressure, the left-hand member becomes C_P, whence

$$\boxed{C_P = C_V + nR.} \tag{2}$$

We have the result, therefore, that the heat capacity at constant pressure of an ideal gas is always larger than that at constant volume, the difference remaining constant and equal to nR.

Since U is a function of θ only, it follows that

$$C_V = \frac{dU}{d\theta} = \text{a function of } \theta \text{ only}$$

and

$$C_P = C_V + nR = \text{a function of } \theta \text{ only}.$$

One more useful equation can be obtained. Since

$$dQ = (C_V + nR)\, d\theta - V\, dP,$$

we get

$$\boxed{dQ = C_P\, d\theta - V\, dP.}$$ (3)

6.6. Experimental Determination of Heat Capacities. It is interesting to compare the deductions of Article 6.5 with the results of experiment. The heat capacities of gases are measured by the electrical method. To measure C_V, the gas is contained in a thin-walled steel flask with a heating wire wound around it. By maintaining an electric current in the wire, an equivalent amount of heat is supplied to the gas, and the specific heat at constant volume is obtained by measuring the temperature rise of the gas. The same method is used to measure C_P except that, instead of confining the gas to a constant volume, the gas is allowed to flow at constant pressure through a calorimeter, where it receives electrically a known equivalent heat per unit of time. From the initial (inlet) and final (outlet) temperatures, the rate of supply of heat, and the rate of flow of gas, C_P is calculated. The results of such measurements on gases at *low pressures* (approximately ideal gases) can be stated in a simple manner in terms of molar heat capacities.

1. *All gases.*

   a. The molar heat at constant volume is independent of the volume.

   b. The molar heat at constant pressure is independent of the pressure.

   c. The molar heat at constant pressure is always larger than the molar heat at constant volume, the difference being equal to R.

2. *Monatomic gases*, such as He, A, and Ne, and most metallic vapors, such as the vapors of Na, Cd, and Hg.

   a. The molar heat at constant volume is constant over a wide temperature range, and is very nearly equal to $\frac{3}{2}R$, or 2.98 cal/mole · deg.

   b. The molar heat at constant pressure is constant over a wide temperature range and is very nearly equal to $\frac{5}{2}R$, or 4.97 cal/mole · deg.

   c. The ratio c_P/c_V is constant over a wide temperature range and is very nearly equal to 1.67.

3. *The so-called permanent diatomic gases*, namely, H_2, D_2, O_2, N_2, NO, and CO.

   a. The molar heat at constant volume is constant at ordinary temperatures, being equal to about $\frac{5}{2}R$, or about 5 cal/mole · deg, and increases as the temperature is raised.

   b. The molar heat at constant pressure is constant at ordinary temperatures, being equal to about $\frac{7}{2}R$, or about 7 cal/mole · deg, and increases as the temperature is raised.

c. The ratio c_P/c_V is constant at ordinary temperatures, being equal to about 1.40, and decreases as the temperature is raised.

4. *Polyatomic gases and gases that are chemically active,* such as CO_2, NH_3, CH_4, Cl_2, Br_2, etc.

c_V, c_P, and c_P/c_V vary with the temperature, the variation being different for each different gas.

These results are all in excellent agreement with the predictions based on statistical mechanics in which an ideal gas is treated as a large number of molecules among which there are no attractive or repulsive forces. By taking into account the translation, rotation, vibration, and electronic transitions of the molecules of a gas, it is possible to show that the molar heat capacity at constant pressure may always be expressed in the form

$$c_P = \text{constant term} + \text{function of temperature}$$
$$= \tfrac{5}{2}R + c_i \qquad \text{(for all monatomic gases)}$$
$$= \tfrac{7}{2}R + c_i \qquad \text{(for all diatomic gases except hydrogen),}$$

where the constant term results from translational and rotational motions

and the variable term c_i arises from vibrations and electronic transitions.

The exceptional behavior of hydrogen is shown in Fig. 6.6. At very low temperatures, c_P drops to a value around 5 cal/mole · deg appropriate to a *monatomic* gas. This behavior is connected with the peculiar rotational properties of molecules at very low temperatures. It would occur with other diatomic gases if it were not for the fact that all diatomic gases except hydrogen liquefy before the temperature gets low enough to give rise to this effect.

The exact form of c_i arises from the vibrational characteristic of molecules and is quite complicated. For example, for carbon monoxide up to $2000°K$,

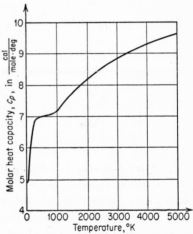

FIG. 6.6. Molar heat capacity at constant pressure of hydrogen.

$$c_P = \frac{7}{2}R + \left(\frac{3080}{\theta}\right)^2 R \frac{e^{3080/\theta}}{(e^{3080/\theta} - 1)^2}.$$

Exact equations of the above type are difficult to handle and are not suitable for the practical calculations of the engineer or physical chemist. Consequently, approximate empiric equations are used. Empiric equations for c_P of some of the most important gases, compiled by Bryant in

1934, are given in Table 6.2. These are correct to about 2 per cent within the temperature range of 300 to 2000°K. In recent years, other more accurate empiric equations have been suggested, some of them being valid up to 3000°K. The simple equations of Bryant, however, will serve the purposes of this book.

TABLE 6.2. MOLAR HEAT CAPACITIES AT CONSTANT
PRESSURE OF IMPORTANT GASES
(W. M. C. BRYANT)
$c_P = a + b\theta + c\theta^2$

Gas	a, $\dfrac{\text{cal}}{\text{mole} \cdot \text{deg}}$	b, $\dfrac{10^{-3}\ \text{cal}}{\text{mole} \cdot \text{deg}^2}$	c, $\dfrac{10^{-6}\ \text{cal}}{\text{mole} \cdot \text{deg}^3}$
H_2	6.88	0.066	+0.279
N_2, HBr	6.30	1.819	−0.345
O_2	6.26	2.746	−0.770
CO, HI	6.25	2.091	−0.459
NO	6.21	2.436	−0.612
HCl	6.64	0.959	−0.057
H_2S	6.48	5.558	−1.204
H_2O	6.89	3.283	−0.343
SO_2	8.12	6.825	−2.103
HCN	7.01	6.600	−1.642
CO_2	6.85	8.533	−2.475
COS	8.32	7.224	−2.146
CS_2	9.76	6.102	−1.894
NH_3	5.92	8.963	−1.764
C_2H_2	8.28	10.501	−2.644
CH_4	3.38	17.905	−4.188

6.7. Quasi-static Adiabatic Process. When an ideal gas undergoes a quasi-static adiabatic process, the pressure, volume, and temperature change in a manner that is described by a relation between P and V, θ and V, or P and θ. In order to derive the relation between P and V, we start with Eqs. (1) and (3) of Art. 6.5. Thus,

$$dQ = C_V\, d\theta + P\, dV,$$
$$dQ = C_P\, d\theta - V\, dP.$$

Since, in an adiabatic process, $dQ = 0$,

$$V\, dP = C_P\, d\theta,$$
$$P\, dV = -C_V\, d\theta.$$

Dividing the first by the second,

$$\frac{dP}{P} = -\frac{C_P}{C_V}\frac{dV}{V}$$

and, denoting the ratio of the heat capacities (which is the same as the ratio of the molar or specific heats) by the symbol γ, we have

$$\frac{dP}{P} = -\gamma \frac{dV}{V}.$$

This equation cannot be integrated until we know something about the behavior of γ. We have seen that for monatomic gases γ is constant, whereas for diatomic and polyatomic gases it may vary with the temperature. It requires, however, a very large change of temperature to produce an appreciable change in γ. For example, in the case of carbon monoxide, a temperature rise from 0 to 2000°C produces a decrease in γ from 1.4 to 1.3. Most adiabatic processes that we deal with do not involve such a large temperature change. We are therefore entitled, in an adiabatic process that involves only a moderate temperature change, to neglect the small accompanying change in γ. Regarding γ therefore as constant and integrating, we obtain

$$\ln P = -\gamma \ln V + \ln \text{const.}$$

or

$$\boxed{PV^\gamma = \text{const.}}$$ (4)

The above equation holds at all equilibrium states through which an ideal gas passes during a quasi-static adiabatic process. It is important to understand that a free expansion is an adiabatic process but not quasi-static. It is therefore entirely fallacious to attempt to apply Eq. (4) to the states traversed by an ideal gas during a free expansion.

A family of curves representing quasi-static adiabatic processes may be plotted on a P-V diagram by assigning different values to the constant in Eq. (4). The slope of any adiabatic curve is

$$\left(\frac{\partial P}{\partial V}\right)_s = -\gamma \text{ const. } V^{-\gamma-1}$$

$$= -\gamma \frac{P}{V},$$

where the subscript s is used to denote an adiabatic process.

Quasi-static isothermal processes are represented by a family of equilateral hyperbolas obtained by assigning different values to θ in the equation $PV = nR\theta$. Since

$$\left(\frac{\partial P}{\partial V}\right)_\theta = -\frac{P}{V},$$

it follows that an adiabatic curve has a steeper negative slope than an isothermal curve at the same point.

The isothermal curves and adiabatic curves of an ideal gas may be shown in a revealing way on a P-V-θ surface. If P, V, and θ are plotted along rectangular axes, the resulting surface is shown in Fig. 6.7 where it may be seen that the adiabatic curves cut across the isotherms.

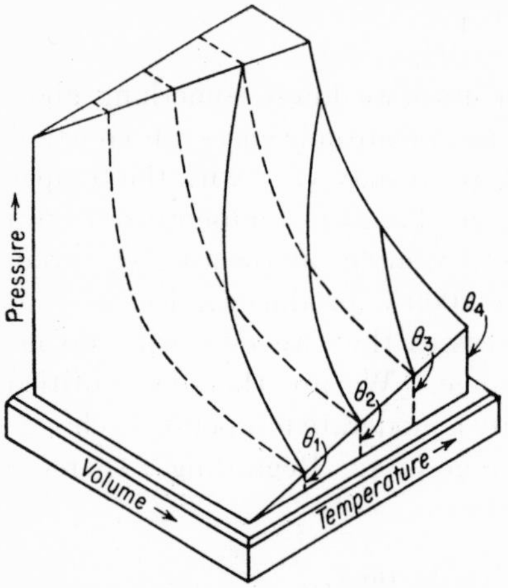

6.8. Clément and Désormes Method of Measuring γ. The earliest and simplest method of measuring the γ of an ideal gas is that of Clément and Désormes. The gas is contained in a vessel at room temperature and at a pressure P_i slightly above atmospheric pressure (see Fig. 6.8). Suppose that the volume of *any small constant mass* of the gas is V_i. By rapidly opening and closing a stopcock (flipping a poppet valve), the small amount of gas under consideration is caused to expand adiabatically until its volume is V_f and its pressure is that of the atmosphere

FIG. 6.7. P-V-θ surface for an ideal gas. Isotherms are represented by dashed curves and adiabatics by full curves.

P_0, the temperature dropping slightly below room temperature. Assuming this adiabatic expansion to be approximately quasi-static, we may write

$$P_iV_i^{\gamma} = P_0V_f^{\gamma}.$$

The gas is allowed to stand for a few minutes at constant volume until its temperature comes back to its initial value, thus causing the pressure

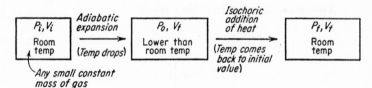

FIG. 6.8. Schematic representation of the method of Clément and Désormes.

to rise to the final value P_f. Since the initial and final temperatures are equal, we have

$$P_iV_i = P_fV_f.$$

Eliminating V_i and V_f from the two equations, we get

$$\frac{P_i}{P_0} = \left(\frac{P_i}{P_f}\right)^{\gamma}.$$

Taking the natural logarithm of both sides and solving for γ, we obtain

$$\gamma = \frac{\ln (P_i/P_0)}{\ln (P_i/P_f)}.$$

The pressures are usually measured with an open U-tube manometer containing a convenient light liquid. Denoting the height of the barometric column of this liquid by h_0, we may write

$$P_i = h_0 + h_i = h_0(1 + h_i/h_0),$$
$$P_0 = h_0,$$
$$P_f = h_0 + h_f = h_0(1 + h_f/h_0),$$

where h_i and h_f are very small compared with h_0. Upon substituting,

$$\gamma = \frac{\ln (1 + h_i/h_0)}{\ln (1 + h_i/h_0) - \ln (1 + h_f/h_0)}.$$

Now it is easy to show that, if x is small compared with unity,

$$\ln (1 + x) = x.$$

Since the ratios h_i/h_0 and h_f/h_0 are small compared with unity, we obtain finally

$$\gamma = \frac{h_i}{h_i - h_f}.$$

6.9. Rüchhardt's Method of Measuring γ.
An ingenious method of measuring γ developed by Rüchhardt in 1929, although no more accurate than the preceding method, will appeal to students who have a liking for mechanics. The gas is contained in a large jar of volume V. Fitted to the jar (see Fig. 6.9) is a glass tube with an accurate bore of cross-sectional area A, in which a metal ball of mass m fits snugly like a piston. Since the gas is slightly compressed by

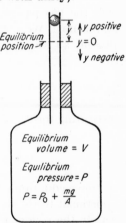

FIG. 6.9. Rüchhardt's apparatus for the measurement of γ.

the steel ball in its equilibrium position, its pressure P is slightly larger than atmospheric pressure P_0. Thus, neglecting friction,

$$P = P_0 + \frac{mg}{A}.$$

If the ball is given a slight downward displacement and then let go, it will oscillate with a period τ. Friction will cause the ball to come to rest eventually. Let the displacement of the ball from its equilibrium position at any moment be denoted by y, where y is positive when the ball is above the equilibrium position and negative below. A small positive displacement causes an increase in volume that is very small compared with the equilibrium volume V and that therefore can be denoted by dV, where

$$dV = yA.$$

Similarly, a small positive displacement causes a decrease in pressure that is very small compared with the equilibrium pressure P and that therefore can be denoted by dP, where dP is a negative quantity. The resultant force $\mathcal{F}$ acting on the ball is equal to $A\,dP$ if we neglect friction, or

$$dP = \frac{\mathcal{F}}{A}.$$

Notice that, when y is positive, dP is negative and therefore $\mathcal{F}$ is negative, that is, $\mathcal{F}$ is a restoring force.

Now, as the ball oscillates fairly rapidly, the variations of P and V are adiabatic. Since the variations are also quite small, the states through which the gas passes can be considered to be approximately states of equilibrium. We may therefore assume that the changes of P and V represent an approximately quasi-static adiabatic process, and we may write

$$PV^\gamma = \text{const.},$$
and
$$P\gamma V^{\gamma-1}\,dV + V^\gamma\,dP = 0.$$

Substituting for dV and dP, we get

$$\mathcal{F} = -\frac{\gamma P A^2}{V}\,y.$$

The above equation expresses the fact that the restoring force is directly proportional to the displacement and in the opposite direction. This is precisely the condition for *simple harmonic motion*, for which the period τ is

$$\tau = 2\pi\sqrt{\frac{m}{-\mathcal{F}/y}}.$$

Consequently,
$$\tau = 2\pi\sqrt{\frac{mV}{\gamma P A^2}}$$

and
$$\gamma = \frac{4\pi^2 mV}{A^2 P \tau^2}.$$

The mass of the ball, the cross-sectional area of the tube, the pressure, and the volume are all known beforehand, and only the period has to be measured to obtain γ. The values obtained by Rüchhardt for air and for CO_2 were in good agreement with those obtained from calorimetric measurements.

6.10. Modifications of Rüchhardt's Method. A clever modification of Rüchhardt's method was suggested by Rinkel in 1929. This method consists of holding the ball in the position where the gas pressure is exactly atmospheric and then letting it drop, measuring the distance L that the ball falls before starting to go up again. Measuring y from this initial position, the gravitational potential energy liberated is mgL, and the work done in compressing the gas is

$$\int_0^L \mathscr{F}\, dy = \frac{\gamma P_0 A^2}{V} \int_0^L y\, dy = \frac{\gamma P_0 A^2 L^2}{2V}$$

whence

$$\frac{\gamma P_0 A^2 L^2}{2V} = mgL,$$

or

$$\gamma = \frac{2mgV}{P_0 A^2 L}.$$

Rinkel's method has the advantage over Rüchhardt's that L may be measured with greater accuracy than τ. Moreover, an error in the measurement of L produces an error in γ determined by only the first power of L, whereas an error in τ produces an error in γ determined by the second power.

Brodersen in 1930 used both methods as accurately as possible by studying the motion of the ball photographically, getting a wavy trace on a moving photographic film. The constants of his apparatus were

Mass of ball, $m = 16.71$ gm
Volume of gas, $V = 6280$ cm^3
Atmospheric pressure, $P_0 = 759.9$ mm Hg
Area of tube, $A = 2.0104$ cm^2

and his results are shown in Table 6.3.

TABLE 6.3. COMPARISON OF RÜCHHARDT'S AND RINKEL'S METHODS

Gas	Rüchhardt's method		Rinkel's method	
	Period τ, sec	$\gamma = \dfrac{4\pi^2 m V}{P A^2 \tau^2}$	Distance L, cm	$\gamma = \dfrac{2mgV}{P A^2 L}$
Air (unpurified and undried)..	0.8547	1.390	36.86	1.373
CO_2 (commercial)...........	0.8896	1.284	38.5	1.301

Both Rüchhardt's and Rinkel's methods involve errors due to three simplifying assumptions, (1) that the gas is ideal, (2) that there is no friction, and (3) that volume changes are strictly adiabatic. Rinkel estimated that the second assumption is responsible for the largest error, amounting to about 3 per cent.

An interesting modification of Rüchhardt's experiment in which accurate account is taken of the real equation of state of the gas, the friction present, and the departure from strict adiabatic conditions was achieved by Clark and Katz in 1940.   The method was improved by Katz, Woods, and Leverton in 1949.   A steel piston at the center of a cylindrical tube divides the gas into two equal parts, as shown in Fig. 6.10.   It is set in vibration at any desired frequency by external coils in which an alternating current of suitable frequency is maintained.   The cylinder is kept in a horizontal position, and friction between the piston and the cylinder is reduced by balancing the weight of the piston by the attraction of an electromagnet.

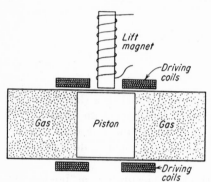

FIG. 6.10. Apparatus of Clark and Katz for measuring γ of a real gas as a function of the pressure.

The amplitude of vibration of the piston is measured with a microscope equipped with a micrometer eyepiece at a number of values of the frequency of the impressed alternating current, and the resonance curve is plotted.   From the resonance frequency and very elaborate calculations not involving the assumptions made by Rüchhardt and Rinkel, γ is calculated.   Since friction was reduced to a great extent by the lift magnet, the corrections amounted to only about 1 per cent.   The authors measured γ at various pressures from 1 to 25 atm and expressed the results in the form of empiric equations, as shown in Table 6.4.

6.11. Velocity of a Longitudinal Wave.   If a compression is produced at one place in a substance, it will travel with a constant velocity $\mathcal{V}$

TABLE 6.4. PRESSURE VARIATION OF γ
$$\gamma = a + bP + cP^2$$

Gas	Temp., °C	a	b, atm^{-1}	c, atm^{-2}	γ extrapolated to zero pressure (ideal gas)
He	23.1	1.6669	−0.0002	0	1.667
A	24.2	1.6667	0.00353	0	1.667
H$_2$	24.4	1.4045	0.00025	0	1.405
N$_2$	23.0	1.4006	0.00221	0	1.401
CO$_2$	29.9	1.2857	0.00629	0	1.286
N$_2$O	25.3	1.2744	0.00225	0.000973	1.274
CH$_4$	25.1	1.3029	−0.00105	0.000484	1.303

depending on certain properties of the substance that we shall now proceed to determine. Directing our attention to a column of material of cross section A, let us suppose that a piston, on the left in Fig. 6.11, actuated by an agent exerting a force $A(P + \Delta P)$ moves to the right with a constant velocity $\mathcal{V}_0$. This sets up a compression traveling with a constant velocity $\mathcal{V}$, so that in time τ the compression has traveled a distance $\mathcal{V}\tau$ while the piston has traveled a distance $\mathcal{V}_0\tau$.

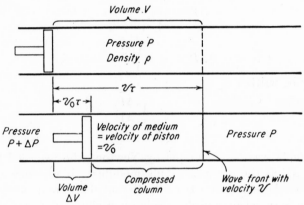

FIG. 6.11. Propagation of a compression with constant velocity $\mathcal{V}$ by motion of a piston with constant velocity $\mathcal{V}_0$. Upper diagram at the start; lower diagram after time τ.

Consider as a "free body" the compressed column whose length, if uncompressed, would be $\mathcal{V}\tau$ and whose uncompressed volume $V = A\mathcal{V}\tau$. If ρ is the density of the normal or uncompressed material, the mass of the free body is $\rho A \mathcal{V}\tau$. At time τ, the

$$\left.\begin{array}{l}\text{Rate of increase of mass of}\\ \text{the compressed column}\end{array}\right\} = \frac{\rho A \mathcal{V}\tau}{\tau} = \rho A \mathcal{V}.$$

The entire compressed column has a velocity $\mathcal{V}_0$ equal to that of the piston. Therefore the

$$\left.\begin{array}{l}\text{Rate of increase of momentum}\\ \text{of the compressed column}\end{array}\right\} = \rho A \mathcal{V}\mathcal{V}_0.$$

The free body is acted on by a force $A(P + \Delta P)$ to the right and a force AP to the left. Therefore, the

$$\left.\begin{array}{l}\text{Unbalanced force on the}\\ \text{compressed column}\end{array}\right\} = A\,\Delta P.$$

Since the unbalanced force is equal to the rate of change of momentum,

$$A \, \Delta P = \rho A \mathscr{V} \mathscr{V}_0,$$

or
$$\Delta P = \rho \mathscr{V}^2 \frac{\mathscr{V}_0}{\mathscr{V}}.$$

The "uncompressed free body" of volume $V = A \mathscr{V} \tau$ has undergone a compression $\Delta V = A \mathscr{V}_0 \tau$. That is,

$$\frac{\Delta V}{V} = \frac{A \mathscr{V}_0 \tau}{A \mathscr{V} \tau} = \frac{\mathscr{V}_0}{\mathscr{V}}.$$

Therefore,
$$\Delta P = \rho \mathscr{V}^2 \frac{\Delta V}{V},$$

which may be written

$$\mathscr{V} = \sqrt{\frac{V \dfrac{\Delta P}{\Delta V}}{\rho}}.$$

This formula was first obtained by Newton, who regarded the quantity $V \, \Delta P / \Delta V$ as the isothermal bulk modulus. It was shown later by Laplace that the expression is really the adiabatic bulk modulus. To see why this is so, let us consider a column of material of cross section A, bounded by two planes, one at the center of a compression and the other at the center of a rarefaction, a distance $\lambda/2$ apart, where λ is the wavelength. Let us suppose that the temperature at the center of the compression exceeds the temperature at the center of the rarefaction by an amount $\Delta \theta$. Then the heat conducted a distance $\lambda/2$ in the time $\lambda/2\mathscr{V}$ (time for the wave to travel the distance $\lambda/2$) is given by

$$\left. \begin{array}{l} \text{Heat conducted in the time for the} \\ \text{wave to travel a distance } \lambda/2 \end{array} \right\} = kA \frac{\Delta \theta}{\lambda/2} \frac{\lambda}{2\mathscr{V}} = kA \frac{\Delta \theta}{\mathscr{V}},$$

where k is the thermal conductivity of the medium. The mass of material between the compression and rarefaction is $\rho A \lambda/2$, and the heat necessary to raise the temperature of this mass by the amount $\Delta \theta$ is

$$\left. \begin{array}{l} \text{Heat necessary to raise temperature} \\ \text{of mass } \rho A \lambda/2 \text{ by } \Delta \theta \end{array} \right\} = \rho A \frac{\lambda}{2} c_V \, \Delta \theta,$$

where c_V is the specific heat at constant volume.

The propagation of the wave would be adiabatic if the conducted heat were much too small to raise the temperature of the mass $\rho A \lambda/2$ by the amount $\Delta \theta$, or

$$\frac{kA \, \Delta \theta}{\mathscr{V}} \ll \rho A \frac{\lambda}{2} c_V \, \Delta \theta \qquad \text{(adiabatic condition)}.$$

This may be written

$$\frac{2k}{\mathscr{V} \rho c_V} \ll \lambda \qquad \text{(adiabatic condition)}.$$

The usual range of wavelengths of compressional waves is from a few centimeters to a few hundred centimeters. Let us compare these values with $2k/\mathscr{V}\rho c_V$. Taking a gas like air as a typical case, we have, roughly,

$$k = 5 \times 10^{-5} \text{ cal/sec} \cdot \text{cm} \cdot \text{deg},$$
$$\mathscr{V} = 3 \times 10^4 \text{ cm/sec},$$
$$\rho = 10^{-3} \text{ gm/cm}^3,$$
$$c_V = 10^{-1} \text{ cal/gm} \cdot \text{deg},$$

and
$$\frac{2k}{\mathscr{V}\rho c_V} = \frac{2 \times 5 \times 10^{-5} \dfrac{\text{cal}}{\text{sec} \cdot \text{cm} \cdot \text{deg}}}{3 \times 10^4 \dfrac{\text{cm}}{\text{sec}} \times 10^{-3} \dfrac{\text{gm}}{\text{cm}^3} \times 10^{-1} \dfrac{\text{cal}}{\text{gm} \cdot \text{deg}}}$$
$$= 3.3 \times 10^{-5} \text{ cm}.$$

In the case of a metal, k would be much larger, but this would be compensated by the much larger values of $\mathscr{V}$ and ρ, and the quantity $2k/\mathscr{V}\rho c_V$ would be still smaller than 3.3×10^{-5} cm. This quantity is therefore seen to be so much smaller than the usual value of a wavelength of a compressional wave (3.3×10^{-5} cm is the wavelength of ultraviolet light) that the adiabatic condition is well fulfilled. We therefore conclude that, in view of the properties of ordinary matter, *the volume changes which take place under the influence of a longitudinal wave at ordinary frequencies are adiabatic* and not isothermal.

Returning now to the expression for the velocity of a longitudinal wave and identifying $V \Delta P/\Delta V$ as the *adiabatic bulk modulus B_S*, we have finally

$$\boxed{\mathscr{V} = \sqrt{\frac{B_S}{\rho}}.}$$

In the case of an ideal gas,

$$B_S = -V\left(\frac{\partial P}{\partial V}\right)_S = \gamma P,$$

and
$$\rho = \frac{M}{v},$$

where M is the molecular weight and v is the molar volume. Hence,

$$\mathscr{V} = \sqrt{\frac{\gamma P v}{M}},$$

or
$$\mathscr{V} = \sqrt{\frac{\gamma R \theta}{M}}.$$

The above formula enables us to calculate γ from experimental measurements of $\mathscr{V}$ and θ. For example, the speed of sound in air at 0°C is about 1100 ft/sec or about 3.31×10^4 cm/sec. We have therefore for air,

$$\mathscr{V}_V = 3.31 \times 10^4 \text{ cm/sec},$$
$$\theta = 273 \text{ deg},$$
$$R = 8.31 \times 10^7 \text{ ergs/mole} \cdot \text{deg},$$
$$M = \tfrac{4}{5} \times 28 + \tfrac{1}{5} \times 32 = 28.8 \text{ gm/mole},$$

whence

$$\begin{aligned}
\gamma &= \frac{M\mathscr{V}^2}{R\theta} \\
&= \frac{28.8 \text{ gm/mole} \times (3.31)^2 \times 10^8 \text{ cm}^2/\text{sec}^2}{8.31 \times 10^7 \text{ ergs/mole} \cdot \text{deg} \times 273 \text{ deg}} \\
&= \frac{3.16 \times 10^{10} \text{ dyne} \cdot \text{cm/mole}}{2.27 \times 10^{10} \text{ ergs/mole}} \\
&= 1.39.
\end{aligned}$$

The speed of a sound wave in a gas can be measured with fair accuracy by means of Kundt's tube. The gas is admitted to a cylindrical tube closed at one end and supplied at the other end with a movable piston capable of being set in vibration parallel to the axis of the tube. In the tube is a small amount of light powder. For a given frequency, a position of the piston can be found at which standing waves are set up. Under these conditions small heaps of powder pile up at the nodes. The distance between any two adjacent nodes is one-half a wavelength, and the speed of the waves is the product of the frequency and the wavelength. Values of γ obtained by this method are in good agreement with those obtained from calorimetric measurements.

PROBLEMS

6.1. Show that the virial expansion

$$Pv = A(1 + B'P + C'P^2 + \cdots)$$

may be written

$$Pv = A\left(1 + \frac{B''}{v} + \frac{C''}{v^2} + \cdots\right)$$

where

$$B'' = AB',$$
$$C'' = A^2[(B')^2 + C'].$$

6.2. (a) The most reliable value of $\lim (Pv)_3$ was obtained by using oxygen. Why?

(b) The value of $\lim (Pv)$ of helium of mass number 3 (He^3) was found to be 0.3459 liter $\cdot$ atm/mole when the gas bulb was surrounded by He^4 at its normal boiling point. What is the NBP of He^4?

6.3. (a) Prove that the volume expansivity β of a real gas and the compressibility factor Z are connected by the following relation:

$$\beta = \frac{1}{\theta} + \frac{1}{Z}\left(\frac{\partial Z}{\partial \theta}\right)_P = \frac{1}{\theta} + \frac{(dB'/d\theta)P + (dC'/d\theta)P^2 + \cdots}{1 + B'P + C'P^2 + \cdots}.$$

(b) Prove that the isothermal compressibility k of a real gas is given by the relation

$$k = \frac{1}{P} - \frac{1}{Z}\left(\frac{\partial Z}{\partial P}\right)_\theta = \frac{1}{P} - \frac{B' + 2C'P + \cdots}{1 + B'P + C'P^2 + \cdots}.$$

(c) Compare these results with those of Prob. 2.3.

6.4. Mercury is poured into the open end of a J-shaped glass tube which is closed at the short end, trapping the air in that end. Assuming air to act like an ideal gas, how much mercury can be poured in before it overflows? The long and short ends are, respectively, 1 m and 50 cm long, and effects due to the curvature of the bottom may be neglected.

6.5. A cylindrical highball glass 15 cm high and 35 cm² in cross section contains water up to the 10-cm mark. A card is placed over the top and held there while the glass is inverted. When the support is removed, what mass of water must leave the glass in order that the rest of the water should remain in the glass, neglecting the weight of the card? (CAUTION: Try this over a sink.)

6.6. In the Woodcock gas thermometer, the gas bulb of volume V is connected by means of a capillary of negligible volume with a pressure gauge at constant room temperature θ' whose volume V' may be considerably *larger* than V. The thermometer is filled with gas to a pressure P_0 when the bulb is at a temperature θ_0. The temperature of the apparatus where the bulb is located is now changed to a value θ, the pressure in the entire thermometer changing to P.

(a) Assuming the gas to be ideal, show that

$$P = \frac{\theta'/\theta_0 + r}{\theta'/\theta + r}P_0,$$

where $r = V'/V$.

(b) Assume $\theta' = 300°K$, $\theta_0 = 20°K$, $P_0 = 1$ atm, and calculate the decrease in P accompanying a decrease in θ from 3 to 2°K when $r = 0.1$, that is, when the "nuisance volume" is small.

(c) Same as (b) except $r = 10$ (large "nuisance volume"). The change in pressure divided by the change in temperature is a measure of the sensitivity of the thermometer. Is it true that by increasing the "nuisance volume" one can increase the sensitivity?

6.7. The ideal gas temperature is defined operationally with a constant-volume gas thermometer thus

$$\theta = \lim_{P_3 \to 0} \theta(P) = 273.16°K \lim \frac{P}{P_3} \qquad (\text{const. } V).$$

To measure θ it is neither accurate nor convenient to measure P/P_3 at smaller and smaller values of P_3, and then to extrapolate. Instead, $\theta(P)$ is measured at *one* value of P_3, namely, 1000 mm of Hg, and a correction factor is applied, which is tantamount to an extrapolation to zero pressure. To calculate the correction factor, first write $\theta(P)$ in the form

$$\theta(P) = 273.16°K \frac{PV}{P_3V} = 273.16°K \frac{Pv}{P_3v},$$

and then use the virial expansion of Prob. 6.1 as far as the second virial coefficient, thus:

$$Pv = A\left(1 + \frac{B''}{v}\right).$$

(a) Prove that

$$\theta = \theta(P)\left[1 - \frac{B'' - B_3''}{v}\right].$$

HINT: Make use of the fact, as seen in Table 6.1, that virial coefficients are small, and also that, when x is small compared with unity,

$$\frac{1}{1 + x} = 1 - x.$$

(b) Using a constant-pressure gas thermometer prove that

$$\theta = \theta(V)[1 - P(B' - B_3')].$$

6.8. The temperature of an ideal gas in a capillary of constant cross-sectional area varies exponentially from one end $(x = 0)$ to the other $(x = L)$, according to the equation

$$\theta = \theta_0 e^{-kx}.$$

If the volume of the capillary is V and the pressure P is uniform throughout, show that the number of moles of gas n is given by

$$PV = nR\frac{kL\theta_0}{e^{kL} - 1}.$$

Show that, as $k \to 0$, $PV \to nR\theta_0$, as it should.

6.9. Prove that the work done by an ideal gas with constant heat capacities during a quasi-static adiabatic expansion is equal to

(a) $$W = C_V(\theta_i - \theta_f).$$

(b) $$W = \frac{P_iV_i - P_fV_f}{\gamma - 1}.$$

(c) $$W = \frac{P_iV_i}{\gamma - 1}\left[1 - \left(\frac{P_f}{P_i}\right)^{\frac{\gamma-1}{\gamma}}\right].$$

6.10. (a) Show that the heat transferred during an infinitesimal quasi-static process of an ideal gas can be written

$$dQ = \frac{C_V}{nR}V\,dP + \frac{C_P}{nR}P\,dV.$$

Applying this equation to an adiabatic process, show that $PV^\gamma = $ const.

(b) An ideal gas of volume 0.05 ft^3 and pressure 120 lb/in.^{2} undergoes a quasi-static adiabatic expansion until the pressure drops to 15 lb/in.^{2} Assuming γ to remain constant at the value 1.4, (1) what is the final volume? (2) how much work is done?

6.11. (a) Derive the following formula for a quasi-static adiabatic process of an ideal gas, assuming γ to be constant:

$$\theta V^{\gamma-1} = \text{const.}$$

(b) At about 100 msec after detonation of a uranium fission bomb, the "ball of fire" consists of a sphere of gas with a radius of about 50 ft and a temperature of 300,000°K. Making very rough assumptions, estimate at what radius its temperature would be 3000°K.

6.12. (a) Derive the following formula for a quasi-static adiabatic process of an ideal gas, assuming γ to be constant:

$$\frac{\theta}{P^{(\gamma-1)/\gamma}} = \text{const.}$$

(b) Helium ($\gamma = \frac{5}{3}$) at 300°K and 1 atm pressure is compressed quasi-statically and adiabatically to a pressure of 5 atm. Assuming that the helium behaves like an ideal gas, what is the final temperature?

6.13. A horizontal insulated cylinder contains a frictionless nonconducting piston. On each side of the piston are 54 liters of an inert monatomic ideal gas at 1 atm and 273°K. Heat is slowly supplied to the gas on the left side until the piston has compressed the gas on the right side to 7.59 atm.

(a) How much work is done on the gas on the right side?

(b) What is the final temperature of the gas on the right side?

(c) What is the final temperature of the gas on the left side?

(d) How much heat is added to the gas on the left side?

6.14. An exhausted chamber with nonconducting walls is connected through a valve to the atmosphere, where the pressure is P_0 and the temperature θ_0. The valve is opened slightly, and air flows into the chamber until the pressure within the chamber is P_0. Assuming the air to behave like an ideal gas with constant heat capacities, show that the final temperature of the air in the chamber is $\gamma\theta_0$.

6.15. A thick-walled insulated metal chamber contains n_i moles of helium at high pressure P_i. It is connected through a valve with a large almost empty gasholder in which the pressure is maintained at a constant value P_0, very nearly atmospheric. The valve is opened slightly and the helium flows slowly and adiabatically into the gasholder until the pressures on the two sides of the valve are equalized. Assuming the helium to behave like an ideal gas with constant heat capacities, show that

(a) The final temperature of the gas in the chamber is

$$\theta_f = \theta_i \left(\frac{P_f}{P_i}\right)^{(\gamma-1)/\gamma},$$

(b) The number of moles of gas left in the chamber is

$$n_f = n_i \left(\frac{P_f}{P_i}\right)^{1/\gamma},$$

(c) The final temperature of the gas in the gasholder is

$$\theta' = \frac{\theta_i}{\gamma} \frac{1 - P_f/P_i}{1 - (P_f/P_i)^{1/\gamma}}.$$

(HINT: See Prob. 4.10.)

6.16. (a) If y is the height above sea level, show that the decrease of atmospheric pressure due to a rise dy is given by

$$\frac{dP}{P} = -\frac{Mg}{R\theta} dy,$$

where M is the molecular weight of the air, g the acceleration of gravity, and θ the absolute temperature at the height y.

(b) If the decrease of pressure in (a) is due to an adiabatic expansion, show that

$$\frac{dP}{P} = \frac{\gamma}{\gamma - 1}\frac{d\theta}{\theta}.$$

(c) From (a) and (b), using some of the numerical data of Art. 6.11, calculate $d\theta/dy$ in degrees per kilometer.

6.17. A steel ball of mass 8 gm is placed in a tube of cross-sectional area 1.2 cm². The tube is connected to an air tank of 6 liters capacity, the pressure of the air being 76 cm Hg. (a) With what period will the ball vibrate? (b) If the ball is held originally at a position where the gas pressure is exactly atmospheric and is then allowed to drop, how far will it go before it starts to come up?

6.18. Carbon dioxide is contained in a vessel whose volume is 5270 cm³. A ball of mass 16.65 gm, placed in a tube of cross-sectional area 2.01 cm², vibrates with a period of 0.834 sec. What is γ when the barometer reads 72.3 cm?

6.19. Mercury is poured into a U tube open at both ends until the total length of the mercury is h.

(a) If the level of mercury on one side of the tube is depressed and then the mercury is allowed to oscillate with small amplitude, show that, neglecting friction, the period τ_1 is given by

$$\tau_1 = 2\pi\sqrt{\frac{h}{2g}}.$$

(b) One end of the U tube is now closed so that the length of the entrapped air column is L, and again the mercury is caused to oscillate. Assuming friction to be negligible, the air to be ideal, and the changes of volume to be adiabatic, show that the period τ_2 is now

$$\tau_2 = 2\pi\sqrt{\frac{h}{2g + \gamma h_0 g/L}},$$

where h_0 is the height of the barometric column.

(c) Show that

$$\gamma = \frac{2L}{h_0}\left(\frac{\tau_1^2}{\tau_2^2} - 1\right).$$

6.20. The speed of a longitudinal wave in a mixture of helium and neon at 300°K was found to be 758 m/sec. What is the composition of the mixture?

6.21. The atomic weight of iodine is 127. A standing wave in iodine vapor at 400°K produces nodes that are 6.77 cm apart when the frequency is 1000 vib/sec. Is iodine vapor monatomic or diatomic?

6.22. An open glass tube of uniform bore is bent into the shape of an L. One arm is immersed in a liquid of density ρ', the other arm, of length l, remaining in the air in a horizontal position. The tube is rotated with constant angular speed ω about the axis of the vertical arm. Prove that the height y to which the liquid rises in the vertical arm is equal to

$$y = \frac{P_0(1 - e^{-\omega^2 l^2 M/2R\theta})}{g\rho'},$$

where P_0 is atmospheric pressure, M is the molecular weight of air, and g is the acceleration of gravity.

$$7$$

The Second Law of Thermodynamics

7.1. Conversion of Work into Heat, and Vice Versa. When two stones are rubbed together under water, the work done against friction is transformed into internal energy tending to produce a rise of temperature of the stones. As soon, however, as the temperature of the stones rises above that of the surrounding water, there is a flow of heat into the water. If the mass of water is large enough or if the water is continually flowing, there will be no appreciable rise of temperature, and the water can be regarded as a heat reservoir. Since the state of the stones is the same at the end of the process as at the beginning, the net result of the process is merely the conversion of mechanical work into heat. Similarly, when an electric current is maintained in a resistor immersed either in running water or in a very large mass of water, there is also a conversion of electrical work into heat, without any change in the thermodynamic coordinates of the wire. In general, work of any kind W may be done upon a system in contact with a reservoir, giving rise to a flow of heat Q without altering the state of the system. The system acts merely as an intermediary. It is apparent from the first law that the work W is equal to the heat Q, or, in other words, the transformation of work into heat is accomplished with 100 per cent efficiency. Moreover, this transformation can be continued indefinitely.

To study the converse process, namely, the conversion of heat into work, we must also have at hand a process or series of processes by means of which such a conversion may continue indefinitely without involving any resultant changes in the state of any system. At first thought, it might appear that the isothermal expansion of an ideal gas might be a suitable process to consider in discussing the conversion of heat into work. In this case there is no internal-energy change since the temperature remains constant, and therefore $W = Q$, or heat has been converted completely into work. This process, however, involves a change of state of the gas. The volume increases and the pressure decreases until atmospheric pressure is reached, at which the process stops. It therefore cannot be used indefinitely.

139

What is needed is a series of processes in which a system is brought back to its initial state, i.e., a *cycle*. All the processes that constitute a cycle may involve a flow of heat to or from the system and the performance of work by or on the system. Let the following notation refer to one complete cycle:

Q_1 = amount of heat absorbed by the system
Q_2 = amount of heat rejected by the system
W = net amount of work done by the system

Both Q_1 and Q_2 have been defined as positive numbers. If Q_1 is larger than Q_2 and W is done by the system, the mechanical device by whose agency the system is caused to undergo the cycle is called a *heat engine*. It is convenient to speak of the system as the *working substance* and to say that the engine operates in a cycle. The purpose of a heat engine is to deliver work continuously to the outside by performing the same cycle over and over again. The net work in the cycle is the output, and the heat absorbed by the working substance is the input. The *thermal efficiency* of the engine η is defined as

$$\text{Thermal efficiency} = \frac{\text{work output in any energy units}}{\text{heat input in the same energy units}}$$

or

$$\eta = \frac{W}{Q_1}.$$

Applying the first law to one complete cycle, remembering that there is no net change of internal energy, we get

$$Q_1 - Q_2 = W,$$

and therefore

$$\eta = \frac{Q_1 - Q_2}{Q_1}$$

or

$$\boxed{\eta = 1 - \frac{Q_2}{Q_1}.}$$

It is seen from this equation that η will be unity (efficiency 100 per cent) when Q_2 is zero. In other words, if an engine can be built to operate in a cycle in which there is no outflow of heat from the working substance, there will be 100 per cent conversion of heat into work. We shall see later under what conditions this is possible in principle and why it is not possible in practice.

The transformation of heat into work is usually accomplished in practice by two general types of engine, the *internal-combustion engine* and the *steam engine*. In both engines, a gas or a mixture of gases contained in a cylinder undergoes a cycle, thus causing a piston to impart to a shaft a motion of rotation against an opposing force. It is necessary in both engines that the gas in the cylinder at some time in the cycle be raised to a high temperature and pressure. In the steam engine this is accomplished by an outside furnace, which, by heat conduction and radiation, causes the water to be heated and changed into steam at high temperature. The high temperature and pressure achieved in the internal-combustion engine, however, are produced by a chemical reaction between a fuel and air that takes place in the cylinder itself. There are two types of internal-combustion engine. In the *gasoline engine*, the combustion of the gasoline and air takes place explosively through the agency of an electric spark. The *diesel engine*, however, uses oil as a fuel, the combustion of which is accomplished more slowly by spraying the oil into the cylinder at a convenient rate.

7.2. Gasoline Engine. In the gasoline engine, the cycle involves the performance of six processes, of which four require motion of the piston and are called *strokes:*

1. *Intake Stroke.* A mixture of gasoline vapor and air is drawn into the cylinder by the suction stroke of the piston. The pressure of the outside is greater than that of the mixture by an amount sufficient to cause acceleration and to overcome friction.

2. *Compression Stroke.* The mixture of gasoline vapor and air is compressed until its pressure and temperature rise considerably. This is accomplished by the compression stroke of the piston, in which friction, acceleration, and heat loss by conduction are present.

3. *Explosion.* Combustion of the hot mixture is caused to take place very rapidly by an electric spark. The resulting combustion products attain a very high pressure and temperature, but the volume remains unchanged. The piston does not move during this process.

4. *Power Stroke.* The hot combustion products expand and push the piston out, thus suffering a drop in pressure and temperature. This is the power stroke of the piston and is also accompanied by friction, acceleration, and heat conduction.

5. *Valve Exhaust.* The combustion products at the end of the power stroke are still at a higher pressure and temperature than the outside. An exhaust valve allows some gas to escape until the pressure drops to that of the atmosphere. The piston does not move during this process.

6. *Exhaust Stroke.* The piston pushes almost all the remaining combustion products out of the cylinder by exerting a pressure sufficiently larger than that of the outside to cause acceleration and overcome friction. This is the exhaust stroke.

In the above processes there are several phenomena that render an exact mathematical analysis almost impossible. Among these are friction, acceleration, loss of heat by conduction, and the chemical reaction between gasoline vapor and air. A drastic but useful simplification is provided by eliminating these troublesome effects. When this is done, we have a sort of idealized gasoline engine that performs a cycle known as an *Otto cycle*.

7.3. Air-standard Otto Cycle. The behavior of a gasoline engine can be approximated by assuming a set of ideal conditions as follows:

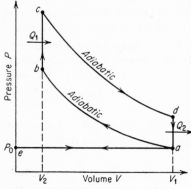

1. The working substance is at all times air, which behaves like an ideal gas with constant heat capacities.

2. All processes are quasi-static.

3. There is no friction.

On the basis of these assumptions the air-standard Otto cycle is composed of six simple processes of an ideal gas; these are plotted on a P-V diagram in Fig. 7.1.

FIG. 7.1. Air-standard Otto cycle.

1. $e \rightarrow a$ represents a quasi-static isobaric intake, at atmospheric pressure. There is no friction, and no acceleration. The volume varies from zero to V_1 as the number of moles varies from zero to n_1 according to the equation

$$P_0 V = nR\theta_a,$$

where P_0 is atmospheric pressure and θ_a is the temperature of the outside air.

2. $a \rightarrow b$ represents a quasi-static, adiabatic compression of n_1 moles of air. There is no friction, and no loss of heat through the cylinder wall. The temperature rises from θ_a to θ_b according to the equation

$$\theta_a V_1^{\gamma-1} = \theta_b V_2^{\gamma-1}.$$

3. $b \rightarrow c$ represents a quasi-static isochoric increase of temperature and pressure of n_1 moles of air, brought about by an absorption of heat from a series of external reservoirs whose temperatures range from θ_b to θ_c. If there were only one reservoir at the temperature θ_c, the flow of heat would not be quasi-static. This process is meant to approximate the effect of the explosion in a gasoline engine.

4. $c \rightarrow d$ represents a quasi-static adiabatic expansion of n_1 moles of air, involving a drop in temperature from θ_c to θ_d according to the equation

$$\theta_c V_2^{\gamma-1} = \theta_d V_1^{\gamma-1}.$$

5. $d \rightarrow a$ represents a quasi-static isochoric drop in temperature and pressure of n_1 moles of air, brought about by a rejection of heat to a

series of external reservoirs ranging in temperature from θ_d to θ_a. This process is meant to approximate the drop to atmospheric pressure upon opening the exhaust valve.

6. $a \to e$ represents a quasi-static isobaric exhaust at atmospheric pressure. The volume varies from V_1 to zero as the number of moles varies from n_1 to zero, the temperature remaining constant at the value θ_a.

The two isobaric processes $e \to a$ and $a \to e$ obviously cancel each other and need not be considered further. Of the four remaining processes, only two involve a flow of heat. There is an absorption of Q_1 units of heat at high temperatures from b to c, and a rejection of Q_2 units of heat at lower temperatures from d to a, as indicated in Fig. 7.1.

Assuming C_V to be constant along the line $b \to c$, we get

$$Q_1 = \int_{\theta_b}^{\theta_c} C_V \, d\theta = C_V(\theta_c - \theta_b).$$

Similarly, for process $d \to a$, regarding Q_2 as a positive number,

$$Q_2 = -\int_{\theta_d}^{\theta_a} C_V \, d\theta = C_V(\theta_d - \theta_a).$$

The thermal efficiency is therefore

$$\eta = 1 - \frac{Q_2}{Q_1} = 1 - \frac{\theta_d - \theta_a}{\theta_c - \theta_b}.$$

The two adiabatic processes provide the equations

$$\theta_d V_1^{\gamma-1} = \theta_c V_2^{\gamma-1},$$
$$\theta_a V_1^{\gamma-1} = \theta_b V_2^{\gamma-1},$$

which yield, after subtraction,

$$(\theta_d - \theta_a)V_1^{\gamma-1} = (\theta_c - \theta_b)V_2^{\gamma-1},$$

or

$$\frac{\theta_d - \theta_a}{\theta_c - \theta_b} = \left(\frac{V_2}{V_1}\right)^{\gamma-1}.$$

Denoting the ratio V_1/V_2 by r, where r is called either the *compression ratio* or the *expansion ratio*, we have finally

$$\eta = 1 - \frac{1}{(V_1/V_2)^{\gamma-1}} = 1 - \frac{1}{r^{\gamma-1}}.$$

In an actual gasoline engine, r cannot be made greater than about 10 because, if r is larger, the rise of temperature upon compression of the mixture of gasoline and air is great enough to cause an explosion before the advent of the spark. This is called *preignition*. Taking r equal to 9 and γ equal to 1.5 (for air γ is more nearly 1.4),

$$\eta = 1 - \frac{1}{\sqrt{9}}$$
$$= 0.67 = 67 \text{ per cent.}$$

It will be shown later that all the troublesome effects present in an actual gasoline engine, such as acceleration, turbulence, and heat conduction by virtue of a finite temperature difference, are such as to make the efficiency much lower than that of the air-standard Otto cycle.

7.4. Diesel Engine. In the diesel engine, only air is admitted on the intake. The air is compressed adiabatically until the temperature is high enough to ignite oil that is sprayed into the cylinder after the compression. The rate of supply of oil is adjusted so that combustion takes place approximately isobarically, the piston moving out during combustion. The rest of the cycle, namely, power stroke, valve exhaust, and exhaust stroke, is exactly the same as in the gasoline engine. The usual troublesome effects, such as chemical combination, friction, acceleration, and heat losses, take place in the diesel engine as in the gasoline engine. Eliminating these effects by making the same assumptions as before, we are left with a sort of idealized diesel engine that

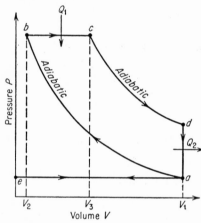

FIG. 7.2. Air-standard Diesel cycle.

performs a cycle known as the *air-standard diesel cycle*. If the line $b \rightarrow c$ in Fig. 7.1 is imagined horizontal instead of vertical, the resulting cycle will be the air-standard diesel cycle. This is shown in Fig. 7.2.

The line $b \rightarrow c$ in Fig. 7.2 represents the quasi-static isobaric absorption of heat from a series of external reservoirs ranging in temperature from θ_b to θ_c. This process is meant to approximate the isobaric burning of the oil. All the other curves have the same meaning as in the case of the air-standard Otto cycle.

Assuming C_P to be constant along the line $b \rightarrow c$, we get

$$Q_1 = \int_{\theta_b}^{\theta_c} C_P \, d\theta = C_P(\theta_c - \theta_b),$$

and, as in the case of the Otto cycle,

$$Q_2 = C_V(\theta_d - \theta_a).$$

Therefore, $$\eta = 1 - \frac{1}{\gamma}\frac{\theta_d - \theta_a}{\theta_c - \theta_b}.$$

This may be transformed into

$$\eta = 1 - \frac{1}{\gamma}\frac{(1/r_E)^\gamma - (1/r_C)^\gamma}{(1/r_E) - (1/r_C)}$$

where $$r_E = \frac{V_1}{V_3} = \text{expansion ratio}$$

and $$r_C = \frac{V_1}{V_2} = \text{compression ratio}.$$

In practice, the compression ratio of a diesel engine can be made much larger than that of a gasoline engine, because there is no fear of preignition since only air is compressed. Taking, for example, $r_C = 15$, $r_E = 5$, and $\gamma = 1.5$,

$$\eta = 1 - \frac{2}{3}\frac{\dfrac{1}{5^{3/2}} - \dfrac{1}{15^{3/2}}}{\dfrac{1}{5} - \dfrac{1}{15}}$$
$$= 1 - 5(0.0895 - 0.0172)$$
$$= 64 \text{ per cent.}$$

The efficiencies of actual diesel engines are, of course, still lower, for the reasons mentioned in connection with the gasoline engine.

In the diesel engine just considered, four strokes of the piston are needed for the execution of a cycle, and only one of the four is a power stroke. Since only air is compressed in the diesel engine, it is possible to do away with the exhaust and intake strokes and thus complete the cycle in two strokes. In the two-stroke-cycle diesel engine, every other stroke is a power stroke, and thus the power is doubled. The principle is very simple: At the conclusion of the power stroke, when the cylinder is full of combustion products, the valve opens, exhaust takes place until the combustion products are at atmospheric pressure, and then, instead of using the piston itself to exhaust the remaining gases, fresh air is blown into the cylinder, replacing the combustion products. A blower, operated by the engine itself, is used for this purpose, and thus it accomplishes in one simple operation what formerly required two separate piston strokes.

7.5. Heat Engine. Kelvin-Planck Statement of the Second Law. We are not in a position, as yet, to describe the details of the cycle performed by a steam engine or to consider the idealization of this cycle, known as the Rankine cycle. It is not necessary, however, to know the exact nature of the steam-engine cycle in order to understand that, during the cycle, water is heated to its boiling point and vaporized and that, for this purpose, there must be a flow of heat from an external reservoir.   Furthermore, it is clear that after expansion the steam must be condensed at a lower temperature, thus involving a flow of heat into an external reservoir.   In the Otto and diesel cycles also, heat was absorbed at high temperatures and rejected at lower temperatures.   Whether the absorption and rejection of heat are quasi-static or not is of no consequence.   We assumed quasi-static conditions in the air-standard Otto and diesel cycles only for purposes of simple calculation.   Usually, there are only two reservoirs, one at a higher temperature than the other, such as the boiler and condenser of a steam engine.   During both absorption and rejection of heat, there is in general a finite temperature difference

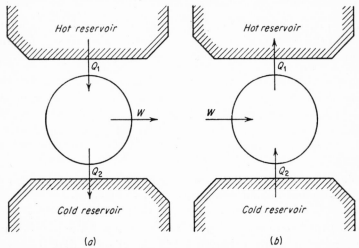

FIG. 7.3. Symbolic representation of (a) a heat engine and of (b) a refrigerator.

between the working substance and the reservoir.   Reduced to its simplest terms, the important characteristics of heat-engine cycles may be summed up as follows:

1. There is some process or series of processes during which there is an absorption of heat from an external reservoir at a high temperature (called simply the "hot reservoir").

2. There is some process or series of processes during which heat is rejected to an external reservoir at a lower temperature (called simply the "cold reservoir").

This is represented schematically in Fig. 7.3(a).   No engine has ever been developed that converts the heat extracted from one reservoir into work without rejecting some heat to a reservoir at a lower temperature. This negative statement, which is the result of everyday experience, constitutes the *second law of thermodynamics* and has been formulated in several ways.   The original statement of Kelvin is "It is impossible by means of inanimate material agency to derive mechanical effect from any portion of matter by cooling it below the temperature of the coldest of the surrounding objects." In the words of Planck, "It is impossible to construct an engine which, working in a complete cycle, will produce no effect other than the raising of a weight and the cooling of a heat reservoir." We may combine these statements into one equivalent statement, to which we shall refer hereafter as the *Kelvin-Planck statement of the second law*, thus:

It is impossible to construct an engine that, operating in a cycle, will produce no effect other than the extraction of heat from a reservoir and the performance of an equivalent amount of work.

If the second law were not true, it would be possible to drive a steamship across the ocean by extracting heat from the ocean or to run a power plant by extracting heat from the surrounding air. The student should notice that neither of these "impossibilities" violates the first law of thermodynamics. After all, both the ocean and the surrounding air contain an enormous store of internal energy, which, in principle, may be extracted in the form of a flow of heat. There is nothing in the first law to preclude the possibility of converting this heat completely into work. The second law, therefore, is not a deduction from the first but stands by itself as a separate law of nature, referring to an aspect of nature different from that contemplated by the first law. The first law denies the possibility of creating or destroying energy; the second denies the possibility of utilizing energy in a particular way. The continual operation of a machine that creates its own energy and thus violates the first law is called *perpetual motion of the first kind*. The operation of a machine that utilizes the internal energy of only one heat reservoir, thus violating the second law, is called *perpetual motion of the second kind*.

7.6. Refrigerator. Clausius Statement of the Second Law. We have seen that a heat engine is a device through whose agency a working substance is taken through a cycle in such a direction that some heat is absorbed while the temperature is high, a smaller amount is rejected at a lower temperature, and a net amount of work is done on the outside. If we imagine a cycle performed in a direction opposite to that of an engine, the net result would be the absorption of some heat at a low temperature, the rejection of a *larger* amount at a higher temperature, and a net amount of work done *on* the working substance. A device that performs a cycle in this direction is called a *refrigerator*, and the working substance is called a *refrigerant*. Figure 7.3(*b*) represents a schematic diagram of a refrigerator.

Let the following notation (all positive quantities) refer to one complete cycle:

Q_1 = amount of heat rejected by the refrigerant
Q_2 = amount of heat absorbed by the refrigerant
W = net work done on the refrigerant

Since the refrigerant undergoes a cycle, there is no change in internal energy, and the first law becomes

$$Q_2 - Q_1 = -W$$

or
$$Q_1 = Q_2 + W.$$

That is, the heat rejected to the hot reservoir is larger than the heat extracted from the cold reservoir by the amount of work done.

The purpose of a refrigerator is to extract as much heat Q_2 as possible from the cold reservoir with the expenditure of as little work W as possible. The quantity that expresses the ability of a refrigerator to do its job is therefore Q_2/W, which is known as the *coefficient of performance*. Details of the refrigeration cycle and a calculation of the coefficient of performance will be given in a later chapter. It is sufficient at this time merely to emphasize that work is always necessary to transfer heat from a cold to a hot reservoir. In household refrigerators, this work is usually done by an electric motor whose cost of operation appears regularly on the monthly bill. It would be a boon to mankind if no external supply of energy were needed, but it must certainly be admitted that experience indicates the contrary. This negative statement leads us to the *Clausius statement of the second law.*

It is impossible to construct a device that, operating in a cycle, will produce no effect other than the transfer of heat from a cooler to a hotter body.

At first sight, the Kelvin-Planck and the Clausius statements appear to be quite unconnected, but we shall see immediately that they are in all respects equivalent.

7.7. Equivalence of Kelvin-Planck and Clausius Statements. Let us adopt the following notation:

K = truth of the Kelvin-Planck statement
$-K$ = falsity of the Kelvin-Planck statement
C = truth of the Clausius statement
$-C$ = falsity of the Clausius statement

Two propositions or statements are said to be equivalent when the truth of one implies the truth of the second and the truth of the second implies the truth of the first. Using the symbol $\supset$ to mean "implies" and the symbol $\equiv$ to denote equivalence, we have, by definition,

$$K \equiv C$$

when
$$K \supset C \quad \text{and} \quad C \supset K.$$

Now, it may easily be shown that

$$K \equiv C$$

also when
$$-K \supset -C \quad \text{and} \quad -C \supset -K.$$

Thus, in order to demonstrate the equivalence of K and C, we have to show that a violation of one statement implies a violation of the second, and vice versa.

1. To prove that $-C \supset -K$, consider a refrigerator, shown in the left-hand side of Fig. 7.4, that requires *no work* to transfer Q_2 units of heat from a cold reservoir to a hot reservoir and that therefore violates the Clausius statement. Suppose that a heat engine (on the right) also operates between the same two reservoirs in such a way that heat Q_2 is delivered to the cold reservoir. The engine, of course, does not violate any law, but the refrigerator and engine *together* constitute a self-acting

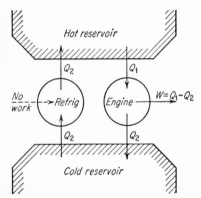 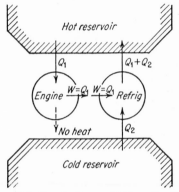

Fig. 7.4. Proof that $-C \supset -K$. The refrigerator on the left is a violation of C; the refrigerator and engine acting together constitute a violation of K.

Fig. 7.5. Proof that $-K \supset -C$. The engine on the left is a violation of K; the engine and refrigerator acting together constitute a violation of C.

device that takes heat $Q_1 - Q_2$ from the hot reservoir and converts *all* this heat into work without producing any change in the cold reservoir. Therefore the refrigerator and engine together constitute a violation of the Kelvin-Planck statement.

2. To prove that $-K \supset -C$, consider an engine, shown on the left-hand side of Fig. 7.5, that rejects no heat to the cold reservoir and that therefore violates the Kelvin-Planck statement. Suppose that a refrigerator (on the right) also operates between the same two reservoirs and uses up all the work liberated by the engine. The refrigerator violates no law, but the engine and refrigerator *together* constitute a self-acting device that transfers heat Q_2 from the cold to the hot reservoir without producing any changes elsewhere. Therefore the engine and refrigerator together constitute a violation of the Clausius statement.

We therefore arrive at the conclusion that both statements of the second law are equivalent. It is a matter of indifference which one is used in a particular argument.

PROBLEMS

7.1. Figure 7.6 represents an imaginary ideal gas engine cycle. Assuming constant heat capacities, show that the thermal efficiency is

$$\eta = 1 - \gamma \frac{(V_1/V_2) - 1}{(P_1/P_2) - 1}.$$

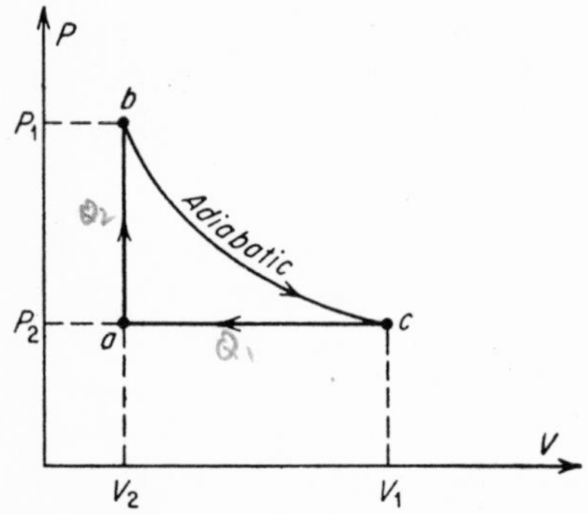

FIG. 7.6.

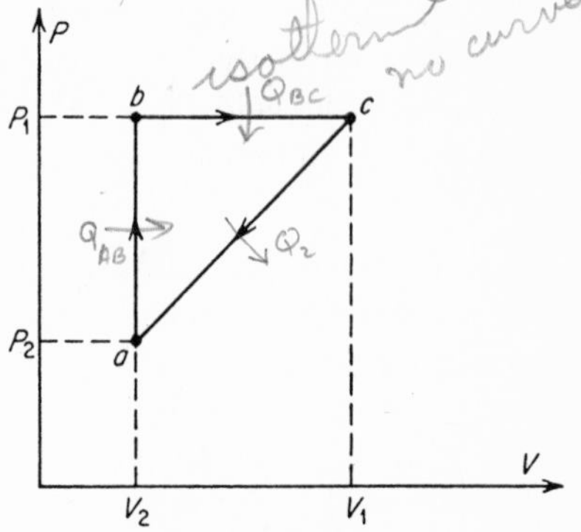

FIG. 7.7.

7.2. Figure 7.7 represents an imaginary ideal gas engine cycle. Assuming constant heat capacities, show that the thermal efficiency is

$$\eta = \frac{1}{2C_V \theta_b} \frac{(P_1 - P_2)(V_1 - V_2)}{[1 - (P_2/P_1)] + \gamma[(V_1/V_2) - 1]}.$$

7.3. A vessel contains 600 cm³ of helium gas at 2°K and $\frac{1}{36}$ atm. Take the zero of internal energy of helium to be at this point.

(a) The temperature is raised at constant volume to 288°K. Assuming helium to behave like an ideal monatomic gas, how much heat is absorbed, and what is the internal energy of the helium? Can this energy be regarded as stored heat or stored work?

(b) The helium is now expanded adiabatically to 2°K. How much work is done and what is the new internal energy? Has heat been converted into work without compensation, thus violating the second law?

(c) The helium is now compressed isothermally to its original volume. What are the quantities of heat and work in this process? What is the efficiency of the cycle? Plot on a P-V diagram.

7.4. Derive the expression for the efficiency of an air-standard diesel cycle in terms of expansion and compression ratios, given in Art. 7.4.

7.5. There are many paramagnetic solids whose internal energy is a function of temperature only, like an ideal gas. In an isothermal demagnetization, heat is absorbed from one reservoir and converted completely into work. Is this a violation of the second law? Why?

7.6. Would an atomic-energy power plant violate either the first law or the second law of thermodynamics? Explain.

7.7. Prove that it is impossible for two quasi-static adiabatics to intersect. (HINT: Assume that they do intersect and complete the cycle with an isothermal. Show that the performance of this cycle violates the second law.)

8

Reversibility and Irreversibility

8.1. Reversibility and Irreversibility. In thermodynamics, work is a macroscopic concept. The performance of work may always be described in terms of the raising or lowering of a weight or the winding or unwinding of a spring, i.e., by the operation of a device that serves to increase or decrease the potential energy of a mechanical system. Imagine, for the sake of simplicity, a suspended weight coupled by means of suitable pulleys to a system so that any work done by or on the system can be described in terms of the raising or lowering of the weight. Imagine, further, a series of reservoirs which may be put in contact with the system and in terms of which any flow of heat to or from the system may be described. We shall refer to the suspended weight and the series of reservoirs as the *local surroundings* of the system. The local surroundings are therefore those parts of the surroundings which interact *directly* with the system. Other mechanical devices and reservoirs that are accessible and that *might* interact with the system constitute the *auxiliary surroundings* of the system, or, for want of a better expression, the *rest of the universe*. The word *universe* is used here in a very restricted technical sense, with no cosmic or celestial implications. The universe merely means a finite portion of the world consisting of the system and those surroundings which may interact with the system.

Now suppose that a process occurs in which (1) the system proceeds from an initial state i to a final state f; (2) the suspended weight is lowered to an extent that W units of work are performed; and (3) a transfer of heat Q takes place from the system to the series of reservoirs. If, at the conclusion of this process, the system may be restored to its initial state i, the weight lifted to its former level, and the reservoirs caused to part with the same amount of heat Q, without producing any changes in any other mechanical device or reservoir in the universe, the original process is said to be *reversible*. In other words, *a reversible process is one that is performed in such a way that, at the conclusion of the process, both the system and the local surroundings may be restored to their initial states,* **without producing any changes in the rest of the universe.** A

151

process that does not fulfill these stringent requirements is said to be *irreversible*.

The question immediately arises as to whether natural processes, i.e., the familiar processes of nature, are reversible or not. The purpose of this chapter is to show that it is a consequence of the second law of thermodynamics that all natural processes are irreversible. By considering representative types of natural processes and examining the features of these processes which are responsible for their irreversibility, we shall then be able to state the conditions under which a process may be performed reversibly.

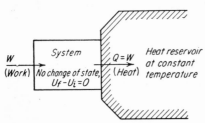

FIG. 8.1. Isothermal transformation of work through a system (which remains unchanged) into internal energy of a reservoir.

8.2. External Mechanical Irreversibility. There is a large class of processes involving the isothermal transformation of work through a system (which remains unchanged) into internal energy of a reservoir. This type of process is depicted schematically in Fig. 8.1 and is illustrated by the following five examples:

1. Irregular stirring of a viscous liquid in contact with a reservoir.

2. Coming to rest of a rotating or vibrating liquid in contact with a reservoir.

3. Inelastic deformation of a solid in contact with a reservoir.

4. Transfer of electricity through a resistor in contact with a reservoir.

5. Magnetic hysteresis of a material in contact with a reservoir.

In order to restore the system and its local surroundings to their initial states without producing changes elsewhere, Q units of heat would have to be extracted from the reservoir and converted completely into work. Since this would involve a violation of the second law, all processes of the above type are irreversible.

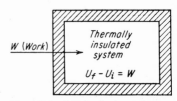

FIG. 8.2. Adiabatic transformation of work into internal energy of a system.

Another set of processes involves the adiabatic transformation of work into internal energy of a system. This is depicted schematically in Fig. 8.2 and is illustrated by the following examples, similar to the preceding list:

1. Irregular stirring of a viscous thermally insulated liquid.

2. Coming to rest of a rotating or vibrating thermally insulated liquid.

3. Inelastic deformation of a thermally insulated solid.

4. Transfer of electricity through a thermally insulated resistor.

5. Magnetic hysteresis of a thermally insulated material.

A process of this type is accompanied by a rise of temperature of the system from, say, θ_i to θ_f. In order to restore the system and its local surroundings to their initial states without producing changes elsewhere, the internal energy of the system would have to be decreased by extracting $U_f - U_i$ units of heat, thus lowering the temperature from θ_f to θ_i, and this heat would have to be completely converted into work. Since this violates the second law, all processes of the above type are irreversible.

The transformation of work into internal energy either of a system or of a reservoir is seen to take place through the agency of such phenomena as viscosity, friction, inelasticity, electric resistance, and magnetic hysteresis. These effects are known as *dissipative effects*, and the work is said to be dissipated. Processes involving the dissipation of work into internal energy are said to exhibit *external mechanical irreversibility*. It is a matter of everyday experience that dissipative effects, particularly friction, are always present in moving devices. Friction, of course, may be reduced considerably by suitable lubrication, but experience has shown that it can never be completely eliminated. If it could, a movable device could be kept in continual operation without violating either of the two laws of thermodynamics. Such a continual motion is known as *perpetual motion of the third kind*.

8.3. Internal Mechanical Irreversibility. The following very important natural processes involve the transformation of internal energy of a system into mechanical energy and then back into internal energy again:

1. Ideal gas rushing into a vacuum (free expansion).
2. Gas seeping through a porous plug (throttling process).
3. Snapping of a stretched wire after it is cut.
4. Collapse of a soap film after it is pricked.

We shall prove the irreversibility of only the first.

During a free expansion, no interactions take place, and hence there are no local surroundings. The only effect produced is a change of state of an ideal gas from a volume V_i and temperature θ to a larger volume V_f and the same temperature θ. To restore the gas to its initial state, it would have to be compressed isothermally to the volume V_i. If the compression were performed quasi-statically and there were no friction between the piston and cylinder, an amount of work W would have to be done by some outside mechanical device and an equal amount of heat would have to flow out of the gas into a reservoir at the temperature θ. If the mechanical device and the reservoir are to be left unchanged, the heat would have to be extracted from the reservoir and converted completely into work. Since this last step is impossible, the process is irreversible.

In a free expansion, immediately after the stopcock is opened, there is a transformation of some of the internal energy into kinetic energy of "mass motion" or "streaming," and then this kinetic energy is dissipated through viscosity into internal energy again. Similarly, when a stretched wire is cut, there is first a transformation of internal energy into kinetic energy of irregular motion and of vibration and then the dissipation of this energy through inelasticity into internal energy again. In all the processes, the first energy transformation takes place as a result of mechanical instability, and the second by virtue of some dissipative effect. A process of this sort is said to exhibit *internal mechanical irreversibility*.

8.4. External and Internal Thermal Irreversibility. Consider the following processes involving a transfer of heat between a system and a reservoir by virtue of a *finite* temperature difference:

1. Conduction or radiation of heat from a system to a cooler reservoir.

2. Conduction or radiation of heat through a system (which remains unchanged) from a hot reservoir to a cooler one.

To restore, at the conclusion of a process of this type, both the system and its local surroundings to their initial states, without producing changes elsewhere, heat would have to be transferred by means of a self-acting device from a cooler to a hotter body. Since this violates the second law (Clausius statement), all processes of this type are irreversible. Such processes are said to exhibit *external thermal irreversibility*.

A process involving a transfer of heat between parts of the same system because of nonuniformity of temperature is also obviously irreversible by virtue of the Clausius statement of the second law. Such a process is said to exhibit *internal thermal irreversibility*.

8.5. Chemical Irreversibility. Some of the most interesting processes that go on in nature involve a spontaneous change of internal structure, chemical composition, density, crystal form, etc. Some important examples follow.

Formation of new chemical constituents:

1. All chemical reactions.

Mixing of two different substances:

2. Diffusion of two dissimilar inert ideal gases.
3. Mixing of alcohol and water.

Sudden change of phase:

4. Freezing of supercooled liquid.
5. Condensation of supersaturated vapor.

Transport of matter between phases in contact:

6. Solution of solid in water.
7. Osmosis.

Such processes are by far the most difficult to handle and must, as a rule, be treated by special methods. Such methods constitute what is known as chemical thermodynamics and are discussed in the last few chapters of this book. It can be shown that the diffusion of two dissimilar inert ideal gases is equivalent to two independent free expansions. Since a free expansion is irreversible, it follows that diffusion is irreversible. The student will have to accept at present the statement that the above processes are irreversible. Processes that involve a spontaneous change of chemical structure, density, phase, etc., are said to exhibit *chemical irreversibility*.

8.6. Conditions for Reversibility. Most processes that occur in nature are included among the general types of process listed in the preceding articles. Living processes, particularly those involving cell division, tissue growth, etc., require a special investigation. There is some difference of opinion about the irreversibility of living processes; at present, the prevailing attitude seems to be that, if one takes into account all the interactions which accompany living processes, such processes are irreversible. Aside from living processes, we are entitled to conclude that it is a direct consequence of the second law of thermodynamics that *all natural processes are irreversible*.

A careful inspection of the various types of natural process shows that all of them involve one or both of the following features: (1) The conditions for mechanical, thermal, or chemical equilibrium, i.e., thermodynamic equilibrium, are not satisfied. (2) Dissipative effects, such as viscosity, friction, inelasticity, electric resistance, and magnetic hysteresis, are present. For a process to be reversible, it must not possess these features. If a process is performed quasi-statically, the system passes through states of thermodynamic equilibrium, which may be traversed just as well in one direction as in the opposite direction. If there are no dissipative effects, all the work done by the system during the performance of a process in one direction can be returned to the system during the reverse process. We are led, therefore, to the conclusion that a process will be reversible when (1) it is performed quasi-statically and (2) it is not accompanied by any dissipative effects.

Since it is impossible to satisfy these two conditions perfectly, it is obvious that a reversible process is purely an ideal abstraction, extremely useful for theoretical calculations (as we shall see) but quite devoid of reality. In this sense, the assumption of a reversible process in thermodynamics resembles the assumptions made so often in mechanics, such as those which refer to weightless strings, frictionless pulleys, and point masses.

A heat reservoir was defined as a body of very large mass capable of absorbing or rejecting an unlimited supply of heat without suffering appreciable changes in its thermodynamic coordinates. The changes that do take place are so very slow and so very minute that dissipative actions never develop. *Therefore, when heat enters or leaves a reservoir, the changes that take place in the reservoir are the same as those which would take place if the same quantity of heat were transferred reversibly.*

It is possible in the laboratory to approximate the conditions necessary for the performance of reversible processes. For example, if a gas is confined in a cylinder equipped with a well-lubricated piston and is allowed to expand very slowly against an opposing force provided either by a weight suspended from a frictionless pulley or by an elastic spring, the gas undergoes an approximately reversible process. A clever imaginary device for ensuring mechanical equilibrium at all times, due to

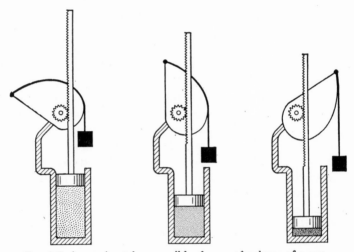

Fig. 8.3. Approximately reversible change of volume of a gas.

Schmidt, is shown in Fig. 8.3. Similar considerations apply to a wire and to a surface film.

A reversible transfer of electricity through an electric cell may be imagined as follows: Suppose that a motor whose coils have a negligible resistance is caused to rotate until its back emf is only slightly different from the emf of the cell. Suppose further that the motor is coupled either to a weight suspended from a frictionless pulley or to an elastic spring. If neither the cell itself nor the connecting wires to the motor have appreciable resistance, a reversible transfer of electricity takes place.

PROBLEM

8.1. Classify and discuss the following natural phenomena from the standpoint of irreversibility: a waterfall, the weathering of rocks, the rusting of iron, a forest fire, the tearing of a piece of cloth, lightning, a compressed spring dissolving in acid, spontaneous combustion of a coal pile, aging of a magnet, shelf aging of an electric cell.

9

The Carnot Cycle and
the Kelvin Temperature Scale

9.1. Carnot Cycle. During a part of the cycle performed by the working substance in an engine, some heat is absorbed from a hot reservoir; during another part of the cycle, a smaller amount of heat is rejected to a cooler reservoir. The engine is therefore said to operate between these two reservoirs. Since it is a fact of experience that some heat is always rejected to the cooler reservoir, the efficiency of an actual engine is never 100 per cent. If we assume that we have at our disposal two reservoirs at given temperatures, it is important to answer the following questions: (1) What is the maximum efficiency that can be achieved by an engine operating between these two reservoirs? (2) What are the characteristics of such an engine? (3) Of what effect is the nature of the working substance?

The importance of these questions was recognized by Nicolas Léonard Sadi Carnot, a brilliant young French engineer who, in the year 1824 before the first law of thermodynamics was firmly established, described in a paper entitled "Sur la puissance motrice du feu" an ideal engine operating in a particularly simple cycle known today as the *Carnot cycle*.

In describing and explaining the behavior of this ideal engine, Carnot made use of three terms: *feu*, *chaleur*, and *calorique*. By *feu*, he meant fire or flame, and when the word is so translated no misconceptions arise. Carnot gave, however, no definitions for *chaleur* and *calorique*, but in a footnote stated that they had the same meaning. If both of these words are translated as heat, then Carnot's reasoning is contrary to the first law of thermodynamics. There is, however, some evidence that, in spite of the unfortunate footnote, Carnot did not mean the same thing by *chaleur* and *calorique*. Carnot used *chaleur* when referring to heat in general, but when referring to the motive power of heat that is brought about when heat enters at high temperature and leaves at low temperature, he used the expression *chute de calorique*, never *chute de chaleur*. It is the opinion of a few scientists that Carnot had in the back of his mind the concept of entropy for which he reserved the term *calorique*. This seems incredible, and yet it is a remarkable circumstance that, if the expression *chute de calorique* is translated "fall of entropy," many of the objections to Carnot's work raised by Kelvin, Clapeyron, Clausius, and others are no longer valid. In spite of possible mistranslations, Kelvin recognized the importance of Carnot's ideas and put them in the form in which they appear today.

A Carnot cycle is a set of processes that can be performed by any thermodynamic system whatever, whether chemical, electrical, magnetic, or otherwise. The system or working substance is imagined first to be in thermal equilibrium with a cold reservoir at the temperature θ_2. Four processes are then performed in the following order:

1. A reversible adiabatic process is performed in such a direction that the temperature rises to that of the hotter reservoir, θ_1.

2. The working substance is maintained in contact with the reservoir at θ_1, and a reversible isothermal process is performed in such a direction and to such an extent that heat Q_1 is absorbed from the reservoir.

3. A reversible adiabatic process is performed in a direction opposite to (1) until the temperature drops to that of the cooler reservoir, θ_2.

4. The working substance is maintained in contact with the reservoir at θ_2, and a reversible isothermal process is performed in a direction opposite to (2) until the working substance is in its initial state. During this process, heat Q_2 is rejected to the cold reservoir.

An engine operating in a Carnot cycle is called a *Carnot engine*. A Carnot engine operates between two reservoirs in a particularly simple way. All the heat that is absorbed is absorbed at a constant high temperature, namely, that of the hot reservoir. Also, all the heat that is rejected is rejected at a constant lower temperature, that of the cold reservoir. Since all four processes are reversible, the Carnot cycle is a reversible cycle.

9.2. Examples of Carnot Cycles. The simplest example of a Carnot cycle is that of a gas (not necessarily an ideal gas) depicted on a P-V diagram in Fig. 9.1. The dotted lines marked $\theta_1\theta_1$ and $\theta_2\theta_2$ are isothermals at the temperatures θ_1 and θ_2, respectively, θ_1 being greater than θ_2. The gas is originally in the state represented by the point a. The four processes are then:

1. $a \rightarrow b$, reversible adiabatic compression until the temperature rises to θ_1.

2. $b \rightarrow c$, reversible isothermal expansion until any desired point such as c is reached.

3. $c \rightarrow d$, reversible adiabatic expansion until the temperature drops to θ_2.

4. $d \rightarrow a$, reversible isothermal compression until the original state is reached.

During the isothermal expansion $b \rightarrow c$, heat Q_1 is absorbed from the hot reservoir at θ_1. During the isothermal compression $d \rightarrow a$, heat Q_2 is rejected to the cooler reservoir at θ_2.

A mixture of liquid and vapor may also be taken through a Carnot cycle. This is shown on a P-V diagram in Fig. 9.2. The dotted line L_1V_1 denotes the isothermal isobaric vaporization of the liquid at the high temperature θ_1; the line L_2V_2 that at the lower temperature θ_2

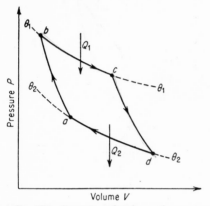

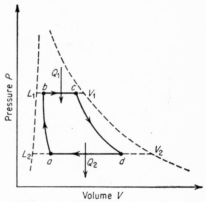

FIG. 9.1. Carnot cycle of a real gas.   FIG. 9.2. Carnot cycle of a mixture of liquid and vapor.

Any point between L and V denotes a mixture of liquid and vapor. Starting at the point a, the four processes are as follows:

1. $a \rightarrow b$, reversible adiabatic compression until the temperature rises to θ_1.

2. $b \rightarrow c$, reversible isothermal isobaric vaporization until any arbitrary point such as c is reached.

3. $c \rightarrow d$, reversible adiabatic expansion until the temperature drops to θ_2.

4. $d \rightarrow a$, reversible isothermal isobaric condensation until the initial state is reached.

A Carnot cycle of a reversible electric cell is depicted on an $\mathcal{E}$-Z diagram in Fig. 9.3. The lines $\theta_1\theta_1$ and $\theta_2\theta_2$ represent isothermals at the temperatures θ_1 and θ_2, respectively. The point a indicates that the cell is well charged. The four processes are:

1. $a \rightarrow b$, reversible adiabatic transfer of electricity from $-$ to $+$ in the outside circuit until the temperature rises to θ_1.

2. $b \rightarrow c$, reversible isothermal transfer of electricity from $+$ to $-$ in the outside circuit until an arbitrary point c is reached.

3. $c \rightarrow d$, reversible adiabatic transfer of electricity until the temperature drops to θ_2.

4. $d \rightarrow a$, reversible isothermal transfer of electricity until the initial state is reached.

As a last example of a Carnot cycle, that of a paramagnetic substance is shown on an $\mathscr{H}$-I diagram in Fig. 9.4. The lines $O\theta_2$ and $O\theta_1$ represent

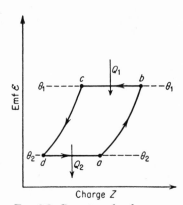

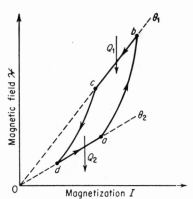

FIG. 9.3. Carnot cycle of a reversible electric cell.

FIG. 9.4. Carnot cycle of a paramagnetic substance.

isothermals at the temperatures θ_2 and θ_1, respectively. Starting at a, the four processes are:

1. $a \rightarrow b$, reversible adiabatic magnetization until the temperature rises to θ_1.

2. $b \rightarrow c$, reversible isothermal demagnetization until an arbitrary point c is reached.

3. $c \rightarrow d$, reversible adiabatic demagnetization until the temperature drops to θ_2.

4. $d \rightarrow a$, reversible isothermal magnetization until the initial state is reached.

The net work done in one cycle by a Carnot engine can be adjusted to any arbitrary amount by choosing the position of the point c, that is, by adjusting the extent of the isothermal process $b \rightarrow c$. It is seen that the coordinates used to plot a Carnot cycle and the shape of the cycle depend on the nature of the working substance. It will be shown, however, in the next chapter that it is possible to find two coordinates in terms of which a graph of any Carnot cycle with *any* working substance is a rectangle. Consequently, we shall represent a Carnot engine symbolically with the aid of a rectangle as shown in Fig. 9.5(a). The letter R inside the rectangle indicates that the Carnot cycle is a reversible cycle.

If an engine is to operate between only two reservoirs and still operate in a reversible cycle, then it must be a Carnot engine.   For example, if an Otto cycle were performed between only two reservoirs, the heat transfers in the two isochoric processes would involve finite temperature differences and, therefore, could not be reversible.   Conversely, if the Otto cycle were performed reversibly, it would require a series of reservoirs, not merely two.   The expression "Carnot engine," therefore, means "a reversible engine operating between only two reservoirs."

9.3. Carnot Refrigerator.   Since a Carnot cycle consists of reversible processes, it may be performed in either direction.   When it is performed in a direction opposite to that shown in the examples, it is a refrigeration cycle.   A Carnot refrigerator is represented symbolically in Fig. 9.5(b).

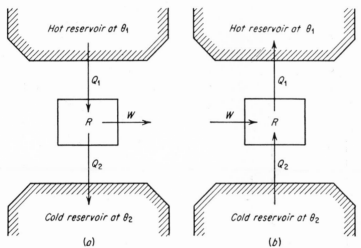

Fig. 9.5. Symbolic representation of (a) Carnot engine and of (b) Carnot refrigerator.

The important feature of a Carnot refrigeration cycle which distinguishes it from any general reversed engine cycle is that the quantities Q_1, Q_2, and W are numerically equal to those quantities when the cycle is performed in the opposite direction.   For example, exactly the same amount of heat that is absorbed by the Carnot engine from the hot reservoir is rejected to the hot reservoir when the cycle is reversed.   This would not be the case if the cycle were not reversible.

9.4. Carnot's Theorem and Corollary.   We are now in a position to prove Carnot's theorem, which is stated as follows: *No engine operating between two given reservoirs can be more efficient than a Carnot engine operating between the same two reservoirs.*

Imagine a Carnot engine R and any other engine I working between the same two reservoirs and adjusted so that they both deliver the same amount of work W.   Thus:

Carnot Engine R	Any Other Engine I
1. Absorbs heat Q_1 from the hot reservoir.	1. Absorbs heat Q_1' from the hot reservoir.
2. Performs work W.	2. Performs work W.
3. Rejects heat $Q_1 - W$ to the cold reservoir.	3. Rejects heat $Q_1' - W$ to the cold reservoir.
4. Efficiency $\eta_R = W/Q_1$.	4. Efficiency $\eta_I = W/Q_1'$.

Let us assume that the efficiency of the engine I is greater than that of R. Thus,

$$\eta_I > \eta_R,$$
$$\frac{W}{Q_1'} > \frac{W}{Q_1},$$

and
$$Q_1 > Q_1'.$$

Now let the engine I drive the Carnot engine R backward as a Carnot refrigerator. This is shown symbolically in Fig. 9.6. The engine and the refrigerator coupled together in this way constitute a self-acting device, since all the work needed to operate the refrigerator is supplied by the engine. The net heat extracted from the cold reservoir is

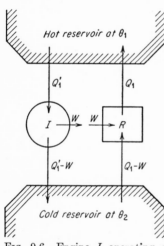

$$Q_1 - W - (Q_1' - W) = Q_1 - Q_1',$$

which is positive. The net heat delivered to the hot reservoir is also $Q_1 - Q_1'$. The effect, therefore, of this self-acting device is to transfer $Q_1 - Q_1'$ units of heat from a cold reservoir to a hot reservoir. Since this is a violation of the second law of thermodynamics (Clausius statement), our original assumption that $\eta_I > \eta_R$ is false and Carnot's theorem is proved. We may express this result in symbols, thus:

FIG. 9.6. Engine I operating a Carnot refrigerator.

$$\eta_I \leq \eta_R.$$

The following corollary to Carnot's theorem may be easily proved: *All Carnot engines operating between the same two reservoirs have the same efficiency.*

Consider two Carnot engines R_1 and R_2, operating between the same two reservoirs. If we imagine R_1 driving R_2 backward, then Carnot's theorem states that

$$\eta_{R_1} \leq \eta_{R_2}.$$

If R_2 drives R_1 backward, then

$$\eta_{R_2} \leq \eta_{R_1}.$$

It therefore follows that

$$\eta_{R_1} = \eta_{R_2}.$$

It is clear from the above result that the nature of the working substance which is undergoing the Carnot cycle has no influence on the efficiency of the Carnot engine.

9.5. Kelvin Temperature Scale. A Carnot engine absorbing Q_1 units of heat from a hot reservoir at a temperature θ_1 and rejecting Q_2 units of heat to a cold reservoir at a temperature θ_2 has an efficiency η_R that is independent of the nature of the working substance. The efficiency therefore depends only on the two temperatures, and we may write

$$\eta_R = 1 - \frac{Q_2}{Q_1} = \phi(\theta_1, \theta_2),$$

where ϕ is an unknown function. Rearranging the above equation, we get

$$\frac{Q_1}{Q_2} = \frac{1}{1 - \phi(\theta_1, \theta_2)} = f(\theta_1, \theta_2),$$

where f is also an unknown function.

Imagine now a Carnot engine operating between reservoirs at θ_2 and θ_3, absorbing Q_2 at θ_2 and rejecting Q_3 at θ_3. The same equation must hold as in the previous case; thus,

$$\frac{Q_2}{Q_3} = f(\theta_2, \theta_3).$$

Since the heat rejected by the first Carnot engine, Q_2, is absorbed by the second Carnot engine, both engines working together constitute a third Carnot engine, which absorbs heat Q_1 from a reservoir at θ_1 and rejects heat Q_3 to a reservoir at θ_3, where

$$\frac{Q_1}{Q_3} = f(\theta_1, \theta_3).$$

Since

$$\frac{Q_1}{Q_2} = \frac{Q_1/Q_3}{Q_2/Q_3},$$

we have the result that

$$f(\theta_1, \theta_2) = \frac{f(\theta_1, \theta_3)}{f(\theta_2, \theta_3)}.$$

Now the temperature θ_3 is arbitrarily chosen; and since it does not appear in the left-hand member of the above equation, it must therefore drop out of the ratio on the right. After it has been canceled, the numerator can be written $\psi(\theta_1)$ and the denominator $\psi(\theta_2)$ where ψ is another unknown function. Thus

$$\frac{Q_1}{Q_2} = \frac{\psi(\theta_1)}{\psi(\theta_2)}.$$

The ratio on the right is defined as the ratio of two *Kelvin temperatures* and is denoted by T_1/T_2. We have, therefore, finally

$$\frac{Q_1}{Q_2} = \frac{T_1}{T_2}.$$

Thus, *two temperatures on the Kelvin scale are to each other as the heats absorbed and rejected, respectively, by a Carnot engine operating between reservoirs at these temperatures.* It is seen that the Kelvin temperature scale is independent of the peculiar characteristics of any particular substance. It therefore supplies precisely what is lacking in the ideal gas scale.

At first thought it might seem that the ratio of two Kelvin temperatures would be impossible to measure, since a Carnot engine is an ideal engine, quite impossible to construct. The situation, however, is not so bad as it seems. The ratio of two Kelvin temperatures is the ratio of two heats that are transferred during two isothermal processes bounded by the same two adiabatics. The two adiabatic boundaries may be located experimentally, and the heats transferred during two isothermal "nearly reversible" processes can be measured with considerable precision. As a matter of fact, this is one of the methods used in measuring temperatures below 1°K.

To complete the definition of the Kelvin scale we proceed, as in Chap. 1, to assign the arbitrary value of 273.16°K to the temperature of the triple point of water T_3. Thus

$$T_3 = 273.16°K.$$

For a Carnot engine operating between reservoirs at the temperatures T and T_3, we have

$$\frac{Q}{Q_3} = \frac{T}{T_3}$$

or

$$T = 273.16°K \frac{Q}{Q_3}.$$

Comparing this with the corresponding equation for the ideal gas temperature θ, namely,

$$\theta = 273.16°K \frac{\lim (PV)}{\lim (PV)_3},$$

it is seen that, in the Kelvin scale, Q plays the role of a "thermometric property." This does not, however, have the objection attached to a coordinate of an arbitrarily chosen thermometer, inasmuch as the behavior of a Carnot engine is independent of the nature of the working substance.

9.6. Absolute Zero. It follows from the equation

$$T = 273.16°K \frac{Q}{Q_3}$$

that the heat transferred isothermally between two given adiabatics decreases as the temperature decreases. Conversely, the smaller the value of Q, the lower the corresponding T. The smallest possible value of Q is zero, and the corresponding T is absolute zero. *Thus, if a system undergoes a reversible isothermal process without transfer of heat, the temperature at which this process takes place is called absolute zero.* In other words, at absolute zero, an isotherm and an adiabatic are identical.

It should be noticed that the definition of absolute zero holds for all substances and is therefore independent of the peculiar properties of any one arbitrarily chosen substance. Furthermore, the definition is in terms of purely macroscopic concepts. No reference is made to molecules or to molecular energy. Whether absolute zero may be achieved experimentally is a question which will be deferred until Chap. 16.

A Carnot engine absorbing heat Q_1 from a hot reservoir at T_1 and rejecting heat Q_2 to a cooler reservoir at T_2 has an efficiency

$$\eta_R = 1 - \frac{Q_2}{Q_1}.$$

Since

$$\frac{Q_2}{Q_1} = \frac{T_2}{T_1},$$

$$\eta_R = 1 - \frac{T_2}{T_1}.$$

For a Carnot engine to have an efficiency of 100 per cent it is clear that T_2 must be zero. Only when the lower reservoir is at absolute zero will all the heat be converted into work. Since nature does not provide us with a reservoir at absolute zero, a heat engine with 100 per cent efficiency is a practical impossibility.

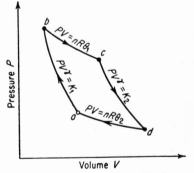

9.7. Carnot Cycle of an Ideal Gas. Equality of Ideal Gas Temperature and Kelvin Temperature. A Carnot cycle of an ideal gas is depicted on a P-V diagram in Fig. 9.7. The two isothermal processes $b \to c$ and

FIG. 9.7. Carnot cycle of an ideal gas.

$d \to a$ are represented by equilateral hyperbolas whose equations are, respectively,

$$PV = nR\theta_1$$

and

$$PV = nR\theta_2.$$

For any infinitesimal reversible process of an ideal gas, the first law may be written

$$dQ = C_V \, d\theta + P \, dV.$$

Applying this equation to the isothermal process $b \to c$, the heat absorbed is found to be

$$Q_1 = \int_{V_b}^{V_c} P \, dV$$

$$= nR\theta_1 \ln \frac{V_c}{V_b}.$$

Similarly, for the isothermal process $d \to a$, the heat rejected (expressed as a positive number) is

$$Q_2 = nR\theta_2 \ln \frac{V_d}{V_a}.$$

Therefore

$$\frac{Q_1}{Q_2} = \frac{\theta_1 \ln (V_c/V_b)}{\theta_2 \ln (V_d/V_a)}.$$

Since the process $a \to b$ is adiabatic, we may write for any infinitesimal portion

$$-C_V \, d\theta = P \, dV$$

or

$$-C_V \, d\theta = \frac{nR\theta}{V} \, dV.$$

Integrating from a to b, we get

$$\frac{1}{nR} \int_{\theta_2}^{\theta_1} C_V \frac{d\theta}{\theta} = \ln \frac{V_a}{V_b}.$$

Similarly, for the adiabatic process $c \to d$,

$$\frac{1}{nR} \int_{\theta_2}^{\theta_1} C_V \frac{d\theta}{\theta} = \ln \frac{V_d}{V_c}.$$

Therefore

$$\ln \frac{V_a}{V_b} = \ln \frac{V_d}{V_c}$$

or

$$\ln \frac{V_c}{V_b} = \ln \frac{V_d}{V_a},$$

and we get, finally,

$$\frac{Q_1}{Q_2} = \frac{\theta_1}{\theta_2}.$$

Since, however, the Kelvin temperature scale is defined by the same sort of equation, we have

$$\frac{\theta_1}{\theta_2} = \frac{T_1}{T_2}.$$

If θ and T refer to any temperature, and θ_3 and T_3 refer to the triple point of water, the preceding equation becomes

$$\frac{\theta}{\theta_3} = \frac{T}{T_3}.$$

Since $\theta_3 = T_3 = 273.16°K$, it follows that

$$\boxed{\theta = T.}$$

The Kelvin temperature is therefore numerically equal to the ideal gas temperature and, in the proper range, may be measured with a gas thermometer.

PROBLEMS

9.1. An inventor claims to have developed an engine that takes in 100,000 Btu at a temperature of 400°K, rejects 40,000 Btu at a temperature of 200°K, and delivers 15 kw · hr of mechanical work. Would you advise investing money to put this engine on the market?

9.2. A Carnot engine absorbs 1000 joules of heat from a reservoir at the temperature of the normal boiling point of water and rejects heat to a reservoir at the temperature of the triple point of water. Find the heat rejected, the work done, and the efficiency.

9.3. Which is the more effective way to increase the efficiency of a Carnot engine: to increase T_1, keeping T_2 constant; or to decrease T_2, keeping T_1 constant?

9.4. Imagine any engine I and a Carnot engine R operating between the same two reservoirs. Suppose that they absorb from the hotter reservoir different amounts of heat, do different amounts of work, but reject to the cooler reservoir the *same* amounts of heat. Prove Carnot's theorem with the aid of the Kelvin-Planck statement of the second law.

9.5. In Art. 9.4 suppose engine I to execute an *irreversible* cycle, and assume $\eta_I = \eta_R$. Show that this assumption leads to a result that is inconsistent with the assumed irreversibility of I, and therefore $\eta_I < \eta_R$.

9.6. Draw a symbolic diagram of a set of Carnot engines with the following characteristics: Each engine absorbs the heat rejected by the preceding one at the temperature at which it was rejected, and each engine delivers the same amount of work. Show that the temperature intervals between which these engines operate are all equal.

9.7. Take a gas whose equation of state is $P(v - b) = R\theta$ and whose c_v is a function of θ only through a Carnot cycle, and prove that $\theta = T$.

10

Entropy

10.1. Clausius' Theorem. Work diagrams in which a generalized force such as P, $\mathcal{F}$, $\mathcal{S}$, $\mathcal{E}$, or $\mathcal{H}$ is plotted against the corresponding generalized displacement V, L, A, Z, I have been used to indicate processes of various systems. An isothermal process or an adiabatic process is represented by a different curve on each diagram. In this chapter it is desired to formulate general principles that apply to all systems. If we let the symbol $\mathcal{Y}$ denote any generalized force and the symbol X its corresponding generalized displacement, a generalized work diagram in which $\mathcal{Y}$ is plotted against X may be used to depict processes common to all systems and will thus be suitable for general discussions.

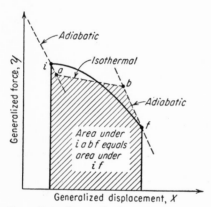

FIG. 10.1. Generalized work diagram. ($i \rightarrow f$, any reversible process; $i \rightarrow a$, reversible adiabatic process; $a \rightarrow b$, reversible isothermal process; $b \rightarrow f$, reversible adiabatic process.)

Consider a reversible process represented by the smooth curve $i \rightarrow f$ on the generalized work diagram shown in Fig. 10.1. The nature of the system is immaterial. The dotted curves through i and f, respectively, represent portions of adiabatic processes. Let us draw a curve $a \rightarrow b$ representing an isothermal process in such a way that the area under the smooth curve if is equal to the area under the zigzag path $iabf$. Then the work done in traversing both paths is the same, or

$$W_{if} = W_{iabf}.$$

Now

$$Q_{if} = U_f - U_i + W_{if},$$

and

$$Q_{iabf} = U_f - U_i + W_{iabf}.$$

Therefore,

$$Q_{if} = Q_{iabf}.$$

But since no heat is transferred in the two adiabatic processes ia and bf, we have

$$Q_{if} = Q_{ab}.$$

If we are given, therefore, a reversible process in which the temperature may change in any manner, it is always possible to find a reversible zigzag path between the same two states, consisting of an adiabatic followed by an isothermal followed by an adiabatic, such that the heat transferred during the isothermal portion is the same as that transferred during the original process.

Now consider the smooth closed curve representing a reversible cycle on the work diagram shown in Fig. 10.2. Since no two adiabatic lines can intersect (see Prob. 7.7), a number of adiabatic lines may be drawn, dividing the cycle into a number of adjacent strips. A zigzag closed path may now be drawn, consisting of alternate adiabatic and isothermal portions, such that the heat transferred during all the isothermal portions is equal to the heat transferred in the original cycle. Consider the two isothermal processes ab at the temperature T_1, during which heat Q_1 is absorbed, and cd at the temperature T_2, during which heat Q_2 is rejected.

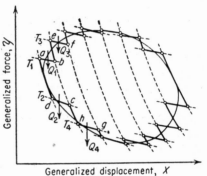

FIG. 10.2. Generalized work diagram. (Smooth closed curve = reversible cycle; zigzag closed path = alternate reversible isothermal and adiabatic processes.)

Since ab and cd are bounded by the same adiabatics, $abcd$ is a Carnot cycle, and we may write

$$\frac{Q_1}{T_1} = \frac{Q_2}{T_2}.$$

For the sake of clearness and simplicity, we have been regarding both Q_1 and Q_2 as positive numbers, thus ignoring the sign convention introduced earlier in this book. Let us now adhere to the sign convention and regard any Q as an algebraic symbol, positive for heat absorbed and negative for heat rejected. We may then write

$$\frac{Q_1}{T_1} + \frac{Q_2}{T_2} = 0,$$

where Q_1 stands for a positive number and Q_2 for a negative number. Since the isothermals ef and gh are bounded by the same two adiabatics, $efgh$ is also a Carnot cycle, and

$$\frac{Q_3}{T_3} + \frac{Q_4}{T_4} = 0.$$

If a similar equation is written for each pair of isothermals bounded by the same two adiabatics and if all the equations are added, the result is obtained that

$$\frac{Q_1}{T_1} + \frac{Q_2}{T_2} + \frac{Q_3}{T_3} + \frac{Q_4}{T_4} + \cdots = 0.$$

Since no heat is transferred during the adiabatic portions of the zigzag cycle, we may write

$$\sum \frac{Q}{T} = 0,$$

where the summation is taken over the complete zigzag cycle.

Now imagine the cycle divided into a very large number of strips by drawing a large number of adiabatics close together. If we connect these adiabatics with small isothermals in the manner already described, a zigzag path may be traced that may be made to approximate the original cycle as closely as we please. When these isothermal processes become infinitesimal, the ratio dQ/T for an infinitesimal isothermal between two adjacent adiabatics is equal to the ratio dQ/T for the infinitesimal piece of the original cycle bounded by the same two adiabatics. In the limit, therefore, we may write, for any reversible cycle,

$$\boxed{\;_R\!\oint \frac{dQ}{T} = 0.\;}$$

The circle through the integral sign signifies that the integration takes place over the complete cycle, and the letter R emphasizes the fact that the equation is true only for a reversible cycle. This result is known as *Clausius' theorem*.

10.2. Entropy and the Mathematical Formulation of the Second Law. Let an initial equilibrium state of any thermodynamic system be represented by the point i on any convenient diagram such as the generalized work diagram of Fig. 10.3. Denote a final equilibrium state by the point f. It is possible to take the system from i to f along any number of different reversible paths since i and f are equilibrium states. Suppose the system is taken from i to f along the reversible path R_1 and then back to i again along another reversible path R_2. The two paths obviously constitute

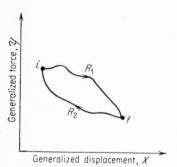

FIG. 10.3. Two reversible paths joining two equilibrium states of a system.

a reversible cycle, and, from Clausius' theorem, we may write

$$\oint_{R_1 R_2} \frac{dQ}{T} = 0.$$

The above integral may be expressed as the sum of two integrals, one for the path R_1 and the other for the path R_2. We have then

$$\int_{R_1}{}_i^f \frac{dQ}{T} + \int_{R_2}{}_f^i \frac{dQ}{T} = 0$$

or

$$\int_{R_1}{}_i^f \frac{dQ}{T} = - \int_{R_2}{}_f^i \frac{dQ}{T}.$$

Since R_2 is a reversible path,

$$- \int_{R_2}{}_f^i \frac{dQ}{T} = \int_{R_2}{}_i^f \frac{dQ}{T},$$

and finally

$$\int_{R_1}{}_i^f \frac{dQ}{T} = \int_{R_2}{}_i^f \frac{dQ}{T}.$$

Since R_1 and R_2 were chosen at random and represent *any* two reversible paths, the above equation expresses the important fact that $_R\int_i^f dQ/T$ *is independent of the reversible path connecting i and f.* It therefore follows that *there exists a function of the thermodynamic coordinates of a system whose value at the final state minus its value at the initial state equals the integral* $_R\int_i^f dQ/T$. This function is called the *entropy* and is denoted by S. If S_i is the entropy at the initial state and S_f that at the final state, then we have the result that

$$\boxed{\int_{R}{}_i^f \frac{dQ}{T} = S_f - S_i,}$$

where the difference $S_f - S_i$ is the *entropy change.*

Finally, if the two equilibrium states i and f are infinitesimally near, the integral sign may be eliminated and $S_f - S_i$ becomes dS. The equation then becomes

$$\boxed{\frac{dQ_R}{T} = dS,}$$

where dS is an exact differential, since it is the differential of an actual function. The subscript R written along with dQ indicates that the preceding equation is true only if dQ is transferred reversibly. *This equation is the mathematical formulation of the second law.*

It should be noticed that the existence of an entropy function is deduced in the same manner as that of an energy function, i.e., by showing that a certain quantity is independent of the path. In neither case, however, does the defining equation enable us to calculate one value of the function.

10.3. Principle of Carathéodory. We have arrived at the mathematical formulation of the second law by the conventional, historical method initiated by the engineer Carnot and elaborated by the physicists Kelvin and Clausius. These men thought in terms of practical engines, ideal engines, and physical models. Starting with a statement expressing the impossibility of converting heat completely into work, or the impossibility of spontaneous heat flow from a colder to a hotter body, an ideal engine of maximum efficiency was described. With the aid of this ideal engine, an absolute temperature scale was defined and the Clausius theorem proved. On the basis of the Clausius theorem, the existence of an entropy function was inferred. From a mathematical point of view, this procedure is somewhat unsatisfactory. The mathematician prefers what is known as an "axiomatic treatment," i.e., a statement of the minimum number of fundamental axioms and then a purely formal mathematical deduction from these axioms.

In 1909, the mathematician Carathéodory set himself the problem of finding a statement of the second law which, without the aid of Carnot engines and refrigerators, but only by mathematical deduction, would lead to the existence of an entropy function satisfying the equation $dQ_R = T\, dS$. He was led to his formulation of the second law by a mathematical theorem which he proved and which may be stated in its simplest form† as follows:

Imagine a space of three dimensions with rectangular coordinates x, y, z. *In the neighborhood of any arbitrary point P_0 there are points which are not accessible from P_0 along solution curves of the equation*

$$A(x, y, z)\, dx + B(x, y, z)\, dy + C(x, y, z)\, dz = 0,$$

if, and only if, the equation is integrable. The equation is said to be integrable if there exist functions $\lambda(x, y, z)$ and $F(x, y, z)$ such that

$$A\, dx + B\, dy + C\, dz = \lambda\, dF.$$

The proof of this purely mathematical theorem is somewhat involved and it will not be given here. It holds for any number of variables.

Let us now consider how this theorem has a bearing on thermodynamics. Consider a system whose states are determined, for the sake of argument, by three thermodynamic coordinates x, y, and z. Then

---

† The simplest formulation of Carathéodory's ideas is given by H. A. Buchdahl in the *American Journal of Physics*, January, 1949. The brief outline given here is based on Buchdahl's presentation.

the first law in differential form may be written

$$dQ = A\,dx + B\,dy + C\,dz,$$

where A, B, and C are functions of x, y, and z. The adiabatic, reversible transitions of this system are subject to the condition

$$dQ = A\,dx + B\,dy + C\,dz = 0.$$

Let us now take as our mathematical statement of the second law the following:

In the neighborhood of any arbitrary initial state P_0 of a physical system there exist neighboring states which are not accessible from P_0 along quasi-static adiabatic paths.

It follows from Carathéodory's theorem that this is possible if and only if there exist functions T and S such that

$$dQ = A\,dx + B\,dy + C\,dz = T\,dS.$$

Thus, by stating the second law in terms of the inaccessibility of certain states by adiabatic paths, and by using a mathematical theorem, Carathéodory inferred the existence of an entropy function and an integrating factor connected with Kelvin temperature. This is the barest outline of the axiomatic treatment and is given only to inspire those of a mathematical turn of mind to read and learn more about it.

10.4. Entropy of an Ideal Gas. If a system absorbs an infinitesimal amount of heat dQ_R during a reversible process, the entropy change of the system is equal to

$$dS = \frac{dQ_R}{T}.$$

It is interesting to notice that, although dQ_R is an inexact differential, the ratio dQ_R/T is exact. The reciprocal of the Kelvin temperature is therefore the integrating factor of dQ_R. If dQ_R is expressed as a sum of differentials involving thermodynamic coordinates, then, upon dividing by T, the expression may be integrated and the entropy of the system obtained. As an example of this procedure, consider one of the expressions for dQ_R of an ideal gas, namely,

$$dQ_R = C_P\,dT - V\,dP.$$

Dividing by T, we get

$$\frac{dQ_R}{T} = C_P\frac{dT}{T} - \frac{V}{T}\,dP$$

or

$$dS = C_P\frac{dT}{T} - nR\frac{dP}{P}.$$

Let us now calculate the entropy change ΔS of the gas between an arbitrarily chosen *standard state* with coordinates T_S, P_S, and any other state with coordinates T, P. Integrating between these two states, we get

$$\Delta S = \int_{T_S}^{T} C_P \frac{dT}{T} - nR \ln \frac{P}{P_S}.$$

Suppose we ascribe to the standard state an entropy S_S and choose *any arbitrary numerical value* for this quantity. Then an entropy S may be associated with the other state where $S - S_S = \Delta S$. To make the discussion simpler, let C_P be constant. Then

$$S - S_S = C_P \ln \frac{T}{T_S} - nR \ln \frac{P}{P_S},$$

and this may be rewritten

$$S = C_P \ln T - nR \ln P + (S_S - C_P \ln T_S + nR \ln P_S).$$

Denoting the quantity in parentheses by the *constant* S_0, we get finally

$$S = C_P \ln T - nR \ln P + S_0.$$

Substituting for T and P thousands of different values, we may calculate thousands of corresponding values of S which, after tabulation, constitute an *entropy table*. Any one value from this table, taken alone, will have no meaning. The difference between two values, however, will be an actual entropy change.

Let us now return to the original differential equation

$$dS = C_P \frac{dT}{T} - nR \frac{dP}{P}.$$

Again, for simplicity, assuming C_P to be constant, we may take the indefinite integral and obtain

$$S = C_P \ln T - nR \ln P + S_0,$$

where S_0 is the constant of integration. Since this is precisely the equation obtained previously, we see that, in taking the indefinite integral of dS, we do not obtain an "absolute entropy," but merely an entropy referred to a nonspecified standard state whose coordinates are contained within the constant of integration. Thus, for an ideal gas

$$S = \int C_P \frac{dT}{T} - nR \ln P + S_0.$$

To calculate the entropy of an ideal gas as a function of T and V, we use the other expression for dQ_R of an ideal gas.   Thus,

$$\frac{dQ_R}{T} = C_V \frac{dT}{T} + \frac{P}{T} dV$$

$$dS = C_V \frac{dT}{T} + nR \frac{dV}{V}.$$

Proceeding in the same way as before, we get for the entropy, referred to an unspecified standard state, the expression

$$S = \int C_V \frac{dT}{T} + nR \ln V + S_0$$

which becomes, if C_V is constant,

$$S = C_V \ln T + nR \ln V + S_0.$$

10.5. T-S Diagram.   For each infinitesimal amount of heat that enters a system during an infinitesimal portion of a reversible process, there is an equation

$$dQ_R = T\, dS.$$

It follows therefore that the total amount of heat transferred in a **reversible** process is given by

$$Q_R = \int_i^f T\, dS.$$

This integral can be interpreted graphically as the area under a curve on a diagram in which T is plotted along the Y axis and S along the X axis.   The nature of the curve on the T-S diagram is determined by the kind of reversible process that the system undergoes.   Obviously, an isothermal process is a horizontal line.

In the case of a reversible adiabatic process, we have

$$dS = \frac{dQ_R}{T}$$

and

$$dQ_R = 0,$$

whence, if T is not zero,

$$dS = 0$$

and S is constant.   Therefore, during a reversible adiabatic process, the entropy of a system remains constant, or, in other words, the system undergoes an *isentropic process*.   An isentropic process on a T-S diagram is obviously a vertical line.   It is therefore clear that the two isothermal and the two adiabatic processes which go to make up a Carnot cycle form a rectangle on a T-S diagram, no matter what the working substance is.   Only reversible processes may be plotted on a T-S diagram since entropy has been defined only for equilibrium states.

The T-S diagram is particularly convenient for representing reversible cycles. The closed curve shown in Fig. 10.4 consisting of an upper portion R_1 and a lower portion R_2 represents a reversible engine cycle. The

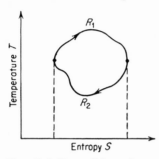

area under R_1 (positive area) is equal to the heat absorbed Q_1, and the area under R_2 (negative area) to the heat rejected Q_2. The area inside the closed curve is therefore $Q_1 - Q_2$ or W. Since the efficiency of the engine is $1 - (Q_2/Q_1)$, it may be measured directly from the diagram.

FIG. 10.4. Reversible cycle on a T-S diagram.

10.6. Entropy and Reversibility. The fact that the area under a curve on a T-S diagram is equal to the heat transferred in a reversible process is of some importance to the mechanical engineer but of little interest to the theoretical physicist. In order to understand the physical meaning of entropy and its significance in the world of science, it is necessary to study all the entropy changes that take place when a system undergoes a process. If we calculate the entropy change of the system and add to this the entropy change of the local surroundings, we obtain a quantity that is the sum of all the entropy changes brought about by this particular process. We may call this the *entropy change of the universe* due to the process in question.

When a finite amount of heat is absorbed or rejected by a reservoir, extremely small changes in the coordinates take place in every unit of mass. The entropy change of a unit of mass is therefore very small. Since, however, the total mass of a reservoir is large, the total entropy change is finite. Suppose that a reservoir is in contact with a system and that heat Q is absorbed by the reservoir at the temperature T. The reservoir undergoes nondissipative changes determined entirely by the quantity of heat absorbed. Exactly the same changes *in the reservoir* would take place if the same amount of heat Q were transferred reversibly. Hence the entropy change of the reservoir is Q/T. Therefore, *whenever a reservoir absorbs heat Q at the temperature T from any system during any kind of process, the entropy change of the* **reservoir** *is Q/T.*

Consider now the entropy change of the universe that is brought about by the performance of any reversible process. The process will, in general, be accompanied by a flow of heat between a system and a set of reservoirs ranging in temperature from T_i to T_f. During *any* infinitesimal portion of the process, an amount of heat $đQ_R$ is transferred between the system and one of the reservoirs at the temperature T. Let $đQ_R$ be a positive number. If $đQ_R$ is absorbed by the system, then

$$dS \text{ of the system} = + \frac{dQ_R}{T},$$

$$dS \text{ of the reservoir} = - \frac{dQ_R}{T},$$

and the entropy change of the universe is zero. If dQ_R is rejected by the system, then obviously

$$dS \text{ of the system} = - \frac{dQ_R}{T},$$

$$dS \text{ of the reservoir} = + \frac{dQ_R}{T},$$

and the entropy change of the universe is again zero. If dQ_R is zero, then neither the system nor the reservoir will have an entropy change and the entropy change of the universe is still zero. Since this is true for any infinitesimal portion of the reversible process, it is true for all such portions, and therefore we may conclude that, *when a reversible process is performed, the entropy of the universe remains unchanged.*

10.7. Entropy and Irreversibility. When a system undergoes an irreversible process between an initial equilibrium state and a final equilibrium state, the entropy change of the system is equal to

$$S_f - S_i = {}_R\!\int_i^f \frac{dQ}{T},$$

where R indicates *any reversible process arbitrarily chosen* by which the system may be brought from the given initial state to the given final state. No integration is performed over the original irreversible path. The irreversible process is replaced by a reversible one. This can easily be done when the initial and the final state of the system are equilibrium states. When either the initial or the final state is a nonequilibrium state, special methods must be used. At first, we shall limit ourselves to irreversible processes all of which involve initial and final states of equilibrium.

Processes Exhibiting External Mechanical Irreversibility. (a) Those involving the isothermal dissipation of work through a system (which remains unchanged) into internal energy of a reservoir, such as

1. Irregular stirring of a viscous liquid in contact with a reservoir.
2. Coming to rest of a rotating or vibrating liquid in contact with a reservoir.
3. Inelastic deformation of a solid in contact with a reservoir.
4. Transfer of electricity through a resistor in contact with a reservoir.
5. Magnetic hysteresis of a material in contact with a reservoir.

In the case of any process involving the isothermal transformation of work W through a system into internal energy of a reservoir, there is no entropy change of the system because the thermodynamic coordinates do not change.   There is a flow of heat Q into the reservoir where $Q = W$. Since the reservoir absorbs Q units of heat at the temperature T, its entropy change is $+Q/T$ or $+W/T$.   The entropy change of the universe is therefore W/T, which is a positive quantity.

(b) Those involving the adiabatic dissipation of work into internal energy of a system, such as

1. Irregular stirring of a viscous thermally insulated liquid.
2. Coming to rest of a rotating or vibrating thermally insulated liquid.
3. Inelastic deformation of a thermally insulated solid.
4. Transfer of electricity through a thermally insulated resistor.
5. Magnetic hysteresis of a thermally insulated material.

In the case of any process involving the adiabatic transformation of work W into internal energy of a system whose temperature rises from T_i to T_f at constant pressure, there is no flow of heat to or from the surroundings, and therefore the entropy change of the local surroundings is zero.   To calculate the entropy change of the system, the original irreversible process must be replaced by a reversible one that will take the system from the given initial state (temperature T_i, pressure P) to the final state (temperature T_f, pressure P).   Let us replace the irreversible performance of work by a reversible isobaric flow of heat from a series of reservoirs ranging in temperature from T_i to T_f.   The entropy change of the system will then be

$$S_f - S_i \text{ (system)} = {}_R\!\int_{T_i}^{T_f} \frac{dQ}{T}.$$

For an isobaric process,

$$dQ_R = C_P \, dT,$$

and

$$S_f - S_i \text{ (system)} = \int_{T_i}^{T_f} C_P \frac{dT}{T}.$$

Finally, if C_P is assumed constant,

$$S_f - S_i \text{ (system)} = C_P \ln \frac{T_f}{T_i},$$

and the entropy change of the universe is $C_P \ln (T_f/T_i)$, which is a positive quantity.

Processes Exhibiting Internal Mechanical Irreversibility.   Those involving the transformation of internal energy of a system into mechanical energy and then back into internal energy again, such as

1. Ideal gas rushing into a vacuum (free expansion).
2. Gas seeping through a porous plug (throttling process).
3. Snapping of a stretched wire after it is cut.
4. Collapse of a soap film after it is pricked.

In the case of a free expansion of an ideal gas, the entropy change of the local surroundings is zero. To calculate the entropy change of the system, the free expansion must be replaced by a reversible process that will take the gas from its original state (volume V_i, temperature T) to the final state (volume V_f, temperature T). Evidently, the most convenient reversible process is a reversible isothermal expansion at the temperature T from a volume V_i to the volume V_f. The entropy change of the system is then

$$S_f - S_i \text{ (system)} = \int_{R\, V_i}^{V_f} \frac{dQ}{T}.$$

For an isothermal process of an ideal gas,

$$dQ_R = P\, dV,$$

and

$$\frac{dQ_R}{T} = nR \frac{dV}{V},$$

whence

$$S_f - S_i \text{ (system)} = nR \ln \frac{V_f}{V_i}.$$

The entropy change of the universe is therefore $nR \ln (V_f/V_i)$, which is a positive number.

Processes Exhibiting External Thermal Irreversibility. Those involving a transfer of heat by virtue of a finite temperature difference, such as

1. Conduction or radiation of heat from a system to its cooler surroundings.

2. Conduction or radiation of heat through a system (which remains unchanged) from a hot reservoir to a cooler one.

In the case of the conduction of Q units of heat through a system (which remains unchanged) from a hot reservoir at T_1 to a cooler reservoir at T_2, the following steps are obvious:

$$S_f - S_i \text{ (system)} = 0.$$

$$S_f - S_i \text{ (hot reservoir)} = -\frac{Q}{T_1}.$$

$$S_f - S_i \text{ (cold reservoir)} = +\frac{Q}{T_2}.$$

$$S_f - S_i \text{ (universe)} = \frac{Q}{T_2} - \frac{Q}{T_1}.$$

Processes Exhibiting Chemical Irreversibility. Those involving a spontaneous change of internal structure, chemical composition, density, etc., such as

1. A chemical reaction.

2. Diffusion of two dissimilar inert ideal gases.

3. Mixing of alcohol and water.

4. Freezing of supercooled liquid.

5. Condensation of a supersaturated vapor.

6. Solution of a solid in water.

7. Osmosis.

Assuming the diffusion of two dissimilar inert ideal gases to be equivalent to two separate free expansions, for one of which

$$S_f - S_i \text{ (universe)} = nR \ln \frac{V_f}{V_i},$$

and taking a mole of each gas with $V_i = v$ and $V_f = 2v$, we obtain

$$S_f - S_i \text{ (universe)} = 2R \ln 2,$$

which is a positive number. All the results of this article are summarized in Table 10.1.

TABLE 10.1. ENTROPY CHANGE OF THE UNIVERSE DUE TO NATURAL PROCESSES

Type of irreversibility	Irreversible process	Entropy change of the system	Entropy change of the local surroundings	Entropy change of the universe
External mechanical irreversibility	Isothermal dissipation of work through a system into internal energy of a reservoir	0	$\dfrac{W}{T}$	$\dfrac{W}{T}$
	Adiabatic dissipation of work into internal energy of a system	$C_P \ln \dfrac{T_f}{T_i}$	0	$C_P \ln \dfrac{T_f}{T_i}$
Internal mechanical irreversibility	Free expansion of an ideal gas	$nR \ln \dfrac{V_f}{V_i}$	0	$nR \ln \dfrac{V_f}{V_i}$
External thermal irreversibility	Transfer of heat through a medium from a hot to a cooler reservoir	0	$\dfrac{Q}{T_2} - \dfrac{Q}{T_1}$	$\dfrac{Q}{T_2} - \dfrac{Q}{T_1}$
Chemical irreversibility	Diffusion of two dissimilar inert ideal gases	$2R \ln 2$	0	$2R \ln 2$

10.8. Entropy and Nonequilibrium States. The calculation of the entropy changes associated with the irreversible processes discussed in Art. 10.7 presented no special difficulties because, in all cases, the system either did not change at all (in which case only the entropy changes of reservoirs had to be calculated) or the terminal states of a system were equilibrium states that could be connected by a suitable reversible process. Consider, however, the following process involving internal thermal irreversibility. A thermally conducting bar, brought to a nonuniform temperature distribution by contact at one end with a hot reservoir and at the other end with a cold reservoir, is removed from the reservoirs and then thermally insulated and kept at constant pressure.   An internal flow of heat will finally bring the bar to a uniform temperature, but the transition will be from an initial nonequilibrium state to a final equilibrium state.   It is obviously impossible to find one reversible process by which the system may be brought from the same initial to the same final state.   What meaning, therefore, may be attached to the entropy change associated with this process?

Let us consider the bar to be composed of an infinite number of infinitesimally thin sections, each of which has a different initial temperature but all of which have the same final temperature.   Suppose we imagine all the sections to be insulated from one another and all kept at the same pressure and then each section to be put in contact successively with a series of reservoirs ranging in temperature from the initial temperature of the particular section to the common final temperature.   This defines an infinite number of reversible isobaric processes, which may be used to take the system from its initial nonequilibrium state to its final equilibrium state.   We shall now define the entropy change as the result of integrating dQ/T over all of these reversible processes.   In other words, in the absence of one reversible process to take the system from i to f, we conceive of an infinite number of reversible processes—one for each volume element.

As an example, consider the uniform bar of length L depicted in Fig. 10.5.   A typical volume element at x has a mass

$$dm = \rho A \, dx$$

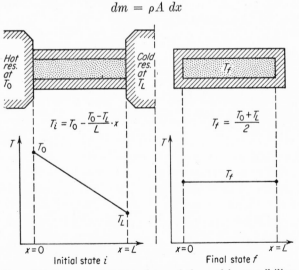

$$T_i = T_0 - \frac{T_0 - T_L}{L} \cdot x$$

$$T_f = \frac{T_0 + T_L}{2}$$

Initial state i Final state f

FIG. 10.5. Process exhibiting internal thermal irreversibility.

where ρ is the density and A the cross-sectional area. The heat capacity of the section is

$$c_P \, dm = c_P \rho A \, dx.$$

Let us suppose that the initial temperature distribution is linear, so that the section at x has an initial temperature

$$T_i = T_0 - \frac{T_0 - T_L}{L} x.$$

If no heat is lost and if we assume for the sake of simplicity that the thermal conductivity, density, and heat capacity of all sections remain constant, then the final temperature will be

$$T_f = \frac{T_0 + T_L}{2}.$$

Integrating dQ/T over a reversible isobaric transfer of heat between the volume element and a series of reservoirs ranging in temperature from T_i to T_f, we get, for the entropy change of *this one volume element*,

$$c_P \rho A \, dx \int_{T_i}^{T_f} \frac{dT}{T} = c_P \rho A \, dx \ln \frac{T_f}{T_i}$$

$$= c_P \rho A \, dx \ln \frac{T_f}{T_0 - \frac{T_0 - T_L}{L} x}$$

$$= -c_P \rho A \, dx \ln \left(\frac{T_0}{T_f} - \frac{T_0 - T_L}{L T_f} x \right).$$

Upon integrating over the whole bar, the total entropy change is

$$S_f - S_i = -c_P \rho A \int_0^L \ln \left(\frac{T_0}{T_f} - \frac{T_0 - T_L}{L T_f} x \right) dx,$$

which, after integration† and simplification, becomes

$$S_f - S_i = C_P \left(1 + \ln T_f + \frac{T_L}{T_0 - T_L} \ln T_L - \frac{T_0}{T_0 - T_L} \ln T_0 \right).$$

To show that the entropy change is positive, let us take a convenient numerical case such as $T_0 = 400°\mathrm{K}$, $T_L = 200°\mathrm{K}$, whence $T_f = 300°\mathrm{K}$. Then,

$$S_f - S_i = 2.30 C_P \left(\frac{1}{2.30} + 2.477 + 2.301 - 2 \times 2.602 \right)$$

$$= 0.021 C_P.$$

The same method may be used to compute the entropy change of a system during a process from an initial nonequilibrium state character-

† $\int \ln (a + bx) \, dx = \frac{1}{b} (a + bx) [\ln (a + bx) - 1]$.

ized by a nonuniform pressure distribution to a final equilibrium state where the pressure is uniform. Examples of such processes are given in the problems at the end of this chapter.

10.9. Principle of the Increase of Entropy. The entropy change of the universe associated with each of the irreversible processes treated up to now was found to be positive. We are led to believe, therefore, that whenever an irreversible process takes place the entropy of the universe increases. To establish this proposition, known as the *entropy principle*, in a general manner, it is sufficient to confine our attention to adiabatic processes only, since we have already seen that the entropy principle is true for all processes involving the irreversible transfer of heat. We start the proof by considering the special case of an adiabatic irreversible process between two equilibrium states of a system.

1. Let the initial state of the system be represented by the point i on the generalized work diagram of Fig. 10.6, and suppose that the system undergoes an *irreversible adiabatic process* to the state f. Then the entropy change is

$$\Delta S = S_f - S_i.$$

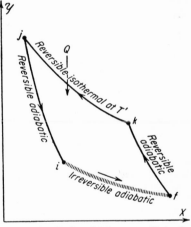

A temperature change may or may not have taken place. Whether or not, let us cause the system to undergo a *reversible adiabatic process* $f \rightarrow k$ in such a direction as to bring its temperature to that of any arbitrarily chosen reservoir, say, at T'. Then, since $S_f = S_k$,

$$\Delta S = S_k - S_i.$$

FIG. 10.6. Cycle which contradicts the second law unless $S_f > S_i$.

Now suppose that the system is brought into contact with the reservoir and caused to undergo a *reversible isothermal process* $k \rightarrow j$ until its entropy is the same as at the beginning. A final *reversible adiabatic process* $j \rightarrow i$ will now bring the system back to its initial state; and since $S_j = S_i$,

$$\Delta S = S_k - S_j.$$

The only heat transfer Q that has taken place in the cycle is during the isothermal process $k \rightarrow j$, where

$$Q = T'(S_j - S_k).$$

A net amount of work W has been done in the cycle, where

$$W = Q.$$

It is clear from the second law of thermodynamics that the heat Q cannot have entered the system, that is, Q cannot be positive, for then we would have a cyclic process in which no effect has been produced other than the extraction of heat from a reservoir and the performance of an equivalent amount of work. Therefore $Q \leq 0$, and

$$T'(S_j - S_k) \leq 0,$$

and finally
$$\Delta S \geq 0.$$

2. If we assume that the original irreversible adiabatic process took place without any change in entropy, then it would be possible to bring the system back to i by means of one reversible adiabatic process. Moreover, since the net heat transferred in this cycle is zero, the net work would also be zero. Therefore, under these circumstances, the system and its surroundings would have been restored to their initial states without producing changes elsewhere, which implies that the original process was reversible. Since this is contrary to our original assertion, the entropy of the system cannot remain unchanged. Therefore

$$\Delta S > 0.$$

3. Let us now suppose that the system is not homogeneous and not of uniform temperature and pressure and that it undergoes an irreversible adiabatic process in which mixing and chemical reaction may take place. If we assume that the system may be subdivided into parts (each one infinitesimal, if necessary) and that it is possible to ascribe a definite temperature, pressure, composition, etc., to each part, so that each part shall have a definite entropy depending on its coordinates, then we may define the entropy of the whole system as the sum of the entropies of its parts. If we now assume that it is possible to take *each part* back to its initial state by means of the reversible processes described in (1), using the same reservoir for each part, then it follows that ΔS of the whole system is positive.

It should be emphasized that we have had to make two assumptions, namely, (1) that the entropy of a system may be defined by subdividing the system into parts and summing the entropies of these parts and (2) that reversible processes may be found or imagined by which mixtures may be unmixed and reactions may be caused to proceed in the opposite direction. The justification for these assumptions rests to a small extent on experimental grounds. Thus, in a later chapter, there will be described a device involving semipermeable membranes whereby a mixture of two different inert ideal gases may be separated reversibly. A similar device through which a chemical reaction may be caused to proceed reversibly in any desired direction may also be conceived. Nevertheless, the main justification for these assumptions and therefore for the entropy principle lies in the fact that they lead to results in complete agreement with experiment; for the experimental physicist, this is sufficient.

The behavior of the entropy of the universe as a result of *any* kind of process may now be represented in the following succinct manner:

$$\Delta S \text{ (universe)} \geq 0,$$

where the equality sign refers to reversible processes and the inequality sign to irreversible processes.

10.10. Application of the Entropy Principle. We have seen that whenever irreversible processes take place the entropy of the universe increases. In the actual operation of a device, such as an engine or a refrigerator, it is often possible to calculate the sum of all the entropy changes. The fact that this sum is positive enables us to draw useful conclusions concerning the behavior of the device. An important example from the field of refrigeration engineering will illustrate the power and simplicity of the entropy principle. Suppose it is desired to freeze water or to liquefy air, i.e., to lower the temperature of a body of finite mass from the temperature T_1 of its surroundings to any desired temperature T_2. A refrigerator operating in a cycle between a reservoir at T_1 and the body itself is utilized, and after a finite number of complete cycles has been traversed, a quantity of heat Q has been removed from the body, a quantity of work W has been supplied to the refrigerator, and a quantity of heat $Q + W$ has been rejected to the reservoir, as shown in Fig. 10.7. Listing the entropy changes, we have

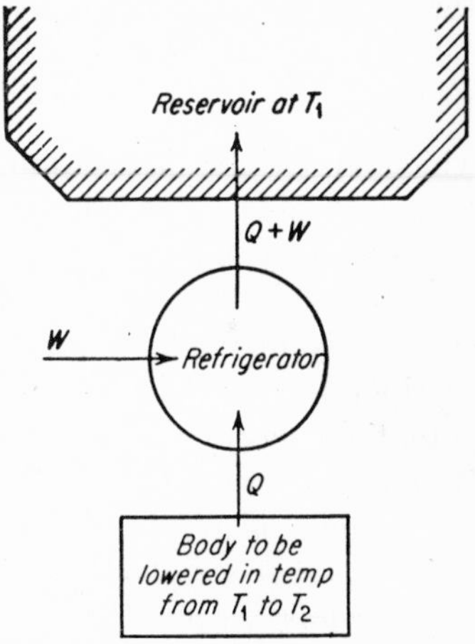

$$\Delta S \text{ of the body} = S_2 - S_1,$$
$$\Delta S \text{ of the refrigerant} = 0,$$
$$\Delta S \text{ of the reservoir} = \frac{Q + W}{T_1}.$$

FIG. 10.7. Operation of a refrigerator in lowering the temperature of a body from that of its surroundings T_1 to any desired value T_2.

Applying the entropy principle,

$$S_2 - S_1 + \frac{Q + W}{T_1} \geq 0.$$

Multiplying by T_1 and transposing, we get

$$W \geq T_1(S_1 - S_2) - Q.$$

It follows that the smallest possible value for W is

$$W \text{ (min)} = T_1(S_1 - S_2) - Q.$$

If tables of the thermodynamic properties of the material are available, a knowledge of the initial and final states is all that is needed to read from the tables the values of $S_1 - S_2$ and, if the body undergoes an isobaric process, of Q. The calculated value of W (min) is used to provide an estimate of the minimum cost of operation of the refrigeration plant.

10.11. Entropy and Unavailable Energy. Suppose that a quantity of heat Q may be extracted from a reservoir at the temperature T and that it is desired to convert as much as possible of this heat into work. If a colder reservoir is at hand, say, at the temperature T', a Carnot engine may be used, which, since it has the greatest efficiency, will supply the greatest amount of work, where

$$W = Q\left(1 - \frac{T'}{T}\right).$$

The lower the temperature of the colder reservoir, the greater will be the output of work. If T_0 is the temperature of the *coldest* reservoir at hand, then

$$W \text{ (max)} = Q\left(1 - \frac{T_0}{T}\right),$$

which represents the maximum amount of energy available for work when Q units of heat are extracted from a reservoir at T. It is obvious, therefore, that any energy which resides within the reservoir at T_0 and which may be extracted only in the form of heat is in a form in which it is completely unavailable for work. The potential energy, however, of a frictionless mechanical device (as measured from the position of lowest potential energy) is in a form in which it is completely available for work. It is desired to establish the proposition that, *whenever an irreversible process takes place, the effect on the universe is the same as that which would be produced if a certain quantity of energy were converted from a form in which it was completely available for work into a form in which it is completely unavailable for work. This amount of energy E is T_0 times the entropy change of the universe brought about by the irreversible process.*

Since the general proof of this proposition is somewhat abstract, let us consider first a special case, namely, the irreversible conduction of heat under a finite temperature gradient. Suppose that heat Q is conducted along a bar from a region at temperature T_1 to a region at temperature T_2. After conduction has taken place, we have heat Q available at the lower temperature T_2, of which the following amount is available for work:

$$\text{Maximum work after conduction} = Q\left(1 - \frac{T_0}{T_2}\right).$$

If conduction had not taken place, heat Q would have been available at the higher temperature T_1, and the maximum amount of work that could have been obtained from this is

$$\text{Maximum work before conduction} = Q\left(1 - \frac{T_0}{T_1}\right).$$

Evidently, the amount of energy E that has become unavailable for work is the difference

$$E = Q\left(1 - \frac{T_0}{T_1}\right) - Q\left(1 - \frac{T_0}{T_2}\right)$$

$$= T_0\left(\frac{Q}{T_2} - \frac{Q}{T_1}\right)$$

$$= T_0 \Delta S \qquad \text{(universe)}.$$

The proposition is therefore seen to be true for the special case of heat conduction. Since it is not possible to handle all irreversible processes in this simple manner, we shall have to adopt a more abstract point of view, in order to establish the proposition generally.

Consider a mechanical device such as a suspended weight or a compressed spring capable of doing work on a system. Suppose the system is in contact with a reservoir at the temperature T. The mechanical device and the reservoir at T constitute the *local surroundings* of the system. Suppose an irreversible process takes place in which the mechanical device does work W on the system, the internal energy of the system changes from U_i to U_f, and heat Q is transferred between the system and the reservoir. Then the first law demands that

$$Q = U_f - U_i + W,$$

and the second law that

$$S_f - S_i \text{ (system and local surroundings)} > 0.$$

Now suppose that it is desired to produce exactly the same changes in the system and the local surroundings that resulted from the performance of the irreversible process, *but by reversible processes only*. This would require, in general, the services of Carnot engines and refrigerators, which, in turn, would have to be operated in conjunction with an auxiliary mechanical device and an auxiliary reservoir. The auxiliary mechanical device may be considered, as usual, to be either a suspended weight or a compressed spring. For the auxiliary reservoir let us choose the one whose temperature is the lowest at hand, say, T_0. These constitute the *auxiliary surroundings*. With the aid of suitable Carnot engines and refrigerators all operating in cycles, in conjunction with the auxiliary surroundings, it is now possible to produce in the system and the local surroundings, by reversible processes only, the same changes that were formerly brought about by the irreversible process. If this is done, the entropy change of the system and the local surroundings is the same as before, since they have gone from the same initial states to the same final states. The auxiliary surroundings, however, must undergo an equal and opposite entropy change, because the net entropy change of the universe during reversible processes is zero.

Since the entropy change of the system and local surroundings is positive, the entropy change of the auxiliary surroundings is negative. Therefore the reservoir at T_0 must have rejected a certain amount of heat, say, E. Since no extra energy has appeared in the system and local surroundings, the energy E must have been transformed into work on the auxiliary mechanical device. We have the result therefore that, *when the same changes which were formerly produced in a system and local surroundings by an irreversible process are brought about reversibly, an amount of energy E leaves an auxiliary reservoir at T_0 in the form of heat, and appears in the form of work on an auxiliary mechanical device.* In other words, energy E is converted from a form in which it was completely unavailable for work into a form in which it is completely available for work. Since the original process was not performed reversibly, the energy E was not converted into work, and therefore E *is the energy that is rendered unavailable for work* because of the performance of the irreversible process.

It is a simple matter to calculate the energy that becomes unavailable during an irreversible process. If the same changes are brought about reversibly, the entropy change of the system and local surroundings is the same as before, namely, $S_f - S_i$. The entropy change of the auxiliary surroundings is merely the entropy change of the auxiliary reservoir due to the rejection of E units of heat at the temperature T_0, that is, $-E/T_0$. Since the sum of the entropy changes of the system, local surroundings, and auxiliary surroundings is zero, we have

$$S_f - S_i - \frac{E}{T_0} = 0,$$

whence

$$\boxed{E = T_0(S_f - S_i).}$$

Therefore, *the energy that becomes unavailable for work during an irreversible process is T_0 times the entropy change of the universe that is brought about by the irreversible process.* Since no energy becomes unavailable during a reversible process, it follows that the maximum amount of work is obtained when a process takes place reversibly.

Since irreversible processes are continually going on in nature, energy is continually becoming unavailable for work. This conclusion, known as the *principle of the degradation of energy,* was first developed by Kelvin and provides an important physical interpretation of that mysterious quantity, the entropy change of the universe. It must be understood that energy which becomes unavailable for work is not energy which is lost. The first law is obeyed at all times. Energy is merely transformed from one form into another. In picturesque language, one may say that energy is "running downhill."

10.12. Entropy and Disorder. It has been emphasized that work, as it is used in thermodynamics, is a macroscopic concept. There must be changes that are describable by macroscopic coordinates. Haphazard motions of individual molecules against intermolecular forces do not constitute work. Work involves order or orderly motion. Whenever work is dissipated into internal energy, the disorderly motion of molecules is increased. Thus, during either the isothermal or adiabatic dissipation of work into internal energy, the disorderly motion of the molecules of either a reservoir or a system is increased. Such processes therefore involve a transition from order to disorder. Similarly, two gases that are mixed represent a higher degree of disorder than when they are separated. It is possible to regard all natural processes from this point of view, and in all cases the result obtained is that *there is a tendency on the part of nature to proceed toward a state of greater disorder.*

The increase of entropy of the universe during natural processes is an expression of this transition. In other words, we may state roughly that *the entropy of a system or of a reservoir is a measure of the degree of molecular disorder existing in the system or reservoir.* To put these ideas on a firm foundation, the concept of disorder must be properly defined. It is shown in statistical mechanics that the disorder of a system may be calculated by the theory of probability and expressed by a quantity B known as the *thermodynamic probability*. The relation between entropy and disorder is then shown to be

$$S = \text{const. } \ln B.$$

By means of this equation a meaning may be given to the entropy of a system in any nonequilibrium state. That is, a nonequilibrium state corresponds to a certain degree of disorder and therefore to a definite entropy.

According to this relation, when the entropy of an isolated system increases, the system is proceeding from a state of lower to a state of higher probability. That is, the direction in which natural processes take place is governed by the laws of probability. *The second law of thermodynamics is therefore seen to be a statistical law.* Consider, for example, the conduction of heat from a hot stove to a kettle of water. According to the statistical interpretation of the second law, we assert, *not* that heat *must* flow from the stove to the water, but that it is highly probable that heat will flow from the stove to the water. It is to be understood that there is always a chance, although an extremely small one, that the reverse may take place.

The statistical character of the second law arises from the fact that the motions of individual molecules cannot be directed or controlled by any human agency. Suppose, for example, that a vessel containing a gas were divided into two compartments by a partition in which there was a small trap door and that, standing by the trap door, there were a superhuman being called a *Maxwell demon*, since the idea was first propounded by James Clerk Maxwell. Suppose that the demon opened the trap door only when fast molecules approached, thus allowing the fast molecules to collect in one compartment and slow ones in the other. This would obviously result in a transition from disorder to order, thus constituting a violation of the second law. If the trap door were left open and unattended by a Maxwell demon, there would be a small probability of a separation of the fast from the slow molecules, but a much larger probability of an even distribution.

In recent years the concept of entropy has been applied to the transmission of information by telegraph or radio. It is an obvious fact that such transmission is attended by errors and interference of various kinds with the result that the final message is less accurate or conveys less information than the original. In other words, when a message occurs, there is a transition to a state of greater inaccuracy. "Information" seems to be related to negative entropy or, as Brillouin puts it, "negentropy."

Imagine a telegraphic system in which the receiver may exist in a large number B_0 of possible states, all of them of the same probability. When information is received, the number of possible states is reduced to B_1. We take the logarithm of the ratio B_0/B_1 as a measure of the information I_1. Thus the equation

$$I_1 = \text{const. } \ln \frac{B_0}{B_1},$$

when compared with the relation between entropy and thermodynamic probability

$$S = \text{const. } \ln B,$$

and when the two constants are considered to be equal, yield the result that

$$S_1 = S_0 - I_1$$

where $S_0 = \text{const. } \ln B_0$ is the initial entropy, and $S_1 = \text{const. } \ln B_1$ is the final entropy with the information I_1. Thus, the information corresponds to a negative term in the final entropy of a physical system, or

$$\text{Information} = \text{negentropy.}$$

This is the barest outline of the foundation of information theory. There is much more that can be done. For further details, the student is referred to "Science and Information Theory" by Léon Brillouin.

10.13. Entropy and Direction. Absolute Entropy. The second law of thermodynamics provides an answer to the question that is not contained within the scope of the first law, namely, "In what direction does a process take place?" The answer is that a process always takes place in such a direction as to cause an increase in the entropy of the universe. In the case of an isolated system it is the entropy of the system that tends to increase. To find out, therefore, the equilibrium state of an isolated system, it is necessary merely to express the entropy as a function of certain coordinates and to apply the usual rules of calculus to render the function a maximum. When the system is not isolated but instead, let us say, is maintained at constant temperature and pressure, there are other entropy changes to be taken into account. It will be shown later, however, that there exists another function, known as the Gibbs function, referring to the system alone whose behavior determines equilibrium under these conditions.

In practical applications of thermodynamics one is interested only in the amount by which the entropy of a system changes in going from an initial to a final state. In cases where it is necessary to perform many such calculations with the minimum of effort, for example, in steam engineering, in problems in refrigeration and gas liquefaction, etc., it is found expedient to set up an *entropy table* in which the "entropy" of the system in thousands of different states is represented by appropriate numbers. This is done by assigning the value zero to the entropy of the system in an arbitrarily chosen standard state and calculating the entropy change from this standard state to all other states. When this is done, it is understood that one value of what is listed as "the entropy" has no meaning, but that the difference between two values is actually the entropy change.

It is a very interesting and also a very important question in physics as to whether there exists an absolute standard state of a system in which the entropy is really zero, so that the number obtained by calculating the entropy change from the zero state to any other represents the "absolute entropy" of the system. It was first suggested by Planck that the entropy of a single crystal of a pure element at the absolute zero of temperature should be taken to be zero. Zero entropy, however, has statistical implications implying, in a rough way, the absence of all molecular, atomic, electronic, and nuclear disorder. Before any meaning can be attached to the idea of zero entropy, one must know all the factors that contribute to the disorder of a system. An adequate discussion requires the application of quantum ideas to statistical mechanics, so that it is perhaps best merely to quote the words of Fowler and Guggenheim, who have considered the subject exhaustively and who summarize the situation as follows:

We may assign, if we please, the value zero to the entropy of all perfect crystals of a single pure isotope of a single element in its idealized state at the absolute zero of temperature, but even this has no theoretical significance on account of nuclear spin weights. For the purpose of calculating experimental results, some conventional zero must be chosen, and the above choice or a similar one is thus often convenient. But its conventional character will no longer be so likely to be overlooked that any importance will in the future be attached to absolute entropy, an idea which has caused much confusion and been of very little assistance in the development of the subject.

10.14. Entropy Flow and Entropy Production. Consider the conduction of heat along a copper wire that lies between a hot reservoir at temperature T_1 and a cooler reservoir at T_2. Suppose the heat current or rate of flow of heat is represented by the symbol I_Q. In unit time, the hot reservoir undergoes a decrease of entropy I_Q/T_1, the copper wire suffers no entropy change because, once in the steady state, its coordinates do not change, and the cooler reservoir undergoes an entropy increase I_Q/T_2. The entropy change of the universe per unit time is $I_Q/T_2 - I_Q/T_1$ which is, of course, positive.

This process may, however, be considered from a point of view in which the attention is focused on the wire, rather than on the universe. Since the hot reservoir underwent an entropy decrease we may say that it lost entropy to the wire, or that *there was a flow of entropy into the wire* equal to I_Q/T_1 per unit time. Since the cooler reservoir underwent an entropy increase, we may say that the reservoir gained entropy from the wire, or that *there was a flow of entropy out of the wire* equal to I_Q/T_2, per unit time. But I_Q/T_2 is greater than I_Q/T_1, and hence this point of view leads us to a situation in which the *flow of entropy out of the wire exceeds the flow in.* If entropy is to be regarded as a quantity that can flow, it is necessary to assume that entropy is produced or generated inside the wire at a rate sufficient to compensate for the difference between the rate of outflow and the rate of inflow. If the rate of production of entropy within the wire is written $dS/d\tau$, we have

$$\frac{dS}{d\tau} = \frac{I_Q}{T_2} - \frac{I_Q}{T_1} = I_Q \frac{T_1 - T_2}{T_1 T_2},$$

and if the temperatures of the reservoirs are $T + \Delta T$ and T, so that only a small temperature difference exists across the wire

$$\frac{dS}{d\tau} = I_Q \frac{\Delta T}{T^2} = \frac{I_Q}{T} \frac{\Delta T}{T}.$$

Since I_Q stands for a heat current, we may interpret I_Q/T as an entropy current I_S, or

$$I_S = \frac{I_Q}{T}.$$

We have therefore the result that, when heat is conducted along a wire across which there is a temperature difference ΔT, *entropy flows through the wire at a rate I_S and entropy is produced within the wire at a rate*

$$\frac{dS}{d\tau} = I_S \frac{\Delta T}{T}.$$

Suppose now that an electric current I is maintained in this same copper wire by virtue of a difference of potential $\Delta\mathcal{E}$ across its ends, while the wire is in contact with a reservoir at the temperature T. Electrical energy of amount $I\,\Delta\mathcal{E}$ is dissipated in the wire per unit time and heat flows out of the wire at the same rate $I\,\Delta\mathcal{E}$, since the wire itself undergoes no energy change. The reservoir undergoes an increase of entropy $I\,\Delta\mathcal{E}/T$ per unit time and there is no entropy change of the wire. Hence the entropy change of the universe per unit time is $I\,\Delta\mathcal{E}/T$, which is positive. Changing our point of view, as before, to a consideration of the wire, we may say that there was no flow of entropy into the wire, but that entropy flowed out at the rate $I\,\Delta\mathcal{E}/T$. To provide for this outflow of entropy, we assume an entropy production inside the wire at the rate

$$\frac{dS}{d\tau} = I \frac{\Delta\mathcal{E}}{T}.$$

If now, *both* a heat current and an electric current exist in the wire simultaneously, we may say that entropy is being generated within the wire by virtue of *both processes* at a rate given by

$$\boxed{\frac{dS}{d\tau} = I_S \frac{\Delta T}{T} + I \frac{\Delta\mathcal{E}}{T}.}$$

It is an interesting fact of experimental physics that, in the absence of a potential difference, a heat current depends only on the temperature difference, but, when there is a potential difference as well, the heat current (also the entropy current) depends on *both* the temperature difference and the potential difference. Similarly, when both temperature and potential differences exist across a wire, the electric current also depends on *both* of these differences. The heat flow (and entropy flow) and the electricity flow are irreversible *coupled flows*, which exist by virtue of a departure from equilibrium conditions in the wire. If the departure from equilibrium is not too great, it may be assumed that both I_S and I are *linear* functions of the temperature and potential differences. Thus,

$$I_S = L_{11} \frac{\Delta T}{T} + L_{12} \frac{\Delta \mathcal{E}}{T},$$

and

$$I = L_{21} \frac{\Delta T}{T} + L_{22} \frac{\Delta \mathcal{E}}{T}$$

are the famous *Onsager equations* which express the linearity between the flows (or currents) and the *generalized forces* $\Delta T/T$ and $\Delta \mathcal{E}/T$. The L's are coefficients connected with electric resistance, thermal conductivity, and the thermoelectric properties of the wire. Only three of the four L's are independent, for it can be proved rigorously by means of statistical mechanics that, if the departure from equilibrium is small,

$$\boxed{L_{12} = L_{21},}$$

which is known as *Onsager's reciprocal relation.*

By means of this strange point of view involving entropy flow and entropy production, and with the aid of Onsager's equations and reciprocal relation, the famous equations for a thermocouple will be derived in Chap. 14.

PROBLEMS

10.1. (*a*) Derive the expression for the efficiency of a Carnot engine directly from a *T*-*S* diagram.

(*b*) Compare the efficiencies of cycles *a* and *b* of Fig. 10.8.

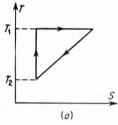 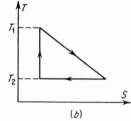

FIG. 10.8.

10.2. Prove that the slope on a *T*-*S* diagram of (*a*) an isochoric curve is T/C_V; (*b*) an isobaric curve is T/C_P.

10.3. Draw rough *T*-*S* diagrams for the following ideal gas cycles: Otto, Diesel, a rectangle on a *P*-*V* diagram, a "right triangle" on a *P*-*V* diagram in which the base is an isobaric, the altitude an isochoric, and the "hypotenuse" an adiabatic.

10.4. Show that the entropy of an ideal gas with constant heat capacities may be written

$$S = C_V \ln P + C_P \ln V + \text{const.}$$

10.5. An electric current of 10 amp is maintained for 1 sec in a resistor of 25 ohms while the temperature of the resistor is kept constant at 27°C.

(a) What is the entropy change of the resistor?

(b) What is the entropy change of the universe?

The same current is maintained for the same time in the same resistor, but now thermally insulated, whose initial temperature is 27°C. If the resistor has a mass of 10 gm and $c_P = 0.20$ cal/gm · deg,

(c) What is the entropy change of the resistor?

(d) What is the entropy change of the universe?

10.6. (a) One kilogram of water at 273°K is brought into contact with a heat reservoir at 373°K. When the water has reached 373°K, what is the entropy change of the water? Of the heat reservoir? Of the universe?

(b) If the water had been heated from 273 to 373°K by first bringing it in contact with a reservoir at 323°K and then with a reservoir at 373°K, what would have been the entropy change of the universe?

(c) Explain how the water might be heated from 273 to 373°K with almost no change of entropy of the universe.

10.7. The molar heat capacity at constant magnetic field of a paramagnetic solid at low temperature varies with the temperature and field according to the relation

$$c_{\mathscr{H}} = \frac{b + C\mathscr{H}^2}{T^2} + DT^3,$$

where b, C, and D are constants. What is the entropy change of n moles of material when the temperature changes from T_i to T_f while $\mathscr{H}$ remains constant at the value $\mathscr{H}_0$?

10.8. A thermally insulated cylinder closed at both ends is fitted with a frictionless heat-conducting piston which divides the cylinder into two parts. Initially the piston is clamped in the center, with 1 liter of air at 300°K and 2 atm pressure on one side and 1 liter of air at 300°K at 1 atm pressure on the other side. The piston is released and reaches equilibrium in pressure and temperature at a new position. Compute the final pressure and temperature and the total increase of entropy. What irreversible process has taken place?

10.9. A piece of hot metal (mass m, specific heat at instant pressure c_P, temperature T_i) is immersed in a cooler liquid (m', c_P', T_i') adiabatically and isobarically. Prove that the condition of equilibrium, namely, $T_f = T_f'$, may be obtained by rendering the entropy change of the universe a maximum subject to the condition that the heat lost by the metal equals the heat gained by the liquid.

10.10. A mass m of water at T_1 is isobarically and adiabatically mixed with an equal mass of water at T_2. Show that the entropy change of the universe is

$$2mc_P \ln \frac{(T_1 + T_2)/2}{\sqrt{T_1 T_2}},$$

and prove that this is positive by drawing a semicircle of diameter $T_1 + T_2$.

10.11. Solve the problem of Art. 10.8 when only the hot reservoir is removed, and show that the entropy change of the universe is

$$C_P \left(1 + \frac{T_0 - T_L}{2T_L} - \frac{T_0}{T_0 - T_L} \ln \frac{T_0}{T_L}\right).$$

10.12. A body of finite mass is originally at a temperature T_1, which is higher than that of a reservoir at the temperature T_2. Suppose an engine operates in a cycle between the body and the reservoir until it lowers the temperature of the body from

T_1 to T_2, thus extracting heat Q from the body.   If the engine does work W, then it will reject heat $Q - W$ to the reservoir at T_2.   Applying the entropy principle, prove that the maximum work obtainable from the engine is

$$W \text{ (max)} = Q - T_2(S_1 - S_2),$$

where $S_1 - S_2$ is the entropy decrease of the body.

10.13. Two identical bodies of constant heat capacity at the temperatures T_1 and T_2, respectively, are used as reservoirs for a heat engine.   If the bodies remain at constant pressure and undergo no change of phase, show that the amount of work obtainable is

$$W = C_P(T_1 + T_2 - 2T_f),$$

where T_f is the final temperature attained by both bodies.   Show that, when W is a maximum,

$$T_f = \sqrt{T_1 T_2}.$$

10.14. Two identical bodies of constant heat capacity are at the same initial temperature T_i.   A refrigerator operates between these two bodies until one body is cooled to the temperature T_2.   If the bodies remain at constant pressure and undergo no change of phase, show that the minimum amount of work needed to do this is

$$W \text{ (min)} = C_P\left(\frac{T_i^2}{T_2} + T_2 - 2T_i\right).$$

10.15. Consider any system immersed in a medium at the constant temperature T_0 and suppose that *the only reservoir with which the system may exchange heat is this medium.*   Let the system undergo a process involving the absorption of heat Q, the performance of work W, and a change of entropy $S_f - S_i$.   Show that

(a) $-\dfrac{U_f - U_i + W}{T_0} + S_f - S_i \geq 0,$

(b) $W \text{ (max)} = U_i - T_0 S_i - (U_f - T_0 S_f),$

(c) $T_0 \,\Delta S \text{ (universe)} = W \text{ (max)} - W \text{ (actual)}.$

10.16. When both a heat current and an electric current are maintained in the same wire simultaneously by a temperature difference ΔT and a potential difference $\Delta \mathcal{E}$, prove that

(a) $\left(\dfrac{\partial I_s}{\partial \Delta \mathcal{E}}\right)_{\Delta T} = \left(\dfrac{\partial I}{\partial \Delta T}\right)_{\Delta \mathcal{E}}.$

(b) $L_{11} = kA/\Delta x$, where k is the thermal conductivity and A and Δx are the area and length, respectively, of the wire.

(c) $L_{22} = T/R$, where R is the electric resistance of the wire.

10.17. Show that, in the case of irreversible coupled flows of heat and electricity,

(a) $T^2 \dfrac{dS}{d\tau} = L_{11}(\Delta T)^2 + (L_{12} + L_{21})\,\Delta T\,\Delta \mathcal{E} + L_{22}(\Delta \mathcal{E})^2,$

(b) $\dfrac{\partial}{\partial \Delta \mathcal{E}}\left(T\dfrac{dS}{d\tau}\right)_{\Delta T} = 2I, \qquad \dfrac{\partial}{\partial \Delta T}\left(T\dfrac{dS}{d\tau}\right)_{\Delta \mathcal{E}} = 2I_s.$

(c) Show that, with ΔT fixed, the equilibrium state obtained when $I = 0$ involves a minimum rate of entropy production.

(d) Show that, with $\Delta \mathcal{E}$ fixed, the equilibrium state obtained when $I_s = 0$ involves a minimum rate of entropy production.

Properties of Pure Substances

11.1. *P-V* Diagram for a Pure Substance. If 1 gm of water at about 94°C is introduced into a vessel about 2 liters in volume from which all the air has been exhausted, the water will evaporate completely and the system will be in the condition known as *unsaturated vapor*, the pressure of the vapor being less than 1 atm. On the *P-V* diagram shown in Fig. 11.1 this state is represented by the point *A*. If the vapor is then

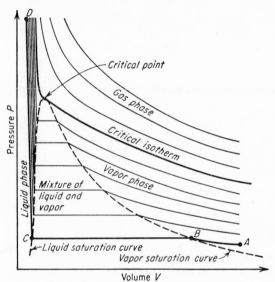

Fig. 11.1. Isotherms of a pure substance.

compressed slowly and isothermally, the pressure will rise until there is *saturated vapor* at the point *B*. If the compression is continued, condensation takes place, the pressure remaining constant so long as the temperature remains constant. The straight line *BC* represents the isothermal isobaric condensation of water vapor, the constant pressure being called the *vapor pressure*. At any point between *B* and *C*, water and steam are in equilibrium; at the point *C*, there is only liquid water, or *saturated liquid*. Since a very large increase of pressure is needed to compress liquid water, the line CD is almost vertical. At any point on the line CD the water is said to be in the *liquid phase*, at any point on AB in the *vapor phase*, and at any point on BC there is equilibrium between the liquid and the vapor phases. $ABCD$ is a typical isotherm of a pure substance on a P-V diagram.

At other temperatures the isotherms are of similar character, as shown in Fig. 11.1. It is seen that the lines representing equilibrium between liquid and vapor phases, or *vaporization lines*, get shorter as the temperature rises until a certain temperature is reached, the *critical temperature*, above which there is no longer any distinction between a liquid and a vapor. The isotherm at the critical temperature is called the *critical isotherm*, and the point that represents the limit of the vaporization lines is called the *critical point*. It is seen that the critical point is a point of inflection on the critical isotherm. The pressure and volume at the critical point are known as the *critical pressure* and the *critical volume*, respectively. All points at which the liquid is saturated lie on the *liquid saturation curve*, and all points representing saturated vapor lie on the *vapor saturation curve*. The two saturation curves denoted by dotted lines meet at the critical point. Above the critical point the isotherms are continuous curves that at large volumes and low pressures approach equilateral hyperbolas, i.e., the isotherms of an ideal gas.

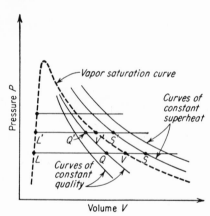

FIG. 11.2. Curves of constant quality and curves of constant superheat.

In Fig. 11.2 the point V refers to saturated vapor at the temperature T_1. If this vapor is heated at constant pressure until its temperature rises to T_2, a point such as S will be reached and the vapor is said to be *superheated*, the difference $T_2 - T_1$ being the *number of degrees superheat*. Superheated vapor is unsaturated vapor. If the line $V'S'$ represents the same number of degrees superheat as the line VS, then all points such as S and S' determine a curve known as a *curve of constant superheat*.

The point V denotes saturated vapor or 100 per cent vapor and 0 per cent liquid. The point L, however, denotes 0 per cent vapor and 100 per cent liquid at the same temperature. At intermediate points such as Q the percentage vapor, or *quality*, varies. If the point Q' represents the same quality with respect to V' that the point Q represents with respect to V, then Q and Q' lie on a curve known as a *curve of constant quality*.

In the two P-V diagrams shown in Figs. 11.1 and 11.2 the low-temperature region representing the solid phase has not been shown. The solid region and the region of equilibrium between solid and vapor are indicated by isotherms of the same general character as those in Fig. 11.1. The horizontal portion of one of these isotherms represents the transition from saturated solid to saturated vapor, or *sublimation*. There is obviously one such line that is the boundary between the liquid-vapor region and the solid-vapor region. This *line* is associated with the *triple point*. In the case of ordinary water, the triple point is at a pressure of 4.58 mm and a temperature of 0.01°C, and the line extends from a volume of 1.00 cm³/gm (saturated liquid) to a volume of 206,000 cm³/gm (saturated vapor).

11.2. Critical Point. It is clear that the critical point is a limiting point at which the volume of a liquid is equal to that of an equal mass of vapor, or, in other words, at which the density of the liquid equals the density of the vapor. If the densities of both liquid and vapor are measured as functions of the temperature and the results are plotted, the critical temperature can be determined from the point where the two curves meet.

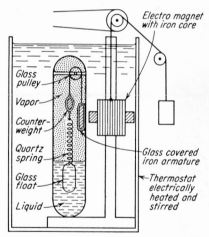

A very delicate method of measuring the density of a liquid and of its vapor was devised by Maass, who with many coworkers has studied the properties of matter in the neighborhood of the critical point. His apparatus is shown in its essential details in Fig. 11.3. The liquid and vapor are contained in a small, heavy-walled pyrex tube. A quartz

FIG. 11.3. Apparatus of Maass for measuring liquid and vapor densities in the neighborhood of the critical point.

spiral, previously calibrated and found to have a modulus of 0.00512 gm/mm, to which is attached a glass float of known mass and volume, is raised or lowered magnetically so that the extension of the spring may be measured when the float is in the liquid or in the vapor. The whole apparatus was immersed in an oil thermostat electrically heated and stirred, the temperature of which could be maintained uniform and constant to a few hundredths of a degree.

Experimental results for propylene are shown in Fig. 11.4. The most interesting behavior is seen to be about the last six degrees before the critical point where the liquid and vapor densities vary only slightly with

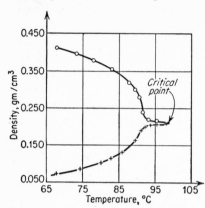

FIG. 11.4. Liquid- and vapor-density curves of propylene, meeting at the critical point.

the temperature and are only slightly different. It is an interesting fact that at no temperature in this region is the meniscus between liquid and vapor visible. It was first thought that the disappearance of the meniscus was the criterion for the attainment of the critical point. Maass, however, showed that the meniscus disappears throughout a range of values of pressure, temperature, and density as shown by the shaded area on the P-V diagram of Fig. 11.5. In this region there are two distinct phases with different densities, but they cannot be distinguished visually. Results of other experiments on critical temperatures, pressures, and densities are given in Table 11.1.

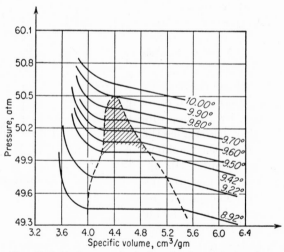

FIG. 11.5. Isotherms of ethylene in the critical region.

11.3. Vapor Pressure of Liquids and Solids. When a liquid or solid is in equilibrium with its vapor at a given temperature, the vapor exerts a pressure that depends only on the temperature. In general, the higher the temperature, the greater the vapor pressure. The temperature at which the vapor pressure equals 760 mm is known as the *normal boiling point*. Vapor pressures from a few millimeters to several atmos-

TABLE 11.1. CRITICAL DATA

Substance	Critical temp., °K	Critical pressure, atm	Critical volume, cm³/mole	Critical density, gm/cm³
Helium (4)....................	5.3	2.26	57.8	0.0693
Helium (3)....................	3.34	1.15		
Hydrogen (normal).............	33.3	12.80	65.0	0.0310
Deuterium (normal)............	38.4	16.4		
Nitrogen......................	126.2	33.5	90.1	0.311
Oxygen.......................	154.8	50.1	78	0.41
Ammonia......................	405.5	111.3	72.5	0.235
Freon 12......................	384.7	39.6	218	0.555
Carbon dioxide................	304.2	72.9	94.0	0.468
Sulfur dioxide.................	430.7	77.8	122	0.524
Water........................	647.4	218.3	56	0.32
Carbon disulfide..............	552	78	170	0.44

pheres can be measured statically with a simple mercury-tube manometer, as shown in Fig. 11.6. The oven is maintained at any desired temperature at which the saturated vapor has a pressure equal to

$$P = P_0 + h.$$

For low vapor pressures, P_0 is made zero, whereas, for high vapor pressures, gas may be admitted to the left-hand tube and the pressure P_0 may be calculated with the aid of Boyle's law. The level of the mercury in the right-hand tube is kept within the oven at all times by adjusting the height of the mercury reservoir. The vapor pressure of mercury is about 0.001 mm at room temperature and therefore introduces no error in the determination of P_0.

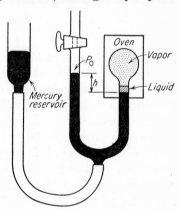

FIG. 11.6. Mercury manometer for measuring the vapor pressure of a liquid.

As the temperature is reduced, a temperature is reached at which some of the liquid starts to solidify. This temperature and the corresponding vapor pressure constitute the triple point at which solid, liquid, and vapor exist in equilibrium. At lower temperatures only solid and vapor are present. The vapor pressure of most solids is very small. Very low vapor pressures from 1 mm down to 10^{-5} mm are measured by determining the rate of evaporation, according to a method devised by Knudsen. The substance is contained in a quartz vessel with a small hole in the top. The vessel is

maintained at constant temperature for a length of time ranging from
3 to 50 hr, and during this time some of the substance evaporates and
escapes through the hole. Measurements of the loss of weight of the
substance in a given time, the temperature, the area of the hole, and other
constants of the apparatus enable one to calculate the vapor pressure.
The theory of this method involves an application of the kinetic theory
of gases, which is beyond the scope of this book.

11.4. P-T Diagram for a Pure Substance. If the vapor pressure of
a solid is measured at various temperatures until the triple point is
reached and then that of the liquid is measured until the critical point is
reached, the results when plotted on
a P-T diagram appear as in Fig. 11.7.
If the substance at the triple point is
compressed until there is no vapor
left and the pressure on the resulting
mixture of liquid and solid is increased, the temperature will have
to be changed for equilibrium to exist
between the solid and the liquid.
Measurements of these pressures and
temperatures give rise to a third
curve on the P-T diagram, starting
at the triple point and continuing
indefinitely. The points representing the coexistence of (1) solid and
vapor lie on the *sublimation curve*, (2) liquid and vapor lie on the *vaporization curve*, (3) liquid and solid lie on the *fusion curve*. In the particular
case of water, the sublimation curve is called the *frost line*, the vaporization curve is called the *steam line*, and the fusion curve is called the *ice line*.

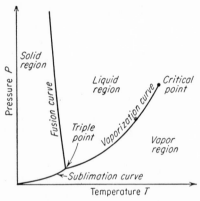

Fig. 11.7. P-T diagram for a substance
such as water.

The slopes of the sublimation and the vaporization curves for all substances are positive. The slope of the fusion curve, however, may be
positive or negative. The fusion curve of most substances has a positive slope. Water is one of the important exceptions. When an equation known as the Clapeyron equation is derived in Chap. 15, it will be
seen that any substance, such as water, which expands upon freezing
has a fusion curve with a negative slope, whereas the opposite is true
for a substance which contracts upon freezing.

11.5. Triple Point. The pressure and temperature at which all three
phases of a pure substance coexist may be measured with the apparatus
that is used to measure vapor pressure. The triple point is merely the
point of intersection of the sublimation and vaporization curves. It
must be understood that only on a P-T diagram is the triple point
represented by a point. On a P-V diagram it is a line, and on a U-V

diagram it is a triangle. Triple-point data for some interesting substances are given in Table 11.2.

TABLE 11.2. TRIPLE-POINT DATA

Substance	Temp., °K	Pressure, mm Hg
Helium (4) (λ point)...........	2.186	38.3
Helium (3)..................	None	None
Hydrogen (normal)...........	13.84	52.8
Deuterium (normal)..........	18.63	128
Neon.......................	24.57	324
Nitrogen....................	63.18	94
Oxygen.....................	54.36	1.14
Ammonia....................	195.40	45.57
Carbon dioxide..............	216.55	3880
Sulfur dioxide...............	197.68	1.256
Water......................	273.16	4.58

In investigating the ice line of water at very high pressures, Bridgman and Tammann discovered five new modifications of ice, designated as ice II, III, V, VI, and VII, ordinary ice being denoted by ice I. Two other modifications of ice, IV and VIII, were found to be unstable. Equilibrium conditions among these forms of ice and liquid give rise to six other triple points, which, along with the low-pressure triple point, are listed in Table 11.3.

TABLE 11.3. TRIPLE POINTS OF WATER

Phases in equilibrium	Pressure	Temp., °C
Ice I, liquid, vapor..............	4.579 mm Hg	+ 0.01
Ice I, liquid, ice III..............	2,115 kg/cm²	−22.0
Ice I, ice II, ice III..............	2,170 kg/cm²	−34.7
Ice II, ice III, ice V.............	3,510 kg/cm²	−24.3
Ice III, liquid, ice V.............	3,530 kg/cm²	−17.0
Ice V, liquid, ice VI.............	6,380 kg/cm²	+ 0.16
Ice VI, liquid, ice VII...........	22,400 kg/cm²	+81.6

11.6. P-V-T Surface. All the information that is represented on both the P-V and the P-T diagrams can be shown on one diagram if the three coordinates P, V, and T are plotted along rectangular axes. The result is called the P-V-T surface. Two such surfaces are shown in Figs. 11.8 and 11.9, the first for a substance like water that expands upon freezing and the second for a substance like CO_2 that contracts upon freezing. These diagrams are not drawn to scale, the volume axis being

considerably foreshortened. If the student imagines a *P-V-T* surface
projected on the *P-V* plane, he will see the usual *P-V* diagram. Upon
projecting the surface on the *P-T* plane, the whole solid-vapor region
projects into the sublimation curve, the whole liquid-vapor region projects
into the vaporization curve, the whole solid-liquid region projects into
the fusion curve, and finally the "triple-point line" projects into the
triple point. The critical point is denoted by the letters *Cr* and the

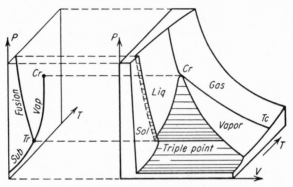

FIG. 11.8. *P-V-T* surface for a substance which expands upon freezing.

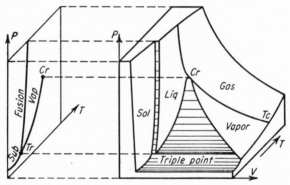

FIG. 11.9. *P-V-T* surface for a substance which contracts upon freezing.

triple point by *Tr*. The critical isotherm is marked T_c. A substance
with no free surface and with a volume determined by that of the container is called a gas when its temperature is above the critical temperature. Otherwise it is called a vapor.

All the triple points of water are shown on the *P-V-T* surface shown in
Fig. 11.10, which was constructed by Verwiebe on the basis of measurements by Bridgman.

The *P-V-T* surface and accompanying *P-T* projection for helium given
in Fig. 11.11 show that helium has a number of remarkable properties.
If we start at the critical point ($T_c = 5.1°$K, $P_c = 2.3$ atm) and lower the

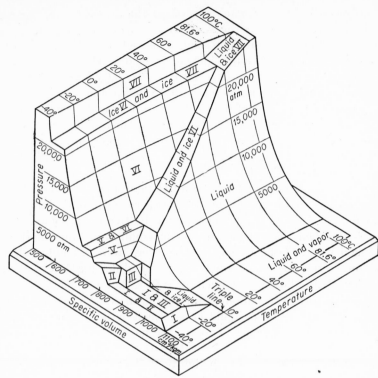

FIG. 11.10. *P-V-T* surface for water, showing all the triple points. Constructed by Verwiebe on the basis of measurements by Bridgman.

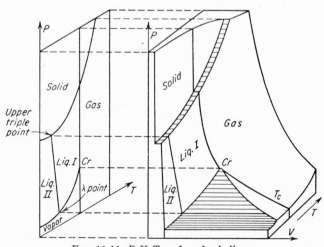

FIG. 11.11. *P-V-T* surface for helium.

temperature, the liquid remaining in equilibrium with its vapor, a triple point is reached (known as the λ point) at which three different phases are in equilibrium but there is no solid.   Instead of solid helium, another modification of liquid helium, known as helium II, is formed.   The coordinates of the λ point are $T = 2.19°K$, $P = 0.0508$ atm (38.65 mm). Further reduction of the temperature (by rapid evaporation) is still not attended by the formation of the solid.   In order to produce solid helium from either liquid I or liquid II, the pressure must be increased to over 25 atm, in which case a triple point (the upper triple point) is reached at which both the liquids and the solid are in equilibrium.   *There is no triple point for solid, liquid, and vapor.*

The transition from liquid I to liquid II takes place with no "latent" heat and with no change of volume.   Such a transition is known as a phase change of the second order and will be treated in some detail in Chap. 15.   When the two liquids are in equilibrium, they both have the same density.   Other properties, however, are remarkably different. For example, the thermal conductivity of liquid helium II is very much larger than that of liquid I, so much so, in fact, that a temperature gradient, which gives rise to bubbling in liquid I, does not exist in liquid II and thus one can tell when liquid II is formed by noting that the liquid suddenly becomes quiescent.   Perhaps the most interesting property of liquid II is its remarkably low viscosity.   It flows very rapidly through capillary tubes and goes through tightly packed porous materials as if through a sieve.   Other interesting properties of liquid helium II are that it has a large heat capacity at constant pressure and a negative volume expansivity.

11.7. Equations of State.   It is impossible to express the complete behavior of a substance over the whole range of measured values of P, V, and T by means of one simple equation.   There have been no less than 56 equations of state suggested within the last 80 years to represent only the liquid, vapor, and liquid-vapor regions, ranging from the ideal gas equation

$$Pv = RT,$$

which holds only at low pressures in the vapor and gas regions, to the Beattie-Bridgeman equation

$$P = \frac{RT(1 - \epsilon)}{v^2}(v + B) - \frac{A}{v^2}$$

where $A = A_0\left(1 - \frac{a}{v}\right)$, $B = B_0\left(1 - \frac{b}{v}\right)$, $\epsilon = \frac{c}{vT^3}$,

which, because of its five adjustable constants, represents with some accuracy the whole range above the triple point.   The student will find a list of these 56 equations starting at page 224 in the "Handbuch der

Experimentalphysik," Vol. VIII, Part 2.   Some of these equations are frankly empirical, designed to represent as closely as possible the measured values of P, V, and T, while others are theoretical, having been calculated on the basis of the kinetic theory of gases.   One of the most famous of the theoretical equations of state, based on assumptions concerning molecular behavior that are still of use today, is the van der Waals equation of state

$$\left(P + \frac{a}{v^2}\right)(v - b) = RT.$$

This equation holds fairly well in the liquid region, the vapor region, and near and above the critical point.

Since the critical point is the limiting position as two points (saturated liquid and saturated vapor) both at the same P and T approach each other, it follows that the slope of the critical isotherm on a P-V diagram is zero at the critical point, or

$$\left(\frac{\partial P}{\partial V}\right)_{T=T_c} = 0.$$

Also, since the critical point is a point of inflection on the critical isotherm,

$$\left(\frac{\partial^2 P}{\partial V^2}\right)_{T=T_c} = 0.$$

These two equations, along with the equation of state itself, enable one to calculate the critical P, V, and T, denoted by P_c, V_c, T_c.   For example, the van der Waals equation can be written

$$P = \frac{RT}{v - b} - \frac{a}{v^2};$$

and, setting the first and second derivatives equal to zero,

$$\left(\frac{\partial P}{\partial v}\right)_T = -\frac{RT}{(v - b)^2} + \frac{2a}{v^3} = 0,$$

and
$$\left(\frac{\partial^2 P}{\partial v^2}\right)_T = \frac{2RT}{(v - b)^3} - \frac{6a}{v^4} = 0.$$

The last two equations become

$$\frac{2a}{v^3} = \frac{RT}{(v - b)^2}$$

and
$$\frac{3a}{v^4} = \frac{RT}{(v - b)^3},$$

whence, dividing the first by the second,

$$v_c = 3b.$$

Substituting this value for v in the first of the two equations, we get

$$T_c = \frac{8a}{27bR}$$

and finally, substituting these two values in the van der Waals equation,

$$P_c = \frac{8a}{27b(2b)} - \frac{a}{9b^2} = \frac{a}{27b^2}.$$

It follows that

$$\frac{RT_c}{P_c v_c} = \frac{R \dfrac{8a}{27bR}}{\dfrac{a}{27b^2} 3b} = \frac{8}{3} = 2.67.$$

If a substance behaved like an ideal gas at the critical point, $RT_c/P_c v_c$ would equal unity. If it obeys the van der Waals equation, this ratio should equal 2.67. In Table 11.4 the measured values of $RT_c/P_c v_c$ are listed for a number of interesting gases, and in no case is this ratio equal to 2.67.

TABLE 11.4. MEASURED VALUES
OF $RT_c/P_c v_c$

Substance	$\dfrac{RT_c}{P_c v_c}$
Water..................	4.46
Carbon dioxide..........	3.48
Oxygen.................	3.42
Argon..................	3.43
Nitrogen...............	3.42
Hydrogen...............	3.03
Helium.................	3.13

Above the critical point, at higher pressure, the van der Waals equation is fairly satisfactory and is useful in many cases. Other equations of state give better values of $RT_c/P_c v_c$ but are no better in describing other properties of gases. The Dieterici and the Berthelot equations will be found in the problems at the end of the chapter. An equation that has been very useful in representing the properties of superheated steam but does not apply at the critical point or in the liquid-vapor region is due to Callendar:

$$v - b = \frac{RT}{P} - \frac{a}{T^n}$$

where $n = 10\frac{1}{3}$.

11.8. T-S Diagram for a Pure Substance. The entropy of a system is a function of the thermodynamic coordinates whose change during a process in which the system goes from an equilibrium state i to another equilibrium state f is equal to

$$S_f - S_i = {}_R\!\int_i^f \frac{\mathrm{d}Q}{T},$$

where the symbol R indicates that the integration is to be performed over any reversible path connecting i and f. If the two equilibrium states are infinitesimally near, then

$$\mathrm{d}Q = T\,dS$$

and

$$\frac{\mathrm{d}Q}{dT} = T\frac{dS}{dT}.$$

At constant volume

$$\boxed{\left(\frac{\mathrm{d}Q}{dT}\right)_V = C_V = T\left(\frac{\partial S}{\partial T}\right)_V,}$$

and at constant pressure

$$\boxed{\left(\frac{\mathrm{d}Q}{dT}\right)_P = C_P = T\left(\frac{\partial S}{\partial T}\right)_P.}$$

If the temperature variation of C_V is known, the entropy change during an isochoric process may be calculated from the equation

$$S_f - S_i \text{ (isochoric)} = \int_i^f \frac{C_V}{T}\,dT.$$

Similarly, for an isobaric process,

$$S_f - S_i \text{ (isobaric)} = \int_i^f \frac{C_P}{T}\,dT.$$

The above equations provide a general method for calculating an entropy change but no way of calculating the absolute entropy of a system in a given state. If a set of tables is required that is to be used to obtain entropy differences and not absolute entropy, then it is a convenient procedure to choose an arbitrary standard state and calculate the entropy change of the system from this standard state to all other states. Thus, in the case of water, the standard state is chosen to be that of saturated water at 0.01°C and its own vapor pressure 4.58 mm, and all entropies are referred to this state.

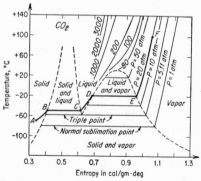

FIG. 11.12. T-S diagram for CO_2. The two dashed lines bounding the solid-liquid region are a guess.

The T-S diagram for a substance such as CO_2 is shown in Fig. 11.12.

The curve from A to F is a typical isobar representing a series of reversible isobaric processes in which solid is transformed finally into vapor. Thus,

AB = isobaric heating of solid to its melting point
BC = isobaric isothermal melting
CD = isobaric heating of liquid to its boiling point
DE = isobaric isothermal vaporization
EF = isobaric heating of vapor (superheating)

The area under the line BC represents the heat of fusion at the particular temperature, and the area under the line DE represents the heat

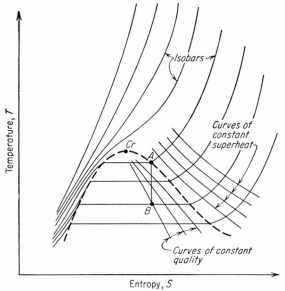

FIG. 11.13. T-S diagram for wet and for superheated steam.

of vaporization. Similarly, the heat of sublimation is represented by the area under any sublimation line. It is obvious from the diagram that the heat of vaporization decreases as the temperature rises and becomes zero at the critical point and also that the heat of sublimation is equal to the sum of the heat of fusion and the heat of vaporization at the triple point.

The T-S diagram for the liquid, liquid-vapor, and vapor regions of water is of some interest to engineers. In Fig. 11.13 such a diagram is shown with isobars, lines of constant quality, and lines of constant superheat. It should be noted that saturated steam such as is indicated at point A, expanding reversibly and adiabatically (isentropically) to the point B, becomes wet, the quality of the steam, or dryness, decreasing the greater the expansion. This is not true for all substances. For example, in the case of benzene, it is evident from the T-S diagram shown in Fig. 11.14 that an isentropic expansion from a saturation point A to a point B causes the vapor to become unsaturated.

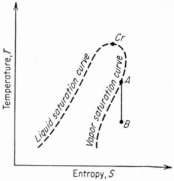

11.9. Gibbs U-V-S Surface. For an infinitesimal process, we have

$$dU = dQ - P\,dV.$$

If the process takes place between two neighboring equilibrium states, we may assume it to be reversible, whence

$$\boxed{dU = T\,dS - P\,dV.}$$

FIG. 11.14. T-S diagram for benzene.

Regarding U as a function of S and V, we may write

$$dU = \left(\frac{\partial U}{\partial S}\right)_V dS + \left(\frac{\partial U}{\partial V}\right)_S dV,$$

from which it follows that

$$\left(\frac{\partial U}{\partial S}\right)_V = T, \qquad \left(\frac{\partial U}{\partial V}\right)_S = -P.$$

It is clear from the above that a surface, generated by plotting U, S, and V, would also indicate the temperature and pressure from the two slopes

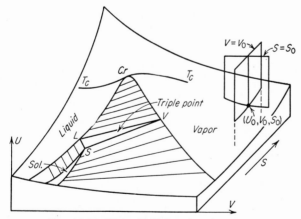

FIG. 11.15. Gibbs U-V-S surface for water.

at any given point. Gibbs was the first to consider such a surface and to point out its interesting properties. A rough diagram of a U-V-S surface for water is given in Fig. 11.15.

Imagine a plane at $S = S_0$ cutting the surface, the intersection being a particular curve whose equation involves U and V. The slope of this curve at some point on the curve, say (U_0, V_0, S_0) is $(\partial U/\partial V)_0$, and the equation of the line tangent to the curve at this point is

$$U - U_0 - \left(\frac{\partial U}{\partial V}\right)_0 (V' - V_0) = 0.$$

Again, upon cutting the surface with a plane at $V = V_0$, a curve is obtained the equation of whose tangent line at the point (U_0, V_0, S_0) is

$$U - U_0 - \left(\frac{\partial U}{\partial S}\right)_0 (S - S_0) = 0.$$

Now the plane that is tangent to the surface at the point (U_0, V_0, S_0) contains these two intersecting tangent lines. Therefore the equation of the plane tangent to the surface at the point (U_0, V_0, S_0) is

$$U - U_0 - \left(\frac{\partial U}{\partial V}\right)_0 (V - V_0) - \left(\frac{\partial U}{\partial S}\right)_0 (S - S_0) = 0.$$

Calling P_0 and T_0 the pressure and temperature, respectively, at the point in question, we have

$$\left(\frac{\partial U}{\partial V}\right)_0 = -P_0,$$

$$\left(\frac{\partial U}{\partial S}\right)_0 = T_0,$$

and the equation of the tangent plane becomes

$$U - U_0 + P_0(V - V_0) - T_0(S - S_0) = 0.$$

Consequently, the P and T of a point determine uniquely a tangent plane at the point. If two different points on the surface therefore refer to the same pressure and temperature, they must both touch the same tangent plane. Further, if P and T are constant along a curve, this whole curve touches the tangent plane and is therefore a straight line. An isothermal isobaric vaporization must therefore be a straight line. Since the whole liquid-vapor region is constructed of such lines, it is a ruled surface. The same is also true of the other two mixture regions. Since all proportions of solid, liquid, and vapor at the triple point exist at the same pressure and temperature, it is clear that the tangent plane determined by this P and T must touch all these points, or, in other words, *the triple point on a U-V-S surface is a plane triangle.* A tangent plane touches the surface in the solid region or the vapor region or the liquid region at only one point.

It should be emphasized that the surface depicted qualitatively in Fig. 11.15 represents only equilibrium states of water. The original surface contemplated by Gibbs included metastable states such as those corresponding to supercooled vapor and supercooled liquid. A model showing these metastable states was first made by Maxwell during Gibbs's lifetime and was presented to him. This model is in the possession of Yale University. A better model of this type was made in 1939 by Clark and Katz. For further details about this surface, the student is referred to the paper by Clark and Katz in the *Transactions of the Royal Society of Canada*, Third Series, Sec. III, Vol. 32, 1939.

11.10. Enthalpy. The enthalpy of a system is defined as

$$H = U + PV.$$

In order to study the properties of this function, consider the change in enthalpy that takes place when a system undergoes an infinitesimal process from an initial equilibrium state to a final equilibrium state. We have

$$dH = dU + P\,dV + V\,dP.$$

But $\qquad\qquad\qquad dQ = dU + P\,dV;$

therefore $\qquad\qquad dH = dQ + V\,dP.$

Dividing both sides by dT,

$$\frac{dH}{dT} = \frac{dQ}{dT} + V\frac{dP}{dT}$$

and, at constant P,

$$\left(\frac{\partial H}{\partial T}\right)_P = \left(\frac{dQ}{dT}\right)_P = C_P \qquad \text{[property (1)].}$$

Since

$$dH = dQ + V\,dP,$$

the change in enthalpy during an isobaric process is equal to the heat that is transferred. That is,

$$\left.\begin{aligned} & H_f - H_i = Q \\[1em] \text{or} \\[1em] & H_f - H_i = \int_i^f C_P\,dT \end{aligned}\right\} \quad \text{(isobaric) [property (2)].}$$

Since isobaric processes are much more important in engineering and chemistry than isovolumic processes, the enthalpy is of greatest use in these branches of science.

The change in enthalpy of a system undergoing an adiabatic process has an interesting graphical interpretation. Since

$$dH = dQ + V\,dP,$$

then, for an adiabatic process,

$$H_f - H_i = \int_i^f V\,dP \qquad \text{(adiabatic) [property (3)].}$$

The above integral represents the area to the left of an adiabatic curve on a P-V diagram.   This area does *not* represent work.

One of the most interesting properties of the enthalpy function is in connection with a *throttling process*.   Imagine a cylinder thermally insulated and equipped with two nonconducting pistons on opposite sides of a porous wall, as shown in Fig. 11.16(i).   The wall, shaded in horizontal lines, is a porous plug, a narrow constriction, or a series of small holes. Between the left-hand piston and the wall there is a gas at a pressure P_i and a volume V_i; and since the right-hand piston is against the wall, any gas being thus prevented from seeping through, the initial state of the gas is an equilibrium state.   Now imagine moving both pistons simultaneously in such a way that a *constant pressure* P_i is maintained on the left-hand side of the wall and a *constant lower pressure* P_f is maintained on the right-hand side.   After all the gas has seeped through the porous wall, the final equilibrium state of the system will be as shown in Fig. 11.16(f).   Such a process is a throttling process.

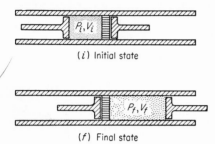

(i) Initial state

(f) Final state

Fig. 11.16. Throttling process.

A throttling process is obviously an irreversible one since the gas passes through nonequilibrium states on its way from the initial equilibrium state to its final equilibrium state.   These nonequilibrium states cannot be described by thermodynamic coordinates, but an interesting conclusion can be drawn about the initial and final equilibrium states.   Applying the first law to the throttling process

$$Q = U_f - U_i + W,$$

we have $Q = 0$

and $$W = \int_0^{V_f} P\,dV + \int_{V_i}^0 P\,dV.$$

Since both pressures remain constant,

$$W = P_f V_f - P_i V_i.$$

The above expression is known in engineering as *flow work*, since it represents the work necessary to keep the gas flowing.   Therefore

$$0 = U_f - U_i + P_f V_f - P_i V_i$$

or $$U_i + P_i V_i = U_f + P_f V_f,$$

and finally

$$H_i = H_f \qquad \text{(throttling process) [property (4)]}.$$

In a throttling process, therefore, the initial and final enthalpies are equal. One is not entitled to say that the enthalpy remains constant since one cannot speak of the enthalpy of a system that is passing through such nonequilibrium states.   In plotting a throttling process on any diagram the initial and final equilibrium states may be represented by points. The intermediate states, however, cannot be plotted.

A continuous throttling process may be achieved by a pump that maintains a constant high pressure on one side of a constriction or porous

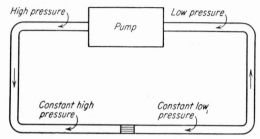

Fig. 11.17. Apparatus for performing a continuous throttling process.

wall and a constant lower pressure on the other side, as shown in Fig. 11.17.   For every unit of mass that undergoes the throttling process, we may write

$$h_i = h_f$$

where the lower-case letters indicate *specific enthalpy*.

TABLE 11.5. COMPARISON OF U AND H

Internal energy U	Enthalpy H
In general $$dU = \text{d}Q - P\,dV$$ $$\left(\frac{\partial U}{\partial T}\right)_V = C_V$$	In general $$dH = \text{d}Q + V\,dP$$ $$\left(\frac{\partial H}{\partial T}\right)_P = C_P$$
Isochoric process $$U_f - U_i = Q$$ $$U_f - U_i = \int_i^f C_V\,dT$$	Isobaric process $$H_f - H_i = Q$$ $$H_f - H_i = \int_i^f C_P\,dT$$
Adiabatic process $$U_f - U_i = -\int_i^f P\,dV$$	Adiabatic process $$H_f - H_i = \int_i^f V\,dP$$
Free expansion $$U_i = U_f$$	Throttling process $$H_i = H_f$$
For an ideal gas $$U = \int C_V\,dT + \text{const.}$$	For an ideal gas $$H = \int C_P\,dT + \text{const.}$$

The four properties of the enthalpy function must be clearly under-stood by the student, for they will be used continually throughout the remainder of this book. The comparison of the internal energy and the enthalpy given in Table 11.5 will help the student to remember these properties.

11.11. Mollier Chart. The properties of the enthalpy function enable one to calculate the change in enthalpy in going from any initial state to any final state, but not to calculate an absolute enthalpy. In order to construct tables of enthalpy it is necessary to choose a standard state the enthalpy at which is arbitrarily designated as zero and in refer-ence to which all other enthalpies are expressed. Such tables may be used to determine enthalpy differences, but one enthalpy will have no meaning. In the case of water the standard state is chosen to be the low-pressure triple point.

We have derived that

$$dH = đQ + V\,dP$$

for an infinitesimal process between two neighboring equilibrium states. Since such a process may be regarded as reversible,

$$đQ = T\,dS$$

and

$$\boxed{dH = T\,dS + V\,dP.}$$

Now H is a function of any two convenient coordinates. Suppose that H is expressed as a function of S and P. Then

$$dH = \left(\frac{\partial H}{\partial S}\right)_P dS + \left(\frac{\partial H}{\partial P}\right)_S dP.$$

Comparing this equation with the preceding one, we get

$$\left(\frac{\partial H}{\partial S}\right)_P = T, \qquad \left(\frac{\partial H}{\partial P}\right)_S = V.$$

The first of these equations shows that the slope of an isobaric curve on an H-S diagram is the Kelvin temperature. An H-S diagram is called a *Mollier diagram*. Figure 11.18 represents a rough sketch of a Mollier diagram for a pure substance such as water. The curve $ABCDEF$ repre-sents a typical reversible isobaric transition from solid at A to vapor at F. Thus,

$AB =$ isobaric heating of solid to melting point (slope increasing)
$BC =$ isobaric isothermal melting of solid (slope constant)
$CD =$ isobaric heating of liquid to boiling point (slope increasing)
$DE =$ isobaric isothermal vaporization of liquid (slope constant)
$EF =$ isobaric superheating of vapor (slope increasing)

All sublimation, fusion, and vaporization lines are straight lines—the higher the temperature, the steeper the slope.

An interesting surface is obtained when H, S, and P are plotted along rectangular axes. A rough sketch of such a surface for water is shown

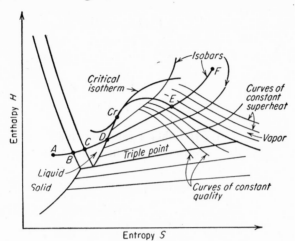

Fig. 11.18. Mollier diagram for water.

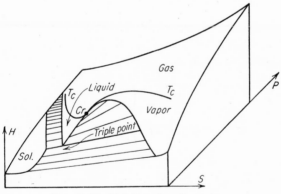

Fig. 11.19. H-S-P surface for water.

in Fig. 11.19. Since

$$\left(\frac{\partial H}{\partial S}\right)_P = T, \qquad \left(\frac{\partial H}{\partial P}\right)_S = V,$$

T and V are indicated at any point by the two slopes that determine a plane tangent to the surface at the point.

11.12. Helmholtz Function. The Helmholtz function is defined as

$$A = U - TS.$$

For an infinitesimal reversible process,

$$dA = dU - T\,dS - S\,dT,$$
and
$$T\,dS = dU + P\,dV.$$

Hence,
$$dA = -P\,dV - S\,dT.$$

From this it follows: (1) For a *reversible isothermal process*,

$$dA = -P\,dV$$
or
$$A_f - A_i = -\int_i^f P\,dV.$$

Hence the change of the Helmholtz function during a reversible isothermal process equals the work done *on* the system.   (2) For a *reversible, isothermal, and isochoric process*,

$$dA = 0$$
or
$$A = \text{const.}$$

These properties are of interest in chemistry and are useful in considering chemical reactions that take place isothermally and isochorically. The main importance, however, of the Helmholtz function is its use in statistical mechanics, where it plays a fundamental role. It is possible by statistical methods to calculate the Helmholtz function of some substances as a function of T and V. The equation of state of a substance is then obtained from the relationship

$$P = -\left(\frac{\partial A}{\partial V}\right)_T$$

and the entropy from

$$S = -\left(\frac{\partial A}{\partial T}\right)_V.$$

11.13. Gibbs Function. The Gibbs function is defined as

$$G = H - TS.$$

For an infinitesimal reversible process,

$$dG = dH - T\,dS - S\,dT.$$

It will be recalled, however, that

$$dH = T\,dS + V\,dP,$$

whence
$$dG = V\,dP - S\,dT.$$

In the case of a *reversible, isothermal, isobaric process,*

$$dG = 0,$$

and
$$G = \text{const.}$$

This is a particularly important result in connection with processes involving a change of phase. Sublimation, fusion, and vaporization take place isothermally and isobarically and can be conceived of as occurring reversibly. Hence, during such processes, the Gibbs function of the system remains constant. If we denote by the symbols g', g'', and g''' the molar Gibbs functions of a saturated solid, saturated liquid, and saturated vapor, respectively, then the equation of the fusion curve is

$$g' = g'',$$

the equation of the vaporization curve is

$$g'' = g''',$$

and the equation of the sublimation curve is

$$g' = g'''.$$

At the triple point two equations hold simultaneously, namely,

$$g' = g'' = g'''.$$

All the g's can be regarded as functions of P and T only, and hence the two equations above serve to determine the P and the T of the triple point uniquely.

The Gibbs function is of the utmost importance in chemistry since chemical reactions can be conceived of as taking place at constant P and T. It is also of some use in engineering.

11.14. Names and Symbols for the Thermodynamic Functions. No science has developed in neat, logical steps. The history of any science shows periods of tremendous growth in which many research workers throughout the world try, discard, and try again new ideas, new definitions, and new symbols. In thermodynamics this situation has been aggravated by the fact that many workers have borne in mind only the particular needs of a special branch of thermodynamics, such as engineering or chemical thermodynamics, without attempting to adopt a point of view suitable for all branches. It is not surprising, therefore, that there are many different names and symbols for the thermodynamic functions.

Practically all authors of modern textbooks are agreed upon the name entropy and the symbol S. For the internal-energy function both E and U are used about equally often. Since neither E nor U is ever used to designate any other function, there is no objection in retaining these two letters as alternate symbols.

The symbol for enthalpy is almost invariably H, but there are three other names that are widely used: heat content, total heat, and heat function. It is the opinion of the author that to designate this function by any expression involving the word "heat" is objectionable, for two reasons: (1) The beginner is apt to receive the erroneous impression that heat, in general, is a function or that a body has a certain amount of heat in it. (2) The change in enthalpy is the heat transferred *only for an isobaric process*. If, for this reason, the enthalpy is called the "heat function at constant pressure," then, to be consistent, we should have to call U the "heat function for constant volume." Since, however, the change in internal energy is equal to the work done in an adiabatic process, we should then have as an alternative name for internal energy the "adiabatic work function." Although the idea of assigning to a function a name that suggests a property of the function is an appealing one, the fact remains that the thermodynamic functions have *many* properties, and it is not satisfactory to choose one property for the purpose of nomenclature.

The situation with regard to the Helmholtz and Gibbs functions is really serious and has led to great confusion and error in calculations, as is shown in the accompanying table.

	Helmholtz function	Gibbs function
Most American chemists....	Work function A	Free energy F
Many physicists............	Free energy F	Thermodynamic potential G
Compromise suggested by several symbols committees.	Helmholtz function A	Gibbs function G

Space is lacking to discuss the arguments for and against these names and symbols. The deplorable fact remains that many physicists and chemists use the same name and the same symbol for two entirely different functions. The only feasible solution, in the opinion of the author, is to compromise by selecting unambiguous, noncommittal names and symbols, giving up entirely the expression "free energy" and the symbol F.

PROBLEMS

11.1. A small amount of liquid is introduced into a glass tube, all air is removed, and the tube is sealed off. Describe the behavior of the meniscus when the temperature of the system is raised,

(a) If the volume of the tube is much greater than the critical volume.

(b) If the volume of the tube is much less than the critical volume.

(c) If the volume of the tube is only slightly different from the critical volume.

11.2. A piece of ice at 0°C is placed alongside of a beaker of water at 0°C in a glass vessel, from which all air has been removed. If the ice, water, and vessel are all maintained at a temperature of 0°C by a suitable thermostat, describe the final equilibrium state inside the vessel.

11.3. A mass m of pure substance is placed in a tube of constant volume V. If there are two phases present, show that

(a) The volume occupied by one phase will be

$$V_1 = \frac{m - \rho_2 V}{\rho_1 - \rho_2},$$

where ρ_1, V_1, and ρ_2, V_2 are the densities and volumes, respectively, of the two phases.

(b) The condition that V_1 will not change as the temperature is increased is given by

$$\frac{V_1}{V_2} = - \frac{d\rho_2/dT}{d\rho_1/dT}.$$

11.4. Using the Dieterici equation of state

$$P = \frac{RT}{v - b} e^{-\frac{a}{RTv}},$$

show that

$$P_c = \frac{a}{4e^2 b^2}, \qquad v_c = 2b, \qquad T_c = \frac{a}{4Rb},$$

and compare the numerical value of $RT_c/P_c v_c$ with the experimental values in Table 11.4.

11.5. Using the Berthelot equation of state

$$P = \frac{RT}{v - b} - \frac{a}{Tv^2},$$

show that

$$P_c = \frac{1}{12b} \sqrt{\frac{2aR}{3b}}, \qquad v_c = 3b, \qquad T_c = \sqrt{\frac{8a}{27bR}},$$

and compare the numerical value of $RT_c/P_c v_c$ with the experimental values in Table 11.4.

11.6. If P, v, T are the actual pressure, volume, and temperature of a gas; P_c, v_c, T_c, the critical pressure, volume, and temperature, then the reduced pressure P_R, the reduced volume v_R, and the reduced temperature T_R are defined as

$$P_R = \frac{P}{P_c}, \qquad v_R = \frac{v}{v_c}, \qquad T_R = \frac{T}{T_c}.$$

Show that, in terms of reduced quantities, the van der Waals equation becomes

$$\left(P_R + \frac{3}{v_R^2} \right) \left(v_R - \frac{1}{3} \right) = \frac{8}{3} T_R.$$

11.7. Expand both the van der Waals and the Dieterici equations of state in the form

$$Pv = RT \left(1 + \frac{B''}{v} + \frac{C''}{v^2} + \cdots \right),$$

and show that, in both cases the second virial coefficient B'' is given by

$$B'' = b - \frac{a}{RT}.$$

11.8. (a) The entropy of saturated water at 100°C is given in the tables as 0.31 cal/gm · deg and that of saturated steam at the same temperature as 1.76 cal/gm · deg. What is the heat of vaporization at this temperature?

(b) The enthalpy of saturated steam at 100°C is given in the tables as 640 cal/gm. From (a) calculate the enthalpy of saturated water at this temperature.

(c) Calculate the Gibbs function of saturated water and of saturated vapor at 100°C, and verify the fact that the two are equal.

11.9. (a) With the aid of a Mollier diagram, show that, when a saturated liquid undergoes a throttling process, cooling and partial vaporization result.

(b) The pressure of CO_2 at the triple point is about 5 atm. Show with the aid of a Mollier diagram that, if saturated liquid CO_2 at room temperature undergoes a throttling process to atmospheric pressure, "dry ice" will be formed.

11.10. Show that, for an ideal gas,

(a) $A = \int C_V \, dT - T \int \frac{C_V}{T} \, dT - nRT \ln V - \text{const.} \ T + \text{const.}$

(b) $G = \int C_P \, dT - T \int \frac{C_P}{T} \, dT + nRT \ln P - \text{const.} \ T + \text{const.}$

(c) Apply the above equations to 1 mole of an ideal monatomic gas.

11.11. Defining the *Massieu function J* by the equation

$$J = -\frac{U}{T} + S,$$

show that

$$dJ = \frac{U}{T^2} \, dT + \frac{P}{T} \, dV.$$

11.12. Defining the *Planck function K* by the equation

$$K = -\frac{H}{T} + S,$$

show that

$$dK = \frac{H}{T^2} \, dT - \frac{V}{T} \, dP.$$

12

The Steam Engine
and the Refrigerator

12.1. Steam Engine. A schematic diagram of an elementary steam power plant is shown in Fig. 12.1. The operation of such a plant can be understood by following the pressure and volume changes of a small constant mass of water as it is conveyed from the condenser, through the boiler, into the expansion chamber, and back to the condenser. The water in the condenser is at a pressure less than atmospheric and at a temperature less than the normal boiling point. By means of a pump it is introduced into the boiler, which is at a much higher pressure and temperature. In the boiler the water is first heated to its boiling point and then vaporized, both processes taking place approximately at constant pressure. The steam is then superheated at the same pressure. It is then allowed to flow into a cylinder, where it expands approximately adiabatically against a piston, or a set of turbine blades, until its pressure and temperature drop to that of the condenser. In the condenser, finally, the steam condenses into water at the same temperature and pressure as at the beginning, and the cycle is complete.

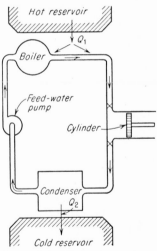

Fig. 12.1. Elementary steam power plant.

In the actual operation of the steam plant there are several processes that render an exact analysis difficult. These are:

1. Acceleration and turbulence caused by the difference of pressure required to cause the flow of the steam from one part of the apparatus to another.

2. Friction.

3. Conduction of heat through the walls during the expansion of the steam.

4. Irreversible heat transfers due to a finite temperature difference between the furnace and the boiler.

A first approximation to the solution of the problem of the steam plant may be made by introducing some simplifying assumptions that, although in no way realizable in practice, provide at least an upper limit to the efficiency of such a plant, and that define a cycle called the *Rankine cycle*, in terms of which the actual behavior of a steam plant may be discussed. The Rankine cycle bears about the same relation to the actual steam

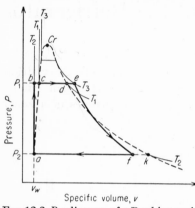

plant as the air-standard Otto cycle does to the automobile engine.

12.2. Rankine Cycle. In Fig. 12.2 three isotherms of water are shown on a P-v diagram, one at T_2 corresponding to the temperature of the condenser, another at T_1 the temperature of the boiler, and a third at a still higher temperature T_3. The dashed curves are the liquid and the vapor saturation curves, respectively. The lower-case letter v is used because it repre-

FIG. 12.2. P-v diagram of a Rankine cycle.

sents the specific volume, i.e., volume per pound. In the Rankine cycle all processes are assumed to be reversible, complications that arise from acceleration, turbulence, friction, and irreversible heat transfers being thus eliminated. Starting at the point a representing the state of 1 lb of saturated liquid water at the temperature and pressure of the condenser, the Rankine cycle comprises the following six processes:

1. $a \rightarrow b$, reversible adiabatic compression of water to the pressure of the boiler P_1 (only a very small change of temperature takes place during this process).

2. $b \rightarrow c$, reversible isobaric heating of water to the boiling point.

3. $c \rightarrow d$, reversible isobaric isothermal vaporization of water into saturated steam.

4. $d \rightarrow e$, reversible isobaric superheating of steam into superheated steam at temperature T_3.

5. $e \rightarrow f$, reversible adiabatic expansion of steam into wet steam.

6. $f \rightarrow a$, reversible isobaric isothermal condensation of steam into saturated water.

During the process $b \rightarrow c$ the substance is imagined to be in contact with a series of reservoirs ranging from a temperature T_2 to a temperature T_1, receiving a small amount of heat from each reservoir. During $c \to d$ there is a flow of heat from one reservoir at T_1, and during $d \to e$ heat is transferred from a series of reservoirs at temperatures ranging from T_1 to T_3. During the condensation process $f \to a$, heat is rejected to a reservoir at the temperature T_2.

Let q_1 denote the total amount of heat absorbed per pound during the three processes $b \to c$, $c \to d$, and $d \to e$. Since all these processes take place at constant pressure,

$$q_1 = h_e - h_b.$$

Similarly, the heat q_2 rejected during the process $f \to a$ (q_2 being treated as a positive quantity) is

$$q_2 = h_f - h_a.$$

Therefore the efficiency is

$$\eta = \frac{q_1 - q_2}{q_1}$$
$$= \frac{h_e - h_b - h_f + h_a}{h_e - h_b}.$$

If h_b is not readily obtainable in the steam tables, it may be expressed in terms of quantities that are listed there. Since $a \to b$ represents an adiabatic process, the area to the left of $a \to b$ is equal to the change of enthalpy, or

$$h_b - h_a = \int_a^b v\, dP.$$

Now, v is practically constant during the process $a \to b$; hence

$$h_b - h_a = v_w(P_1 - P_2)$$

where v_w is the volume of a pound of water in the condenser. Substituting for h_b, we get finally

$$\eta = \frac{h_e - h_f - (P_1 - P_2)v_w}{h_e - h_a - (P_1 - P_2)v_w}.$$

The expression $(P_1 - P_2)v_w$ is known as the *feed-pump term*.

12.3. Steam Tables. The properties of water and steam are tabulated in the steam tables for all states corresponding to points on the saturation lines and in the superheat region, but not in the mixture region. A horizontal row of numbers in the steam tables refers to one pressure. Excerpts from typical steam tables are given in Table 12.1 for two different pressures. v stands for specific volume in cubic feet per pound, h for specific enthalpy in Btu per pound, and s for specific entropy in Btu per pound degree F. The values of h and s are computed on the basis that h and s of saturated water at 32°F and at the corresponding vapor pressure 0.0887 lb/in.^{2} are zero.

TABLE 12.1. EXCERPTS FROM STEAM TABLES

Pressure and corresponding saturation temperature		Saturated water	Saturated steam	120°	200°	220°	240°
1 lb/in.^{2} corresponding to saturation temperature of 101.74°F	v	0.02	333.6	344.6	392.6	404.5	416.5
	h	69.7	1106.0	1114.3	1150.4	1159.5	1168.5
	s	0.1326	1.9782	1.9928	2.0512	2.0647	2.0779

Pressure and corresponding saturation temperature		Saturated water	Saturated steam	420°	440°	460°	480°
300 lb/in^2 corresponding to saturation temperature of 417.33°F	v	0.0189	1.5433	1.5513	1.6090	1.6638	1.7165
	h	393.8	1202.8	1204.8	1219.1	1232.5	1245.3
	s	0.5879	1.5104	1.5126	1.5286	1.5434	1.5572

To calculate the efficiency of the Rankine cycle in any actual case where

$$\eta = \frac{h_e - h_f - (P_1 - P_2)v_w}{h_e - h_a - (P_1 - P_2)v_w},$$

the values of h_e (in the superheat region), h_a (on the liquid saturation line), and v_w (also on the liquid saturation line) may be found in the tables. The value of h_f, however, in the mixture region, is not listed. It can be calculated as follows: At all points along the line $k \rightarrow a$ (isothermal isobaric condensation of steam) the Gibbs function of the system remains constant (see Art. 11.13). Thus

$$g_f = g_k$$

or

$$h_f - T_2 s_f = h_k - T_2 s_k.$$

But since the process $e \rightarrow f$ is isentropic,

$$s_f = s_e,$$

whence

$$h_f = h_k - T_2(s_k - s_e)$$

and h_f can be calculated in terms of quantities all of which are listed in the steam tables.

As a numerical example, consider the following simple problem: Calculate the efficiency of an engine operating in a Rankine cycle with a boiler pressure of 300 lb/in.^{2} and a boiler temperature of 480°F, the temperature of the condenser being 101.74°F.   From the preceding tables,

$$h_a = \begin{cases} \text{enthalpy per lb of saturated liquid at saturation pres-} \\ \text{sure of 1 lb/in.}^2 \text{ corresponding to a saturation temper-} \\ \text{ature of 101.74°F} \end{cases}$$

$$= 69.7 \text{ Btu/lb.}$$

$$h_e = \begin{cases} \text{enthalpy per lb of superheated vapor at pressure of} \\ \text{300 lb/in.}^2 \text{ and temperature 480°F} \end{cases}$$

$$= 1245.3 \text{ Btu/lb.}$$

$$h_f = \text{enthalpy per lb of wet vapor} = h_k - T_2(s_k - s_e)$$
$$= 1106.0 \ \text{Btu/lb} - (102 + 460) \ \text{deg} \ (1.9782 - 1.5572)$$
$$\text{Btu/lb} \cdot \text{deg}$$
$$= 869 \text{ Btu/lb.}$$

$$v_w(P_1 - P_2) = \frac{0.02 \text{ ft}^3/\text{lb} \ (300 - 1) \text{ lb/in.}^2 \times 144 \text{ in.}^2/\text{ft}^2}{778 \text{ ft} \cdot \text{lb/Btu}}$$

$$= 1.11 \text{ Btu/lb.}$$

$$\eta = \frac{1245 - 869 - 1.11}{1245 - 69.7 - 1.11} = 0.32 = 32 \text{ per cent.}$$

In the actual steam plant there are so many irreversible processes that the efficiency is much lower.   In this simple plant an efficiency of about 10 or 15 per cent might be expected.

If x_f denotes the quality of the steam at the end of the expansion stroke at f, then the mixture contains x_f lb of vapor and $1 - x_f$ lb of liquid.   The entropy at f is therefore

$$s_f = x_f s_k + (1 - x_f)s_a$$

But
$$s_f = s_e,$$

whence, solving for x_f,

$$x_f = \frac{s_e - s_a}{s_k - s_a}.$$

In the preceding problem,

$$x_f = \frac{1.5572 - 0.1326}{1.9782 - 0.1326} = 0.77 = 77 \text{ per cent dry.}$$

12.4. T-s and h-s Diagrams of Rankine Cycle.   The T-s diagram of a Rankine cycle is shown in Fig. 12.3.   It should be noted that the points a and b are practically coincident since the process $a \to b$ (forcing the water into the boiler), being reversible and adiabatic, involves no entropy change and only a small temperature change.

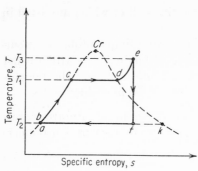

FIG. 12.3. T-s diagram of a Rankine cycle.   FIG. 12.4. Mollier diagram of a Rankine cycle.

The most useful diagram for representing a Rankine cycle is the Mollier diagram given in Fig. 12.4. It has already been shown that

$$\left(\frac{\partial h}{\partial s}\right)_P = T,$$

or the slope of an isobaric on a Mollier diagram is the Kelvin temperature. Since the processes $b \to c$, $c \to d$, and $d \to e$ are all isobaric, it is clear that:

1. The slope of $b \to c$ increases from about T_2 to T_1.
2. The slope of $c \to d$ remains constant at T_1.
3. The slope of $d \to e$ increases from T_1 to T_3.

Mollier diagrams for steam showing isothermals, isobarics, lines of constant superheat, and lines of constant quality are usually included with the steam tables. On such a chart all the quantities necessary for the calculation of the efficiency of the Rankine cycle can be read off, and no extra calculations are necessary.

12.5. Principles of Refrigeration. The purpose of a refrigerator is to extract as much heat as possible from a cold reservoir with the expenditure of as little work as possible. The "output," so to speak, is the heat extracted from the cold reservoir, and the "input" is work. A convenient measure, therefore, of the performance of a refrigerator is expressed by the *coefficient of performance* ω, where

$$\omega = \frac{\text{heat extracted from the cold reservoir}}{\text{work done on the refrigerant}}.$$

If, in one or more cycles, heat Q_2 is extracted from the cold reservoir and work W is done,

$$\omega = \frac{Q_2}{W} = \frac{Q_2}{Q_1 - Q_2},$$

and, in the special case of a Carnot refrigerator, where the Q's are proportional to the Kelvin temperatures,

$$\omega_R = \frac{T_2}{T_1 - T_2} \qquad \text{(Carnot refrigerator).}$$

Consider a refrigerator that extracts heat Q_2 from a reservoir at T_2, has work W done on it, and rejects heat $Q_2 + W$ to a hotter reservoir at T_1. Since the refrigerant has undergone a cycle, its entropy change is zero, and therefore the total entropy change of the universe is merely the sum of the entropy changes of the hot and cold reservoirs. Hence, applying the entropy principle,

$$\frac{W + Q_2}{T_1} - \frac{Q_2}{T_2} \geq 0,$$

or

$$W + Q_2 \left(1 - \frac{T_1}{T_2}\right) \geq 0,$$

or

$$W \geq Q_2 \left(\frac{T_1 - T_2}{T_2}\right),$$

whence

$$W \text{ (min)} = \frac{Q_2}{\dfrac{T_2}{T_1 - T_2}} = \frac{Q_2}{\omega_R},$$

which shows that the minimum amount of work is required by a Carnot refrigerator, or that a Carnot refrigerator has the maximum coefficient of performance.

In practical problems on refrigeration, however, particularly those involving gas liquefaction, the body from which heat is to be extracted is not a reservoir but a substance of finite mass whose temperature decreases during the operation of the refrigerator. In such cases, it is often necessary to calculate the minimum work to perform a given amount of refrigeration in order to estimate the operating cost of the plant. This is easily done as follows: Suppose that a refrigerator operating in a cycle extracts heat Q from a body of finite mass, thus lowering its temperature to T_2. If work W is done, then heat $W + Q$ is rejected to the hotter reservoir at T_1. Applying the entropy principle,

$$\frac{W + Q}{T_1} - (S_i - S_2) \geq 0,$$

where $S_i - S_2$ is the decrease in entropy of the body. Hence

$$W \geq T_1(S_i - S_2) - Q,$$

and the minimum amount of work is

$$W \text{ (min)} = T_1(S_i - S_2) - Q.$$

If the body remains at constant pressure during the refrigeration, $Q = H_i - H_2$, and

$$W \text{ (min)} = T_1(S_i - S_2) - (H_i - H_2).$$

12.6. Refrigeration Cycle. A schematic diagram of an elementary refrigeration plant is shown in Fig. 12.5. As usual, we consider the pressure and volume changes of a constant mass of fluid as it is conveyed from the liquid storage, where it is at the temperature and pressure of the condenser through the throttling valve, through the evaporator, into the compressor, and finally back to the condenser.

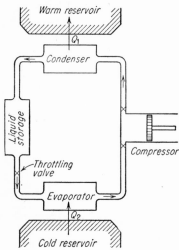

FIG. 12.5. Elementary refrigeration plant.

In the condenser the refrigerant is at a high pressure and at as low a temperature as can be obtained with air or water cooling. The refrigerant is always of such a nature that, at this pressure and temperature, it is a saturated liquid. It can be seen from the Mollier diagram that, when a saturated liquid undergoes a throttling process, cooling and partial vaporization are bound to take place. In the evaporator it is completely vaporized, the heat of vaporization being supplied by the materials to be cooled. The vapor is then compressed approximately isentropically, thus suffering a rise of temperature and becoming a superheated vapor. In the condenser the superheated vapor is cooled until it condenses and becomes completely liquefied.

Complications due to irreversible processes involving turbulence, acceleration, friction, finite temperature differences, etc., will be eliminated as usual by idealizing the refrigeration plant and describing an *ideal refrigeration cycle.*

In Fig. 12.6 three isotherms of a fluid such as ammonia are shown on a *P-v* diagram, one at T_1, corresponding to the temperature of the condenser, another at T_2, the temperature of the evaporator, and a third at T_3, the temperature attained

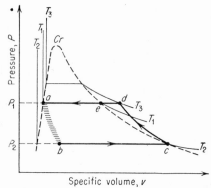

FIG. 12.6. *P-v* diagram of the refrigeration cycle.

at the end of the compression.   We shall assume that all processes *except the throttling process* are reversible.

Starting at the point a representing the state of 1 lb of saturated liquid at the temperature and pressure of the condenser, the refrigeration cycle comprises the following five processes:

1. $a \rightarrow b$, *irreversible* throttling process involving a drop of pressure and temperature.   Only the initial and final states can be plotted.

2. $b \rightarrow c$, reversible isothermal isobaric vaporization.

3. $c \rightarrow d$, reversible adiabatic compression.

4. $d \rightarrow e$, reversible isobaric cooling of superheated vapor until saturated.

5. $e \rightarrow a$, reversible isothermal isobaric condensation of vapor to saturated liquid.

During the process $b \rightarrow c$, the refrigerant is imagined to be in contact with a reservoir at T_2 from which heat is extracted.   During the process

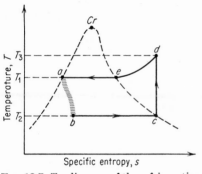

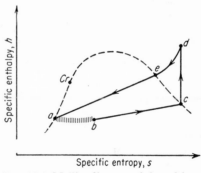

Fig. 12.7. *T-s* diagram of the refrigeration cycle.

Fig. 12.8. Mollier diagram of the refrigeration cycle.

$d \rightarrow e$, the refrigerant is imagined in contact with a series of reservoirs at temperatures from T_3 to T_1 to each of which a small amount of heat is supplied.   Finally, during the process $e \rightarrow a$, heat is transferred from the refrigerant to a reservoir at the temperature T_1.

The *T-s* diagram of the refrigeration cycle is shown in Fig. 12.7 and the Mollier diagram in Fig. 12.8.   The student should have no difficulty in understanding these diagrams without any explanation.

12.7. Coefficient of Performance.   The coefficient of performance of a refrigerator has been defined as

$$\omega = \frac{\text{heat removed from lower reservoir } q_2}{\text{net work done during the cycle } w}$$

or

$$\omega = \frac{q_2}{q_1 - q_2},$$

where all q's are positive numbers. Since $b \rightarrow c$ is an isobaric process,

$$q_2 = h_c - h_b;$$

and since $d \rightarrow e \rightarrow a$ is isobaric,

$$q_1 = h_d - h_a.$$

Consequently $$\omega = \frac{h_c - h_b}{h_d - h_a - h_c + h_b}.$$

But since $a \rightarrow b$ is a throttling process,

$$h_a = h_b$$

and therefore $$\omega = \frac{h_c - h_a}{h_d - h_c}.$$

If the process $a \rightarrow b$ were not a throttling process but instead were a reversible adiabatic expansion, the coefficient of performance would be still larger than in the above ideal case. Of course, in the case of the actual refrigerator, not only is the process $a \rightarrow b$ irreversible, but all the other processes involve irreversible effects, and therefore the coefficient of performance is lower than the expression just derived.

As a numerical example, consider the following ideal case: The temperature in the evaporator of an ammonia refrigerating plant is 5°F, and the temperature at which the ammonia condenses in the condenser is 86°F.

From tables of the properties of ammonia,

$h_a = \left\{ \begin{array}{l} \text{enthalpy per lb of saturated liquid at 86°F, corresponding to} \\ \text{a saturation pressure of 169.2 lb/in.}^2 \end{array} \right.$

$\quad = 138.9$ Btu/lb.

$h_c = \left\{ \begin{array}{l} \text{enthalpy per lb of saturated vapor at 5°F, corresponding to} \\ \text{a saturation pressure of 34.3 lb/in.}^2 \end{array} \right.$

$\quad = 613.3$ Btu/lb.   (Entropy at $c = 1.3253$ Btu/lb · deg.)

$h_d = \left\{ \begin{array}{l} \text{enthalpy per lb of superheated vapor, after isentropic com-} \\ \text{pression at the entropy 1.3253 Btu/lb · deg to the pressure of} \\ \text{169.2 lb/in.}^2 \end{array} \right.$

$\quad = \left\{ \begin{array}{l} \text{enthalpy per lb of superheated vapor at a temperature of} \\ \text{210°F (from chart)} \end{array} \right.$

$\quad = 713$ Btu/lb.

Therefore, $$\omega = \frac{613.3 - 138.9}{713 - 613.3}$$

$$= \frac{474.4}{99.7}$$

$$= 4.76.$$

To find the quality x of the mixture at the conclusion of the throttling process, we equate the enthalpies at states a and b, thus:

$$h_a = xh_c + (1 - x)h_k,$$

where h_k refers to saturated liquid at the low temperature and pressure. Therefore,

$$
\begin{aligned}
x &= \frac{h_a - h_k}{h_c - h_k} \\
&= \frac{138.9 - 48.3}{613.3 - 48.3} \\
&= 16 \text{ per cent.}
\end{aligned}
$$

The initial and final pressures needed to produce a temperature drop from 86 to 5°F by a throttling process, and the quality after throttling, are listed in Table 12.2 for a number of widely used refrigerants.

TABLE 12.2. PRESSURES FOR TEMPERATURE DROP FROM 86 TO 5°F AND QUALITY AFTER THROTTLING

Refrigerant	Initial pressure corresponding to temperature of 86°F, lb/in.^{2}	Final pressure corresponding to temperature of 5°F, lb/in.^{2}	Quality after throttling, per cent
Sulfur dioxide, SO_2...............	66.5	11.8	16.5
Methyl chloride, CH_3Cl...........	94.7	21.2	16.8
Dichlorodifluoromethane, CCl_2F_2 (Freon 12)....................	108	26.5	26.5
Ammonia, NH_3..................	169	34.3	16

12.8. Heating by Refrigeration. The preceding calculation shows that the coefficient of performance of a refrigerator may be considerably larger than unity. Assuming for the sake of argument the value 5,

$$\omega = \frac{Q_2}{W} = 5.$$

But

$$Q_2 = Q_1 - W;$$

hence

$$\frac{Q_1 - W}{W} = 5,$$

$$\frac{Q_1}{W} = 6,$$

and therefore the heat liberated at the higher temperature is equal to six times the work done. If the work is supplied by an electric motor, for every Btu of electrical energy supplied 6 Btu of heat will be liberated; whereas if 1 Btu of electrical energy were dissipated in a resistor, one could obtain at most 1 Btu of heat. Consequently, it would seem to be highly advantageous to heat a house by refrigerating the outdoors.

This was first pointed out by Lord Kelvin in 1852, who designed a

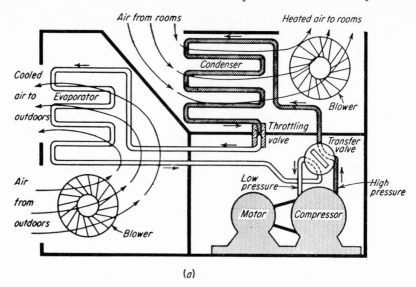

(a)

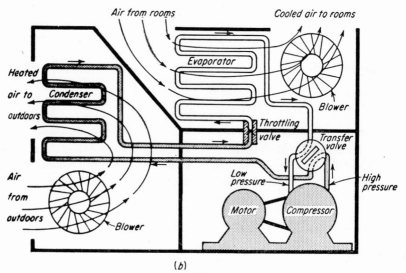

(b)

FIG. 12.9. (a) Heating the house by refrigerating the outside air. (b) Cooling the house by heating the outside air.

machine for the purpose. The device, however, was never built, and it remained for Haldane, about 75 years later, to utilize the principle and heat his house in Scotland by refrigerating the outdoor air supplemented by city water. Since about 1938, many devices known as "heat pumps" have appeared on the market for warming the house in winter by refrigerating either the ground or the outside air, or the water supplied in the mains. By turning a valve and reversing the flow of refrigerant, the heat pump may also be used to cool the house in summer as shown in Fig. 12.9. Various commercial units have coefficients of performance ranging from about 2 to about 7. The design, installation, and operation of such units is now an important branch of engineering.

12.9. Servel Electrolux Refrigerator. The most important feature of the refrigeration cycle is the throttling process, in which the refrigerant is transferred from a region of high pressure to a region of lower pressure, thus suffering a drop in temperature of 70 to 80°F. For purposes of kitchen refrigeration, the drop in pressure must be about 10 atm. This pressure difference is maintained as a rule by a compressor or pump of a reciprocating or rotary type operated by an electric motor. This involves moving parts, with consequent problems of lubrication, vibration, and noise. Moreover, to maintain a constant temperature, a thermostat is used to start the motor when the temperature rises above a fixed value and to stop the motor when the temperature drops below a lower value. The starting and stopping of the motor may produce a flicker in the electric lights and also a click in a nearby radio.

An interesting modification of such a system by which a refrigerant is taken around the refrigeration cycle without employing any machinery with moving parts and which operates continuously is the Electrolux refrigerator. This was invented by two Swedish engineers, Carl Munters and Baltzar von Platen, while they were still undergraduates at the Royal Institute of Technology in Stockholm. It is represented schematically in Fig. 12.10. The refrigerant is ammonia liberated by a solution of ammonia in water. The ammonia is transferred from one region to another through an atmosphere of hydrogen. The total pressure, which is equal to the sum of the partial pressure of ammonia and the partial pressure of the hydrogen, is *constant* at all points of the system. There is therefore no need for any valves.

The operation of the Electrolux is understood best by noting, in Fig. 12.10, that there are three distinct complete circuits all operating at the same time.

1. *The Ammonia Circuit.* Droplets of water in which ammonia is dissolved separated by small amounts of ammonia vapor are raised in the liquid lift, which operates in the same way as a coffee percolator. Ammonia vapor escapes from the vapor and liquid separator, goes up to the condenser, which is cooled with the aid of radiating fins, and liquefies. It then joins a stream of hydrogen and vaporizes in an atmosphere of hydrogen while going through the evaporator, thus extracting heat from the tray of ice cubes. The mixture of ammonia vapor and hydrogen then comes in contact with water in the absorber, the ammonia dissolving and the hydrogen continuing through. The dissolved ammonia then returns to the generator.

2. The Water Circuit. The water that separates out in the vapor and liquid separator runs down into the absorber, where it dissolves ammonia vapor. The concentrated solution proceeds to the generator, from which it is driven into the liquid lift and raised again to the separator.

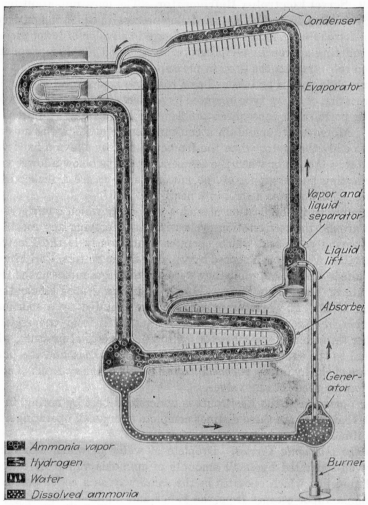

Fig. 12.10. Simplified diagram of the Servel Electrolux refrigerator. (*Courtesy Servel, Inc.*)

3. The Hydrogen Circuit. Hydrogen, which is not soluble in water, leaves the absorber and enters the evaporator, where it aids in vaporizing the liquid ammonia. The hydrogen, mixed with ammonia vapor, passes back to the absorber, where the ammonia is dissolved and the hydrogen is free once again.

The refrigeration cycle of the Servel Electrolux refrigerator may be represented schematically in the manner shown in Fig. 12.11.   Heat Q_3 is extracted from the gas flame at T_3, heat Q_2 is extracted from the cold reservoir at T_2, and heats Q_1' and Q_1'' are rejected to the intermediate reservoir at room temperature.   In one complete cycle there is no net change of energy, and no external work is done.   Consequently, the net heat is zero, or

$$Q_2 + Q_3 - Q_1' - Q_1'' = 0.$$

Since Q_2 represents, so to speak, the output and Q_3 the input, the coefficient of performance in this case is

$$\frac{Q_2}{Q_3} = \frac{Q_1' + Q_1''}{Q_3} - 1.$$

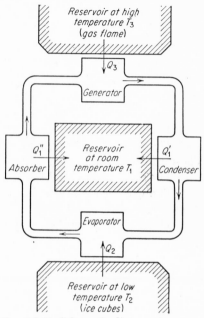

FIG. 12.11. Schematic diagram to represent the thermodynamic behavior of the Electrolux refrigerator.

12.10. Flow Processes.   A distinction was made at the beginning of this book between internal energy of a system and external or mechanical energy of the system as a whole. Hitherto we have dealt with systems whose kinetic and potential energies as a whole either have been zero or, if present, have not in any way entered into the problem.   In engineering it is often necessary to deal with a system (such as a pound of steam) which is moving with high speed and of which the kinetic energy is changing during a process, thus involving a transformation of external energy into either internal energy or work. Any process involving a moving system where there is a transformation of external energy into internal energy or work is called a *flow process*.   To express the first law of thermodynamics for a flow process it is necessary merely to include those terms which express the kinetic and potential energy of the system as a whole along with the usual terms involving internal energy, heat, and work.

Imagine a fluid flowing through a device shown schematically in Fig. 12.12 in such a manner that, in the steady state, a constant pressure P_i is maintained on one side and a constant pressure P_f on the other.   If we consider the passage of 1 lb of fluid through the device, the following properties of the fluid will change:

1. The internal energy, by an amount $u_f - u_i$.

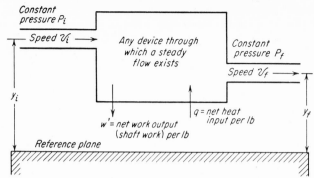

FIG. 12.12. Flow process.

2. The kinetic energy, by an amount $(1/2g)(\mathcal{V}_f^2 - \mathcal{V}_i^2)$.

3. The potential energy, by an amount $y_f - y_i$.

There will be a total amount of work as follows:

1. The shaft work equal to w'.

2. The work necessary to force 1 lb of fluid into the chamber at constant pressure P_i, equal to $-P_i v_i$.

3. The work done on the outside by 1 lb of fluid in leaving the chamber at constant pressure P_f, equal to $P_f v_f$.

Denoting by q the net amount of heat absorbed and applying the principle of the conservation of energy, we get

$$q = u_f - u_i + \frac{\mathcal{V}_f^2 - \mathcal{V}_i^2}{2g} + y_f - y_i + P_f v_f - P_i v_i + w'.$$

Remembering that $h = u + Pv$, we may write this equation

$$\boxed{q = h_f - h_i + \frac{\mathcal{V}_f^2 - \mathcal{V}_i^2}{2g} + y_f - y_i + w'.}$$

1. In the case of a *nozzle* or a *venturi meter*, there is a large change of speed of the moving fluid because of a change of cross-sectional area of the pipe, without any shaft work being done or any transfer of heat. Hence, in the horizontal case,

$$\frac{\mathcal{V}_f^2 - \mathcal{V}_i^2}{2g} = h_i - h_f.$$

2. In the case of a *turbine*, the change of kinetic energy is very often negligibly small, and the process is almost adiabatic, whence, for horizontal flow,

$$w' = h_i - h_f.$$

3. In the case of a *throttle* or *throttling valve*, the fluid has a negligibly small initial speed, and any speed that is attained within the valve is

almost immediately dissipated into internal energy after passage through the valve.   Moreover, no shaft work is done, and no heat is transferred. Consequently, for horizontal flow,

$$h_i = h_f.$$

The student will recognize this result as one of the three fundamental properties that were discussed when the enthalpy function was first introduced.

PROBLEMS

Steam tables and refrigeration data are needed for some of these problems.

12.1. Show from the steam tables that, at any pressure,

$$g \text{ (saturated liquid)} = g \text{ (saturated vapor)}.$$

12.2. An engine operating in a Rankine cycle uses dry saturated steam at 300 lb/in². abs. pressure.   The temperature of the water in the condenser is 60°F.
(a) Calculate the thermal efficiency of this engine.
(b) What is the quality of the steam at the end of the expansion stroke?

12.3. An engine operating in a Rankine cycle uses superheated steam at a pressure of 300 lb/in.² abs. at 300°F superheat.   The temperature of the condenser water is 60°F.
(a) Calculate the thermal efficiency of this engine.
(b) What is the quality of the steam at the end of the expansion stroke?

12.4. Calculate the minimum amount of work needed to convert 100 lb of water at 32°F and 1 atm into ice at the same temperature and pressure, using a reservoir at 86°F.   (The heat of fusion of ice is 144 Btu/lb.)

12.5. (a) Calculate the minimum amount of work necessary to freeze 10 gm of water from 27 to −13°C at constant atmospheric pressure, using a reservoir at 27°C. (c_P of ice = 0.50 cal/gm · deg C.)
(b) Calculate the coefficient of performance.

12.6. Saturated water at 15 lb/in.² undergoes a throttling process to a final pressure of 1 lb/in.².   Calculate the quality of the resulting mixture.

12.7. Wet steam at 100 lb/in.² undergoes a throttling process and becomes superheated steam at atmospheric pressure and 240°F.   Find the original quality of the steam.

12.8. (a) Calculate the coefficient of performance of a Carnot refrigerator operating between the temperatures of 86 and 5°F.   (b) Compare this value with the coefficient of performance of the ideal refrigeration cycle, using the refrigerants sulfur dioxide, methyl chloride, dichlorodifluoromethane, with the condenser at 86°F and the evaporator at 5°F.

12.9. An exhausted chamber with nonconducting walls is connected through a valve with a steam main through which steam at 100 lb/in.² and 500°F is flowing. The valve is opened and steam flows into the chamber until the pressure within the chamber is 100 lb/in.²   Find the temperature of the steam in the chamber when flow stops.

12.10. A steady flow of steam enters a heating coil at 150 lb/in.² and 400°F and leaves it at 140 lb/in.² and 600°F.
(a) If the kinetic energies at entrance and exit are negligible and the coil is horizontal, how much heat is transferred to each pound of steam?

(b) If the coil is 100 ft high and the flow is downward and the entrance and exit velocities are, respectively, 200 and 280 ft/sec, how much heat is transferred per pound?

12.11. A steam turbine receives a steam flow of 10,000 lb/hr and delivers 500 kw. Neglecting heat loss,

(a) Find the change in enthalpy across the turbine if the velocities at entrance and exit and the difference of elevation at entrance and exit are negligible.

(b) Find the change in enthalpy across the turbine if the velocity at entrance is 200 ft/sec, the velocity at exit is 1200 ft/sec, and the inlet pipe is 10 ft above the exhaust.

12.12. Apply the general energy equation of steady flow to two neighboring regions of a pipe an infinitesimal distance from each other. Show that, in the case of an ideal fluid flowing with no viscosity and no wall friction, in the absence of shaft work, the general equation may be separated into two independent equations,

$$dq = du + P\,dv,$$

$$0 = v\,dP + d\left(\frac{\mathcal{V}^2}{2g}\right) + dy \qquad \text{(Bernoulli's equation).}$$

12.13. Apply Bernoulli's equation to the frictionless flow of an ideal *incompressible* fluid in a horizontal pipe of variable cross section. Show that, at any place in the pipe,

$$P + \frac{\rho}{2}\,\mathcal{V}^2 = \text{const.}$$

where ρ is the density. Show also that, at any place in the pipe where the cross-sectional area is A,

$$\rho A \mathcal{V} = \text{const.}$$

12.14. An ideal incompressible fluid flows with no friction through a horizontal pipe of variable cross section. Show that

$$\mathcal{V} = \sqrt{\frac{2(P - P_0)}{\rho\left[\left(\dfrac{A}{A_0}\right)^2 - 1\right]}}$$

where P, $\mathcal{V}$, A refer to one part of the pipe and P_0, A_0 to another part. (This is the principle of the venturi meter.)

12.15. At the inlet to a certain nozzle the enthalpy of the fluid is 1300 Btu/lb, and the velocity is 200 ft/sec. At the discharge side the enthalpy of the fluid is 1200 Btu/lb. The nozzle is horizontal, and the flow is adiabatic.

(a) Find the velocity at the nozzle exit.

(b) If the inlet area is 1 ft² and the specific volume at inlet is 3 ft³/lb, find the rate of flow in pounds per second.

(c) If the specific volume at the nozzle discharge is 8 ft³/lb, find the exit area of the nozzle.

12.16. Steam approaches a horizontal nozzle at a pressure of 100 lb/in.² and a temperature of 500°F at negligible velocity. It reaches the discharge end of the nozzle at a pressure of 70 lb/in.² and a temperature of 420°F. Assuming the flow to be isentropic,

(a) Find the velocity in the nozzle discharge.

(b) Find the area of the nozzle-discharge cross section required to pass a flow of 1 lb/sec.

12.17. An ideal gas with constant heat capacities is caused to flow adiabatically through a nozzle from a region where the pressure and temperature are P_i and T_i, respectively, to a constricted region where the values are P and T. Assuming the initial velocity to be negligible,

(a) Show that the final velocity $\mathscr{V}$ is

$$\mathscr{V} = \sqrt{2gc_PT_i\left(1 - \frac{T}{T_i}\right)}.$$

(b) Assuming the expansion in the nozzle to be isentropic, show that $P V^\gamma = const.$

$$\mathscr{V} = \sqrt{2gc_PT_i\left[1 - \left(\frac{P}{P_i}\right)^{\frac{\gamma-1}{\gamma}}\right]}$$

$$= \sqrt{2g\frac{\gamma}{\gamma-1}RT_i\left[1 - \left(\frac{P}{P_i}\right)^{\frac{\gamma-1}{\gamma}}\right]}.$$

$P V = n P \theta$

$V = \dfrac{n R \theta}{P.}$

13

Applications of Thermodynamics to Pure Substances

13.1. Two Mathematical Theorems. *Theorem 1.* If a relation exists among x, y, and z, we may imagine z expressed as a function of x and y; whence

$$dz = \left(\frac{\partial z}{\partial x}\right)_y dx + \left(\frac{\partial z}{\partial y}\right)_x dy.$$

If we let

$$M = \left(\frac{\partial z}{\partial x}\right)_y \quad \text{and} \quad N = \left(\frac{\partial z}{\partial y}\right)_x,$$

then

$$dz = M\, dx + N\, dy,$$

where z, M, and N are all functions of x and y. Differentiating M partially with respect to y and N with respect to x, we get

$$\left(\frac{\partial M}{\partial y}\right)_x = \frac{\partial^2 z}{\partial x\, \partial y}$$

$$\left(\frac{\partial N}{\partial x}\right)_y = \frac{\partial^2 z}{\partial y\, \partial x}.$$

Since the two second derivatives on the right are equal, it follows that

$$\boxed{\left(\frac{\partial M}{\partial y}\right)_x = \left(\frac{\partial N}{\partial x}\right)_y.}$$

This is known as the *condition for an exact differential*.

Theorem 2. If a quantity f is a function of x, y, and z, and a relation exists among x, y, and z, then f may be regarded as a function of *any two* of x, y, and z. Similarly, any one of x, y, and z may be considered to be a function of f and one other of x, y, and z. Thus, regarding x to be a function of f and y,

$$dx = \left(\frac{\partial x}{\partial f}\right)_y df + \left(\frac{\partial x}{\partial y}\right)_f dy.$$

Considering y to be a function of f and z,

$$dy = \left(\frac{\partial y}{\partial f}\right)_z df + \left(\frac{\partial y}{\partial z}\right)_f dz.$$

Substituting this expression for dy in the preceding equation, we get

$$dx = \left[\left(\frac{\partial x}{\partial f}\right)_y + \left(\frac{\partial x}{\partial y}\right)_f \left(\frac{\partial y}{\partial f}\right)_z\right] df + \left[\left(\frac{\partial x}{\partial y}\right)_f \left(\frac{\partial y}{\partial z}\right)_f\right] dz.$$

But
$$dx = \left(\frac{\partial x}{\partial f}\right)_z df + \left(\frac{\partial x}{\partial z}\right)_f dz.$$

Equating the dz terms of the last two equations, we get

$$\boxed{\begin{aligned} \left(\frac{\partial x}{\partial y}\right)_f \left(\frac{\partial y}{\partial z}\right)_f &= \left(\frac{\partial x}{\partial z}\right)_f, \\ \left(\frac{\partial x}{\partial y}\right)_f \left(\frac{\partial y}{\partial z}\right)_f \left(\frac{\partial z}{\partial x}\right)_f &= 1. \end{aligned}}$$

13.2. Maxwell's Equations. A chemical system has been defined as any system of constant mass whose equilibrium states are describable by the three thermodynamic coordinates P, V, and T. In describing the behavior of such a system it is convenient to make use of the four functions:

1. The internal energy U.
2. The enthalpy $H = U + PV$.
3. The Helmholtz function $A = U - TS$.
4. The Gibbs function $G = H - TS$.

Any one of these may be regarded as a function of *any two* of P, V, and T. Suppose for example that both U and S are expressed as functions of V and T, thus:

$$U = \text{function of } (V, T),$$
and
$$S = \text{function of } (V, T).$$

The second equation may be imagined to be solved for T in terms of S and V; substituting this value of T in the first equation, we should then have

$$U = \text{function of } (S, V).$$

Consequently, we may go further and say that any **one of** the eight quantities P, V, T, S, U, H, A, and G may be expressed as a function of *any two others*.

Now imagine a chemical system undergoing an infinitesimal reversible process from one equilibrium state to another.

1. The internal energy changes by an amount

$$dU = dQ - P\,dV$$
$$= T\,dS - P\,dV$$

where U, T, and P are all imagined to be functions of S and V.

2. The enthalpy changes by an amount

$$dH = dU + P\,dV + V\,dP$$
$$= T\,dS + V\,dP$$

where H, T, and V are all imagined to be functions of S and P.

3. The Helmholtz function changes by an amount

$$dA = dU - T\,dS - S\,dT$$
$$= -P\,dV - S\,dT$$

where A, P, and S are all imagined to be functions of V and T.

4. The Gibbs function changes by an amount

$$dG = dH - T\,dS - S\,dT$$
$$= V\,dP - S\,dT$$

where G, V, and S are all imagined to be functions of P and T.

Since U, H, A, and G are actual functions, their differentials are exact differentials of the type

$$dz = M\,dx + N\,dy$$

where z, M, and N are all functions of x and y. Therefore

$$\left(\frac{\partial M}{\partial y}\right)_x = \left(\frac{\partial N}{\partial x}\right)_y.$$

Applying this result to the four exact differentials dU, dH, dA, and dG,

$$dU = T\,dS - P\,dV; \quad \text{hence} \quad \left(\frac{\partial T}{\partial V}\right)_S = -\left(\frac{\partial P}{\partial S}\right)_V, \quad (1)$$

$$dH = T\,dS + V\,dP; \quad \text{hence} \quad \left(\frac{\partial T}{\partial P}\right)_S = \left(\frac{\partial V}{\partial S}\right)_P, \quad (2)$$

$$dA = -P\,dV - S\,dT; \quad \text{hence} \quad \left(\frac{\partial P}{\partial T}\right)_V = \left(\frac{\partial S}{\partial V}\right)_T, \quad (3)$$

$$dG = V\,dP - S\,dT; \quad \text{hence} \quad \left(\frac{\partial V}{\partial T}\right)_P = -\left(\frac{\partial S}{\partial P}\right)_T. \quad (4)$$

The four equations on the right are known as *Maxwell's equations*. It is not necessary for the student to memorize them since they are so easily derived. Maxwell's equations do not refer to a process but merely express relations that hold at any equilibrium state of a chemical system.

13.3. First $T\,dS$ Equation.   The entropy of a chemical system can be imagined as a function of T and V; whence

$$dS = \left(\frac{\partial S}{\partial T}\right)_V dT + \left(\frac{\partial S}{\partial V}\right)_T dV$$

and

$$T\,dS = T\left(\frac{\partial S}{\partial T}\right)_V dT + T\left(\frac{\partial S}{\partial V}\right)_T dV.$$

It was shown in Art. 11.8 that

$$T\left(\frac{\partial S}{\partial T}\right)_V = C_V;$$

and, from Maxwell's third equation,

$$\left(\frac{\partial S}{\partial V}\right)_T = \left(\frac{\partial P}{\partial T}\right)_V,$$

whence

$$\boxed{T\,dS = C_V\,dT + T\left(\frac{\partial P}{\partial T}\right)_V dV.}$$

We shall call the above equation the *first $T\,dS$ equation*.   It is useful in a variety of ways.   For example, 1 mole of a van der Waals gas undergoes a reversible isothermal expansion from a volume v_i to a volume v_f. How much heat has been transferred?

For 1 mole,

$$T\,ds = c_V\,dT + T\left(\frac{\partial P}{\partial T}\right)_V dv.$$

Using the van der Waals equation of state,

$$P = \frac{RT}{v-b} - \frac{a}{v^2},$$

and

$$\left(\frac{\partial P}{\partial T}\right)_V = \frac{R}{v-b};$$

hence

$$T\,ds = c_V\,dT + RT\frac{dv}{v-b}.$$

Since T is constant, $c_V\,dT = 0$ and, since the process is reversible, $q = \int T\,ds$.   Therefore

$$q = RT\int_{v_i}^{v_f}\frac{dv}{v-b},$$

and finally

$$q = RT\ln\frac{v_f - b}{v_i - b}.$$

13.4. Second $T\,dS$ Equation. If the entropy of a chemical system is regarded as a function of T and P, then

$$dS = \left(\frac{\partial S}{\partial T}\right)_P dT + \left(\frac{\partial S}{\partial P}\right)_T dP$$

and

$$T\,dS = T\left(\frac{\partial S}{\partial T}\right)_P dT + T\left(\frac{\partial S}{\partial P}\right)_T dP.$$

But

$$T\left(\frac{\partial S}{\partial T}\right)_P = C_P;$$

and, from Maxwell's fourth equation,

$$\left(\frac{\partial S}{\partial P}\right)_T = -\left(\frac{\partial V}{\partial T}\right)_P,$$

whence

$$\boxed{T\,dS = C_P\,dT - T\left(\frac{\partial V}{\partial T}\right)_P dP.}$$

We shall call the above equation the *second $T\,dS$ equation*. Two important applications follow.

1. *Reversible Isothermal Change of Pressure.* When T is constant,

$$T\,dS = -T\left(\frac{\partial V}{\partial T}\right)_P dP$$

and

$$Q = -T\int\left(\frac{\partial V}{\partial T}\right)_P dP.$$

Remembering that the coefficient of volume expansion is

$$\beta = \frac{1}{V}\left(\frac{\partial V}{\partial T}\right)_P,$$

we obtain

$$Q = -T\int V\beta\,dP,$$

which can be integrated when the dependence of V and β on the pressure is known. In the case of a solid or liquid, neither V nor β is very sensitive to a change in pressure. For example, in the case of mercury, Bridgman found that as the pressure was increased from zero to 1000 atm at 0°C the volume of 1 mole of mercury changed from 14.72 to 14.67 cm³, a change of only ⅓ per cent; and the volume expansivity changed from 181×10^{-6} deg^{-1} to 174×10^{-6} deg^{-1}, a 4 per cent change. The volume and the expansivity of most solids and liquids behave similarly, and therefore V and β may be taken out from under the integral sign and replaced by average values, $\bar V$ and $\bar\beta$. (A bar over a quantity indicates an average value.)   We have then

$$Q = -T\bar{V}\bar{\beta} \int_{P_i}^{P_f} dP$$

or
$$Q = -T\bar{V}\bar{\beta}(P_f - P_i).$$

It is seen from this result that, as the pressure is increased isothermally, heat will flow *out* if $\bar{\beta}$ is positive but, for a substance with a negative expansivity (such as water between 0 and 4°C), an isothermal increase of pressure causes an absorption of heat.

If the pressure on 1 mole of mercury at 0°C is increased reversibly and isothermally from zero to 1000 atm, the heat transferred will be

$$q = -T\bar{v}\bar{\beta}(P_f - P_i),$$

where $T = 273$ deg

$\bar{v} = 14.7$ cm³/mole

$\bar{\beta} = 178 \times 10^{-6}$ deg⁻¹

$P_i = 0$

$P_f = 1000$ atm $= 1.013 \times 10^9$ dynes/cm²

Hence

$$q = -\frac{273 \text{ deg} \times 14.7 \text{ cm}^3/\text{mole} \times 178 \times 10^{-6} \text{ deg}^{-1} \times 1.013 \times 10^9 \text{ dynes/cm}^2}{4.19 \times 10^7 \text{ ergs/cal}}$$

$$= -\frac{72.3 \times 10^7 \text{ dyne} \cdot \text{cm/mole}}{4.19 \times 10^7 \text{ ergs/cal}}$$

$$= -17.3 \text{ cal/mole}.$$

It is interesting to compare the heat liberated with the work done during the compression.

$$w = \int P \, dv;$$

but at constant temperature

$$dv = \left(\frac{\partial v}{\partial P}\right)_T dP,$$

and
$$w = \int \left(\frac{\partial v}{\partial P}\right)_T P \, dP.$$

Remembering that the isothermal compressibility (reciprocal of isothermal bulk modulus) is

$$k = -\frac{1}{v}\left(\frac{\partial v}{\partial P}\right)_T,$$

then
$$w = -\int_{P_i}^{P_f} vkP \, dP.$$

The isothermal compressibility is also fairly insensitive to a change of pressure. Bridgman showed that the compressibility of mercury at 0°C changed from 3.88×10^{-12} to 3.79×10^{-12} cm²/dyne (a 2 per cent change) as the pressure was increased from zero to 1000 atm. We may therefore again replace v and k by average values and obtain

$$w = - \frac{\bar{v}\bar{k}}{2} (P_f^2 - P_i^2);$$

and taking for mercury

$$\bar{k} = 3.84 \times 10^{-12} \text{ cm}^2/\text{dyne},$$

we get

$$w = - \frac{14.7 \text{ cm}^3/\text{mole} \times 3.84 \times 10^{-12} \text{ cm}^2/\text{dyne} \times (1.01)^2 \times 10^{18} \text{ (dynes/cm}^2)^2}{2 \times 4.19 \times 10^7 \text{ ergs/cal}}$$

$$= - \frac{5.76 \times 10^7 \text{ dyne} \cdot \text{cm/mole}}{8.38 \times 10^7 \text{ ergs/cal}}$$

$$= -0.687 \text{ cal/mole}.$$

It is seen, therefore, that, when the pressure on a mole of mercury at 0°C is increased from zero to 1000 atm, 17.3 cal of heat is liberated but only 0.687 cal of work is done! The extra amount of heat comes, of course, from the store of internal energy, which has changed by an amount

$$u_f - u_i = q - w$$
$$= -17.3 \text{ cal/mole} + 0.687 \text{ cal/mole}$$
$$= -16.6 \text{ cal/mole}.$$

A similar result is obtained in the case of any substance with a positive expansivity. For a substance with a negative expansivity, heat is absorbed and the internal energy is increased.

2. *Reversible Adiabatic Change of Pressure.* Since the entropy remains constant,

$$T \, dS = 0 = C_P \, dT - T \left(\frac{\partial V}{\partial T} \right)_P dP$$

or

$$dT = \frac{T}{C_P} \left(\frac{\partial V}{\partial T} \right)_P dP$$

$$= \frac{TV\beta}{C_P} \, dP.$$

In the case of a solid or liquid, an increase of pressure of as much as 1000 atm produces only a small temperature change. Also, experiment shows that C_P hardly changes even for an increase of 10,000 atm. The above equation, therefore, when applied to a solid or a liquid, may be written

$$\Delta T = \frac{T\bar{V}\bar{\beta}}{\bar{C}_P} (P_f - P_i).$$

It is clear from the above that an adiabatic increase of pressure will produce an increase of temperature in any substance with a positive expansivity and a decrease in temperature in a substance with a negative expansivity.

If the pressure on a mole of mercury at 0°C is increased isentropically from zero to 1000 atm, the temperature change will be

$$\Delta T = \frac{T\bar{v}\bar{\beta}}{\bar{c}_P} (P_f - P_i)$$

where $\bar{c}_P$ is 6.69 cal/mole · deg. ˙ Hence

$$\Delta T = \frac{273 \text{ deg} \times 14.7 \text{ cm}^3/\text{mole} \times 178 \times 10^{-6} \text{ deg}^{-1}}{6.69 \text{ cal/mole} \cdot \text{deg} \times 4.19 \times 10^7 \text{ ergs/cal}} \times 1.013 \times 10^9 \text{ dynes/cm}^2$$

$$= \frac{72.3 \times 10^7 \text{ dyne} \cdot \text{cm/mole}}{28.0 \times 10^7 \text{ ergs/mole} \cdot \text{deg}}$$

$$= 2.58 \text{ deg.}$$

13.5. Energy Equation.   If a chemical system undergoes an infinitesimal reversible process between two equilibrium states, the change of internal energy is

$$dU = T \, dS - P \, dV;$$

and (the first $T \, dS$ equation),

$$T \, dS = C_V \, dT + T \left(\frac{\partial P}{\partial T}\right)_V dV.$$

Combining both equations, we get

$$dU = C_V \, dT + \left[T \left(\frac{\partial P}{\partial T}\right)_V - P \right] dV,$$

in which U is imagined as a function of T and V.   But

$$dU = \left(\frac{\partial U}{\partial T}\right)_V dT + \left(\frac{\partial U}{\partial V}\right)_T dV,$$

and consequently

$$\boxed{\left(\frac{\partial U}{\partial V}\right)_T = T \left(\frac{\partial P}{\partial T}\right)_V - P.}$$

The above equation, known as the *energy equation*, enables us to draw conclusions about the internal energy of any chemical system whose equation of state is known.   For example:

1. *Ideal Gas*

$$P = \frac{nRT}{V},$$

$$\left(\frac{\partial P}{\partial T}\right)_V = \frac{nR}{V},$$

and
$$\left(\frac{\partial U}{\partial V}\right)_T = T\frac{nR}{V} - P = 0.$$

Therefore U does not depend on V but is a function of T only.

2. *Van der Waals Gas* (*1 Mole*)

$$P = \frac{RT}{v - b} - \frac{a}{v^2}$$

$$\left(\frac{\partial P}{\partial T}\right)_V = \frac{R}{v - b},$$

and
$$\left(\frac{\partial u}{\partial v}\right)_T = T\frac{R}{v - b} - \frac{RT}{v - b} + \frac{a}{v^2}$$

$$= \frac{a}{v^2}.$$

Consequently,

$$du = c_V\, dT + \frac{a}{v^2}\, dv,$$

and
$$u = \int c_V\, dT - \frac{a}{v} + \text{const.}$$

It follows, therefore, that the internal energy of a van der Waals gas increases as the volume increases, the temperature remaining constant.

13.6. Difference in Heat Capacities. Equating the first and second $T\, dS$ equations,

$$C_P\, dT - T\left(\frac{\partial V}{\partial T}\right)_P dP = C_V\, dT + T\left(\frac{\partial P}{\partial T}\right)_V dV;$$

solving for dT,

$$dT = \frac{T\left(\frac{\partial P}{\partial T}\right)_V}{C_P - C_V}\, dV + \frac{T\left(\frac{\partial V}{\partial T}\right)_P}{C_P - C_V}\, dP.$$

But
$$dT = \left(\frac{\partial T}{\partial V}\right)_P dV + \left(\frac{\partial T}{\partial P}\right)_V dP.$$

Therefore
$$\left(\frac{\partial T}{\partial V}\right)_P = \frac{T\left(\frac{\partial P}{\partial T}\right)_V}{C_P - C_V}$$

and
$$\left(\frac{\partial T}{\partial P}\right)_V = \frac{T\left(\frac{\partial V}{\partial T}\right)_P}{C_P - C_V}.$$

Both the above equations yield the result that

$$C_P - C_V = T \left(\frac{\partial V}{\partial T}\right)_P \left(\frac{\partial P}{\partial T}\right)_V.$$

It was shown in Art. 2.4 that

$$\left(\frac{\partial P}{\partial T}\right)_V = -\left(\frac{\partial V}{\partial T}\right)_P \left(\frac{\partial P}{\partial V}\right)_T.$$

Substituting the above value of $(\partial P/\partial T)_V$ in the equation just derived for the difference in the heat capacities, we obtain finally

$$\boxed{C_P - C_V = -T \left(\frac{\partial V}{\partial T}\right)_P^2 \left(\frac{\partial P}{\partial V}\right)_T.}$$

This is one of the most important equations of thermodynamics and shows that

1. Since $(\partial P/\partial V)_T$ is always negative for all known substances and $(\partial V/\partial T)_P^2$ must be positive, then $C_P - C_V$ can never be negative, or C_P *can never be less than* C_V.

2. As $T \to 0$, $C_P \to C_V$, or *at the absolute zero the two heat capacities are equal.*

3. $C_P = C_V$ when $(\partial V/\partial T)_P = 0$. For example, at 4°C, at which the density of water is a maximum, $C_P = C_V$.

Laboratory measurements of the heat capacity of solids and liquids usually take place at constant pressure and therefore yield values of C_P. It would be extremely difficult to measure with any degree of accuracy the C_V of a solid or liquid. Values of C_V, however, must be known for purposes of comparison with theory. The equation for the difference in the heat capacities is very useful in calculating C_V in terms of C_P and other measurable quantities. Remembering that

$$\beta = \frac{1}{V} \left(\frac{\partial V}{\partial T}\right)_P$$

and

$$k = -\frac{1}{V} \left(\frac{\partial V}{\partial P}\right)_T,$$

we may write the equation in the form

$$C_P - C_V = \frac{TV \left[\frac{1}{V}\left(\frac{\partial V}{\partial T}\right)_P\right]^2}{-\frac{1}{V}\left(\frac{\partial V}{\partial P}\right)_T}$$

$$\boxed{C_P - C_V = \frac{TV\beta^2}{k}.}$$

As an example of the use of the above equation let us calculate the molar heat capacity at constant volume of mercury at 0°C and 1 atm pressure. From experiment we have

$$c_P = 6.69 \text{ cal/mole} \cdot \text{deg},$$
$$T = 273 \text{ deg},$$
$$v = 14.72 \text{ cm}^3/\text{mole},$$
$$\beta = 181 \times 10^{-6} \text{ deg}^{-1},$$
$$k = 3.88 \times 10^{-12} \text{ cm}^2/\text{dyne},$$

whence

$$c_P - c_V = \frac{273 \text{ deg} \times 14.72 \text{ cm}^3/\text{mole} \times (181)^2 \times 10^{-12} \text{ deg}^{-2}}{3.88 \times 10^{-12} \text{ cm}^2/\text{dyne}}$$
$$= 3.39 \times 10^7 \text{ ergs/mole} \cdot \text{deg}$$
$$= \frac{3.39 \times 10^7 \text{ ergs/mole} \cdot \text{deg}}{4.19 \times 10^7 \text{ ergs/cal}}$$
$$= 0.809 \text{ cal/mole} \cdot \text{deg}$$

and
$$c_V = (6.69 - 0.809) \text{ cal/mole} \cdot \text{deg}$$
$$= 5.88 \text{ cal/mole} \cdot \text{deg}.$$

Finally,

$$\gamma = \frac{c_P}{c_V}$$
$$= \frac{6.69}{5.88} = 1.14.$$

13.7. Ratio of Heat Capacities. The two $T\,dS$ equations are

$$T\,dS = C_P\,dT - T\left(\frac{\partial V}{\partial T}\right)_P dP,$$

$$T\,dS = C_V\,dT + T\left(\frac{\partial P}{\partial T}\right)_V dV.$$

At constant S,

$$C_P\,dT_S = T\left(\frac{\partial V}{\partial T}\right)_P dP_S,$$

$$C_V\,dT_S = -T\left(\frac{\partial P}{\partial T}\right)_V dV_S.$$

Dividing,

$$\frac{C_P}{C_V} = -\left[\frac{\left(\frac{\partial V}{\partial T}\right)_P}{\left(\frac{\partial P}{\partial T}\right)_V}\right]\left(\frac{\partial P}{\partial V}\right)_S.$$

But the quantity in square brackets is equal to

$$-\left(\frac{\partial V}{\partial P}\right)_T.$$

Therefore

$$\boxed{\frac{C_P}{C_V} = \frac{(\partial P/\partial V)_S}{(\partial P/\partial V)_T}.}$$

The *adiabatic compressibility* is defined as the reciprocal of the adiabatic bulk modulus, or

$$k_S = -\frac{1}{V}\left(\frac{\partial V}{\partial P}\right)_S;$$

and, as usual,

$$k = -\frac{1}{V}\left(\frac{\partial V}{\partial P}\right)_T.$$

We have therefore

$$\frac{C_P}{C_V} = \gamma = \frac{k}{k_S},$$

from which k_S may be calculated.   In the case of mercury at 0°C and 1 atm pressure,

$$\gamma = 1.14,$$
$$k = 3.88 \times 10^{-12} \text{ cm}^2/\text{dyne},$$

whence

$$k_S = \frac{3.88 \times 10^{-12} \text{ cm}^2/\text{dyne}}{1.14}$$
$$= 3.41 \times 10^{-12} \text{ cm}^2/\text{dyne}.$$

13.8. Expansivity.   The volume expansivity of a gas may be calculated from the equation of state or more simply from any empiric equation representing the relation between volume and temperature at constant pressure.   The volume expansivity of liquids and solids is usually calculated from an empiric equation representing the relation between density and temperature at constant pressure.   Since the specific volume v is the reciprocal of the density ρ, it follows that

$$\beta = -\frac{1}{\rho}\frac{\partial \rho}{\partial T}.$$

In cases where it is inconvenient or inadvisable to measure the density of a solid over a wide temperature range, the volume expansivity may be calculated from the linear expansivity.   Suppose that the three rectangular dimensions of a solid are L_1, L_2, and L_3.   Then

$$V = L_1 L_2 L_3,$$
$$\frac{\partial V}{\partial T} = L_2 L_3 \frac{\partial L_1}{\partial T} + L_1 L_3 \frac{\partial L_2}{\partial T} + L_1 L_2 \frac{\partial L_3}{\partial T},$$
$$\frac{1}{V}\frac{\partial V}{\partial T} = \frac{1}{L_1}\frac{\partial L_1}{\partial T} + \frac{1}{L_2}\frac{\partial L_2}{\partial T} + \frac{1}{L_3}\frac{\partial L_3}{\partial T},$$

and

$$\beta = \alpha_1 + \alpha_2 + \alpha_3,$$

where α_1, α_2, and α_3 are the linear expansivities along the three directions. If the solid is isotropic, then

$$\alpha_1 = \alpha_2 = \alpha_3 = \alpha$$

and

$$\beta = 3\alpha.$$

There are many methods of measuring the linear expansivity of solids. If the solid can be obtained in the form of a bar, the simplest method is to make two scratches on the bar and place it horizontally in a temperature bath. The scratches are viewed through separate microscopes, which are mounted on a rigid stand kept at constant temperature. If a change in length $L - L_0$ is produced by a change in temperature $t - t_0$, then

$$\bar{\alpha} = \frac{1}{L_0}\frac{L - L_0}{t - t_0}$$

where $\bar{\alpha}$, the average coefficient, is very nearly equal to the true coefficient when $t - t_0$ is small.

If the linear expansivity of fused quartz is measured by this method, then the expansivities of other materials may be obtained by measuring the expansion relative to quartz. An instrument used for this purpose is the *Abbe-Pulfrich dilatometer*, depicted in Fig. 13.1(a). The material B, whose upper surface is plane and well polished, is placed inside a quartz ring A, whose height is a trifle greater than the material. A cover plate C is placed on the quartz ring, and interference fringes are obtained as a result of reflections from the two surfaces close together. The device is made so that the air space between these two surfaces is wedge-shaped, with an angle that remains constant as both the quartz ring and the material expand.

If n fringes travel across the field of view while the temperature changes from t_0 to t, then the optical path difference has changed by $n\lambda$, where λ is the wavelength of the light, and the thickness of the air space has changed by $n\lambda/2$. If L is the length of the specimen and L_Q that of the quartz, while L_0 is the original length of both the specimen and the quartz ring, then

$$\frac{L_Q - L}{L_0} = \frac{n\lambda}{2L_0}.$$

If, therefore, $n\lambda/2L_0$ is plotted against t and the slope of the resulting curve is taken at various temperatures, the difference in the expansivities is obtained. Thus

$$\alpha_Q - \alpha = \frac{d}{dt}\left(\frac{n\lambda}{2L_0}\right).$$

Another interferometric dilatometer has been developed for high-precision work. This experimental arrangement, first suggested by

Fizeau and later developed by Merrit, Austin, Nix, and MacNair at the Bell Telephone Laboratories, is shown in Fig. 13.1(b). Three samples of the material to be studied, B, are cut in the shape of small pyramids a few millimeters high and are used to separate two quartz plates A and C, so that the air space between the plates is wedge-shaped. Interference fringes are produced by reflections from the upper surface of A and the lower surface of C, and as the temperature is changed these fringes move across the field of view.

A small segment of the lower surface of plate A is made smooth, so that interference fringes may be produced by reflections from the upper and lower surfaces of this part of the plate. As the temperature is

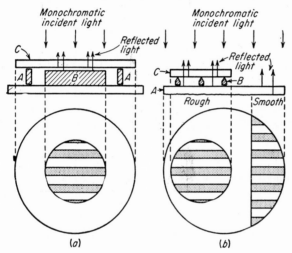

FIG. 13.1. (a) Abbe-Pulfrich dilatometer. (b) Fizeau dilatometer, as improved by Merrit.

changed, these fringes also move because of the expansion and changing index of refraction of plate A. By previous calibration, the number of these fringes that move may be used to determine the temperature. This part of the apparatus therefore acts as a refraction thermometer. The system is immersed in a specially designed thermostat whose temperature is varied very slowly in a period of as much as 70 hr; during this time both fringe systems are photographed at regular intervals by an automatically operated motion-picture camera. As in the case of the Pulfrich dilatometer, the linear expansivity is

$$\alpha = \frac{d}{dt}\left(\frac{n\lambda}{2L_0}\right).$$

In order to avoid the delay involved in photographic processing, the National Bureau of Standards has developed a photoelectric interferometer in which the movement of interference fringes is detected by a photomultiplier tube and the number of fringes is automatically plotted on a recorder against the measured temperature of the specimen. Thus, all hand operations are eliminated and the data are presented on a chart in a form suitable for immediate determination of expansivities.

In general, the volume expansivity of all materials depends on both the temperature and the pressure. As an example of the way β depends

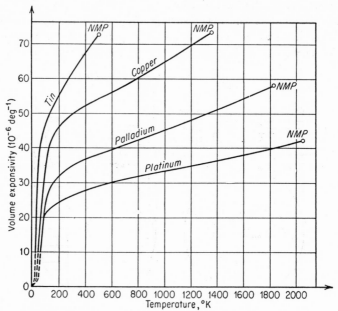

Fig. 13.2. Normal temperature variation of the volume expansivity of metals. (NMP stands for the normal melting point.)

on pressure, consider the values for mercury listed in Table 13.4. It requires an enormous change of pressure to give rise to an appreciable change in β. At ordinary pressures of 1 to 10 atm, β can be regarded as practically constant for most materials.

The temperature variation of β is much more significant. This is shown for copper at atmospheric pressure in Table 13.5 and is plotted for four different metals in Fig. 13.2. It is seen that the volume expansivity decreases as the temperature is lowered, approaching zero as the temperature approaches absolute zero. Most pure solids behave in a manner similar to that shown in Fig. 13.2, but there are several interesting exceptions. A type of iron known as α iron, for example, behaves normally from 0 to about 1000°K; then its volume expansivity takes a sudden drop, becoming negative at about 1100°K.

The curves drawn in Fig. 13.2 show an interesting regularity, namely, the higher the melting point, the lower the volume expansivity.   As a result, in the temperature interval from absolute zero to the melting point, all metals expand approximately the same fraction of their original volumes.   It seems as though a metal like tin, realizing it is going to melt soon, expands rapidly with the temperature, whereas platinum, with a high melting point, slows down its rate.

One of the most interesting substances is water.   The temperature variation of β of both ice and water is given in Table 13.1 and is plotted

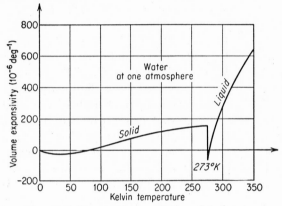

FIG. 13.3. Temperature variation of β of water.

in Fig. 13.3.   It is a remarkable fact that the volume expansivity is negative at very low temperatures and also in the well-known region from 0 to 4°C.

TABLE 13.1. TEMPERATURE VARIATION OF β OF ICE
AND OF WATER

Temp., °K	Volume expansivity, 10^{-6} deg^{-1}	Temp., °K	Volume expansivity, 10^{-6} deg^{-1}
0	0	279	+ 32
23	− 18.3	281	+ 61
73	+ 2.4	283	+ 89
123	+ 50.4	293	+208
173	+102	303	+304
223	+137	313	+390
273 (solid)	+158	323	+465
273 (liquid)	− 67	333	+522
275	− 31	343	+586
277	+ 1	353	+643

13.9. Compressibility.   The isothermal compressibility of a gas may be calculated from an empiric equation expressing the dependence of

V upon P at constant temperature. In the case of solids and liquids the change in volume (or the change in one dimension) produced by a known change in pressure is measured at constant temperature and the average compressibility calculated from the expression

$$\bar{k} = -\frac{1}{V_0}\frac{V - V_0}{P - P_0}.$$

If the change in pressure is not too large, $\bar{k}$ is approximately the true isothermal compressibility.

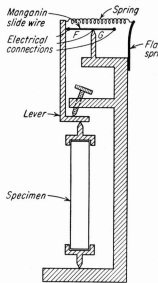

Manganin slide wire

Electrical connections

Spring

F G

Flat spring

Lever

Specimen

FIG. 13.4. Bridgman piezometer.

In the apparatus known as a *piezometer* used by Bridgman for solids, a bar of the solid is contained in a strong iron container filled with oil. The pressure of the oil is varied by a hydrostatic press, and the change in length of the solid relative to that of the iron container is measured by the motion it produces in a high-resistance manganin wire, which moves past a fixed contact G, as shown in Fig. 13.4. The resistance of the part of the wire between the end F and the fixed contact G is measured with the aid of a potentiometer. The quantity that is measured is the linear compressibility; i.e.,

$$\delta = -\frac{1}{L}\frac{\partial L}{\partial P}.$$

If the three rectangular dimensions of the solid are L_1, L_2, and L_3, then

$$V = L_1L_2L_3,$$

$$\frac{\partial V}{\partial P} = L_2L_3\frac{\partial L_1}{\partial P} + L_1L_3\frac{\partial L_2}{\partial P} + L_1L_2\frac{\partial L_3}{\partial P},$$

$$\frac{1}{V}\frac{\partial V}{\partial P} = \frac{1}{L_1}\frac{\partial L_1}{\partial P} + \frac{1}{L_2}\frac{\partial L_2}{\partial P} + \frac{1}{L_3}\frac{\partial L_3}{\partial P},$$

and

$$k = -\frac{1}{V}\frac{\partial V}{\partial P} = \delta_1 + \delta_2 + \delta_3.$$

If the solid is isotropic, all the δ's are equal and

$$k = 3\delta.$$

In general, the isothermal compressibility of all substances is a function of both pressure and temperature. The pressure dependence is exemplified by the values given in Table 13.4 for mercury at 0°C. It is seen that the change is only about 20 per cent for an increase of pressure of 7000 kg/cm². The effect of temperature on the isothermal compressibility is somewhat greater, as shown in Table 13.5 for copper at atmospheric pressure. The isothermal compressibility of copper is plotted against the Kelvin temperature in Fig. 13.5. Above about 100°K the rise of k is approximately linear.

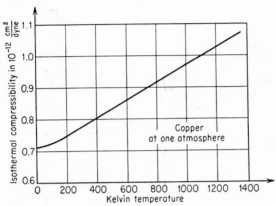

FIG. 13.5. Temperature variation of k of copper.

The adiabatic compressibility is obtained most readily by measuring the velocity of sound $\mathscr{V}$ and using the equation derived in Chap. 6, namely, $\mathscr{V} = \sqrt{1/\rho k_s}$. Eliminating C_V from the equations derived in this chapter,

$$\frac{c_P}{c_V} = \frac{k}{k_s},$$

and

$$c_P - c_V = \frac{Tv\beta^2}{k},$$

TABLE 13.2. VELOCITY OF SOUND AND COMPRESSIBILITY OF WATER

Temp., °C	$\mathscr{V}$, km/sec	β, 10^{-6} (deg)$^{-1}$	c_P, joule / gm · deg	ρ, gm / cm³	k, 10^{-12} cm² / dyne	k_s, 10^{-12} cm² / dyne
0	1.404	−67	4.2177	0.99986	50.8	50.8
10	1.448	89	4.1922	0.99973	48.1	48.0
20	1.483	208	4.1819	0.99823	45.8	45.5
30	1.510	304	4.1785	0.99568	44.6	43.9
40	1.530	390	4.1786	0.99225	43.8	42.7
50	1.544	465	4.1807	0.98807	43.7	42.0
60	1.552	522	4.1844	0.98324	43.7	41.5
70	1.555	586	4.1896	0.97781	44.1	41.3
80	1.555	643	4.1964	0.97183	44.8	41.3

we get the useful relation

$$k - k_s = \frac{Tv\beta^2}{c_P}.$$

It follows therefore that

$$k_s = \frac{1}{\rho \mathscr{V}^2}, \quad \text{and} \quad k = \frac{1}{\rho}\left(\frac{1}{\mathscr{V}^2} + \frac{\beta^2 T}{c_P}\right).$$

The data needed to calculate k_s and k of water between 0 and 80°C are listed in Table 13.2, and both k_s and k are plotted in Fig. 13.6.

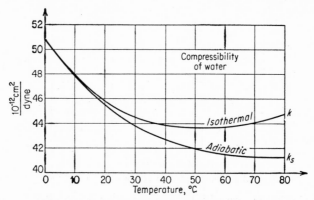

FIG. 13.6. Temperature variation of isothermal and adiabatic compressibilities of water.

13.10. Heat Capacity at Constant Pressure. The experimental measurement of c_P has already been discussed in Art. 4.11 and a type of calorimeter suitable for low-temperature work described. One important result of such measurements is the discovery that the c_P of solids and liquids is extremely insensitive to changes in the pressure. For example, for a change of pressure from 0 to 7000 kg/cm² the c_P of mercury changes from 6.69 to 6.68 cal/mole · deg.

The temperature dependence of c_P, however, is of considerable importance in physics and chemistry. In Table 13.5 the values of c_P of copper are given over a very wide temperature range. These values are plotted in Fig. 13.7. It is seen that c_P approaches zero as the temperature approaches zero and that, as the temperature rises, c_P continually increases without approaching a constant value. This is the normal behavior of c_P and applies for most pure metals and many compounds. There are, of course, exceptions, among which α iron is interesting. In the temperature range from 1000 to 1100°K where the volume expansivity of α iron takes a sudden drop, the c_P takes a sudden rise and then drops just as rapidly. Of even more interest is the behavior of certain paramagnetic salts in the neighborhood of absolute zero. Below 2°K,

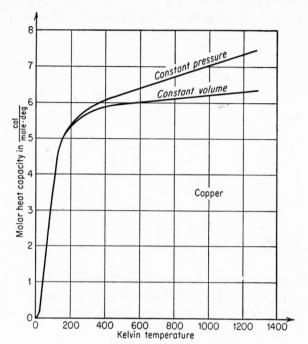

FIG. 13.7. Temperature variation of c_P and c_V of copper.

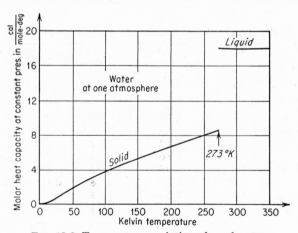

FIG. 13.8. Temperature variation of c_P of water.

c_P rises and then, as the temperature approaches zero, approaches zero again. This behavior is of great importance in connection with the production of very low temperatures by adiabatic demagnetization and will be discussed in Chap. 16.

The behavior of ice is quite normal until the melting point is reached, at which c_P rises to a value more than twice as large, as shown in Table 13.3 and Fig. 13.8.

TABLE 13.3. TEMPERATURE VARIATION OF c_P OF H_2O

Temp., °K	c_P, cal/mole · deg	Temp., °K	c_P, cal/mole · deg
0	0	233	7.63
10	0.66	253	8.14
20	0.423	273 (solid)	8.64
40	1.57	273 (liquid)	18.09
60	2.39	280	18.03
80	3.09	300	18.00
100	3.75	340	18.03
150	5.16	373	18.09
200	6.57		

13.11. Heat Capacity at Constant Volume. It has been mentioned that the c_V of solids and liquids is almost impossible to measure and must therefore be calculated from known values of c_P with the aid of the equation

$$c_P - c_V = \frac{Tv\beta^2}{k}.$$

TABLE 13.4. PRESSURE VARIATION OF PROPERTIES OF MERCURY AT 0°C

P, kg/cm²	v, cm³/mole	β 10^{-6} deg^{-1}	k, 10^{-12} cm²/dyne	c_P, cal mole · deg	$c_P - c_V$ $= \frac{Tv\beta^2}{Jk}$	c_V, cal mole · deg	γ
0	14.72	181	3.88	6.69	0.810	5.88	1.14
1000	14.67	174	3.79	6.69	0.768	5.92	1.13
2000	14.62	168	3.69	6.69	0.731	5.96	1.12
3000	14.57	164	3.60	6.68	0.709	5.97	1.12
4000	14.51	160	3.48	6.68	0.695	5.98	1.12
5000	14.45	158	3.38	6.68	0.695	5.98	1.12
6000	14.42	155	3.25	6.68	0.694	5.99	1.11
7000	14.38	152	3.12	6.68	0.692	5.99	1.11

In Table 13.4 this calculation is shown for mercury at 0°C at a number of different pressures. It is seen that the c_V of mercury varies less than 2 per cent for a pressure change of 7000 kg/cm². The c_V of other substances is also quite insensitive to a change of pressure.

The temperature variation of c_V, however, is very pronounced and is also of great theoretical significance. In Table 13.5 all the quantities

TABLE 13.5. TEMPERATURE VARIATION OF PROPERTIES OF COPPER
Values in parentheses are extrapolated

$T,$ °K	$v,$ cm³/mole	$\beta,$ 10^{-6} deg⁻¹	$k,$ 10^{-12} cm²/dyne	$c_P,$ $\dfrac{\text{cal}}{\text{mole} \cdot \text{deg}}$	$c_P - c_V$ $= \dfrac{Tv\beta^2}{Jk}$	$c_V,$ $\dfrac{\text{cal}}{\text{mole} \cdot \text{deg}}$	γ
0	(7.0)	(0)	(0.710)	(0)	0	0	1.00
50	(7.002)	(11.5)	(0.712	1.38	0.00154	1.38	1.00
100	(7.008)	31.5	0.721	3.88	0.0230	3.86	1.00
150	(7.018)	41.0	0.733	5.01	0.0577	4.95	1.01
200	(7.029)	45.6	0.748	5.41	0.0931	5.32	1.02
250	7.043	48.0	0.762	5.65	0.127	5.52	1.02
300	7.062	49.2	0.776	5.87	0.157	5.71	1.03
500	7.115	54.2	0.837	6.25	0.298	5.95	1.05
800	7.256	60.7	0.922	6.70	0.555	6.14	1.09
1200	7.452	69.7	1.030	7.34	1.00	6.34	1.16

that are used to calculate c_V of copper are listed, along with the final values of c_V. These are plotted along with c_P in Fig. 13.7. It is to be noted that c_V and c_P are practically identical at low temperatures but become quite different at high temperatures where c_V, unlike c_P, approaches a constant value in the neighborhood of 6 cal/mole · deg. This is the normal behavior of most pure metals and compounds.

A tremendous amount of data is required to set up a table such as Table 13.5. The complete temperature dependence of molar volume, volume expansivity, isothermal compressibility, and molar heat at constant pressure is not known for all the substances whose temperature variation of c_V must be known. It is therefore fortunate that an approximate relation exists which is sufficiently accurate to allow the calculation of $c_P - c_V$ in a much simpler manner. If we rewrite the equation

$$c_P - c_V = \frac{v\beta^2 T}{k}$$

in the form

$$c_P - c_V = \frac{v\beta^2}{kc_P^2} c_P^2 T,$$

and denote by the symbol A

$$A = \frac{v\beta^2}{kc_P^2},$$

experiment shows that A remains approximately constant as the temperature changes. The approximate constancy of A is shown in the case of copper in Table 13.6, where it is seen that A does not depart appreciably from the average value of 1.55×10^{-5} mole/cal. With this simplification, the equation for the difference in the heat capacities takes

TABLE 13.6. VALUES OF
A FOR COPPER

Temp., °K	$A = v\beta^2/Jkc_P^2$, $10^{-5}\dfrac{\text{mole}}{\text{cal}}$
0	
50	1.61
100	1.54
150	1.53
200	1.60
250	1.59
300	1.52
500	1.57
800	1.55
1200	1.55

the form

$$c_P - c_V = Ac_P^2 T,$$

where A is a constant which can be calculated from *one* value of each of v, k, β, and c_P at *one* convenient temperature. The equation in this form, known as the *Nernst-Lindemann equation*, is the one that has actually been used to calculate the temperature variation of c_V of most solids.

The results of such calculations for a few representative substances are shown in Fig. 13.9. In all cases, c_V approaches zero as the temperature

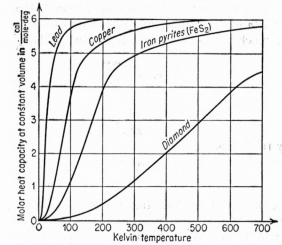

FIG. 13.9. Temperature variation of c_V of solids.

approaches zero and approaches a constant value of about 6 cal/mole · deg as the temperature is raised. The actual temperature region, however, where c_V becomes 6 cal/mole · deg is different for each substance, being around 100°K for Pb and about 2000°K for diamond. In many cases this asymptotic value is reached in the neighborhood of room temperature, about 300°K. Since at this temperature c_V and c_P are not very different, the c_P of many substances has a value in the neighborhood of 6 cal/mole · deg at room temperature. This fact was first noticed by Dulong and Petit, in recognition of whom the value of 6 cal/mole · deg approached by the c_V of all solids at high temperatures is called the *Dulong and Petit value*. The c_V's of some substances, notably Na, Cu, Fe, and FeS$_2$, exceed the Dulong and Petit value at very high temperature.

13.12. Theory of Heat Capacity of Solids. The reason that the c_V of a solid is of more theoretical interest than c_P is found in the fact that $c_V = (\partial u/\partial T)_V$ where u, the molar internal energy, may be calculated with the aid of statistical mechanics. In general, this calculation is extremely complicated because many different phenomena contribute to the internal energy of the solid. Suppose, for example, that the solid is a crystal having a lattice composed of molecules each one of which consists of several atoms, and suppose, furthermore, that there is about one free electron per molecule. Then the total internal energy may be due to:

1. Translational motions of the free electrons.
2. Vibrations of the molecules about their equilibrium positions, called briefly *lattice vibrations*.
3. Vibrations of atoms within each molecule.
4. Partial rotation of the molecules.
5. Excitation of upper energy levels of the molecules.
6. Anomalous effects.

It is fortunate that all these effects do not take place in all solids. For example, in the case of nonmetals, motions of free electrons do not exist, and in the case of metals the lattice consists of single atoms the component parts of which do not rotate or vibrate. Furthermore, all effects do not take place in all temperature ranges. Thus, the motions of the free electrons of metals have an appreciable effect on the heat capacity only at very low temperatures, below about 20°K. Above this temperature they may be ignored. Similarly, excitation of upper energy levels takes place only at very high temperatures and can therefore be ignored at moderate temperatures.

Taking into account only pure lattice vibrations and assuming that the number of such vibrations per unit frequency range at the frequency ν varies directly as ν^2 up to a maximum frequency ν_m, Debye was able to calculate the resulting c_V and to express the result in the form

$$c_V = 3RD\left(\frac{T}{\Theta}\right),$$

where R is the universal gas constant, Θ is a constant, known as the *Debye temperature*, proportional to ν_m, and D is a complicated function, as follows:

$$D\left(\frac{T}{\Theta}\right) = 12\left(\frac{T}{\Theta}\right)^3 \int_0^{\frac{\Theta}{T}} \frac{y^3\,dy}{e^y - 1} - 3\,\frac{\Theta/T}{e^{\Theta/T} - 1}.$$

In view of the simplifying assumptions made by Debye, this expression may be expected to break down at very high temperatures and, in the case of metals, at very low temperatures. Within these two extremes, if no anomalous effects take place, one may expect Debye's formula to agree fairly well with experiment.

The function $D(T/\Theta)$ unfortunately cannot be expressed in simpler form but must be evaluated numerically. The resulting values of c_V are tabulated in Table 13.7 and plotted in Fig. 13.10, where it is seen

TABLE 13.7. DEBYE'S VALUE OF c_V AS A FUNCTION T/Θ

T/Θ	c_V, cal/mole · deg	T/Θ	c_V, cal/mole · deg
0.000	0.0000	0.6	5.193
0.025	0.0073	0.7	5.383
0.050	0.0580	0.8	5.515
0.075	0.1953	0.9	5.604
0.10	0.4514	1.0	5.670
0.15	1.269	1.5	5.824
0.20	2.198	2	5.884
0.25	2.996	3	5.919
0.3	3.615	4	5.937
0.4	4.437	∞	5.958
0.5	4.913		

that the general shape of the curve is the same as that found by experiment. The value of Θ corresponding to a particular substance may be found by comparing the experimental c_V curve with the Debye c_V curve and choosing that value of Θ which will make the two curves coincide. The Dulong and Petit value arises from the Debye formula from the circumstance that, as $T/\Theta \rightarrow \infty$ (roughly, when $T \gg \Theta$),

$$D\left(\frac{T}{\Theta}\right) \rightarrow 1$$

and $$c_V \rightarrow 3R.$$

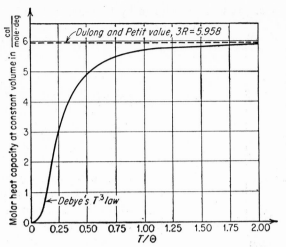

Fig. 13.10. Debye's value of c_V as a function of T/Θ.

The fact that the c_V of some substances exceeds the Dulong and Petit value is due to the high temperature effects listed at the beginning of this article, which are not taken into account in the Debye theory.

As $T/\Theta \to 0$, it may be shown that

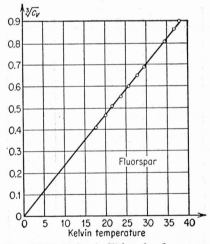

$$D\left(\frac{T}{\Theta}\right) \to \frac{4\pi^4}{5}\left(\frac{T}{\Theta}\right)^3,$$

and hence at very low temperature

$$c_V = \frac{12\pi^4 R}{5\Theta^3}T^3,$$

which, expressed in calories per mole degree, becomes

$$c_V = \frac{464.4}{\Theta^3}T^3.$$

This equation, known as Debye's T^3 law, holds for most nonmetals in the region of low temperatures. This is shown in the case of fluorspar,

Fig. 13.11. Debye's T^3 law for fluorspar.

CaF_2, in Fig. 13.11, where $\sqrt[3]{c_V}$ is plotted against T. The corresponding value of Θ may be obtained from the slope of the line. A few values of Θ are given in the last column of Table 13.8.

The Debye temperature Θ is proportional to the maximum frequency of vibration of the crystal lattice and this, in turn, may be shown to depend on the melting temperature T_m, the molecular weight M, and the molar volume v.　It was first shown by Lindemann that

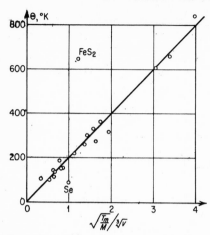

$$\Theta = \frac{\text{const.}}{\sqrt[3]{v}}\sqrt{\frac{T_m}{M}}.$$

The quantities in this equation are listed in Table 13.8 and the equation itself is tested in Fig. 13.12 by plotting Θ against $\sqrt{T_m/M}/\sqrt[3]{v}$. The equation is found to hold quite well for all the substances listed except FeS_2 (iron pyrites) and Se (selenium).　The value of the constant, which is the slope of the line, is very nearly 200.

FIG. 13.12. Dependence of Debye Θ of nonmetals on melting temperature T_m, molecular weight M, and molar volume v. (Slope = 200.)

To account for the behavior of metals at very low temperatures, it is necessary to extend Debye's theory to take account of the motions of the free electrons.　This

TABLE 13.8. PROPERTIES OF NONMETALS

Solid	T_m, °K	M, gm/mole	ρ, gm/cm³	$v = M/\rho$, cm³/mole	$\sqrt[3]{v}$	$\dfrac{\sqrt{T_m/M}}{\sqrt[3]{v}}$	Θ, °K
H_2O	273	18	0.92	19.6	2.7	1.45	315
I	387	254	4.93	51.6	3.72	0.331	106
Se	490	79	4.80	16.5	2.55	0.977	89
AgBr	703	188	6.47	29.0	3.07	0.628	144
Te	723	128	6.02	21.3	2.77	0.860	153
AgCl	728	143	5.56	25.7	2.95	0.766	183
RbI	913	213	3.55	60.0	3.91	0.530	100
RbBr	953	165	3.35	49.3	3.67	0.655	135
KI	958	166	3.13	53.0	3.76	0.638	115
KBr	1003	119	2.75	43.4	3.52	0.823	152
KCl	1049	74.6	1.98	37.7	3.35	1.12	218
NaCl	1074	58.5	2.17	27.0	3.00	1.43	300
As	1090	74.9	5.73	13.1	2.36	1.62	275
LiF	1143	25.9	2.60	10.0	2.16	3.04	607
Ge	1232	72.6	5.35	13.6	2.38	1.73	362
FeS_2	1444	120	5.00	24.0	2.88	1.21	645
ZnS	1511	97.5	4.10	23.8	2.88	1.37	260
CaF_2	1633	78.1	3.18	24.6	2.91	1.57	331
Si	1683	28.1	2.33	12.1	2.30	3.37	658
TiC_2	2108	79.9	4.26	18.8	2.66	1.93	318
MgO	3173	40.3	3.58	11.3	2.24	3.96	820
Diamond	3800	12	3.51	3.42	1.51	12.1	1860–2400

was first done by Sommerfeld on the basis of a theory by Fermi, with the result that

$$c_V = \frac{464.4}{\Theta^3} T^3 + \gamma' T,$$

where the first term on the right is seen to be the Debye T^3 law express-

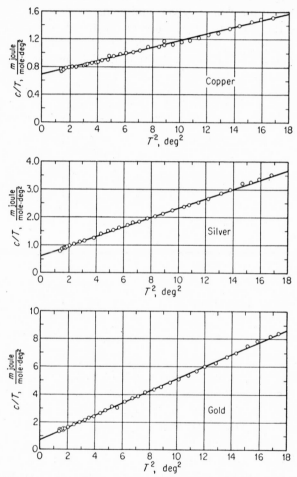

FIG. 13.13. Heat-capacity measurements of Corak, Garfunkel, Satterthwaite, and Wexler.

ing the contribution of the lattice vibrations to the heat capacity, and the second term, linear in T, is the electronic contribution to the heat capacity. The constant γ', different for different metals, will be called the *electronic constant*. It is not to be confused with the ratio of C_P to C_V.

Experimental verification of the Debye-Sommerfeld equation is shown by plotting c_V/T against T^2 (at low temperatures only), since

$$\frac{c_V}{T} = \frac{464.4}{\Theta^3} T^2 + \gamma',$$

which is a straight line with a slope equal to $464.4/\Theta^3$, and a y intercept equal to γ'. The three graphs of Fig. 13.13, obtained by Corak, Garfunkel, Satterthwaite, and Wexler show how well the Debye-Sommerfeld theory is verified for copper, silver, and gold.

Values of the Debye temperature Θ are listed for many metals in Table 13.9 along with the atomic weight M, the density ρ, and the melting temperature T_m. The validity of Lindemann's equation is shown

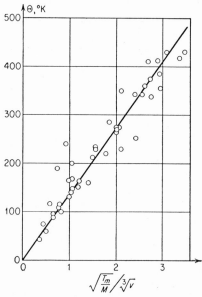

FIG. 13.14. Dependence of Debye Θ of metals on melting temperature T_m, atomic weight M, and molar volume v. (Slope = 137.)

by the graph in Fig. 13.14 where Θ is seen to be proportional to $\sqrt{T_m/M}/\sqrt[3]{v}$, as in the case of nonmetals, but with a different constant of proportionality, namely, 137.

Values of the electronic constant γ' are listed in Table 13.10. There is no simple relation between the electronic constant of a metal and any of its well-known macroscopic properties. The theoretical interpretation of γ' is quite involved and requires for its understanding a knowledge of quantum statistics and the band theory of metals. From these theories one is led to suspect a relation between γ' and the number of electrons outside of closed shells. These numbers are given in Table 13.10 and, in Fig. 13.15 it may be seen that, in a very rough way, γ' increases as the number of electrons outside of closed shells increases from 1 to 5, and

TABLE 13.9. DEBYE TEMPERATURES OF METALS

Metal	M, gm/mole	ρ, gm/cm^3	T_m, °K	$\sqrt[3]{v}$	$\dfrac{\sqrt{T_m/M}}{\sqrt[3]{v}}$	Θ, °K
Ag	108	10.5	1234	2.18	1.55	229
Al	27.0	2.70	933	2.16	2.72	375
Au	197	19.3	1336	2.17	1.20	164
Ba	137	3.5	983	3.40	0.788	116
Be	9.01	1.85	1556	1.70	7.74	1160
Bi	209	9.80	544	2.77	0.582	117
Ca	40.1	1.55	1123	2.96	1.77	220
Cd	112	8.64	594	2.35	0.98	165
Co	58.9	8.9	1768	1.88	2.92	385
Cr	52.0	7.20	2173	1.93	3.35	418
Cs	133	1.89	302	4.13	0.365	43
Cu	63.5	8.92	1357	1.93	2.40	343
Fe	55.9	7.86	1803	1.93	2.94	355
Ga	69.7	5.93	303	2.28	0.92	240
Gd	157	7.95	1600	2.70	1.18	152
Hf	179	13.3	2250	2.38	1.49	213
Hg	201	13.6	234	2.46	0.439	75
In	115	7.30	430	2.51	0.770	109
Ir	193	22.4	2727	2.05	1.84	285
K	39.1	0.86	336	3.57	0.822	100
La	139	6.15	1193	2.83	0.994	143
Li	6.94	0.534	459	2.35	3.46	430
Mg	24.3	1.74	924	2.41	2.56	342
Mn	54.9	7.20	1533	1.97	2.68	410
Mo	96.0	10.2	2893	2.11	2.61	360
Nb	92.9	8.55	2688	2.22	2.42	252
Na	23.0	0.97	371	2.87	1.40	160
Ni	58.7	8.90	1725	1.88	2.88	413
Pb	207	11.3	601	2.64	0.647	96.3
Pd	107	12.0	1825	2.07	2.00	275
Pt	195	21.5	2042	2.10	1.54	233
Rb	85.5	1.53	312	3.82	0.500	59
Re	186	20.5	3440	2.10	2.05	275
Rh	103	12.4	2233	2.21	2.10	350
Sb	122	6.68	904	2.64	1.03	140
Sn	119	5.75	505	2.74	0.753	195
Sr	87.6	2.6	1030	3.23	1.06	148
Ta	181	16.6	3278	2.03	2.10	230
Th	232	11.2	1968	2.74	1.06	168
Ti	47.9	4.5	1950	2.07	3.08	430
Tl	204	11.9	575	2.58	0.650	87.9
U	238	18.7	1406	2.33	1.04	200
V	51.0	5.96	2190	2.39	2.74	338
W	184	19.3	3653	2.22	2.00	270
Zn	65.4	7.14	693	2.09	1.56	235
Zr	91.2	6.4	2125	2.43	1.99	265

TABLE 13.10. ELECTRONIC CONSTANTS OF METALS

Metal	γ', 10^{-4} cal/mole · deg^2	Electrons outside closed shells	Metal	γ', 10^{-4} cal/mole · deg^2	Electrons outside closed shells
Ag	1.45–1.60	1	Nb	17.5–20.4	5
Al	3.27–3.48	3	Na	4.3	1
Au	1.67	1	Ni	17.4	10
Be	0.53	2	Os	5.62	8
Bi	0.114–0.186	5	Pb	7.48–8.0	4
Ca	2.9	2	Pd	22.4–31.0	10
Cd	1.5–1.7	2	Pr	22	5
Co	12.0	9	Pt	16.1–16.5	10
Cr	3.7–3.8	6	Re	5.85	7
Cu	1.60–1.80	1	Rh	10.0–11.7	9
Fe	12.0	8	Ru	8.0	8
Ga	1.2	3	Sn	4.18–4.46	4
Gd	16	10	Ta	13.0–14.0	5
Graphite	0.074		Th	11.2–13.3	4
Hf	6.3–6.8	4	Ti	8.0–8.5	4
Hg	5.3	2	Tl	7.5	3
In	4.0–4.33	3	U	26	6
Ir	7.5–7.6	9	V	21.1–22.1	5
La	16–24	3	W	1.8–5.0	6
Mg	3.15–3.25	2	Zn	1.25–1.50	2
Mn	32.9–43	7	Zr	6.92–7.25	4
Mo	5.05–5.25	6			

then starts low again and increases from 6 to 10. There are four out-standing exceptions to this rule: Mn, La, Bi, and U.

13.13. Grüneisen's Equation. As the temperature approaches zero, both c_V and β approach zero. The ratio c_V/β, however, approaches a constant which is characteristic of the substance. Grüneisen was the first to apply statistical mechanics to a monatomic solid, assuming the potential energy of any two atoms to consist of two terms: one corresponding to an attraction varying inversely as the distance between atoms r to the mth power, and the other to a repulsion varying inversely as r^n. The details of the theory cannot be given here, but one result is an approximate relation between c_V and β as follows:

$$\frac{c_V}{\beta} = \frac{[(c_V/\beta)_0 - bu]^2}{(c_V/\beta)_0},$$

$$\left(\frac{c_V}{\beta}\right)_0 = \frac{c_V}{\beta} \text{ at } T = 0,$$

$$u = \int_0^T c_V \, dT,$$

$$b = \frac{m + n + 3}{6}.$$

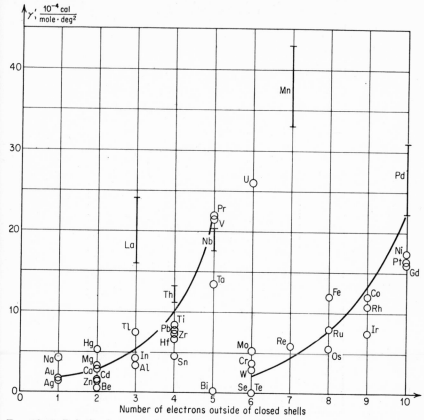

FIG. 13.15. Relation between electronic constant and the number of electrons outside closed shells.

To test this equation experimentally it is convenient to plot $\sqrt{c_V/\beta}$ against u, for the resulting equation

$$\sqrt{\frac{c_V}{\beta}} = \sqrt{\left(\frac{c_V}{\beta}\right)_0} - \frac{b}{\sqrt{(c_V/\beta)_0}}\, u$$

is a straight line with y intercept equal to $\sqrt{(c_V/\beta)_0}$ and slope equal to $-b/\sqrt{(c_V/\beta)_0}$. Values of u may be found either by measuring areas under c_V vs. T curves with a planimeter, or by using Debye's equation. Such graphs are shown in Fig. 13.16 for six metals, and it may be seen that Grüneisen's equation holds quite well. Values of $(c_V/\beta)_0$ are listed for 24 metals in Table 13.11, along with the ratio of molar volume v to compressibility k.

It is a consequence of Grüneisen's theory that both $(c_V/\beta)_0$ and $(v/k)_0$ should be approximately proportional to the melting temperature.

TABLE 13.11. PROPERTIES OF METALS

Metal	$(c_V/\beta)_0$, k cal ────── mole	v/k, k cal ────── mole	$\Gamma = \dfrac{v/k}{(c_V/\beta)_0}$	T_m, °K
Ag	112	244	2.18	1234
Al	84.1	177	2.10	933
Au	149	452	3.04	1336
Be	106	125	1.18	1556
Bi	150	168	1.12	544
Ca	96.0	111	1.16	1123
Cr	277	360	1.30	2173
Cu	120	234	1.94	1357
Fe	167	284	1.70	1803
Mn	85.0	221	2.60	1533
Mo	363	625	1.71	2893
Nb	291	463	1.59	2688
Ni	152	296	1.95	1725
Pb	80.8	190	2.35	601
Pd	170	415	2.44	1825
Pt	221	592	2.68	2042
Rh	230	506	2.20	2233
Sb	179	165	0.92	904
Sn	112	200	1.81	505
Ta	307	535	1.75	3278
Th	185	240	1.30	1968
V	216	227	1.05	2190
W	445	775	1.74	3653
Zn	68.6	128	1.87	693

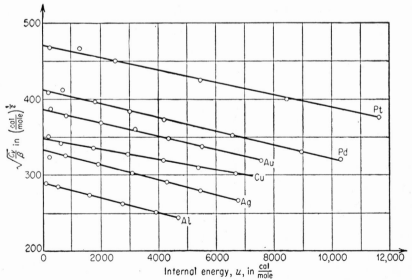

FIG. 13.16. Graphs to test the validity of Grüneisen's equation.

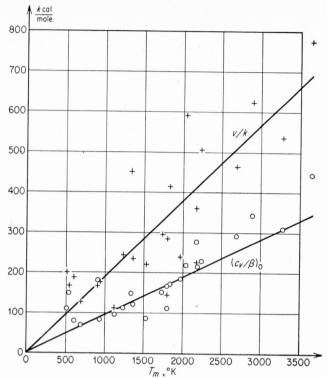

FIG. 13.17. Approximate proportionality of both $(c_V/\beta)_0$ (circles) and v/k (crosses) with the melting temperature of metals.

These quantities are plotted against T_m in Fig. 13.17 where the proportionality is seen to be very rough indeed. The ratio

$$\Gamma = \frac{(v/k)_0}{(c_V/\beta)_0},$$

known as *Grüneisen's constant*, would be strictly constant if $(c_V/\beta)_0$ and $(v/k)_0$ were strictly proportional to T_m. It may be seen from the fourth column of Table 13.11 that Γ is in the neighborhood of 2 for most metals.

PROBLEMS

13.1. Determine whether the following differential expressions are exact or not. If they are, find the functions of which these expressions are the differentials:

(a) $y\,dx + x\,dy$.
(b) $y\,dx - x\,dy$.
(c) $x\,dx + y\,dy$.
(d) $x\,dx - y\,dy$.
(e) $-dx/x^2y + dy/xy^2$.
(f) $R(1 + B'P)\,dT + RTB'\,dP$ (R and B' are constants).

13.2. Starting with the first Maxwell equation, derive the remaining three by using only the relations

$$\left(\frac{\partial x}{\partial y}\right)_z \left(\frac{\partial y}{\partial z}\right)_x \left(\frac{\partial z}{\partial x}\right)_y = -1,$$

$$\left(\frac{\partial x}{\partial y}\right)_f \left(\frac{\partial y}{\partial z}\right)_f \left(\frac{\partial z}{\partial x}\right)_f = +1.$$

13.3. Derive the following equations:

(a) $U = A - T\left(\dfrac{\partial A}{\partial T}\right)_V = -T^2\left(\dfrac{\partial A/T}{\partial T}\right)_V.$

(b) $C_V = -T\left(\dfrac{\partial^2 A}{\partial T^2}\right)_V.$

(c) $H = G - T\left(\dfrac{\partial G}{\partial T}\right)_P = -T^2\left(\dfrac{\partial G/T}{\partial T}\right)_P.$ (Gibbs-Helmholtz equation.)

(d) $C_P = -T\left(\dfrac{\partial^2 G}{\partial T^2}\right)_P.$

13.4. (a) Derive the equation

$$\left(\frac{\partial C_V}{\partial V}\right)_T = T\left(\frac{\partial^2 P}{\partial T^2}\right)_V.$$

(b) Prove that C_V of an ideal gas is a function of T only.

(c) In the case of a gas obeying the equation of state

$$\frac{Pv}{RT} = 1 + \frac{B''}{v},$$

where B'' is a function of T only, show that

$$C_V = -\frac{RT}{v}\frac{d^2}{dT^2}(B''T) + (C_V)_0,$$

where $(C_V)_0$ is the value at very large volumes.

13.5. (a) Derive the equation

$$\left(\frac{\partial C_P}{\partial P}\right)_T = -T\left(\frac{\partial^2 V}{\partial T^2}\right)_P.$$

(b) Prove that C_P of an ideal gas is a function of T only.

(c) In the case of a gas obeying the equation of state

$$\frac{Pv}{RT} = 1 + B'P,$$

where B' is a function of T only, show that

$$C_P = -RTP\frac{d^2}{dT^2}(B'T) + (C_P)_0,$$

where $(C_P)_0$ is the value at very low pressures.

13.6. From the fact that dV/V is an exact differential, derive the relation

$$\left(\frac{\partial \beta}{\partial P}\right)_T = -\left(\frac{\partial k}{\partial T}\right)_P.$$

13.7. Derive the third $T\,dS$ equation,

$$T\,dS = C_V\left(\frac{\partial T}{\partial P}\right)_V dP + C_P\left(\frac{\partial T}{\partial V}\right)_P dV,$$

and show that the three $T\,dS$ equations may be written

(1) $$T\,dS = C_V\,dT + \frac{\beta T}{k}\,dV,$$

(2) $$T\,dS = C_P\,dT - V\beta T\,dP,$$

(3) $$T\,dS = \frac{C_V k}{\beta}\,dP + \frac{C_P}{\beta V}\,dV.$$

13.8. (a) Prove that

$$\left(\frac{\partial u}{\partial P}\right)_T = -T\left(\frac{\partial v}{\partial T}\right)_P - P\left(\frac{\partial v}{\partial P}\right)_T.$$

(b) Taking for the equation of state of a real gas at moderately low pressures

$$\frac{Pv}{RT} = 1 + B'P,$$

where B' is a function of T only, show that

$$\left(\frac{\partial u}{\partial P}\right)_T = -RT\,\frac{d}{dT}\,(B'T).$$

Does this result agree with the experiments of Rossini and Frandsen described in Chap. 6?

13.9. The pressure on 500 gm of copper is increased reversibly and isothermally from zero to 5000 atm at 100°K.

(a) How much heat in calories is transferred during the compression?

(b) How much work is done during the compression?

(c) Determine the change of internal energy.

(d) What would have been the rise of temperature if the copper had been subjected to a reversible adiabatic compression?

(Assume the density, volume expansivity, isothermal compressibility, and heat capacity to remain practically constant. The values are given in Table 13.5.)

13.10. The pressure on 200 gm of water is increased reversibly and isothermally from 1 to 3000 atm at 0°C.

(a) How much heat is transferred?

(b) How much work is done?

(c) Calculate the change in internal energy.

($\beta = -67 \times 10^{-6}$ deg^{-1} and $k = 43 \times 10^{-12}$ cm^2/dyne.)

13.11. The pressure on 1 gm of water is increased from 0 to 1000 atm reversibly and adiabatically. Calculate the temperature change when the initial temperature has the three different values given below:

Temp., °C	Specific volume v, cm^3/gm	β, deg^{-1}	c_P, cal/gm · deg
0	1.000	$- 67 \times 10^{-6}$	1.0087
5	1.000	$+ 15 \times 10^{-6}$	1.0048
50	1.012	$+465 \times 10^{-6}$	0.9983

13.12. Measurements of thermal expansion and compressibility of a gas yield the equations

$$\left(\frac{\partial v}{\partial T}\right)_P = \frac{R}{P} + \frac{a}{T^2},$$

$$\left(\frac{\partial v}{\partial P}\right)_T = -Tf(P),$$

where a is a constant and $f(P)$ is a function of the pressure only. At low pressures, the heat capacity at constant pressure has the value for a monatomic ideal gas. Show that:

(a) $f(P) = \dfrac{R}{P^2}$.

(b) The equation of state is

$$Pv = RT - \frac{aP}{T}.$$

(c) $c_P = \dfrac{2aP}{T^2} + \dfrac{5}{2} R$.

13.13. Derive the equations:

(a) $C_V = -T \left(\dfrac{\partial P}{\partial T}\right)_V \left(\dfrac{\partial V}{\partial T}\right)_S$.

(b) $\left(\dfrac{\partial V}{\partial T}\right)_S = -\dfrac{C_V k}{\beta T}$.

(c) $\dfrac{(\partial V/\partial T)_S}{(\partial V/\partial T)_P} = \dfrac{1}{1 - \gamma}$.

13.14. Derive the equations:

(a) $C_P = T \left(\dfrac{\partial V}{\partial T}\right)_P \left(\dfrac{\partial P}{\partial T}\right)_S$.

(b) $\left(\dfrac{\partial P}{\partial T}\right)_S = \dfrac{C_P}{V \beta T}$.

(c) $\dfrac{(\partial P/\partial T)_S}{(\partial P/\partial T)_V} = \dfrac{\gamma}{\gamma - 1}$.

13.15. At 0°C, aluminum has the following properties: atomic weight = 27.0 gm/mole, density = 2.70 gm/cm^3, c_P = 0.220 cal/gm · deg, β = 71.4 $\times$ 10^{-6} deg^{-1}, k = 1.34 $\times$ 10^{-12} cm^2/dyne. Calculate, at 0°C, (a) the molar heat capacity at constant volume; (b) the ratio γ; (c) the adiabatic compressibility; (d) the constant A in the Nernst-Lindemann equation.

13.16. At 0°C, nickel has the following properties: atomic weight = 58.7 gm/mole, density = 8.90 gm/cm³, c_P = 0.109 cal/gm · deg, β = 40.0 × 10^{-6} deg⁻¹, k = 0.568 × 10^{-12} cm²/dyne. Calculate, at 0°C, (a) the molar heat capacity at constant volume; (b) the ratio γ; (c) the adiabatic compressibility; (d) the constant A in the Nernst-Lindemann equation.

13.17. (a) Prove that the slope of a curve on a Mollier diagram representing a reversible isothermal process is equal to

$$T - \frac{1}{\beta}.$$

(b) Prove that the slope of a curve on a Mollier diagram representing a reversible isochoric process is equal to

$$T + \frac{\gamma - 1}{\beta}.$$

13.18. The Nernst-Lindemann constant A may be written with sufficient accuracy in terms of c_V, thus

$$A = \frac{\beta^2 v}{c_V^2 k}.$$

With the aid of the experimental data given in Art. 13.13, show that, approximately,

$$A = \frac{0.0214 \text{ mole} \cdot \text{deg/cal}}{T_m},$$

where T_m is the melting temperature. Using this equation, calculate A for copper and compare this value with the value given in Art. 13.11.

14

Applications of Thermodynamics
to Special Systems

14.1. Joule-Kelvin Effect (Porous-plug Experiment). In the porous-plug experiment a gas is made to undergo a continuous throttling process. By means of a pump a constant pressure is maintained on one side of a porous plug and a constant lower pressure on the other side. In the original experiments of Joule and Kelvin a cotton plug was used and the gas flowed through it parallel to the axis of the pipe. In modern measurements a cup of a strong porous material capable of withstanding a large force allows the gas to seep through in a radial direction. Rigid precautions are taken to provide adequate thermal insulation for the plug and the portion of the pipe near the plug. Suitable manometers and thermometers are used to measure the pressure and temperature of the gas on both sides of the plug.

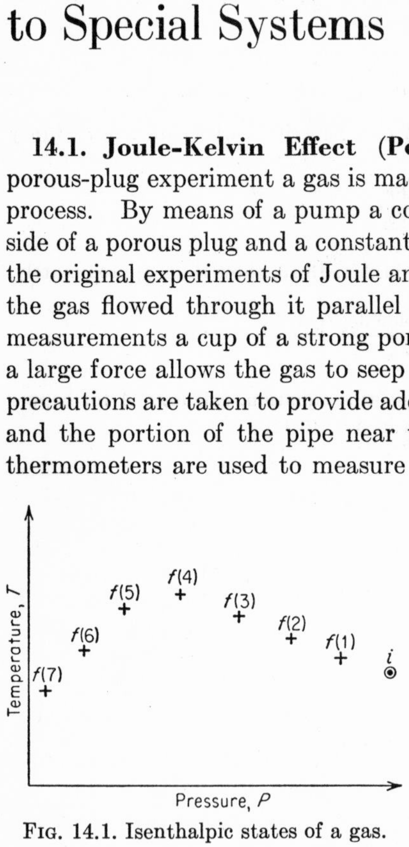

The experiment is performed in the following way: The pressure and temperature on the high-pressure side of the plug P_i and T_i are chosen arbitrarily. The pressure on the other side of the plug P_f is then set at any value less than P_i, and the temperature of the gas T_f is measured. P_i and T_i are kept the same, and P_f is changed to another value and the corresponding T_f is measured. This is done for a number of different values of P_f, the corresponding T_f being measured in each case. P_f is the independent variable of the experiment and T_f the dependent variable. The results provide a set of discrete points on a T-P diagram, one point being $P_i T_i$ and the others being the various P_f's and T_f's indicated in Fig. 14.1 by numbers (1) to (7). Although the points shown in the figure do not refer to any particular gas, they are typical of most gases. It can

Fig. 14.1. Isenthalpic states of a gas.

280

be seen that, if a throttling process takes place between the states $P_i T_i$ and $P_f T_f$ (3), there is a rise of temperature.   Between $P_i T_i$ and $P_f T_f$ (7), however, there is a drop of temperature.   In general, the temperature change of a gas upon seeping through a porous plug depends on the three quantities P_i, T_i, and P_f and may be an increase or a decrease or there may be no change whatever.

According to the principles developed in Art. 11.10, the eight points plotted in Fig. 14.1 represent equilibrium states of some constant mass of the gas, say, 1 gm, at which the gas has the same enthalpy.   All equilibrium states of the gas corresponding to this enthalpy must lie on some curve, and it is reasonable to assume that this curve can be obtained by drawing a smooth curve through the discrete points.   Such a curve is called an *isenthalpic curve*.   The student must understand that *an isenthalpic curve is not the graph of a throttling process*.   No such graph can be drawn because in any throttling process the intermediate states traversed by a gas cannot be described by means of thermodynamic coordinates.   An isenthalpic curve is the locus of all points representing equilibrium states of the same enthalpy.   The porous-plug experiment is performed to provide a few of these points, the rest being obtained by interpolation.

The temperature on the high-pressure side T_i is now changed to another value, P_i being kept the same. P_f is again varied and the corresponding T_f's measured.   Upon plotting the new $P_i T_i$ and the new P_f's and T_f's, another discrete set of points is obtained, which determines another isenthalpic curve corresponding to a different enthalpy.   In this way, a series of isenthalpic curves is obtained.   Such a series is shown in Fig. 14.2 for nitrogen.

The numerical value of the slope of an isenthalpic curve on a T-P diagram at any point is called the *Joule-Kelvin coefficient* and will be denoted by μ.   Thus

$$\mu = \left(\frac{\partial T}{\partial P}\right)_h.$$

The locus of all points at which the Joule-Kelvin coefficient is zero, i.e., the locus of the maxima of the isenthalpic curves, is known as the *inversion curve* and is shown in Fig. 14.2 as a dotted closed curve.   The region inside the inversion curve where μ is positive is called the region of cooling, whereas outside, where μ is negative, is the region of heating.

If a vertical line is drawn at some arbitrarily chosen pressure, it will intersect the isenthalpic curves at a number of points at which μ may be obtained by measuring the slopes of the isenthalpics at these points. We should then have a set of values of μ referring to the same pressure but to different temperatures.   This can then be repeated at another

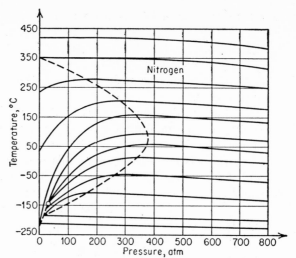

FIG. 14.2. Isenthalpic curves and inversion curve for nitrogen.   The encircled point is the critical point.   (*After Roebuck.*)

pressure.   The data in Table 14.1 were obtained in this way from very careful measurements by Roebuck and Osterberg.

TABLE 14.1. JOULE-KELVIN COEFFICIENTS AND HEAT CAPACITIES

t, °C	Helium at 1 atm		Nitrogen at 1 atm	
	c_P, cal/gm · deg	μ, deg/atm	c_P, cal/gm · deg	μ, deg/atm
300	1.271	−0.0597	0.2501	+0.0139
200	1.264	−0.0641	0.2490	+0.0558
100	1.257	−0.0638	0.2476	+0.1291
75	1.255	−0.0635	0.2472	+0.1555
50	1.254	−0.0631	0.2469	+0.1854
25	1.252	−0.0624	0.2467	+0.2216
0	1.250	−0.0616	0.2466	+0.2655
−100	1.243	−0.0584	0.2473	+0.6487
−155	1.239	−0.0503	0.2478	+1.449
−180	1.237	−0.0412	0.2480	+2.391

The slope of an isenthalpic curve on a T-P diagram, i.e., the *Joule-Kelvin coefficient*, is

$$\mu = \left(\frac{\partial T}{\partial P}\right)_h.$$

In general, the difference in specific enthalpy between two neighboring equilibrium states is

$$dh = T\,ds + v\,dP,$$

and, according to the second $T \, ds$ equation,

$$T \, ds = c_P \, dT - T \left(\frac{\partial v}{\partial T} \right)_P dP.$$

Substituting for $T \, ds$, we get

$$dh = c_P \, dT - \left[T \left(\frac{\partial v}{\partial T} \right)_P - v \right] dP$$

or

$$dT = \frac{1}{c_P} \left[T \left(\frac{\partial v}{\partial T} \right)_P - v \right] dP + \frac{1}{c_P} \, dh.$$

Regarding T as a function of P and h,

$$dT = \left(\frac{\partial T}{\partial P} \right)_h dP + \left(\frac{\partial T}{\partial h} \right)_P dh$$

whence, since $\mu = (\partial T / \partial P)_h$,

$$\boxed{\mu = \frac{1}{c_P} \left[T \left(\frac{\partial v}{\partial T} \right)_P - v \right].}$$

This is the thermodynamic equation for the Joule-Kelvin coefficient. It is evident that, for an ideal gas,

$$\mu = \frac{1}{c_P} \left(T \frac{R}{P} - v \right) = 0.$$

The most important application of the Joule-Kelvin effect is in the liquefaction of gases.

14.2. Liquefaction of Gases by the Joule-Kelvin Effect. An inspection of the isenthalpic curves and the inversion curve of Fig. 14.2 shows that, for the Joule-Kelvin effect to give rise to cooling, the initial temperature of the gas must be below the point where the inversion curve cuts the temperature axis, i.e., below the maximum inversion temperature. For many gases, room temperature is already below the maximum inversion temperature so that no precooling is necessary. Thus, if air is compressed to a pressure of 200 atm and a temperature of 52°C, then, after throttling to a pressure of 1 atm, it will be cooled to 23°C. On the other hand, if helium, originally at 200 atm and 52°C, is throttled to 1 atm, its temperature will rise to 64°C.

Figure 14.3 shows that, for the Joule-Kelvin effect to produce cooling in hydrogen, the hydrogen must be cooled below 200°K. Liquid nitrogen is used in most laboratories for this purpose. To produce Joule-Kelvin cooling in helium, the helium is first cooled with the aid of liquid hydrogen. Only the bottom part of the inversion curve for helium is known with some certainty. Table 14.2 gives the maximum inversion temperatures of a few gases commonly used in low-temperature work.

TABLE 14.2. MAXIMUM INVERSION TEMPERATURES

Gas	Maximum inversion temp., °K
Carbon dioxide............	~1500
Argon...................	723
Nitrogen................	621
Air....................	603
Hydrogen...............	202
Helium.................	~25–60

It is clear from Fig. 14.2 that, once a gas has been precooled to a temperature lower than the maximum inversion temperature, the optimum pressure from which to start throttling corresponds to a point on the inversion curve. Starting at this pressure and ending at atmospheric pressure, the largest temperature drop is produced. This, however, is not large enough to

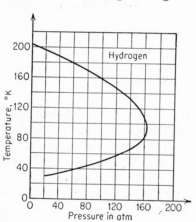

FIG. 14.3. Inversion curve for hydrogen.

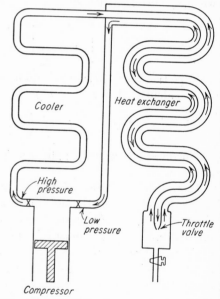

FIG. 14.4. Liquefaction of a gas by means of the Joule-Kelvin effect.

produce liquefaction. Consequently, the gas that has been cooled by throttling is used to cool the incoming gas, which, after throttling, becomes still cooler. After many repetitions of these successive coolings, the gas is lowered to such a temperature that, after throttling, it becomes partly liquefied. The device used for this purpose is a *countercurrent heat exchanger* and is shown in Fig. 14.4.

The gas, after precooling, is sent through the middle tube of a long coil of double-walled pipe. After throttling, it flows back through the outer annular space surrounding the middle pipe.   For the heat exchanger to be efficient, the temperature of the gas as it leaves must differ only slightly from the temperature at which it entered.   To accomplish this, the heat exchanger must be quite long and well insulated, and the gas must flow through it with sufficient speed to cause turbulent flow so that there is good thermal contact between the opposing streams of gas.

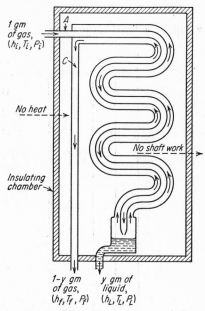

When the steady state is finally reached, liquid is formed at a constant rate: for every gram of gas supplied, a certain fraction y is liquefied, and the fraction $1 - y$ is returned to the pump.   Considering only the heat exchanger and throttling valve completely insulated, as shown in Fig. 14.5, we have a flow process in which no shaft work is done and no heat is transferred, the kinetic- and potential-energy terms being negligible.   It

FIG. 14.5. Throttling valve and heat exchanger in the steady state.

therefore follows that the specific enthalpy of the entering gas is equal to the enthalpy of y gm of emerging liquid plus the enthalpy of $1 - y$ gm of emerging gas.   If

h_i = specific enthalpy of entering gas at T_i, P_i,
h_L = specific enthalpy of emerging liquid at T_L, P_L,
h_f = specific enthalpy of emerging gas at T_f, P_f,

then
$$h_i = y h_L + (1 - y) h_f$$

or
$$y = \frac{h_f - h_i}{h_f - h_L}.$$

Now, in the steady state, h_L is determined by the pressure on the liquid, which fixes the temperature, and hence is constant. h_f is determined by the pressure drop in the return tube and the temperature at C, which is only a little below that at A.   Hence, it remains constant. h_i refers to a temperature T_i that is fixed, but at a pressure that may be chosen at will.   Therefore, the fraction liquefied y may be varied only by varying h_i.   Since

$$y = \frac{h_f - h_i}{h_f - h_L},$$

y will be a maximum when h_i is a minimum; and since h_i may be varied

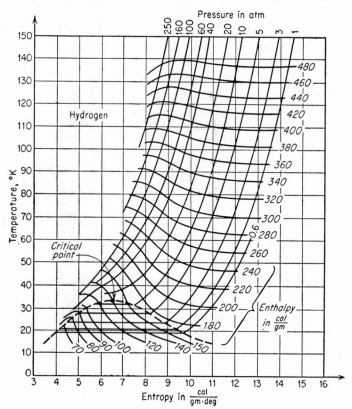

Fig. 14.6. Temperature-entropy diagram for hydrogen.   (*Woolley, Scott, and Brickwedde.*)

only by varying the pressure, the condition that it be a minimum is that

$$\left(\frac{\partial h_i}{\partial P}\right)_{T=T_i} = 0.$$

But
$$\left(\frac{\partial h}{\partial P}\right)_T = -\left(\frac{\partial h}{\partial T}\right)_P \left(\frac{\partial T}{\partial P}\right)_h = -c_P\mu.$$

Hence, for y to be a maximum,

$$\mu = 0 \quad \text{at} \quad T = T_i,$$

or the *point T_i, P_i, must lie on the inversion curve.*

In the design of a gas-liquefaction unit a T-S diagram showing isobars and isenthalps is particularly useful. For example, to calculate the fraction liquefied in the steady state y, the three enthalpies h_i, h_f, and h_L may be obtained directly from such a diagram. T-S diagrams for hydrogen and for helium are shown in Figs. 14.6 and 14.7.

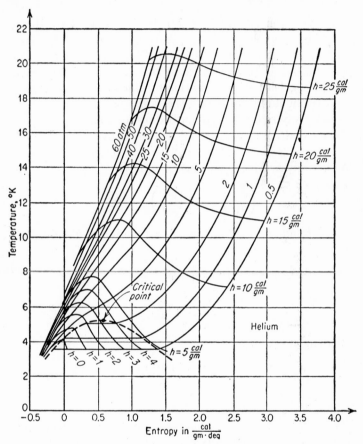

FIG. 14.7. Temperature-entropy diagram for helium.   (*Zelmanov.*)

14.3. Black-body Radiation.

The thermal radiation in equilibrium with the interior walls of an enclosure possesses an energy that is independent of the materials comprising the walls and depends on the temperature and the volume. It can be shown that the energy varies directly with the volume, or, in other words, the ratio of energy to volume is a function of the temperature only. The energy divided by the volume is called the *energy density* and is denoted by u. Thus

$$u = \frac{U}{V} = \text{function of } T \text{ only.}$$

One of the most important consequences of electromagnetic theory is that radiation exerts a pressure. It can be shown that the pressure exerted by the black-body radiation in an enclosure is given by

$$P = \frac{u}{3}.$$

Black-body radiation is therefore completely specified by the pressure of the radiation, the volume of the radiation, and the temperature of the walls with which the radiation is in equilibrium. This temperature is sometimes called the "temperature of the radiation," for convenience. Strictly speaking, it is not the radiation to which the temperature applies, but the matter in equilibrium with the radiation.

Since black-body radiation is described by the coordinates P, V, and T, it may be treated as a chemical system and any one of the equations derived in Chap. 13 may be applied to it. A particularly important result can be obtained from the energy equation

$$\left(\frac{\partial U}{\partial V}\right)_T = T\left(\frac{\partial P}{\partial T}\right)_V - P.$$

Since $U = Vu$ and $P = u/3$ where u is a function of T only, the energy equation becomes

$$u = \frac{T}{3}\frac{du}{dT} - \frac{u}{3}$$

and reduces to

$$\frac{du}{u} = 4\frac{dT}{T}.$$

Integrating the above, we get

$$\ln u = \ln T^4 + \ln b$$

or

$$\boxed{u = bT^4,}$$

where b is a constant. This is known as the *Stefan-Boltzmann law*.

In Chap. 5 an expression was given for the energy of the radiation emitted per second by a unit area of a black body, i.e., the radiant emittance $\mathcal{R}_B$. It can be shown that the following relation exists between the radiant emittance and the energy density:

$$\mathcal{R}_B = \frac{c}{4}u,$$

where c is the speed of light. Therefore, for a black body,

$$\mathcal{R}_B = \frac{cb}{4}T^4$$
$$= \sigma T^4,$$

which is the equation given in Chap. 5. The constant b is equal to

$$b = \frac{4\sigma}{c}$$
$$= \frac{4 \times 5.67 \times 10^{-5} \text{ erg/sec} \cdot \text{cm}^2 \cdot \text{deg}^4}{3 \times 10^{10} \text{ cm/sec}}$$
$$= 7.56 \times 10^{-15} \text{ erg/cm}^3 \cdot \text{deg}^4.$$

Since $P = u/3$ and $u = bT^4$, the equation of state of black-body radiation takes the interesting form

$$P = \frac{b}{3} T^4,$$

and
$$\left(\frac{\partial P}{\partial T}\right)_V = \frac{dP}{dT} = \frac{4}{3} bT^3.$$

Also, since $U = VbT^4$,

$$C_V = \left(\frac{\partial U}{\partial T}\right)_V = 4VbT^3.$$

The first $T \, dS$ equation,

$$T \, dS = C_V \, dT + T \left(\frac{\partial P}{\partial T}\right)_V dV,$$

therefore becomes
$$T \, dS = 4VbT^3 \, dT + \tfrac{4}{3}bT^4 \, dV,$$

which may be used in two ways.

1. *Reversible Isothermal Change of Volume.* If black-body radiation, in equilibrium with the walls of a cavity at the temperature T, is caused to expand isothermally, heat will have to be supplied to the walls to keep the temperature constant. Thus

$$T \, dS = \tfrac{4}{3}bT^4 \, dV$$

and
$$Q = \tfrac{4}{3}bT^4(V_f - V_i).$$

2. *Reversible Adiabatic Change of Volume.* Suppose that black-body radiation, in equilibrium with an extremely small piece of matter such as a grain of coal dust, is contained in a cylinder with perfectly reflecting walls. If the radiation is caused to expand against a piston, the expansion will be adiabatic since there is no exchange of energy between the walls and the radiation. The work done on the surroundings is accomplished at the expense of the internal energy of both the piece of coal and the radiation. If the grain of coal dust has an extremely minute mass, its heat capacity may be regarded as negligible in comparison with that of the radiation. During the expansion, the radiation is always in equilibrium with the coal dust; but since the energy density of the radiation is decreasing, the temperature of the coal dust also decreases. The final

temperature of the coal dust can be found by setting $dS = 0$ in the first $T\,dS$ equation. Thus

$$\tfrac{4}{3}bT^4\,dV = -4VbT^3\,dT,$$

or

$$\frac{dV}{V} = -3\,\frac{dT}{T},$$

and, after integration,

$$VT^3 = \text{const.}$$

The above equation shows that, if the volume of black-body radiation were increased adiabatically by a factor of 8, the radiation would then be capable of existing in equilibrium with matter at a temperature of one-half the original temperature.

14.4. Stretched Wire. In the case of an infinitesimal reversible process of a stretched wire, the two laws of thermodynamics yield the equation

$$T\,dS = dU - \mathcal{F}\,dL.$$

Therefore, to obtain any desired equation for a stretched wire, it is necessary merely to choose the corresponding equation for a chemical system and replace P by $-\mathcal{F}$ and V by L. Thus, the second $T\,dS$ equation becomes

$$T\,dS = C_\mathcal{F}\,dT + T\left(\frac{\partial L}{\partial T}\right)_\mathcal{F}\,d\mathcal{F}.$$

The application of this equation to isothermal and adiabatic processes is exemplified by some of the problems at the end of the chapter.

14.5. Surface Film. To obtain any desired equation for a surface film, it is necessary merely to replace in the corresponding equation for a chemical system V by A and P by $-\mathscr{S}$. Thus, the first $T\,dS$ equation becomes

$$T\,dS = C_A\,dT - T\left(\frac{\partial \mathscr{S}}{\partial T}\right)_A\,dA.$$

Imagine a small amount of liquid in the form of a droplet with a very small surface film. Suppose that the surface film is expanded isothermally with the aid of a suitable wire framework until the area A is very much larger than the original value. Then, *if the surface tension is a function of the temperature only*, the heat transferred is

$$Q = -T\,\frac{d\mathscr{S}}{dT}\,(A - 0),$$

and the work done is

$$W = -\mathscr{S}(A - 0).$$

From the first law,

$$U - U_0 = \left(\mathscr{S} - T\,\frac{d\mathscr{S}}{dT}\right)A,$$

where U_0 is the energy of the liquid with practically no surface and U is the energy of the liquid with the surface of area A. Hence

$$\frac{U - U_0}{A} = \mathscr{S} - T\frac{d\mathscr{S}}{dT}.$$

The left-hand member is interpreted as the energy per unit area associated with the surface only, i.e., the *surface energy per unit area*. It is seen that $(U - U_0)/A$ has the same dimensions as $\mathscr{S}$; that is, ergs per square centimeter equals dynes per centimeter. With the aid of the above

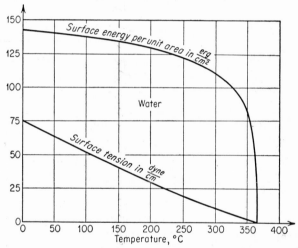

FIG. 14.8. Temperature variation of surface tension and surface energy per unit area of water.

equation, the surface energy per unit area of a film may be calculated once the surface tension has been measured as a function of temperature.

In the neighborhood of the critical temperature the surface tension of all liquids is zero. The surface tension of a pure liquid in equilibrium with its vapor can usually be represented by a formula of the type

$$\mathscr{S} = \mathscr{S}_0\left(1 - \frac{t}{t'}\right)^n$$

where $\mathscr{S}_0$ is the surface tension at 0°C, t' is a temperature a few degrees below the critical temperature, and n is a constant between 1 and 2. For example, in the case of water, $\mathscr{S}_0 = 75.5$ dynes/cm, $t' = 368$°C, and $n = 1.2$. Since $d\mathscr{S}/dT$ is the same as $d\mathscr{S}/dt$, all the quantities necessary to calculate $(U - U_0)/A$ are at hand. The steps in the calculation are given in Table 14.3, and both $\mathscr{S}$ and $(U - U_0)/A$ are plotted in Fig. 14.8.

TABLE 14.3. CALCULATION OF SURFACE ENERGY OF A WATER FILM

Temp., °C	Temp., °K	$\mathscr{S}$, dynes/cm	$\dfrac{d\mathscr{S}}{dT}$	$T\dfrac{d\mathscr{S}}{dT}$	$\dfrac{U - U_0}{A} = \mathscr{S} - T\dfrac{d\mathscr{S}}{dT}$, ergs/cm^2
0	273	75.5	−0.248	− 67.6	143
50	323	63.1	−0.241	− 77.8	141
100	373	51.5	−0.233	− 86.8	138
150	423	40.0	−0.223	− 94.3	134
200	473	29.0	−0.212	−100	129
250	523	18.9	−0.197	−103	122
300	573	9.6	−0.176	−101	111
350	623	1.6	−0.126	− 78.5	80.1
368	641	0	0	0	0

The surface energy per unit area is an important quantity in the kinetic theory of liquids. According to this theory, evaporation takes place when a molecule of liquid possesses sufficient energy to escape through the film at the surface of the liquid. A relation exists, therefore, between the heat of vaporization and the surface energy. If the student compares the surface-energy curve of Fig. 14.8 with the heat-of-vaporization curve of Fig. 15.3 (page 321), he will notice that both quantities vary with the temperature in a similar manner, both becoming zero in the neighborhood of the critical temperature.

14.6. Reversible Cell. Equations for a reversible cell composed of solids and liquids only may be obtained from corresponding equations for a chemical system by replacing V by Z and P by $-\mathscr{E}$. Thus, the first $T\,dS$ equation becomes

$$T\,dS = C_Z\,dT - T\left(\frac{\partial \mathscr{E}}{\partial T}\right)_Z dZ;$$

and, for a saturated reversible cell whose emf depends on the temperature only, the equation becomes

$$T\,dS = C_Z\,dT - T\frac{d\mathscr{E}}{dT}\,dZ.$$

In the case of a *reversible isothermal transfer of a quantity of electricity* $Z_f - Z_i$,

$$Q = -T\frac{d\mathscr{E}}{dT}(Z_f - Z_i),$$

where $Z_f - Z_i$ is negative when positive electricity is transferred externally from the positive to the negative electrode. During this process, the cell delivers an amount of work

$$W = -\mathscr{E}(Z_f - Z_i).$$

If jF coulombs of positive electricity are transferred from positive to negative externally, where j is the valence and F is Faraday's constant, then

$$Z_f - Z_i = -jF,$$

whence

$$Q = jFT \frac{d\mathcal{E}}{dT}$$

and

$$W = jF\mathcal{E}.$$

From the first law, the change in internal energy is

$$U_f - U_i = -jF \left(\mathcal{E} - T \frac{d\mathcal{E}}{dT} \right).$$

When a process takes place at constant pressure with a negligible volume change, the change of internal energy is equal to the change of enthalpy. For

$$H = U + PV$$

and

$$dH = dU + P\,dV + V\,dP,$$

whence, under the conditions mentioned,

$$dH = dU.$$

For the reversible transfer of jF coulombs of electricity through a reversible cell whose volume does not change appreciably at constant atmospheric pressure, we may therefore write

$$H_f - H_i = -jF \left(\mathcal{E} - T \frac{d\mathcal{E}}{dT} \right).$$

In order to interpret this change of enthalpy, let us take the particular case of the Daniell cell. The transfer of positive electricity externally from the copper to the zinc electrode is accompanied by the reaction

$$Zn + CuSO_4 \rightarrow Cu + ZnSO_4.$$

When jF coulombs are transferred, 1 mole of each of the initial constituents disappears and 1 mole of each of the final constituents is formed. The change of enthalpy in this case is equal to the enthalpy of 1 mole of each of the final constituents minus the enthalpy of 1 mole of each of the initial constituents at the same temperature and pressure. This is called the *heat of reaction* and is denoted by ΔH and expressed in calories. Therefore,

$$\Delta H = -\frac{jF}{J} \left(\mathcal{E} - T \frac{d\mathcal{E}}{dT} \right).$$

Since

$$\frac{F}{J} = \frac{96,500 \text{ coulombs}}{4.186 \text{ joules/cal}}$$
$$= 23,070 \text{ cal/volt},$$

we get finally

$$\Delta H = -23,070 \frac{cal}{volt} \, j \left(\mathcal{E} - T \frac{d\mathcal{E}}{dT} \right).$$

In the case of a saturated reversible cell in which gases are liberated, it can be shown rigorously (see Prob. 14.26) that

$$\Delta H = -23,070 \frac{cal}{volt} \, j \left[\mathcal{E} - T \left(\frac{\partial \mathcal{E}}{\partial T} \right)_P \right].$$

The important feature of this equation is that it provides a method of measuring the heat of reaction of a chemical reaction without resorting to calorimetry.   If the reaction can be made to proceed in an electric cell, all that is necessary is to measure the emf of the cell as a function of the temperature at constant atmospheric pressure.   The heat of reaction is therefore measured with a potentiometer and a thermometer. Both measurements can be made with great accuracy, and hence this method yields by far the most accurate values of the heat of reaction. It is interesting to compare values of ΔH obtained electrically with those measured calorimetrically.   This is shown for a number of cells in Table 14.4.   Most of the values of ΔH are negative.   A negative ΔH indicates a rejection of heat, i.e., an exothermic reaction.

TABLE 14.4. REVERSIBLE CELLS

Reaction	Temp., T, °K	Valence, j	Emf, $\mathcal{E}$, volts	$\frac{d\mathcal{E}}{dT}$, volts/deg	ΔH (electric method), cal	ΔH (calorimetric method), cal
$Zn + CuSO_4 = Cu + ZnSO_4$	273	2	1.0934	-0.0004533	$-56,090$	$-55,200$
$Zn + 2AgCl = 2Ag + ZnCl_2$	273	2	1.0171	-0.0002103	$-49,540$	$-49,080$
$Cd + 2AgCl = 2Ag + CdCl_2$	298	2	0.6753	-0.00065	$-40,076$	$-39,530$
$Pb + 2AgI = 2Ag + PbI_2$	298	2	0.2135	-0.000173	$-12,230$	$-12,200$
$Ag + \frac{1}{2}Hg_2Cl_2 = Hg + AgCl$	298	1	0.0455	$+0.000338$	$+ 1,300$	$+ 900$
$Pb + Hg_2Cl_2 = 2Hg + PbCl_2$	298	2	0.5356	$+0.000145$	$-22,900$	$-23,400$
$Pb + 2AgCl = 2Ag + PbCl_2$	298	2	0.4900	-0.000186	$-25,100$	$-24,900$

14.7. Dielectric in a Parallel Plate Capacitor.   Consider a capacitor consisting of two parallel conducting plates of area A, whose linear dimensions are large in comparison with their separation l, filled with an isotropic solid or liquid dielectric.   If a potential difference $\mathcal{E}$ is established across the plates, one plate is given a charge $+Z$ and the other $-Z$.   If the charge of the capacitor is changed by an amount dZ, the work done is

$$\bar{d}W = -\mathcal{E} \, dZ,$$

the minus sign indicating that an increase of charge (positive dZ) requires work done *on* the capacitor. Work supplied by an outside source accomplishes two objectives: (1) an increase in the electric field E in the space between the two plates and (2) an increase in the polarization of the dielectric. We therefore seek to find the contribution of each of these terms to the total work $-\mathcal{E} \, dZ$.

If E is the electric intensity in the dielectric, then the potential difference $\mathcal{E}$ is equal to

$$\mathcal{E} = El.$$

Also, $Z = C\mathcal{E}$, where C, the capacitance, is given by

$$C = \frac{\epsilon_r A}{4\pi l},$$

with ϵ_r equal to the *dielectric coefficient*, or *relative permittivity*. Therefore

$$Z = \frac{\epsilon_r A}{4\pi l} \, El,$$

and since the displacement $D = \epsilon_r E$,

$$Z = \frac{A}{4\pi} \, D,$$

$$dZ = \frac{A}{4\pi} \, dD.$$

We have, therefore,

$$dW = -\mathcal{E} \, dZ$$

$$= -El \frac{A}{4\pi} \, dD,$$

and since the volume $V = Al$,

$$\boxed{dW = -\frac{V}{4\pi} E \, dD} \qquad \text{(total)}.$$

This expression is equivalent to $-\mathcal{E} \, dZ$ and represents the total work done on or by the capacitor when the displacement is changed by an amount dD.

But

$$D = E + 4\pi \frac{P'}{V},$$

where P' is the polarization, i.e., the total electric moment of the dielectric produced either by orientation of elementary dipoles or by the production of induced dipoles. Therefore

$$dW = -\frac{V}{4\pi} E \, dE - E \, dP',$$

where the first term represents the work required to increase the field by an amount dE, and the second to increase the polarization of the dielectric by dP'. If there were no matter present in the space between the plates, the first term would represent the total work, and therefore the work done *by the dielectric* is

$$\boxed{\; dW = -E \, dP' \;} \qquad \text{(dielectric only)}.$$

The close parallelism between the electric and the magnetic situations is emphasized in Table 14.5.

TABLE 14.5. COMPARISON OF MAGNETIC AND ELECTRIC SYSTEMS

	Magnetic	Electric
Total work..........................	$-\dfrac{V}{4\pi}\, \mathcal{H}\, dB$	$-\dfrac{V}{4\pi}\, E \, dD$
Work done to increase the field.........	$-\dfrac{V}{4\pi}\, \mathcal{H}\, d\mathcal{H}$	$-\dfrac{V}{4\pi}\, E \, dE$
Work done by the material............	$-\mathcal{H}\, dI$	$-E \, dP'$

The thermodynamic coordinates of a dielectric are therefore E, P', and T, and an equation of state is a relation among them. If the temperature is not too low, a typical equation of state is

$$\frac{P'}{V} = \left(a + \frac{b}{T}\right) E.$$

The thermodynamic equations appropriate to a dielectric may be easily obtained from those of a chemical system by replacing P by $-E$, and V by P'. Thus, the second $T \, dS$ equation becomes

$$T \, dS = C_E \, dT + T \left(\frac{\partial P'}{\partial T}\right)_E dE.$$

This equation may be applied to (1) a reversible isothermal change of field, or (2) a reversible adiabatic change of field. The temperature change accompanying process (2) is known as the *electrocaloric effect*. Changes of polarization that accompany changes of temperature are sometimes known as *pyroelectric effects*.

14.8. The Piezoelectric Effect. An elastic substance describable with the aid of the coordinates $\mathcal{F}$, L, T undergoes adiabatic temperature changes or isothermal entropy changes when the tension or the length is changed. Such effects may be called *thermoelastic*. An isotropic dielectric whose coordinates are E, P', T undergoes adiabatic temperature changes or isothermal entropy changes when the electric intensity or the polarization is changed. Such effects may be called *pyroelectric*. If a system in an electric field undergoes isothermal or adiabatic changes of polarization when the tension is varied, or isothermal or adiabatic changes of tension when the electric intensity is varied, the system is said to be *piezoelectric*. These phenomena are called *piezoelectric effects*. (The first two syllables are pronounced like "pie" and "ease.")

It may be seen from Fig. 14.9 that piezoelectric effects are really a combination of thermoelastic and pyroelectric effects. The simplest type of piezoelectric material under the simplest type of stress, say a pure tension in only one direction, and in a uniform electric field in that direction, is described with the aid of the five coordinates $\mathscr{F}, L, E, P', T$. In actual cases of crystals such as rochelle salt, quartz, and ammonium dihydrogen phosphate, one is concerned with

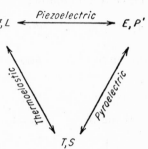

Fig. 14.9. Relation between piezoelectric, thermoelastic, and pyroelectric effects.

several components of stress and of strain, with each component related to the field as well as to the several components of the other, so that the equations are quite involved. We limit ourselves here to the simplest possible situation.

For an infinitesimal, reversible process, the first and second laws yield

$$T \, dS = dU - \mathscr{F} \, dL - E \, dP'.$$

The entropy is a function of three variables, any one of the following sets: $T, \mathscr{F}, E$; or $T, \mathscr{F}, P'$; or T, L, E; or T, L, P'. Choosing the first set, we get

$$T \, dS = T \left(\frac{\partial S}{\partial T} \right)_{\mathscr{F},E} dT + T \left(\frac{\partial S}{\partial \mathscr{F}} \right)_{E,T} d\mathscr{F} + T \left(\frac{\partial S}{\partial E} \right)_{T,\mathscr{F}} dE.$$

The first expression on the right is easily recognized as the heat capacity at constant tension and field; thus

$$T \left(\frac{\partial S}{\partial T} \right)_{\mathscr{F},E} = C_{\mathscr{F},E}.$$

The other two derivatives may be evaluated most readily with the aid of a "piezoelectric Gibbs function," thus

$$G' = U - TS - \mathscr{F}L - EP'.$$

Taking the differential of this function, we get

$$dG' = dU - T \, dS - S \, dT - \mathscr{F} \, dL - L \, d\mathscr{F} - E \, dP' - P' \, dE,$$

and realizing that
$$T \, dS = dU - \mathcal{F} \, dL - E \, dP',$$
we get
$$dG' = -S \, dT - L \, d\mathcal{F} - P' \, dE.$$

Three results follow:

(1) At const. $\mathcal{F}$, $dG'_\mathcal{F} = -S \, dT_\mathcal{F} - P' \, dE_\mathcal{F}$, $\left(\dfrac{\partial S}{\partial E}\right)_{T,\mathcal{F}} = \left(\dfrac{\partial P'}{\partial T}\right)_{E,\mathcal{F}}$,

(2) At const. E, $dG'_E = -S \, dT_E - L \, d\mathcal{F}_E$, $\left(\dfrac{\partial S}{\partial \mathcal{F}}\right)_{T,E} = \left(\dfrac{\partial L}{\partial T}\right)_{\mathcal{F},E}$,

(3) At const. T, $dG'_T = -L \, d\mathcal{F}_T - P' \, dE_T$, $\left(\dfrac{\partial L}{\partial E}\right)_{T,\mathcal{F}} = \left(\dfrac{\partial P'}{\partial \mathcal{F}}\right)_{T,E}$.

Using results (1) and (2), the expression for $T \, dS$ becomes

$$T \, dS = C_{\mathcal{F},E} \, dT + T\left(\frac{\partial L}{\partial T}\right)_{\mathcal{F},E} d\mathcal{F} + T\left(\frac{\partial P'}{\partial T}\right)_{\mathcal{F},E} dE,$$

which may be used to calculate isothermal entropy changes or adiabatic temperature changes when $\mathcal{F}$ or E or both are changed.

Result (3) is a relation between what are known as *piezoelectric coefficients*,

$$\left(\frac{\partial L}{\partial E}\right)_{T,\mathcal{F}} = \left(\frac{\partial P'}{\partial \mathcal{F}}\right)_{T,E},$$

since one expresses the effect of a change of electric field on the length and the other the effect of a change of tension on the polarization.

If the other sets of coordinates are used, different functions are appropriate, the $T \, dS$ equations are different, and different piezoelectric coefficients are obtained, as shown in Table 14.6.

14.9. Thermoelectric Phenomena. When two dissimilar metals are connected and the junctions held at different temperatures, there are five phenomena that take place simultaneously, the Seebeck effect, the Joule effect, the conduction of heat, the Peltier effect, and the Thomson effect. It is necessary to consider each effect briefly.

1. *Seebeck Effect.* There is a thermal emf between the two junctions whose value $\mathcal{E}$ depends on the materials and on the two temperatures. If the circuit is broken at any point, the two ends may be joined to a wire of some third metal, forming two new junctions. If these junctions are maintained at the same temperature, the thermal emf is not altered. With this precaution, a galvanometer, a potentiometer, or a motor may be inserted into the circuit, as shown in Fig. 1.9.

When one junction is held at the constant temperature of melting ice, the variation of the thermal emf with the temperature of the other junc-

TABLE 14.6. ALTERNATE EXPRESSIONS FOR THE PIEZOELECTRIC EFFECT

Coordinates	Appropriate thermodynamic function, $T\,dS$ equation, relation between piezoelectric coefficients
$T, \mathcal{F}, E$	(Piezoelectric Gibbs function) $G' = U - TS - \mathcal{F}L - EP'$
	$(T\,dS\ \text{Eq.})\ T\,dS = C_{\mathcal{F},E}\,dT + T\left(\dfrac{\partial L}{\partial T}\right)_{\mathcal{F},E} d\mathcal{F} + T\left(\dfrac{\partial P'}{\partial T}\right)_{\mathcal{F},E} dE$
	$\left(\begin{array}{c}\text{Piezoelectric} \\ \text{coefficients}\end{array}\right)\left(\dfrac{\partial L}{\partial E}\right)_{T,\mathcal{F}} = \left(\dfrac{\partial P'}{\partial \mathcal{F}}\right)_{T,E}$
$T, \mathcal{F}, P'$	(Thermoelastic Gibbs function) $G'' = U - TS - \mathcal{F}L$
	$(T\,dS\ \text{Eq.})\ T\,dS = C_{\mathcal{F},P'}\,dT + T\left(\dfrac{\partial L}{\partial T}\right)_{\mathcal{F},P'} d\mathcal{F} + \left(\dfrac{\partial E}{\partial T}\right)_{\mathcal{F},P'} dP'$
	$\left(\begin{array}{c}\text{Piezoelectric} \\ \text{coefficients}\end{array}\right) - \left(\dfrac{\partial L}{\partial P'}\right)_{T,\mathcal{F}} = \left(\dfrac{\partial E}{\partial \mathcal{F}}\right)_{T,P'}$
T, L, E	(Pyroelectric Gibbs function) $G''' = U - TS - EP'$
	$(T\,dS\ \text{Eq.})\ T\,dS = C_{L,E}\,dT + T\left(\dfrac{\partial \mathcal{F}}{\partial T}\right)_{L,E} dL + \left(\dfrac{\partial P'}{\partial T}\right)_{L,E} dE$
	$\left(\begin{array}{c}\text{Piezoelectric} \\ \text{coefficients}\end{array}\right) - \left(\dfrac{\partial P'}{\partial L}\right)_{T,E} = \left(\dfrac{\partial \mathcal{F}}{\partial E}\right)_{T,L}$
T, L, P'	(Helmholtz function)$A = U - TS$
	$(T\,dS\ \text{Eq.})\ T\,dS = C_{L,P'}\,dT + T\left(\dfrac{\partial \mathcal{F}}{\partial T}\right)_{L,P'} dL + \left(\dfrac{\partial E}{\partial T}\right)_{L,P'} dP'$
	$\left(\begin{array}{c}\text{Piezoelectric} \\ \text{coefficients}\end{array}\right)\left(\dfrac{\partial \mathcal{F}}{\partial P'}\right)_{T,L} = \left(\dfrac{\partial E}{\partial L}\right)_{T,P'}$

tion is found to obey the equation

$$\mathcal{E} = \alpha_1 t + \frac{\alpha_2}{2}\,t^2 + \frac{\alpha_3}{3}\,t^3,$$

where t is the Celsius temperature and the α's are constants depending on the materials.   Numerical data are given for a few interesting thermocouples in Table 14.7, and the results are plotted in Fig. 14.10.   To obtain the emf when the cold junction is at a temperature other than 0°C, it is necessary merely to add a constant term.   It follows from this that the value of the derivative $d\mathscr{E}/dT$ at one junction is independent of the temperature of the other junction.

2. *Joule Effect.* If the thermal emf is not balanced by an external emf, a current I exists whose value may be adjusted by varying the

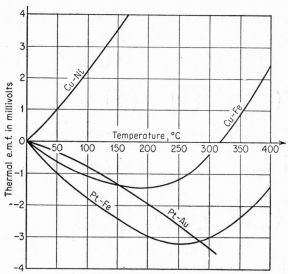

FIG. 14.10. Temperature variation of thermal emf.

external emf. If there is no external circuit, all the electrical energy developed by the thermocouple is dissipated into internal energy. This is the well-known *Joule effect.* Under these conditions,

$$\mathscr{E}I = I^2R$$

where R is the resistance of the thermocouple.

TABLE 14.7. THERMOELECTRIC DATA

$$\mathscr{E} = \alpha_1 t + \frac{\alpha_2}{2} t^2 + \frac{\alpha_3}{3} t^3, \quad \text{volts}$$

Thermocouple	α_1	α_2	α_3
Cu-Fe	-13.403×10^{-6}	$+0.0275 \times 10^{-6}$	$+0.00026 \times 10^{-6}$
Cu-Ni	$+20.39 \times 10^{-6}$	$+0.0453 \times 10^{-6}$	0
Pt-Fe	-19.272×10^{-6}	$+0.0089 \times 10^{-6}$	$+0.00026 \times 10^{-6}$
Pt-Au	-5.991×10^{-6}	-0.0360×10^{-6}	$+0.000005 \times 10^{-6}$

If, however, the resistance of the thermocouple is made very small and a motor whose resistance is also extremely small is connected to the thermocouple, the back emf of the motor can be imagined to be made almost equal to the thermal emf by suitably adjusting the speed. Under these conditions, the Joule effect in both the thermocouple and the motor can be imagined to be reduced to a negligible value, and the electrical energy developed by the thermocouple can be imagined to be converted completely into mechanical work.

3. *Conduction of Heat.* Imagine a thermocouple the junctions of which are at the temperatures T_1 and T_2, respectively $(T_1 > T_2)$, and which has been broken at one point, the two ends being maintained at some intermediate temperature T by means of an insulating reservoir. There is no thermoelectric current, and therefore no Joule effect, but heat is lost by the reservoir at T_1 and gained by that at T_2, with no net gain or loss to the reservoir at T. The wires can be imagined to be suitably lagged so that there is no appreciable lateral transfer of heat across the surfaces of the wires. In this way, we may imagine that the *conducted heat* has been measured for various values of the temperature difference $T_1 - T_2$.

4. *Peltier Effect.* Imagine a thermocouple with its junctions at the same temperature. If, by means of an outside battery, a current is produced in the thermocouple, the temperatures of the junctions are changed by an amount that is not entirely due to the Joule effect. This additional temperature change is the *Peltier effect.* Allowing for the Joule effect, the heat that must be either supplied or extracted to restore a junction to its initial temperature is called the *Peltier heat.* The Peltier effect takes place whether the current is provided by an outside source or is generated by the thermocouple itself.

The Peltier heat is measured by creating a known current in a junction initially at a known temperature and measuring the rate at which the temperature of the junction changes. The junction itself is used as a sort of calorimeter. From the rate of change of temperature and the heat capacity of the junction, the rate at which heat is transferred is calculated. After subtracting the I^2R loss and correcting for the conducted heat, which was determined from previous experiments, the Peltier heat is finally obtained. Extensive measurements have yielded the following results:

a. The rate at which Peltier heat is transferred is proportional to the first power of the current or equal to πI. The quantity π is called the *Peltier coefficient* and is equal to the heat transferred when unit quantity of electricity traverses the junction.

b. The Peltier heat is reversible. When the direction of the current is reversed, the magnitude remaining the same, the Peltier heat is the same, but in the opposite direction.

c. The Peltier coefficient depends on the temperature and the materials of a junction, being independent of the temperature of the other junction. Some numerical values are given in Table 14.8.

5. *Thomson Effect.* The conduction of heat along the wires of a thermocouple carrying no current gives rise to a uniform temperature distribution in each wire. If a current exists, the temperature distribution in each wire is altered by an amount that is not entirely due to the Joule effect. This additional change in the temperature distribution is called the *Thomson effect.* Allowing for the Joule effect, the heat that must be either supplied or extracted laterally at all places along the wires to restore the initial temperature distribution is called the *Thomson heat.*

To measure the Thomson heat at a small region of any one wire, it is necessary to produce a known temperature gradient in the region and to pass a known current either up or down the gradient. The rate at which Thomson heat is transferred is equal to the rate at which electrical energy is dissipated minus the rate at which heat is conducted. Since the Joule effect can be calculated and the conducted heat is known from previous experiments, the Thomson heat can be obtained. The following conclusions may be drawn from such measurements:

a. The rate at which Thomson heat is transferred into a small region of a wire carrying a current I and supporting a temperature difference dT is equal to $\sigma I\, dT$, where σ is called the *Thomson coefficient.*

b. The Thomson heat is reversible.

c. The Thomson coefficient depends on the material of the wire and on the mean temperature of the small region under consideration. Some numerical values are given in Table 14.9.

14.10. Thermodynamic Analysis of the Thermocouple. The Seebeck Effect. The application of thermodynamics to the thermocouple has had a long and interesting history. Lord Kelvin was the first to realize that the two irreversible phenomena, the Joule effect and the conduction of heat, could not be eliminated by merely choosing wires of proper dimensions. For, if the wires are made very thin in order to cut down heat conduction, the electric resistance increases; whereas, if the wires are made thick to cut down the electric resistance, the heat conduction increases. In spite of this, Kelvin assumed that the irreversible effects could be ignored on the ground that they seemed to be independent of the reversible Peltier and Thomson effects. By considering the purely reversible transfer of unit quantity of electricity through a thermocouple circuit, Kelvin set the sum of all the entropy changes equal to zero and derived relations which have been amply checked and which are undoubtedly correct. The stubborn fact remains, however, that the Seebeck, Peltier, and Thomson effects are inextricably linked with the irreversible effects.

Attempts to resolve these difficulties were made by Bridgman, by Tolman and Fine, and by Meixner, but they were not entirely free from objection. The solution is to be found in the macroscopic treatment of irreversible coupled flows developed by Onsager and introduced briefly in Chap. 10.   The following is a simplified version of Onsager's method, based on a paper by H. B. Callen.

A small temperature difference ΔT established across a wire disturbs the thermal equilibrium and gives rise to a heat current I_Q.   Since a cool reservoir at one end of the wire is gaining entropy *from the wire* at a greater rate than that at which a warmer reservoir at the other end is losing it *to the wire*, we say that entropy is being produced *in the wire* at a rate

$$\frac{dS}{d\tau} = I_Q \frac{\Delta T}{T^2} = I_S \frac{\Delta T}{T},$$

where I_S is the entropy current equal to I_Q/T.

A small potential difference $\Delta \mathcal{E}$ established across a wire disturbs the electrical equilibrium and gives rise to an electric current I.   Since a reservoir at temperature T which maintains the wire at a uniform temperature is gaining entropy and there is no entropy input to the wire, we say that entropy is being produced in the wire at a rate

$$\frac{dS}{d\tau} = I \frac{\Delta \mathcal{E}}{T}.$$

When both a temperature difference ΔT and a potential difference $\Delta \mathcal{E}$ exist across the wire, the rate of entropy production is the sum, or

$$\frac{dS}{d\tau} = I_S \frac{\Delta T}{T} + I \frac{\Delta \mathcal{E}}{T}.$$

If departure from equilibrium is not too great, the entropy and electricity flow are coupled in a simple manner, both flows depending *linearly* on both $\Delta T/T$ and $\Delta \mathcal{E}/T$, thus

$$\boxed{I_S = L_{11} \frac{\Delta T}{T} + L_{12} \frac{\Delta \mathcal{E}}{T}} \tag{1}$$

$$\boxed{I = L_{21} \frac{\Delta T}{T} + L_{22} \frac{\Delta \mathcal{E}}{T}.} \tag{2}$$

The coefficients L_{11} and L_{22} have simple interpretations in terms of thermal conductivity and electric conductivity, respectively.   The quantities L_{12} and L_{21} are coupling coefficients.   They represent the effect of a potential difference on an entropy current, and the effect of a temperature difference on an electric current, respectively.   Onsager proved by means of the *microscopic* point of view, that

$$L_{12} = L_{21},$$

which is now known as *Onsager's reciprocal relation.*

If ΔT is set equal to zero in both Eqs. (1) and (2), and then the equations are divided, we get

$$\left(\frac{I_S}{I}\right)_{\Delta T=0} = \frac{L_{12}}{L_{22}}.$$

The ratio on the left is a measure of the entropy that is carried along with the electricity when the temperature is uniform. It is therefore called the *entropy transport parameter* and is denoted by S^*. Thus,

$$S^* = \left(\frac{I_S}{I}\right)_{\Delta T=0} = \frac{L_{12}}{L_{22}}, \tag{3}$$

and depends on the material and temperature of the wire. S^* plays a fundamental role in the theory of the thermocouple.

When there is no current, Eq. (2) provides the relation

$$(\Delta\mathcal{E})_{I=0} = -\frac{L_{21}}{L_{22}}\Delta T,$$

which becomes, upon insertion of the Onsager reciprocal relation,

$$(\Delta\mathcal{E})_{I=0} = -\frac{L_{12}}{L_{22}}\Delta T. \tag{4}$$

Therefore, using Eqs. (3) and (4), we get the useful relation

$$\boxed{-(\Delta\mathcal{E})_{I=0} = S^*\,\Delta T.} \tag{5}$$

We are now in a position to calculate the Seebeck emf generated in the thermocouple depicted in Fig. 14.11. The junction e of the wires

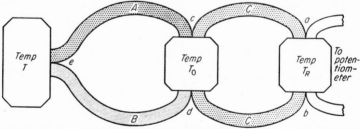

FIG. 14.11. Thermocouple consisting of wires A and B connected to copper wires C and C and thence to the binding posts of a potentiometer.

A and B is maintained at the temperature T while the two junctions, c and d, each with copper, are maintained at temperature T_0 (usually that of an ice bath). The two copper wires marked C are connected to the brass binding posts of a potentiometer, forming two more junctions each of which is at room temperature T_R. The potentiometer is supposed to be balanced, so that $I = 0$ and $\mathcal{E}_a - \mathcal{E}_b$ is the Seebeck emf, $\mathcal{E}_{A,B}$.

Equation (5) may be applied to each of the wires marked A, B, and C, the entropy transport parameters being S_A^*, S_B^*, and S_C^*. Replacing $\Delta\mathcal{E}$ and ΔT by $d\mathcal{E}$ and dT, and integrating from one end of each wire to the other, we have

$$\mathcal{E}_a - \mathcal{E}_c = \int_{T_R}^{T_0} S_C^* \, dT,$$

$$\mathcal{E}_c - \mathcal{E}_e = \int_{T_0}^{T} S_A^* \, dT,$$

$$\mathcal{E}_e - \mathcal{E}_d = \int_{T}^{T_0} S_B^* \, dT,$$

$$\mathcal{E}_d - \mathcal{E}_b = \int_{T_0}^{T_R} S_C^* \, dT.$$

When these equations are added, the left side becomes $\mathcal{E}_a - \mathcal{E}_b = \mathcal{E}_{A,B}$. On the right side, the first and last terms cancel, so that

$$\boxed{\mathcal{E}_{A,B} = \int_{T_0}^{T} (S_A^* - S_B^*) \, dT.} \qquad (6)$$

14.11. The Peltier and Thomson Effects. When an electric current traverses a junction of two dissimilar metals, the heat that must be supplied or withdrawn, over and above the Joule heat, to keep the junction at a constant temperature is called the Peltier heat. This may be calculated readily in terms of the quantities introduced in the previous article. Consider the thermojunction e of Fig. 14.11, depicted in greater detail in Fig. 14.12. Even though the junction is at a uniform temperature, there is a heat current $I_{Q,A}$ into the junction and another heat current $I_{Q,B}$ out of the junction, both carried along with the electric current I. I is taken arbitrarily in the direction from

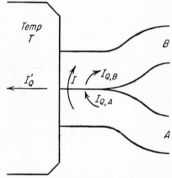

FIG. 14.12. Thermojunction of wires A and B in contact with a reservoir at T. An electric current I exists across the junction, thereby creating the heat currents $I_{Q,A}$ and $I_{Q,B}$. I_Q' is the heat that must be withdrawn in order to keep the junction at constant temperature.

A to B. The difference between $I_{Q,A}$ and $I_{Q,B}$ must be withdrawn along with $I^2 R_j$ (where R_j is the resistance of the junction) in order to keep the temperature constant. Calling the heat to be withdrawn I_Q', we have

$$I_Q' = I^2 R_j + (I_{Q,A})_{\Delta T = 0} - (I_{Q,B})_{\Delta T = 0},$$

and, by definition, the Peltier heat is

$$\pi_{A,B} I = I_Q' - I^2 R_j = (I_{Q,A})_{\Delta T = 0} - (I_{Q,B})_{\Delta T = 0}$$

Since S^* is defined to be $(I_S/I)_{\Delta T = 0}$ and I_S is I_Q/T, it follows that

$$(I_Q)_{\Delta T = 0} = I T S^*.$$

The Peltier coefficient therefore becomes

$$\pi_{A,B} = T(S_A^* - S_B^*).$$ (7)

Since S_A^* and S_B^* depend on the nature of the metals and on the temperature, it follows that the Peltier coefficient depends on the same quantities, but is independent of the temperature of any other junction in the circuit.

To understand the Thomson effect, consider a small portion of wire supporting a temperature difference ΔT, and a potential difference $\Delta \mathcal{E}$ as shown in Fig. 14.13. When an electric current I exists in the wire, the heat current at the hot end, $I_{Q,T+\Delta T}$, differs from that at the cooler end, $I_{Q,T}$. The heat current I_Q' that must be *absorbed* laterally along the

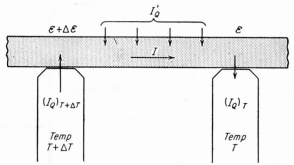

FIG. 14.13. Temperature difference and potential difference across a small portion of wire of resistance ΔR. The Thomson heat is the heat that must be absorbed, in addition to the Joule heat, to keep the same temperature distribution that existed in the absence of an electric current.

wire, in addition to the production rate of Joulean heat $I \Delta \mathcal{E}$ (or $I^2 \Delta R$) in order to maintain the same temperature difference that existed in the absence of the electric current, is the Thomson heat per unit time. The rate of transfer of Thomson heat is written $\sigma I \Delta T$, where σ is called the Thomson coefficient.

Referring to Fig. 14.13, we see that

$$I_Q' = I \Delta \mathcal{E} + (I_Q)_{T+\Delta T} - (I_Q)_T.$$

Now, at a uniform temperature T, the entropy transport parameter S^* was defined as I_S/I or I_Q/TI, whence $I_Q = ITS^*$. When the temperature is not uniform, we may consider S^* to have a different value at different points in the wire. Thus, at a place where the temperature is $T + \Delta T$,

$$(I_Q)_{T+\Delta T} = I(T + \Delta T)\left(S^* + \frac{dS^*}{dT}\Delta T\right).$$

Therefore

$$I'_Q = I \left[\Delta\mathcal{E} + (T + \Delta T) \left(S^* + \frac{dS^*}{dT} \Delta T \right) - TS^* \right]$$

$$= I \left(\Delta\mathcal{E} + T \frac{dS^*}{dT} \Delta T + S^* \Delta T \right).$$

Now, Eq. (2) for the electric current, namely,

$$I = L_{21} \frac{\Delta T}{T} + L_{22} \frac{\Delta\mathcal{E}}{T},$$

may be written

$$\Delta\mathcal{E} = \frac{IT}{L_{22}} - \frac{L_{21}}{L_{22}} \Delta T,$$

and must reduce to Ohm's law when $\Delta T = 0$. Hence

$$\frac{T}{L_{22}} = \Delta R.$$

From Eq. (3),

$$S^* = \frac{L_{12}}{L_{22}},$$

or, making use of the reciprocal relation,

$$S^* = \frac{L_{21}}{L_{22}}.$$

Therefore,

$$\Delta\mathcal{E} = I \Delta R - S^* \Delta T.$$

Substituting this value of $\Delta\mathcal{E}$ into the equation for I'_Q, we get

$$I'_Q = I \left(I \Delta R - S^* \Delta T + T \frac{dS^*}{dT} \Delta T + S^* \Delta T \right),$$

or $\qquad I'_Q = I^2 \Delta R + IT \frac{dS^*}{dT} \Delta T.$

By definition of the rate of transfer of Thomson heat,

$$\sigma I \Delta T = -(I'_Q - I^2 \Delta R)$$

$$= -IT \frac{dS^*}{dT} \Delta T,$$

and finally

$$\sigma = -T \frac{dS^*}{dT}.$$

Returning to the thermocouple of Fig. 14.11,

$$\boxed{\sigma_A - \sigma_B = -T \frac{d}{dT} (S_A^* - S_B^*).}$$
(8)

Let us collect Eqs. (6), (7), and (8):

$$\mathscr{E}_{A,B} = \int_{T_0}^{T} (S_A^* - S_B^*)\, dT, \tag{6}$$

$$\pi_{A,B} = T(S_A^* - S_B^*), \tag{7}$$

$$\sigma_A - \sigma_B = -T \frac{d}{dT}(S_A^* - S_B^*). \tag{8}$$

It is seen what a fundamental role is played by the entropy transport parameter. The thermocouple equations, first derived by Lord Kelvin, are two relations among $\mathscr{E}_{A,B}$, $\pi_{A,B}$, and $\sigma_A - \sigma_B$. To obtain these equations, we differentiate Eq. (6), holding T_0 constant and get

$$\frac{d\mathscr{E}_{A,B}}{dT} = S_A^* - S_B^*.$$

Substituting this result into Eq. (7),

$$\boxed{\frac{\pi_{A,B}}{T} = \frac{d\mathscr{E}_{A,B}}{dT},} \tag{9}$$

and substituting it into Eq. (8),

$$\boxed{\sigma_A - \sigma_B = -T \frac{d^2\mathscr{E}_{A,B}}{dT^2}.} \tag{10}$$

These are the famous thermocouple equations. From these equations it is possible to calculate the Peltier coefficient of any junction and the difference of the Thomson coefficients of the two wires at any temperature, once the temperature dependence of the thermal emf is known.

TABLE 14.8. TEST OF EQUATION $\pi/T = d\mathscr{E}/dT$

Thermocouple	Temp., °K	π/T (measured), μv/deg	$d\mathscr{E}/dT$ (measured), μv/deg
Cu-Ni	273	18.6	20.39
	287	20.2	21.0
	295	20.5	21.4
	302	22.3	21.7
	373	24.4	24.9
Fe-Hg	292	16.7	16.66
	330	16.2	16.14
	373	15.6	15.42
	405	14.9	14.81
	456	13.9	13.74

To test the first equation it is necessary to compare measured values of π/T with measured values of $d\mathcal{E}/dT$. A few measurements are given in Table 14.8, where it is seen that the agreement is satisfactory. The test of the second equation given in Table 14.9 does not provide quite so good an agreement because of the greater difficulty in measuring Thomson coefficients.

TABLE 14.9. TEST OF EQUATION $\dfrac{\sigma_A - \sigma_B}{T} = -\dfrac{d^2\mathcal{E}}{dT^2}$

Thermocouple	Temp., °K	σ_{Cu}, μv/deg	$\sigma_{Cu} - \sigma$, μv/deg	$\dfrac{\sigma_{Cu} - \sigma}{T}$, μv/deg^2	$\dfrac{d^2\mathcal{E}}{dT^2}$, μv/deg^2
Cu-Pt	273	1.6	−10.7	−0.039	+0.036
	293	1.6	−10.7	−0.037	+0.036
	373	2.0	−11.1	−0.030	+0.036
Cu-Fe	273	1.6	− 5.6	−0.020	+0.028
	373	2.0	−14.4	−0.039	+0.033

14.12. Paramagnetic Solid at Ordinary Temperatures. Most experiments on paramagnetic solids are performed at constant atmospheric pressure and involve only minute volume changes, which, as a first approximation, may be ignored. Under these conditions a paramagnetic solid may be described by means of the coordinates $\mathcal{H}$, I, and T. Experiment shows that the magnetization of a certain class of paramagnetic crystals depends on the ratio $\mathcal{H}/T$, increasing almost linearly at small values of $\mathcal{H}/T$ and approaching a constant saturation value as $\mathcal{H}/T$ becomes large. When T is of the order of 300°K, or room temperature, and at moderate fields, the magnetization varies almost linearly with $\mathcal{H}/T$, or

$$I = C\,\frac{\mathcal{H}}{T}$$

which is Curie's equation. At lower temperatures and at correspondingly lower fields, Curie's law still holds until a temperature is reached at which Curie's law breaks down. This temperature is usually below 1°K. Weiss's equation, namely,

$$I = \frac{C\mathcal{H}}{T - N\rho C},$$

describes the behavior of another class of paramagnetic solids at ordinary temperatures but also breaks down as T approaches absolute zero.

Any thermodynamic equation for a paramagnetic solid may be obtained from the corresponding one for a chemical system by replacing V by I

and P by $-\mathcal{H}$. Thus the two $T\,dS$ equations become

$$T\,dS = C_I\,dT - T\left(\frac{\partial \mathcal{H}}{\partial T}\right)_I dI,$$

$$T\,dS = C_{\mathcal{H}}\,dT + T\left(\frac{\partial I}{\partial T}\right)_{\mathcal{H}} d\mathcal{H}.$$

The following applications of the second $T\,dS$ equation are of particular interest:

1. *Reversible Isothermal Change of Field.* When T is constant

$$T\,dS = T\left(\frac{\partial I}{\partial T}\right)_{\mathcal{H}} d\mathcal{H}$$

and, for a finite change of field from $\mathcal{H}_i$ to $\mathcal{H}_f$,

$$Q = T\int_{\mathcal{H}_i}^{\mathcal{H}_f}\left(\frac{\partial I}{\partial T}\right)_{\mathcal{H}} d\mathcal{H}.$$

When the field is kept constant, an increase in temperature of a paramagnetic solid *always* causes a decrease in magnetization. Hence $(\partial I/\partial T)_{\mathcal{H}}$ is negative, and the preceding equation shows that heat is rejected when the field is increased and absorbed when the field is decreased isothermally.

2. *Reversible Adiabatic Change of Field.* When S is constant,

$$C_{\mathcal{H}}\,dT = -T\left(\frac{\partial I}{\partial T}\right)_{\mathcal{H}} d\mathcal{H}.$$

If the substance is initially at a temperature of about 300°K, experiment shows that an adiabatic change of field produces a temperature change that is only a small fraction of the initial temperature. We may therefore regard both T and $C_{\mathcal{H}}$ as practically constant, whence, for a finite change of field, the equation becomes

$$\boxed{\Delta T = -\frac{T}{C_{\mathcal{H}}}\int_{\mathcal{H}_i}^{\mathcal{H}_f}\left(\frac{\partial I}{\partial T}\right)_{\mathcal{H}} d\mathcal{H}}$$

in which $C_{\mathcal{H}}$ may be replaced by C_P without appreciable error. It is seen from the above equation that, when the field is increased adiabatically, a temperature rise takes place. Conversely, an adiabatic demagnetization produces a drop in temperature. This phenomenon is sometimes called the *magnetocaloric effect.*

One of the most interesting examples of the magnetocaloric effect is in connection with a ferromagnetic substance that, above a temperature called the *Curie point,* behaves like a paramagnetic solid. The Curie point of iron is 765°C, and that of nickel is 358°C. In experiments on ferromagnetic substances, the ΔT produced by a known change of field is measured and separate experiments are made to determine $(\partial I/\partial T)_{\mathscr{H}}$. The thermodynamic formula is then used to calculate $C_{\mathscr{H}}$. Recent experiments on iron and nickel show that a magnetocaloric effect of 1 to 2° can be obtained in the neighborhood of the Curie point when the field is changed by 10,000 oersteds.   In this temperature region, $C_{\mathscr{H}}$ exhibits an anomalous behavior.

The most important application of the magnetocaloric effect is in the production of extremely low temperatures, below those obtainable with the aid of liquid helium alone. This will be discussed thoroughly in Chap. 16.

PROBLEMS

14.1. (a) Show that

$$\mu c_P = T^2 \left(\frac{\partial v/T}{\partial T} \right)_P.$$

In the region of moderate pressures, the equation of state of 1 mole of a gas may be written

$$\frac{Pv}{RT} = 1 + B'P + C'P^2,$$

where the second and third virial coefficients B' and C' are functions of the temperature only.

(b) Show that as the pressure approaches zero,

$$\mu c_P \rightarrow RT^2 \frac{dB'}{dT}.$$

(c) Show that the equation of the inversion curve is

$$P = - \frac{dB'/dT}{dC'/dT}.$$

14.2. The Joule-Kelvin coefficient μ is a measure of the temperature change during a throttling process. A similar measure of the temperature change produced by an isentropic change of pressure is provided by the coefficient μ_s, where

$$\mu_s = \left(\frac{\partial T}{\partial P} \right)_S.$$

Prove that

$$\mu_s - \mu = \frac{V}{C_P}.$$

14.3. Indicate on a rough freehand T-S diagram the states of a substance at various places in a Joule-Kelvin liquefier when it is liquefying gas at a constant rate.

14.4. Refer to Art. 10.10 in which the entropy principle is used to calculate the minimum amount of work in refrigeration. What is the minimum amount of work in kilowatt-hours that must be supplied to a refrigerator to convert 1 kg of hydrogen originally at 70°K and 1 atm into liquid at 20°K and 1 atm, using a reservoir at 70°K? (Look up entropy and enthalpy values in Fig. 14.6.)

14.5. What is the minimum amount of work in kilowatt-hours that must be supplied to a refrigerator to convert 1 kg of helium originally at 15°K and 1 atm into liquid at 4.2°K at 1 atm, using a reservoir at 15°K? (See Fig. 14.7.)

14.6. In a Joule-Kelvin liquefier, helium enters the heat exchanger at 14°K and 20 atm and leaves at 13°K and 1 atm. If liquid is formed at 1 atm, what is the fraction liquefied?

14.7. In a Joule-Kelvin liquefier, hydrogen enters the heat exchanger at 68°K and 100 atm and leaves at 62°K and 1 atm. If liquid is formed at 1 atm, what is the fraction liquefied?

14.8. Prove that, for black-body radiation,

(a) $PV^{4/3}$ = const., for an isentropic process,

(b) $\dfrac{S}{V} = \dfrac{4}{3} bT^3$,

(c) $C_P = \infty$,

(d) $G = 0$.

14.9. The tension in a steel wire of length 1 m, diameter 1 mm, and temperature 300°K is increased reversibly and isothermally from zero to 10^8 dynes.

(a) How much heat in joules is transferred?

(b) How much work in joules is done?

(c) What is the change in internal energy?

(d) What would be the temperature change if the process were performed isentropically?

Assume the following quantities to remain constant:

$\rho = 7.86$ gm/cm^3

$\alpha = 12.0 \times 10^{-6}$ deg^{-1}

$Y = 2.00 \times 10^{12}$ dynes/cm^2

$C_{\mathscr{F}} = 0.115$ cal/gm · deg.

14.10. The equation of state of an ideal elastic cylinder is

$$\mathscr{F} = KT \left(\frac{L}{L_0} - \frac{L_0^2}{L^2} \right),$$

where K is a constant and L_0, the length at zero tension, is a function of T only. If the cylinder is stretched reversibly and isothermally from $L = L_0$ to $L = 2L_0$, show that

(a) The heat transferred is

$$Q = -KTL_0(1 + \tfrac{5}{2}\alpha_0 T)$$

where α_0, the linear expansivity at zero tension, is

$$\alpha_0 = \frac{1}{L_0} \frac{dL_0}{dT}.$$

(b) The change of internal energy is

$$\Delta U = -\tfrac{5}{2} KT^2 L_0 \alpha_0.$$

14.11. In the case of an ideal elastic substance whose equation of state is given in Prob. 14.10, prove that:

(a) $\left(\dfrac{\partial U}{\partial L}\right)_T = AY\alpha_0 T.$

(b) $\left(\dfrac{\partial U}{\partial \mathscr{F}}\right)_T = L\alpha_0 T.$

14.12. When rubber is unstretched, X-ray diffraction experiments indicate an amorphous structure. When it is stretched, a crystalline structure is found, indicating that the large chainlike molecules are oriented.

(a) Is $(\partial S/\partial \mathscr{F})_T$ positive or negative?

(b) Prove that the linear expansivity is negative.

14.13. When zinc sulfate (valence = 2) reacts chemically with copper, at a temperature of 273°K and at atmospheric pressure, the heat evolved in the reaction is 2.31×10^8 joules/kilomole. The emf of a Daniell cell at 273°K is 1.0934 volts, and the emf decreases with temperature at the rate of 4.533×10^{-5} volt/deg. How does the calculated heat of reaction compare with the measured value?

14.14. The emf of the cell Zn, $ZnCl_2$, Hg_2Cl_2, Hg is given by the equation

$$\mathscr{E} = 1.0000 + 0.000094(t - 15).$$

Write the reaction, and calculate the heat of reaction at 100°C.

14.15. (a) Prove that for a dielectric

$$\left(\frac{\partial U}{\partial E}\right)_T = T\left(\frac{\partial P'}{\partial T}\right)_E + E\left(\frac{\partial P'}{\partial E}\right)_T.$$

(b) Assuming the equation of state to be

$$P' = \chi VE,$$

where the susceptibility χ is a function of T only, and the volume V is constant, show that the energy per unit volume of the dielectric is equal to

$$\frac{U}{V} = f(T) + \frac{E^2}{2}\left(\chi + T\frac{d\chi}{dT}\right),$$

where $f(T)$ is an undetermined function of temperature.

(c) Prove that the energy per unit volume of an electric field in a vacuum is

$$\frac{E^2}{8\pi}.$$

(d) Using the relation $\epsilon_r = 1 + 4\pi\chi$, show that the *total* energy per unit volume

$$\frac{U}{V} \text{ (dielectric plus field)} = f(T) + \frac{\epsilon_r E^2}{8\pi}\left(1 + \frac{T}{\epsilon_r}\frac{d\epsilon_r}{dT}\right).$$

14.16. (a) Show that for a dielectric the difference in the heat capacities is given by

$$C_E - C_{P'} = T\frac{\left(\dfrac{\partial P'}{\partial T}\right)_E}{\left(\dfrac{\partial P'}{\partial E}\right)_T}.$$

(b) If $P' = \chi VE$, show that

$$\frac{C_E - C_{P'}}{V} = \frac{T}{\chi}\left(\frac{d\chi}{dT}\right)^2 E^2.$$

(c) If $\chi = C/T$, show that

$$\frac{C_E - C_{P'}}{V} = \frac{\chi}{T} E^2.$$

14.17. In the case of a dielectric whose equation of state is $P' = CVE/T$, show that

(a) The heat transferred in a reversible isothermal change of field is

$$Q = -\frac{CV}{2T}(E_f^2 - E_i^2).$$

(b) The small temperature change accompanying a reversible adiabatic change of field is

$$\Delta T = \frac{CV}{2C_E T}(E_f^2 - E_i^2).$$

14.18. Using the data for the platinum-iron thermocouple given in Table 14.7, (a) calculate the Peltier heat transferred at a junction at temperatures of 300°C and 500°C by a current of 1 ma in an hour. (b) At what temperature is the Peltier heat zero? (c) What is the difference in the Thomson coefficients at 300°C and at 500°C?

14.19. In Fig. 14.14 is depicted an idealized apparatus similar to that used to explain a throttling process. There is, however, a big difference. The throttling

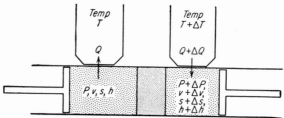

Fig. 14.14. Thermal effusion (Knudsen effect) of a gas through a porous plug.

process is strictly adiabatic, whereas the gas flowing through the porous plug in Fig. 14.14 is maintained at a *constant temperature* and pressure on the left side and at a constant *higher* temperature on the right. If the pores in the plug are small enough, the pressure on the right will be found to be higher than that on the left. This process is called *thermal effusion* or the *Knudsen effect*.

Suppose that both pistons are moved to the right simultaneously, thereby maintaining a constant pressure P on the left and a constant pressure $P + \Delta P$ on the right. Under these circumstances, let n moles of gas be transferred in time τ. In this time, suppose the gas loses heat Q at temperature T and gains heat $Q + \Delta Q$ at the temperature $T + \Delta T$.

(a) Show that the entropy produced in time τ is

$$\Delta S = Q\frac{\Delta T}{T^2} - \frac{\Delta Q}{T} + n\,\Delta s.$$

(b) Apply the first law and obtain

$$\Delta Q = n\,\Delta h.$$

(c) Show that

$$\frac{\Delta S}{\tau} = \frac{Q}{\tau}\frac{\Delta T}{T^2} - \frac{n}{\tau}\frac{v}{T}\Delta P$$

$$= I_S\frac{\Delta T}{T} - I_n v\frac{\Delta P}{T}.$$

(d) Express I_S and $-I_n$ as linear functions of $\Delta T/T$ and $\Delta P/T$.

(e) Show that

$$\frac{L_{12}}{L_{22}} = -\left(\frac{I_S}{I_n v}\right)_{\Delta T=0},$$

and

$$\frac{L_{21}}{L_{22}} = -\left(\frac{\Delta P}{\Delta T}\right)_{I_n=0}.$$

(f) Show that

$$\left(\frac{\Delta P}{\Delta T}\right)_{I_n=0} = \frac{(I_S/I_n)_{\Delta T=0}}{v} = \frac{S^*}{v}.$$

(g) The quantity S^* is the entropy accompanying the transport of 1 mole of gas through the plug. It is found from kinetic theory to be $R/2$. Prove that

$$\frac{P_1}{P_2} = \sqrt{\frac{T_1}{T_2}},$$

where the subscripts 1 and 2 refer to opposite sides of the plug.

14.20. Two moles of gadolinium sulfate obeying Curie's law are in a magnetic field of 20,000 oersteds and at a temperature of 15°K. The field is reduced reversibly and isothermally to zero. Assuming the molar heat capacity at constant field to vary according to the equation

$$C_{\mathscr{H}} = \frac{A + C\mathscr{H}^2}{T^2},$$

with $A = 2.66 \times 10^7$ erg · deg/mole, and C, the Curie constant, equal to 7.85 cm³ · deg/mole,

(a) How much heat in calories is transferred?
(b) How much work in calories is done?
(c) What is the internal energy change?
(d) What would be the final temperature if the process were performed reversibly and adiabatically?

14.21. Show that, when Curie's law is obeyed,

(a) U and C_I are functions of T only.

(b) $S = \int C_I\frac{dT}{T} - \frac{I^2}{2C} + \text{const.}$

(c) $C_{\mathscr{H}} - C_I = \frac{I^2}{C}.$

(d) $\left(\frac{\partial C_{\mathscr{H}}}{\partial \mathscr{H}}\right)_T = \frac{2C\mathscr{H}}{T^2}.$

14.22. Take a paramagnetic solid obeying Curie's law through a Carnot cycle, and verify that

$$\frac{Q_1}{Q_2} = \frac{T_1}{T_2}.$$

14.23. (a) Write down the magnetic analogue of the equation in Prob. 13.8(a). For a magnetic substance whose equation of state is $I = f(\mathcal{H}/T)$, where f is *any* function, no matter how complicated, prove that (b) U is a function of T only, (c) C_I is a function of T only, (d) $C_{\mathcal{H}} = C_I - \mathcal{H}(\partial I/\partial T)_{\mathcal{H}}$.

14.24. From the microscopic point of view, the disorder of a paramagnetic solid may be increased in two ways, by increasing the temperature and by decreasing the magnetization. From this point of view, explain why a reversible adiabatic demagnetization should be accompanied by a decrease in temperature.

14.25. A thermodynamic system is described with the aid of the five coordinates P, V, T, $\mathcal{Y}$, X, where

$$T\, dS = dU + P\, dV - \mathcal{Y}\, dX.$$

Prove that, if $G = U + PV - TS$, as usual,

(a) $dG = -S\, dT + V\, dP + \mathcal{Y}\, dX$.

(b) $-\left(\dfrac{\partial S}{\partial P}\right)_{X,T} = \left(\dfrac{\partial V}{\partial T}\right)_{X,P}$.

(c) $-\left(\dfrac{\partial S}{\partial X}\right)_{P,T} = \left(\dfrac{\partial \mathcal{Y}}{\partial T}\right)_{P,X}$.

(d) $\left(\dfrac{\partial V}{\partial X}\right)_{T,P} = \left(\dfrac{\partial \mathcal{Y}}{\partial P}\right)_{T,X}$.

14.26. Using the five coordinates P, V, T, $\mathcal{E}$, Z to describe a reversible cell in which gases may be liberated, show that

(a) $dG = -S\, dT + V\, dP + \mathcal{E}\, dZ$.

(b) $-\left(\dfrac{\partial S}{\partial Z}\right)_{T,P} = \left(\dfrac{\partial \mathcal{E}}{\partial T}\right)_{P,Z}$.

(c) $dH = T\, dS + V\, dP + \mathcal{E}\, dZ$.

(d) $\left(\dfrac{\partial H}{\partial Z}\right)_{T,P} = \mathcal{E} - T\left(\dfrac{\partial \mathcal{E}}{\partial T}\right)_{P,Z}$.

(e) For a saturated cell, $\Delta H = -\dfrac{jF}{J}\left[\mathcal{E} - T\left(\dfrac{\partial \mathcal{E}}{\partial T}\right)_P\right]$.

14.27. Using the five coordinates P, V, T, $\mathcal{J}$, A to describe a surface film and its accompanying liquid, show that

(a) $dG = -S\, dT + V\, dP + \mathcal{J}\, dA$.

(b) $\left(\dfrac{\partial \mathcal{J}}{\partial P}\right)_{T,A} = \left(\dfrac{\partial V}{\partial A}\right)_{T,P}$.

15

Change of Phase

15.1. First-order Transition. Clapeyron's Equation. In the familiar phase transitions—melting, vaporization, and sublimation—as well as in some less familiar transitions such as from one crystal modification to another, the temperature and pressure remain constant while the entropy and volume change. Consider n_0 moles of material in phase i with molar entropy $s^{(i)}$ and molar volume $v^{(i)}$. Both $s^{(i)}$ and $v^{(i)}$ are functions of T and P and hence remain constant during the phase transition which ends with the material in phase f with molar entropy $s^{(f)}$ and molar volume $v^{(f)}$. The different phases are indicated by superscripts in order to reserve subscripts to specify different states of the same phase or different substances. Let x equal the fraction of the initial phase which has been transformed into the final phase at any moment. Then the entropy and volume of the mixture at any moment, S and V, respectively, are given by

$$S = n_0(1 - x)s^{(i)} + n_0 x s^{(f)},$$
$$V = n_0(1 - x)v^{(i)} + n_0 x v^{(f)},$$

and S and V are seen to be linear functions of x.

If the phase transition takes place reversibly, the heat (commonly known as a latent heat) transferred per mole is given by

$$l = T(s^{(f)} - s^{(i)}).$$

The existence of a latent heat, therefore, means merely that there is a change of entropy. Since

$$dg = -s\,dT + v\,dP,$$

$$s = -\left(\frac{\partial g}{\partial T}\right)_P,$$

and

$$v = \left(\frac{\partial g}{\partial P}\right)_T,$$

we may characterize the familiar phase transitions by either of the following equivalent statements:

1. There are changes of entropy and volume.

2. The first-order derivatives of the Gibbs function change discontinuously.

Any phase change that satisfies these requirements is known as a *phase change of the first order*. First-order transitions are represented crudely by the three graphs on the left-hand side of Fig. 15.1. The changes that take place according to the three graphs on the right-hand

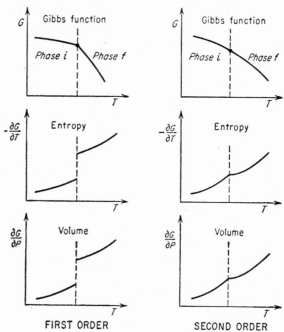

FIG. 15.1. First- and second-order phase transitions.

side of Fig. 15.1 are characteristic of a *phase change of the second order*, since, as we shall see later, in such a phase change the second-order derivatives of the Gibbs function change discontinuously.

In the case of a first-order phase transition, consider the reversible isothermal isobaric change of 1 mole of substance from phase i to phase f. Using the first $T\,ds$ equation,

$$T\,ds = c_V\,dT + T\left(\frac{\partial P}{\partial T}\right)_V dv,$$

and integrating over the whole change of phase, remembering that $(\partial P/\partial T)_V$ is independent of v, we get

$$T(s^{(f)} - s^{(i)}) = T\frac{dP}{dT}(v^{(f)} - v^{(i)}).$$

The left-hand member of this equation is the latent heat per mole, and hence

$$\boxed{\frac{dP}{dT} = \frac{l}{T(v^{(J)} - v^{(i)})}.}$$

This equation, known as *Clapeyron's equation*, applies to any first-order change of phase or transition that takes place at constant T and P.

Throughout this chapter we shall make use of the following notation: one prime for saturated solid, two primes for saturated liquid, and three primes for saturated vapor; subscripts fu for fusion, va for vaporization and su for sublimation. With this notation, Clapeyron's equation for fusion becomes

$$\frac{dP}{dT} = \frac{l_{fu}}{T(v'' - v')}.$$

Since l_{fu} and T are positive, the slope of the fusion curve is determined by the difference $v'' - v'$. If the substance expands on melting, $v'' > v'$ and the slope is positive. This is the usual case. Water, however, contracts on melting and has therefore a fusion curve with a negative slope. It is clear that, in the case of vaporization and sublimation, v''' is very much greater than either v'' or v', and hence dP/dT of these curves is always positive. These principles are illustrated in Figs. 11.7 to 11.11.

It is instructive to derive Clapeyron's equation in another way. It was shown in Chap. 11 that the Gibbs function remains constant during a reversible process taking place at constant temperature and pressure. Hence, for a change of phase at T and P,

$$g^{(i)} = g^{(J)};$$

and, for a phase change at $T + dT$ and $P + dP$,

$$g^{(i)} + dg^{(i)} = g^{(J)} + dg^{(J)}.$$

Subtracting, we get

$$dg^{(i)} = dg^{(J)},$$

or

$$-s^{(i)}\, dT + v^{(i)}\, dP = -s^{(J)}\, dT + v^{(J)}\, dP.$$

Therefore,

$$\frac{dP}{dT} = \frac{s^{(J)} - s^{(i)}}{v^{(J)} - v^{(i)}},$$

and, finally,

$$\frac{dP}{dT} = \frac{l}{T(v^{(J)} - v^{(i)})}.$$

15.2. Vaporization. The latent heat of vaporization may be measured with the aid of the apparatus depicted in Fig. 15.2. A liquid L_2 whose heat of vaporization is to be measured is contained in a small vessel and has immersed in it a small heating coil R_2 as shown in Fig.

15.2. Completely surrounding this vessel is a temperature bath consisting of a mixture of air and the vapor of another liquid L_1. By choosing a suitable liquid L_1 and keeping it at its boiling point by means of the heating coil R_1 in the presence of air at the proper pressure, the temperature bath may be maintained at any desired temperature. At this chosen temperature, the liquid L_2 is in equilibrium with its vapor. The small vessel containing L_2 communicates with another vessel on the outside (not shown in the figure), which may be maintained at any desired temperature by a separately controlled heating or cooling device.

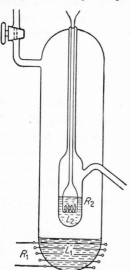

If the temperature of the outside container is maintained at less than that of L_2, a pressure gradient is produced, and some of L_2 will distill over. By maintaining a small current i in the heating coil R_2, the temperature of L_2 is kept equal to that of its surroundings, and the energy necessary to vaporize it is thus supplied. There is therefore a steady distillation of L_2 into the outside container, the heat of vaporization being supplied by the heating coil R_2 and the heat of condensation being withdrawn by the surroundings of the outside container. Moreover, all the energy supplied by the heater R_2 is used to vaporize L_2 since there is no heat loss between the inner tube and its surroundings. Consequently, if n moles are vaporized in a time τ, the heat of vaporization per mole is

FIG. 15.2. Apparatus for measuring heat of vaporization.

$$l_{va} = \frac{\mathscr{E} i \tau}{Jn}.$$

With apparatus similar to that just described, Henning, Aubrey, and Griffiths, and others have measured the heat of vaporization of water at various temperatures. The experimental results are plotted in Fig. 15.3. If Fig. 15.3 is compared with Fig. 14.8 (page 291), it will be seen that the temperature dependence of the heat of vaporization is similar to that of the surface energy per unit area.

The volume, enthalpy, entropy, and Gibbs function of saturated water and steam at various temperatures are given in Table 15.1. The heat of vaporization in joules per gram may be found by subtracting h'' from h'''.

The heat of vaporization may be measured indirectly and noncalorimetrically by measuring the vapor pressure as a function of the temperature and using Clapeyron's equation. Thus,

$$l_{va} = T \frac{dP}{dT} (v''' - v'').$$

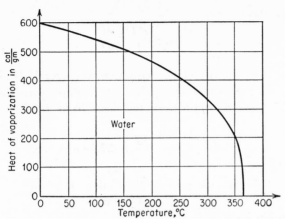

FIG. 15.3. Temperature variation of heat of vaporization of water.

At temperatures considerably below the critical temperature, $v''' \gg v''$, whence v'' can be dropped out. Assuming the vapor to behave like an ideal gas,

$$v''' = \frac{RT}{P},$$

TABLE 15.1. PROPERTIES OF SATURATED WATER AND STEAM (OSBORNE, STIMSON, AND GINNINGS, 1939)

Temp., °C	P, 10^6 dyne / cm²	v'', cm³ / gm	v''', cm³ / gm	h'', joule / gm	h''', joule / gm	s'', joule / gm·deg	s''', joule / gm·deg	g, joule / gm
0	0.006108	1.00021	206,288	0.0006	2501	0.0000	9.1544	0.00
10	0.012271	1.00035	106,422	42.036	2519	0.1511	8.8995	−0.76
20	0.023368	1.00184	57,836	83.904	2538	0.2964	8.6663	−3.0
30	0.042417	1.00442	32,929	125.71	2556	0.4367	8.4523	−6.8
40	0.073750	1.00789	19,546	167.50	2574	0.5723	8.2560	−11.7
50	0.12335	1.0121	12,045	209.30	2592	0.7038	8.0751	−18.1
60	0.19919	1.0171	7677.6	251.13	2609	0.8311	7.9085	−25.7
70	0.31160	1.0228	5045.3	293.01	2626	0.9550	7.7544	−34.7
80	0.47358	1.0290	3408.3	334.95	2643	1.0752	7.6116	−44.8
90	0.70108	1.0359	2360.9	376.98	2660	1.1924	7.4785	−56.0
100	1.01325	1.0435	1673.0	419.11	2676	1.3071	7.3546	−68.6
110	1.4326	1.0515	1210.1	461.34	2691	1.4185	7.2386	−82.2
120	1.9853	1.0603	891.7	503.76	2706	1.5278	7.1297	−96.9
130	2.7011	1.0697	668.3	546.34	2721	1.6345	7.0271	−112.6
140	3.6135	1.0798	508.7	589.17	2734	1.7392	6.9304	−129.4
150	4.7596	1.0906	392.6	632.21	2747	1.8418	6.8383	−147.2
200	15.550	1.1565	127.2	852.39	2793	2.3308	6.4317	−250.4
250	39.776	1.2512	50.06	1085.8	2801	2.7934	6.0721	−375.6
300	85.917	1.4036	21.64	1344.9	2749	3.2548	5.7049	−520.7
350	165.37	1.741	8.80	1671.2	2564	3.7786	5.2117	−683.4
374.15	221.29	3.1	3.1	2085	2085	4.4062	4.4062	−767.1

and the equation becomes

$$l_{va} = \frac{RT^2}{P} \cdot \frac{dP}{dT}.$$

As an example of the use of this equation, consider H_2O at 100°C and at 760 mm. Experiment shows that, as the temperature increases from 99 to 101°C, the vapor pressure increases from 733.7 to 788.0 mm. Therefore,

$$\frac{dP}{dT} = \frac{788.0 - 733.7}{101 - 99} = 27.15 \text{ mm/deg}$$

and

$$l_{va} = \frac{1.99 \text{ cal/mole} \cdot \text{deg} \times (373)^2 \text{ deg}^2 \times 27.15 \text{ mm/deg}}{760 \text{ mm}}$$

$$= 9864 \text{ cal/mole}$$

$$= {}^{9864}\!/_{18} = 548 \text{ cal/gm}.$$

This value is about 2 per cent larger than the correct value because of the assumption that the vapor behaves like an ideal gas.

It is an interesting fact that the entropy change accompanying the vaporization of 1 mole of liquid at its normal boiling point T_b is approximately the same for many liquids, about 20 cal/mole · deg. This is known as *Trouton's rule* and is illustrated in Table 15.2.

TABLE 15.2. TROUTON'S RULE

Sub-stance	T_b, °K	l_{va}, cal/mole	l_{va}/T_b, cal/mole · deg	Sub-stance	T_b, °K	l_{va}, cal/mole	l_{va}/T_b, cal/mole · deg
Ne	27.2	415	15.3	CH_4	112	1955	17.5
A	87.3	1560	17.9	CF_4	145	3010	20.7
Kr	120	2158	18.0	CCl_4	350	7140	20.4
Xe	165	3021	18.3	CH_2O	254	5850	23.0
Rn	211	3920	18.6	CF_2Cl_2	243	4850	20.0
F_2	85.0	1562	18.4	$CHCl_3$	334	6970	20.8
Cl_2	239	4878	20.4	C_2N_2	252	5576	22.1
HCl	188	3860	20.5	C_2H_6	185	3517	19.1
HBr	206	4210	20.4	C_6H_6	353	7350	20.8
HI	238	4724	19.9	$(C_2H_5)_2O$	307	6470	21.1
N_2	77.3	1330	17.2	Li	1599	30,800	19.3
O_2	90.2	1630	18.1	Na	1156	21,800	18.8
NO	121	3293	27.1	K	1030	18,600	18.1
H_2O	373	9717	26.0	Rb	985	17,100	17.4
CS_2	319	6400	20.0	Cs	986	15,700	15.9
SO_2	263	5955	22.6	Hg	630	14,100	22.4
H_2S	213	4463	21.0	Ga	2540	62,000	24.4
N_2O	185	3956	21.4	In	2273	51,600	22.7
NH_3	240	5581	23.3	Cd	1040	23,900	22.9

15.3. Fusion. The simplest method of measuring the heat of fusion of a solid is to supply electrical energy at a constant rate and measure the temperature at convenient time intervals. Plotting the temperature against the time, a heating curve is obtained in which the phase transition appears as a straight line, as shown in Fig. 15.4. The apparatus, shielding, precautions, etc., are exactly the same as those required in the measurement of heat capacity, described in Chap. 4. If n moles of solid melt in time $\Delta\tau$, with electrical energy supplied at the rate $\mathcal{E}i$, then

$$l_{fu} = \frac{\mathcal{E}i\,\Delta\tau}{Jn}.$$

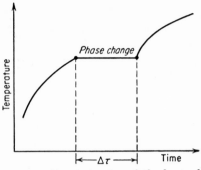

FIG. 15.4. Determination of the heat of fusion from a heating curve.

If T_m is the normal melting point of a solid, the entropy change associated with melting is l_{fu}/T_m. It may be seen from Table 15.3 that this entropy change is not as constant as that associated with vaporization. Fusion is a much more difficult phenomenon to understand on a molecular level.

TABLE 15.3. ENTROPY CHANGE ACCOMPANYING FUSION AT THE NORMAL MELTING POINT

Substance	T_m, °K	l_{fu}, cal/mole	l_{fu}/T_m, cal/mole · deg	Substance	T_m, °K	l_{fu}, cal/mole	l_{fu}/T_m, cal/mole · deg
Li	459	830	1.80	CF_4	84.6	168	2.0
Na	370	630	1.70	CCl_4	250	647	2.6
K	335	570	1.70	CBr_4	181	878	2.4
Rb	311	520	1.70	CH_4	91.5	224	2.45
Cs	299	500	3.4	C_2H_6	101	668	6.57
Cu	1356	2750	2.0	C_4H_{10}	134	1050	7.85
Ag	1233	2630	2.2	C_5H_{12}	143	2000	13.9
Au	1336	3180	2.4	C_6H_{14}	118	3110	17.5
Zn	692	1700	2.4	C_8H_{18}	216	4930	22.8
Cd	594	1500	2.5	$C_{18}H_{38}$	300	10,000	33.3
Hg	234	560	2.4	CH_3OH	176	757	4.30
Al	933	1910	2.0	C_2H_5OH	156	1105	7.05
Ga	303	1320	4.4	C_3H_7OH	147	1241	8.47
Tl	580	1470	2.6	C_4H_9OH	184	2215	12.1
Pb	590	1120	1.90	$C_5H_{11}OH$	194	2348	12.1
Ne	24.5	80.1	1.66	$C_6H_{13}OH$	226	3678	16.7
A	83.8	281	1.68	$C_{18}H_{37}OH$	331	11,700	35.4
K	116	391	1.70				

15.4. Sublimation. Heats of sublimation are usually measured indirectly by measuring the vapor pressure and using Clapeyron's equation. The same assumptions are made as in the case of vaporization, namely,

$$v''' \gg v',$$

and

$$v''' = \frac{RT}{P}.$$

Clapeyron's equation can then be written

$$l_{su} = R\,\frac{dP/P}{dT/T^2}$$
$$= -R\,\frac{d\ln P}{d(1/T)}$$
$$= -2.30R\,\frac{d\log P}{d(1/T)},$$

from which it can be seen that l_{su} is equal to $-2.30R$ times the slope of the curve obtained when $\log P$ is plotted against $1/T$. Vapor pressures of solids are usually measured over only a small range of temperature. Within this range the graph of $\log P$ against $1/T$ is practically a straight line, or

$$\log P = -\frac{\text{const.}}{T} + \text{const.}$$

For example, within the temperature interval from 700 to 739°K, the vapor pressure of magnesium satisfies with reasonable accuracy the equation

$$\log P = -\frac{7527}{T} + 8.589.$$

In the case of zinc between 575 and 630°K, the vapor pressure is given by

$$\log P = -\frac{6787}{T} + 8.972.$$

Therefore from 700 to 739°K the heat of sublimation of magnesium is $2.30R \times 7527 = 34{,}436$ cal/mole; for zinc between 575 and 630°K, $l_{su} = 2.30R \times 6787 = 31{,}054$ cal/mole. At other temperatures the heat of sublimation is different. If reliable vapor-pressure data existed over other temperature ranges, the temperature variation of l_{su} could be obtained. As a rule, however, this is impossible because at low temperatures the vapor pressure of a solid is too small to measure. In the following pages we shall derive *Kirchhoff's equation* for the heat of sublimation at any desired temperature.

An infinitesimal change of molar enthalpy between two states of equilibrium of a chemical system is given by

$$dh = T\,ds + v\,dP.$$

Introducing the second $T\,ds$ equation, we get

$$dh = c_P\,dT + \left[v - T\left(\frac{\partial v}{\partial T}\right)_P\right]dP$$
$$= c_P\,dT + v(1 - \beta T)\,dP.$$

A finite change of enthalpy between the two states $P_i T_i$ and $P_f T_f$ is

$$h_f - h_i = \int_i^f c_P\,dT + \int_i^f v(1 - \beta T)\,dP.$$

Let us apply this equation to a solid whose initial state i' is at zero pressure and at the temperature of absolute zero and whose final state f' is that of a saturated solid (solid about to sublime) represented by a point

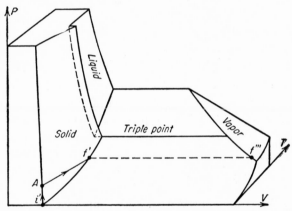

FIG. 15.5. Portion of the P-V-T surface below the triple point.

on the solid-saturation curve below the triple point. These two states are shown on a P-V-T surface in Fig. 15.5. To calculate the enthalpy change from i' to f' we may integrate along any reversible path from i' to f'. The most convenient is the path represented by the two steps $i' \rightarrow A$ and $A \rightarrow f'$, the first being isothermal at absolute zero and the second isobaric at the pressure P. Denoting the final enthalpy by h' and the initial by h_0',

$$h' - h_0' = \int_{i'}^A v(1 - \beta T)\,dP + \int_A^{f'} c_P\,dT$$
$$= \int_0^P v'\,dP + \int_0^T c_P'\,dT,$$

where v' is the molar volume of the solid at absolute zero and c_P' the molar heat capacity at the constant pressure P. Now the pressure at all points on the sublimation curve is very small for most solids. For example, for ordinary ice it ranges from 0 to about 5 mm, for cadmium from 0 to 0.1 mm. Therefore, if we limit the application of this formula to solids at temperatures where the vapor pressure is very small, we may ignore $\int_0^P v' \, dP$, and

$$ h' = \int_0^T c'_P \, dT + h'_0. $$

Since the c'_P of a solid does not vary appreciably with the pressure, the value of c'_P at atmospheric pressure may be used in the above integral.

The enthalpy of the saturated vapor indicated by point f''' in Fig. 15.5 may be calculated on the basis of the assumption that the saturated vapor at such a low pressure behaves like an ideal gas. Going back to the general equation $c_P = (\partial h/\partial T)_P$ and remembering that the enthalpy of an ideal gas is a function of the temperature only, we have

$$ dh''' = c'''_P \, dT. $$

Integrating from absolute zero to T, we have

$$ h''' = \int_0^T c'''_P \, dT + h'''_0, $$

where h'''_0 is the molar enthalpy of a saturated vapor at absolute zero.

Consider now the reversible sublimation of 1 mole of a solid at the temperature T and pressure P corresponding to the transition from f' to f''' in Fig. 15.5. We have

$$ l_{su} = h''' - h' $$
$$ = \int_0^T c'''_P \, dT - \int_0^T c'_P \, dT + h'''_0 - h'_0. $$

Since the two integrals approach zero as T approaches zero, it follows that

$$ l_{su} \to h'''_0 - h'_0 \qquad \text{as} \qquad T \to 0, $$

and $h'''_0 - h'_0$ *is the heat of sublimation at absolute zero*, which is denoted by l_0. Hence,

$$ \boxed{\; l_{su} = \int_0^T c'''_P \, dT - \int_0^T c'_P \, dT + l_0. \;} $$

This equation is known as *Kirchhoff's equation*. It is only an approximate equation, being subject to the restrictions that the pressure is low and that the saturated vapor behaves like an ideal gas.

Kirchhoff's equation may be used in the case of a solid with a monatomic vapor in the following way: A temperature T_1 is chosen in the neighborhood of which the vapor pressure is large enough to be measured. From measurements of the vapor pressure at temperatures near T_1 and the application of Clapeyron's equation, the heat of sublimation l_{su} at the temperature T_1 is calculated as in the preceding article. The value of $\int_0^{T_1} c_P''' \, dT$ at T_1 is $\frac{5}{2} RT_1$. The value of $\int_0^{T_1} c_P' \, dT$ is obtained by plotting c_P against T and taking the area from 0 to T_1. Using Kirchhoff's equation, l_0 may then be calculated. This was done for magnesium and zinc by Coleman and Egerton, whose results are given in Table 15.4.

TABLE 15.4. DETERMINATION OF l_0 FROM KIRCHHOFF'S EQUATION

Substance	T_1, °K	l_{su} at T_1, cal/mole	$\int_0^{T_1} c_P''' \, dT = \frac{5}{2} RT_1$, cal/mole	$\int_0^{T_1} c_P' \, dT$, cal/mole	l_0, cal/mole
Magnesium..	719.3	34,436	3573	3985	34,848
Zinc........	602.3	31,054	2992	3308	31,370

The heat of sublimation is not very sensitive to a change of temperature. From absolute zero up to the melting point it changes by only

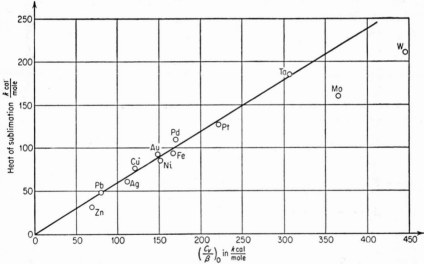

FIG. 15.6. Relation between heat of sublimation and the limiting value of the ratio of heat capacity at constant volume to thermal expansivity.

a few per cent. In Table 15.5 the heat sublimation at some unspecified temperature is listed for 35 different substances. These values may be taken roughly to be values of l_0. A correlation between the heat of sublimation and the limiting value of c_v/β is shown in Fig. 15.6. It may be seen that, approximately

$$l_{su} = 0.6 \left(\frac{c_v}{\beta} \right)_0 .$$

TABLE 15.5. HEAT OF SUBLIMATION
In kcal/mole

Substance	l_{su}	Substance	l_{su}	Substance	l_{su}
Ag	68	K	19.8	Rh	115
Au	92	La	90	Ru	120
Ba	49	Mg	34.8	Se	70
Ca	48	Mn	74	Sr	47
Cd	26.8	Mo	160	Ta	185
Co	85	Ne	34.9	Ti	100
Cr	88	Ni	85	V	85
Cs	18.8	Os	125	W	210
Cu	81	Pb	48	Y	90
Fe	94	Pd	110	Zn	31.4
Hg	14.6	Pt	127	Zr	110
Ir	120	Rb	18.9		

15.5. Equation of the Sublimation Curve. If the vapor in equilibrium with a solid is assumed to behave like an ideal gas, and the volume of the solid is neglected in comparison with that of the vapor, Clapeyron's equation becomes

$$\frac{dP}{P} = \frac{l_{su}}{RT^2} \, dT.$$

If, in addition to these assumptions, we suppose that the vapor pressure is very small, Kirchhoff's equation may be used. Thus,

$$l_{su} = l_0 + \int_0^T c_P''' \, dT - \int_0^T c_P' \, dT.$$

It was pointed out in Art. 6.6 that the molar heat capacity of an ideal gas can be represented as the sum of a constant term and a term which is a function of the temperature. Thus

$$c_P''' = c_0''' + c_i''',$$

where c_0''' is equal to $\frac{5}{2}R$ for all monatomic gases, and to $\frac{7}{2}R$ for all diatomic gases except hydrogen. The factor c_i''' has the property that it approaches zero rapidly as T approaches zero. Kirchhoff's equation may therefore be written

$$l_{su} = l_0 + c_0''' T + \int_0^T c_i''' \, dT - \int_0^T c_P' \, dT,$$

and, after substitution in Clapeyron's equation, we get

$$\frac{dP}{P} = \frac{l_0}{RT^2} \, dT + \frac{c_0'''}{RT} \, dT + \frac{\int_0^T c_i''' \, dT}{RT^2} \, dT - \frac{\int_0^T c_P' \, dT}{RT^2} \, dT.$$

Integrating this equation, we get finally

$$
\ln P = -\frac{l_0}{RT} + \frac{c_0'''}{R}\ln T + \frac{1}{R}\int_0^T \frac{\int_0^T c_i''' \, dT}{T^2}\, dT - \frac{1}{R}\int_0^T \frac{\int_0^T c_P' \, dT}{T^2}\, dT + i,
$$

where i is a constant of integration. This relation is the *equation of the sublimation curve*. It is not rigorous, but it is accurate enough to be used in conjunction with experimental measurements of the vapor pressure of solids. Such measurements are usually attended by errors that are much greater than those brought about by the simplifying assumptions introduced in the derivation.

If the vapor in equilibrium with a solid is monatomic, c_0''' has the value of $\frac{5}{2}R$ and c_i''' is zero. The equation of the sublimation curve then becomes

$$
\ln P = -\frac{l_0}{RT} + \frac{5}{2}\ln T - \frac{1}{R}\int_0^T \frac{\int_0^T c_P' \, dT}{T^2}\, dT + i.
$$

Changing to common logarithms and expressing the pressure in atmospheres, we get

$$
\log P = -\frac{l_0}{2.30RT} + \frac{5}{2}\log T - \frac{1}{2.30R}\int_0^T \frac{\int_0^T c_P' \, dT}{T^2}\, dT
$$
$$
+ \frac{i}{2.30} - \log 1{,}013{,}600.
$$

The last two terms are known as the *practical vapor-pressure constant i'*. Thus,

$$
i' = \frac{i}{2.30} - \log 1{,}013{,}600
$$
$$
= \frac{i}{2.30} - 6.006.
$$

Finally, expressing the pressure in millimeters, introducing the numerical values

$$
2.30R = 4.573,
$$
$$
\log 760 = 2.881,
$$

and calling

$$
B = \frac{1}{2.30R}\int_0^T \frac{\int_0^T c_P' \, dT}{T^2}\, dT,
$$

the equation becomes

$$
\log P = -\frac{l_0}{4.573T} + \frac{5}{2}\log T - B + i' + 2.881.
$$

This is the form in which the equation is most useful to the physicist or chemist in the laboratory.

The sublimation equation is used in two ways, (1) to obtain experimental measurements of the vapor-pressure constant i' which are to be compared with theoretical calculations of i' and (2) to calculate the vapor pressure of a substance at temperatures at which P is too small to measure. In both cases, the integral B must be evaluated on the basis either of experimental measurements of c'_P or of theoretical values for c'_P. In order to do this, c'_P is plotted against T from absolute zero to as high a temperature as is necessary. The area under the curve at various values of T is measured with a planimeter, and the temperature variation of $\int_0^T c'_P \, dT$ is thus obtained. These values are now divided by T^2 and plotted on another graph against T. The area under this new curve at various values of T provides finally the temperature variation of B.

If measurements of the vapor pressure exist over a wide temperature range, the numerical value of $\log P - \frac{5}{2} \log T + B$ is plotted against $1/T$. Since

$$\log P - \frac{5}{2} \log T + B = - \frac{l_0}{4.573} \cdot \frac{1}{T} + i' + 2.881,$$

the resulting graph is a straight line whose

$$\text{Slope} = - \frac{l_0}{4.573},$$
$$\text{Intercept} = i' + 2.881.$$

The data for cadmium are listed in Table 15.6. The vapor-pressure

TABLE 15.6. DATA FOR THE DETERMINATION OF i' OF CADMIUM

Kelvin temperature	$\log P$	$\frac{5}{2} \log T$	B	$\log P - \frac{5}{2} \log T + B$	$1/T$
360	−7.44	6.38	1.82	−12.00	0.00278
380	−6.57	6.45	1.88	−11.14	0.00263
400	−5.80	6.50	1.94	−10.36	0.00250
450	−4.17	6.63	2.08	− 8.72	0.00222
500	−2.86	6.75	2.20	− 7.41	0.00200
550	−1.77	6.85	2.32	− 6.30	0.00182
594	−0.99	6.94	2.41	− 5.52	0.00168

measurements were made by Egerton and Raleigh and the measurements of B by Lange and Simon. From the graph shown in Fig. 15.7, l_0 is found to be 26,740 cal/mole and i' to be 1.50.

If measurements of the vapor pressure exist only in a small temperature interval around the temperature T_1 (which is the usual case), then

Kirchhoff's equation is first used to obtain the value of l_0. The value of i' is then calculated from

$$i' + 2.881 = \log P_1 - \frac{5}{2} \log T_1 + B_1 + \frac{l_0}{4.573} \frac{1}{T_1}$$

where P_1 and B_1 are measurements of the vapor pressure and the double integral, respectively, at the temperature T_1. This is the way in which

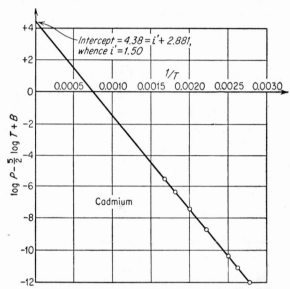

FIG. 15.7. Graph for the determination of the vapor-pressure constant of cadmium.

Coleman and Egerton measured the vapor-pressure constants of magnesium and zinc. Their data are given in Table 15.7.

TABLE 15.7. DETERMINATION OF i' OF MAGNESIUM AND ZINC

Substance	T_1	l_0	$\log P_1$	B_1	i'
Magnesium.............	719.3	34,850	−4.755	1.772	0.47
Zinc..................	602.3	31,370	−5.178	1.956	1.21

It is shown in statistical mechanics that the vapor-pressure constant is given by the equation

$$i' = -1.589 + 1.5 \log M + \log \nu_0^G,$$

where M is the molecular weight of the substance and ν_0^G is a quantity referring to both the vapor and the solid. Values of this quantity along with measured and calculated values of i' are given in Table 15.8. The agreement between theory and experiment is quite good in view of the experimental difficulties.

TABLE 15.8. COMPARISON BETWEEN CALCULATED AND MEASURED VALUES OF i'

Substance	Molecular weight M	ν_0^G	i (theor.)	i' (theor.)	i' (measured)
Neon.....................	20.2	1	14.6	0.373	0.40
Sodium..................	23.0	2	15.6	0.754	0.78
Magnesium..............	24.3	1	14.9	0.489	0.47
Zinc.....................	65.4	1	16.4	1.13	1.21
Cadmium................	112	1	17.3	1.49	1.50
Mercury.................	201	1	18.1	1.87	1.83
Thallium................	204	2	18.8	2.18	2.37

15.6. Second-order Transition. Ehrenfest's Equations. In Fig. 15.1, a second-order phase transition is seen to be one that takes place at constant temperature and pressure with no change of entropy or volume. The first-order derivatives of the Gibbs function therefore change continuously as the substance passes from one phase to the other. There are only a few transitions that seem to satisfy these requirements, and even in these cases it is still somewhat doubtful as to whether, for example, there is no latent heat or merely an extremely small latent heat. The following processes are among those which are generally regarded by most physicists as second-order phase transitions:

1. A ferromagnetic material such as iron or nickel becomes paramagnetic at the Curie point.

2. A superconducting metal becomes an ordinary conductor in the absence of a magnetic field at a definite transition temperature.

3. Certain alloys and chemical compounds undergo an "order-disorder" transition at a definite temperature.

4. Liquid helium II becomes liquid helium I at various temperatures and pressures, such as the λ point where $T = 2.19°K$ and $P = 38.65$ mm.

In all these processes, one or more of the quantities c_P, k, and β show discontinuous changes during the phase transition. In some cases, the changes are very small, leading us to believe that a discontinuous change in all three quantities is a necessary property of a second-order transition. Since

$$\frac{c_P}{T} = \left(\frac{\partial s}{\partial T}\right)_P = \frac{\partial}{\partial T}\left[-\left(\frac{\partial g}{\partial T}\right)_P\right]_P = -\frac{\partial^2 g}{\partial T^2},$$

$$kv = -\left(\frac{\partial v}{\partial P}\right)_T = -\frac{\partial}{\partial P}\left[\left(\frac{\partial g}{\partial P}\right)_T\right]_T = -\frac{\partial^2 g}{\partial P^2},$$

$$\beta v = \left(\frac{\partial v}{\partial T}\right)_P = \frac{\partial}{\partial T}\left[\left(\frac{\partial g}{\partial P}\right)_T\right]_P = \frac{\partial^2 g}{\partial T\,\partial P},$$

it follows that a second-order transition is characterized by discontinuous changes in the second-order derivatives of the Gibbs function. We may find relations between the changes in these quantities and the pressure and temperature, as follows: Indicating the two phases in question by the superscripts i and f, we have

$$s^{(i)} = s^{(f)} \qquad (\text{at } T, P)$$

and $\qquad s^{(i)} + ds^{(i)} = s^{(f)} + ds^{(f)} \qquad (\text{at } T + dT, P + dP)$,

whence $\qquad\qquad\qquad T\, ds^{(i)} = T\, ds^{(f)}$.

Using the second $T\, ds$ equation, we get

$$c_P^{(i)}\, dT - Tv\beta^{(i)}\, dP = c_P^{(f)}\, dT - Tv\beta^{(f)}\, dP,$$

and, finally,

$$\boxed{\dfrac{dP}{dT} = \dfrac{c_P^{(f)} - c_P^{(i)}}{Tv(\beta^{(f)} - \beta^{(i)})}.}$$

For the same phase transition we have also

$$v^{(i)} = v^{(f)} \qquad (\text{at } T, P)$$

and $\qquad v^{(i)} + dv^{(i)} = v^{(f)} + dv^{(f)} \qquad (\text{at } T + dT, P + dP)$,

whence $\qquad\qquad\qquad dv^{(i)} = dv^{(f)}$.

Since $dv = (\partial v/\partial T)_P\, dT + (\partial v/\partial P)_T\, dP$, we have

$$v\beta^{(i)}\, dT - vk^{(i)}\, dP = v\beta^{(f)}\, dT - vk^{(f)}\, dP,$$

or

$$\boxed{\dfrac{dP}{dT} = \dfrac{\beta^{(f)} - \beta^{(i)}}{k^{(f)} - k^{(i)}}.}$$

These two equations are known as *Ehrenfest's equations*.

15.7. Examples of Second-order Phase Transitions. There is very good experimental evidence that the transition from liquid helium I to liquid helium II is a phase transition of the second order. No latent heat has ever been detected, and the density of helium I is the same as that of helium II at the λ point.

The slope of the vaporization curve, i.e., the curve which is the locus of all points representing pressures and temperatures at which liquid helium II is in equilibrium with vapor, is given by Clapeyron's equation, thus

$$\frac{dP}{dT} \text{ (liquid II and vapor)} = \frac{s''' - s^{II}}{v''' - v^{II}},$$

whereas $\qquad \dfrac{dP}{dT}$ (liquid I and vapor) $= \dfrac{s''' - s^{I}}{v''' - v^{I}}$.

Since, at the λ point, $s^{I} = s^{II}$ and $v^{I} = v^{II}$, it follows that the slope of the vaporization curve undergoes no discontinuity at the λ point. This is also in agreement with the experimental facts as depicted in the phase diagram of Fig. 15.8.

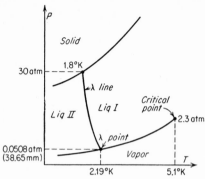

FIG. 15.8. Phase diagram for helium.

Therefore, assuming the transition from liquid I to liquid II to be of the second order, we may apply Ehrenfest's first equation to calculate the slope of the λ line at the λ point. Taking the experimental values

$$T = 2.19°K$$
$$v = 6.84 \text{ cm}^3/\text{gm}$$
$$c_P^{(I)} = 1.2 \text{ cal/gm} \cdot \text{deg}$$
$$c_P^{(II)} = 2.9 \text{ cal/gm} \cdot \text{deg}$$
$$\beta^{(I)} = 0.02 \text{ deg}^{-1}$$
$$\beta^{(II)} = -0.04 \text{ deg}^{-1}$$

we get, at the λ point,

$$\frac{dP}{dT} = \frac{c_P^{(I)} - c_P^{(II)}}{Tv(\beta^{(I)} - \beta^{(II)})}$$
$$= \frac{(1.2 - 2.9) \times 4.19 \times 10^7}{2.19 \times 6.84(0.02 + 0.04) \times 1.01 \times 10^6}$$
$$= -78 \text{ atm/deg,}$$

which agrees well with the measured value of -81 atm/deg. Using the

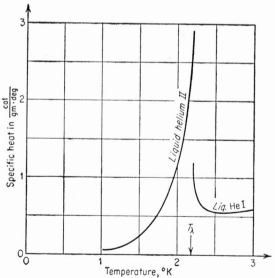

FIG. 15.9. Variation of the specific heat of liquid helium with temperature in the neighborhood of the λ point.

second Ehrenfest equation, we get for the change of compressibility the value -6.2×10^{-10}, which is too small to measure accurately.

The discontinuity in the specific heat of liquid helium at the λ point is shown in Fig. 15.9. The expression "λ point" derives from the shape of this curve which somewhat resembles a capital Greek lambda, Λ. Such a variation of specific heat with temperature is a characteristic of a phase change of the second order.

In a normal sample of natural helium, helium of mass number 4 predominates. About one part in a million, however, consists of helium of mass number 3, sometimes called light helium. Ordinary helium and light helium differ markedly in their properties as shown in Table 15.9.

TABLE 15.9. PROPERTIES OF He^4 AND He^3

	He^4	He^3
Critical temperature, °K............	5.20	3.35
Critical pressure, mm Hg............	1718	390
Critical density, gm/cm³............	0.07	0.042
Normal boiling point, °K............	4.216	3.195

By making use of the difference in properties of the two kinds of helium, which will be discussed more fully in Chap. 16, and also by artificial production of He^3 by radioactive decay of tritium, it is possible to produce mixtures of any desired percentage of He^3. It is a very interesting fact that such mixtures have λ points whose temperatures decrease as the enrichment of He^3 increases. The results of Abraham, Weinstock, and Osborne are shown in Table 15.10.

TABLE 15.10. λ POINTS
IN He^4-He^3 MIXTURES

Mole per cent of He^3	λ point °K
0	2.19
2.4	2.00
10.7	1.92
20.3	1.63
28.2	1.56
92.1	<1.05

Up to the present writing (1956), no λ point has been found for pure liquid He^3, and it is believed on theoretical grounds that none exists.

PROBLEMS

15.1. Prove that, during a phase transition of the first order, (a) the entropy of the entire system is a linear function of the total volume; (b) the energy change is given by

$$\Delta U = L \left(1 - \frac{P}{T} \frac{dT}{dP} \right).$$

15.2. Prove that the difference between the latent heat of any phase transition at T, P and that at $T + dT, P + dP$ is

$$dl = (c_P^{(f)} - c_P^{(i)})\, dT + [v^{(f)}(1 - \beta^{(f)}T) - v^{(i)}(1 - \beta^{(i)}T)]\, dP.$$

15.3. Show that the fractional change of boiling point of a liquid is approximately one-tenth the fractional change of pressure, provided (a) the molar volume of vapor is much larger than the molar volume of liquid; (b) the vapor behaves like an ideal gas; (c) Trouton's rule holds.

15.4. A liquid and vapor in equilibrium undergo a change of temperature dT and a change of pressure dP. Any constant mass of vapor undergoes a change of volume dv'''. Assuming the $v''' \gg v''$ and that the vapor behaves like an ideal gas, show that the "expansivity at constant saturation" is

$$\frac{1}{v'''} \frac{dv'''}{dT} = \frac{1}{T} \left(1 - \frac{l_{va}}{RT} \right).$$

15.5. The vapor pressure of mercury at 399°K and at 401°K is found to be 0.988 mm and 1.084 mm of mercury, respectively. Calculate the latent heat of vaporization of liquid mercury at 400°K.

15.6. The vapor pressure of many liquids is well represented by the equation

$$\ln P = B - \frac{A}{T},$$

where A/T is always greater than 5. (a) Assuming the saturated vapor to obey the ideal gas equation, what is the equation of the vapor saturation curve on a P-v diagram? (b) Show that the slope of this curve is greater than that of an isotherm of an ideal gas, but less than that of an adiabatic of an ideal gas whose $\gamma > 1.25$.

15.7. The specific heat at constant saturation of saturated vapor is defined as

$$c_{sat}''' = T \frac{ds'''}{dT}$$

and of saturated liquid as

$$c_{sat}'' = T \frac{ds''}{dT}.$$

(a) Show that

$$\frac{dl_{va}}{dT} - \frac{l_{va}}{T} = c_{sat}''' - c_{sat}''.$$

(b) From the data in Fig. 15.3 calculate c_{sat}''' of H_2O at 100°C, assuming c_{sat}'' to be 1 cal/gm · deg.

(c) Prove that the difference between the specific heat at constant saturation and the specific heat at constant pressure for either liquid or vapor is equal to

$$c_S - c_P = -Tv\beta \left(\frac{dP}{dT} \right)_{va}.$$

15.8. Water at its freezing point, T_i, P_i, completely fills a strong steel container. The temperature is reduced to T_f at constant volume, the pressure rising to P_f.

(a) Show that the fraction y of water that freezes is given by

$$y = \frac{v_f'' - v_i''}{v_f'' - v_f'}.$$

(b) State explicitly the simplifying assumptions that must be made in order that y may be written

$$y = \frac{v''[\beta''(T_f - T_i) - k''(P_f - P_i)]}{v_f'' - v_f'}.$$

(c) ·Calculate y for $i = 0°C$, 1 atm; $f = -5°C$, 590 atm; $\beta'' = -67 \times 10^{-6}$ deg⁻¹; $k'' = 12 \times 10^{-12}$ cm²/dyne; $v_f'' - v_f' = -0.102$ cm³/gm.

15.9. Ice at its melting point T_i, P_i, undergoes an isentropic compression to the state T_f, P_f.

(a) Show that the fraction x of ice that is melted is given by

$$x = -\frac{s_f' - s_i'}{s_f'' - s_f'}.$$

(b) State explicitly the simplifying assumptions that must be made in order that x may be written

$$x = -\frac{c_P'(T_f - T_i) - T_f v'\beta'(P_f - P_i)}{(l_{fu})_f}.$$

(c) Calculate x for $i = 0°C$, 1 atm; $f = -5°C$, 590 atm; $c_P' = 0.48$ cal/gm · deg; $v' = 1.09$ cm³/gm; $\beta' = 158 \times 10^{-6}$ deg⁻¹; $(l_{fu})_f = 79$ cal/gm.

15.10. (a) Prove that, for a single phase

$$\left(\frac{\partial P}{\partial T}\right)_S = \frac{c_P}{Tv\beta}.$$

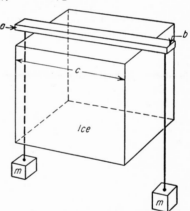

(b) Calculate $(\partial P/\partial T)_S$ for ice at $-3°C$, using the numerical data of Prob. 15.9(c).

(c) Ice is originally at $-3°C$ and 1 atm. The pressure is increased adiabatically until the ice reaches the melting point. At what temperature and pressure is this melting point? [HINT: At what point does a line whose slope is $(\partial P/\partial T)_S$ cut a line whose slope is that of the fusion curve, -133 atm/deg?]

15.11. A steel bar in the form of a rectangular parallelepiped of height a and breadth b is placed on a cake of ice with its ends extending a trifle, as shown in Fig. 15.10. A body of mass m is hung at each end of the bar. The whole system is at 0°C.

FIG. 15.10. A body of mass m is hung at each end of the bar. The whole system is at 0°C.

(a) Show that the decrease in temperature of the ice directly under the bar is

$$\Delta T = \frac{2mgT(v' - v'')}{bcl_{fu}}.$$

(b) Ice melts (see Prob. 15.9) under the bar and refreezes above the bar (*regelation*). Heat is therefore liberated above the bar, is conducted through the metal and a layer of water under the metal, and is absorbed by ice under the layer of water. Show that the speed with which the bar sinks through the ice is

$$\frac{dy}{d\tau} = \frac{U'T(v' - v'')2mg}{\rho l_{fu}^2 bc}.$$

where U' is the over-all heat transfer coefficient of the composite heat conducting path consisting of the metal and the water layer.

(c) Assuming the water layer to have a thickness of about 0.001 cm and a thermal conductivity of 0.00133 cal/sec · cm · deg, the bar to be 10 cm long with a and b each equal to 1 mm, with what speed will the bar descend when $m = 10$ kg?   (The thermal conductivity of steel is 0.15 cal/sec · cm · deg.)

15.12. Prove that the slope of the sublimation curve of a substance at the triple point is greater than that of the vaporization curve at the same point.

15.13. Iodine crystals have an atomic weight of 127 gm/mole and a specific heat of 0.047 cal/gm · deg.   Iodine vapor may be assumed to be an ideal diatomic gas with a constant c_P.   At 301°K, the vapor pressure is 515 dynes/cm²; at 299°K it is 435 dynes/cm².   Compute the latent heat of sublimation at 300°K, at absolute zero, and at 200°K.

15.14. The vapor pressure, in millimeters of mercury, of solid ammonia is given by

$$\ln P = 23.03 - \frac{3754}{T},$$

and that of liquid ammonia by

$$\ln P = 19.49 - \frac{3063}{T}.$$

(a) What is the temperature of the triple point?

(b) What are the latent heats of sublimation and vaporization?

(c) What is the latent heat of fusion at the triple point?

15.15. Given a thermally insulated cylinder containing water at 350°C.   Resting on the liquid and exerting a pressure equal to the vapor pressure is a thermally insulated, perfectly lubricated, nonleaking piston.   The piston is allowed to move out slowly so that the water vapor expands isentropically until the triple point is reached.

(a) Neglecting the heat capacity of the cylinder, prove that the fraction x of liquid vaporized is

$$x = \frac{s_i'' - s_f''}{s_f''' - s_f''}.$$

(b) Using the table on page 321, calculate x.

15.16. Assuming the evaporation of electrons from a hot wire (thermionic effect) to be thermodynamically equivalent to the sublimation of a solid, show that the pressure of the electron gas in equilibrium with a metal is given by

$$P = aT^{5/2}e^{-l_0/RT},$$

provided the electrons outside the metal constitute an ideal monatomic gas and the electrons inside the metal contribute nothing to the heat capacity of the metal.   (The second assumption is a poor one.)

16

The Physics
of Very Low Temperatures

16.1. Gas Liquefaction. The use of the Joule-Kelvin effect to produce liquefaction of gases has two advantages: (1) There are no moving parts at low temperature that would be difficult to lubricate. (2) The lower the temperature, the larger the drop in temperature for a given pressure drop, as shown by the values of μ for nitrogen in Table 14.1. For the purpose of liquefying hydrogen and helium, however, it has a serious disadvantage, namely, the large amount of precooling that is necessary. The hydrogen must be precooled with liquid nitrogen, and the helium must be precooled with liquid hydrogen, which makes the liquefaction of these gases very expensive.

An approximately reversible adiabatic expansion against a piston or a turbine blade always produces a decrease in temperature, no matter what the original temperature. If, therefore, a gas like helium could be made to do external work adiabatically through the medium of an engine or a turbine, then, with the aid of a heat exchanger, the helium could be liquefied without precooling. But this method has the disadvantage that the temperature drop on adiabatic expansion decreases as the temperature decreases.

A combination of both methods has been used successfully. Thus, adiabatic reversible expansion is used to achieve a temperature within the inversion curve, and then the Joule-Kelvin effect completes the liquefaction. Kapitza was the first to liquefy helium in this way, with the aid of a small expansion engine that was lubricated by the helium itself. Later he liquefied air with the aid of a small centrifugal turbine a trifle larger than a watch.

The latest development in the field of gas liquefaction is the Collins helium liquefier, in which helium undergoes adiabatic expansion in a reciprocating engine. The expanded gas is then used to cool the incoming gas in the usual countercurrent heat exchanger. When the temperature is low enough, the gas passes through a throttling valve and

Joule-Kelvin cooling is used to complete the liquefaction. The unit consists of a four-stage compressor, a gasholder, a purefier, and a cryostat containing the engines, heat exchangers, Dewar flasks, vacuum pumps, and all switches and gauges, as shown in Fig. 16.1. It is manufactured by the A. D. Little Co. of Massachusetts.

Precooling with liquid nitrogen may be used but is not essential. Starting with helium at room temperature, it takes only 2 or 3 hr for

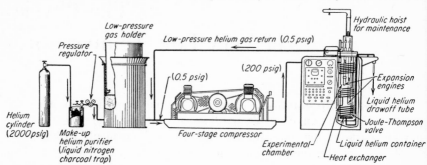

FIG. 16.1. Schematic diagram of the Collins helium-liquefying plant.

liquid helium to be produced, and when a few liters have collected, the liquid may be transferred to an external Dewar. Installation of Collins helium liquefiers in many laboratories throughout the world has expedited low-temperature physics to a great extent.

When a gas is liquefied, the normal boiling point (or, in the case of carbon dioxide, the normal sublimation point) and the triple-point temperatures and pressures must be determined with great accuracy. Temperatures are usually measured with a helium-gas thermometer according to the principles developed in Chap. 1. The bulb of the gas thermometer is often incorporated within the liquefaction apparatus. Pressures are

TABLE 16.1. USEFUL FIXED POINTS IN LOW-TEMPERATURE PHYSICS

Gas	Critical point	Normal boiling point	Triple point	Normal sublimation point
Carbon dioxide...............	304°K	....	216.6°K	194.7°K
	73 atm	....	5.11 atm	760 mm
Nitrogen..................	126.26°K	77.32°K	63.14°K	
	33.54 atm	760 mm	94 mm	
Hydrogen..................	33°K	20.37°K	13.96°K	
	12.8 atm	760 mm	54.1 mm	
Helium 4..................	5.20°K	4.216°K	2.186°K	
	1718 mm	760 mm	37.86 mm	
Helium 3..................	3.35°K	3.195°K	?	
	890 mm	760 mm	?	

usually measured with a mercury manometer, sighted througn the tele-scope of a cathetometer. Once these temperatures and pressures are measured, they may be used as fixed points for the calibration of gas thermometers of simpler design. Some of the most important fixed points of low-temperature physics are listed in Table 16.1.

The lowest temperature that can be reached easily with liquid helium is about 1°K. This is achieved by pumping the vapor away as fast as possible through as wide a tube as possible. With special high-speed

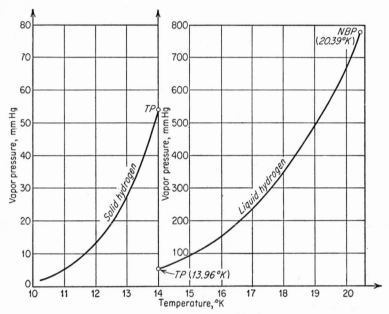

FIG. 16.2. Vapor pressure of hydrogen.

pumps, temperatures as low as 0.7°K have been reached, but this is rare. Temperatures lower than 0.7°K cannot be reached by pumping liquid helium because a film of liquid helium II creeps up the walls of the pumping tube, vaporizes, and then recondenses. This phenomenon will be discussed later on in this chapter.

The next step is to measure the vapor pressure at a large number of different temperatures. Some results of such measurements are shown in Figs. 16.2 and 16.3. With the aid of these curves, measurements of vapor pressure with a mercury manometer serve to determine temper-atures. Thus a hydrogen vapor-pressure thermometer may be used in the range from 20 to 10°K, and a helium vapor-pressure thermometer from 4 to 1°K. In the uncomfortable region from 10 to 4°K, helium gas thermometry is often used, and below 1°K magnetic methods, to be explained later in this chapter, are employed.

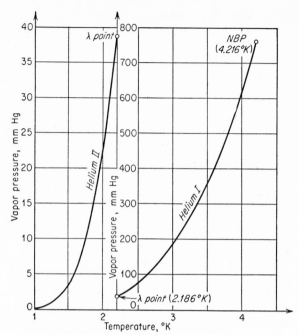

FIG. 16.3. Vapor pressure of helium.

16.2. The Helium Vapor-pressure–temperature Scale. Many of the phenomena discussed in this chapter occur in the temperature range from 1 to 4°K. The experimental apparatus is usually surrounded by a bath of liquid helium and a measurement of the pressure of the vapor in equilibrium either with the liquid bath itself or of some liquid helium in a separate bulb, in conjunction with a vapor-pressure–temperature table, serves to determine the temperature of the apparatus and of any secondary thermometer mounted on the apparatus. Everything depends on how accurately the relation between helium vapor pressure and temperature is known.

Up to 1955, various approximate thermodynamic P-T relations, similar to the sublimation equation given in Art. 15.4, were used and provided values of temperature adequate for many of the research projects. In the early 1950's, however, the development of secondary thermometers such as carbon resistors and paramagnetic salts, to be described in Art. 16.3, gave rise to a host of temperature measurements which could be compared with the results obtained from P-T tables. Small anomalies began to show up and these could be explained only as discontinuities and inconsistencies in the vapor-pressure–temperature relationship.

In the spring of 1955, Clement and his coworkers at the U.S. Naval Research Laboratory developed an empirical P-T relation that resolved practically all the existing discrepancies within a few millidegrees. Not long after, Van Dijk and his colleagues at Leiden derived the following thermodynamic equation between P and T in which departure from ideality of the helium vapor was taken into account as well as the pressure dependence of the enthalpy of the liquid:

$$\ln P = -\frac{l_0}{RT} + \frac{5}{2}\ln T - \frac{1}{RT}\int_0^T s''\,dT + \frac{1}{RT}\int_0^P v''\,dP$$
$$-\frac{2B}{v'''} + \ln\frac{Pv'''}{RT} + i_0,$$

where P is in millimeters of mercury, $l_0 = 59.50$ joules/mole, and $i_0 = 12.2440$. Using the latest values for the various properties of liquid and gaseous helium, Van Dijk published a table of P and T values which was just as successful as Clement's in resolving the existing difficulties and had the further advantage of a thermodynamic background.

16.3. Secondary Thermometers in the Low-temperature Region. The gas thermometer and the vapor-pressure thermometer are elaborate, exacting, and sluggish devices. To measure heat capacities, thermal conductivities, and several other physical quantities of interest at low temperatures, many measurements of small temperature changes must be made quickly and accurately. For these purposes secondary thermometers must be used.

One of the first to be employed was a resistance thermometer made of carbon. Pieces of paper with carbon deposited on them or strips of carbon prepared by painting with colloidal suspensions have two advantages. They have extremely small heat capacities and can therefore follow temperature changes quickly, and their electric resistance, which increases rapidly as the temperature is reduced, is insensitive to the presence of a magnetic field. The main disadvantage of such thermometers is their lack of reproducibility. They must be calibrated anew each time they are used.

In 1951, Clement and Quinell discovered that carbon composition radio resistors, made by Allen-Bradley and rated from $\frac{1}{2}$ to 1 watt, had all the properties most desired in a low-temperature secondary thermometer, namely, high sensitivity, reproducibility, and insensitivity to magnetic fields. The reasons for these desirable properties are not understood, but to such thermometers are attributed the accuracy of much of the work done in low-temperature physics since 1951.

In using small radio resistors as thermometers, the plastic coating is first removed and replaced by a thin coat of lacquer. The thermometer is then attached to the experimental apparatus or placed in a hole drilled for that purpose. The resistance is measured at a number of temperatures which are known from measurements of the helium vapor pressure.

These known T's and R's are used to determine the constants K, A, and B in an empirical formula, such as

$$\log_{10} R + \frac{K}{\log_{10} R} = A + \frac{B}{T}.$$

Sometimes a four-constant formula is needed. An example of the sensitivity of a carbon radio resistor is provided by the numbers in Table 16.2.

TABLE 16.2. SENSITIVITY OF
CARBON RADIO RESISTOR

Temp., °K	R, ohms	dR/dT, ohms/deg
Room temperature	55	
20.37	134.4	4.595
14.00	179.6	11.16
4.20	1061.8	583.4
2.40	5108	7012

The attention of physicists is being drawn more and more toward germanium and silicon as possible low-temperature thermometers. Geballe and his coworkers at the Bell Telephone Laboratories have developed germanium samples "doped" with 2.2×10^{17} excess arsenic atoms per cubic centimeter which are sealed in helium-filled capsules. These have proved to be quite sensitive and accurately reproducible. Such thermometers have the advantage that the processes responsible for the resistance change are at least partly understood.

Some paramagnetic salts obey Curie's law or Weiss's law very closely down to 1°K and even lower. If the Curie constant and the Weiss constant are determined by measurements at known temperatures, then the magnetic salt may be used as a thermometer. In the liquid helium range, the change of magnetization of all paramagnetic salts is rather small. To measure temperature to 1 millidegree, the magnetization must be measured with tremendous accuracy with the aid of a specially constructed a-c mutual inductance bridge. The magnetic thermometer is of most importance in the temperature range below 1°K, where its magnetization changes by a large amount for a small temperature change. In this range it will be of great use in calibrating secondary thermometers.

In recent years acoustic interferometers have been developed for measuring the speed of longitudinal waves in a gas with an accuracy of at least one part in four thousand. The fundamental principle is simple. A resonating quartz source emits ultrasonic waves which travel through a column of helium gas and are reflected from a parallel surface back to the source. The existence of a standing wave is sharply defined by electrical indications of the quartz crystal loading. The displacement of the reflecting plate between positions at which standing waves are observed is equal to an integral number of half wavelengths. Thus, if the wavelength is measured and the frequency is known, the speed of the waves in the helium gas is determined.

Taking into account the small departure of low-pressure helium gas from the ideal gas condition, and its effect on γ, it may be shown that

$$\mathscr{V} = \sqrt{\frac{\gamma_0\, RT}{M}} \left[1 + \left(a + \frac{b}{T} \right) \rho \right],$$

where ρ is the density, γ_0 is the limiting value of γ as ρ approaches zero, and a and b are constants. If ρ is small enough, the correction term does not have to be known with great accuracy. It is hoped that the acoustic interferometer with low-density helium gas may serve as an absolute standardizing thermometer for calibrating secondary thermometers, particularly in the temperature range from 5 to 10°K where there are no fixed points.

16.4. Properties of Paramagnetic Salts. In statistical mechanics an ideal gas is treated as an assembly of molecules that are, on the average, so far apart that forces of interaction among neighboring molecules may be ignored. With this simplification, the ideal gas equation may be derived. When the molecules are paramagnetic and the gas is placed in an external magnetic field, the resultant magnetic moment or magnetization of the gas may be calculated, provided again that mutual interactions are neglected. This calculation was first performed by Langevin and later extended by Brillouin. If I is the molar magnetization of the gas at temperature T and in an external field of magnetic intensity $\mathscr{H}$, Brillouin showed that

$$I = \frac{N g \mu_B}{2} \left[(2J + 1) \coth (2J + 1) \frac{g \mu_B \mathscr{H}}{2kT} - \coth \frac{g \mu_B \mathscr{H}}{2kT} \right],$$

where N is Avogadro's number, k is Boltzmann's constant, μ_B is the Bohr magneton, and g and J are atomic constants that differ from atom to atom. If the hyperbolic cotangent is expressed in terms of e^x and e^{-x} and the exponentials are expanded in series, it may be shown that, as x approaches zero,

$$\lim_{x \to 0} \coth x = \frac{1}{x} + \frac{x}{3}.$$

For small values of the ratio $\mathscr{H}/T$, Brillouin's equation then reduces to Curie's law,

$$I = \frac{C \mathscr{H}}{T},$$

where the molar Curie constant is

$$C = \frac{N g^2 \mu_B^2 J (J + 1)}{3k}.$$

In solid, crystalline paramagnetic salts such as those listed in Table 16.3, the paramagnetic structures are *ions* occupying positions in the crystal lattice far removed from one another. There are so many non-magnetic atoms between the paramagnetic ions, or in other words, the

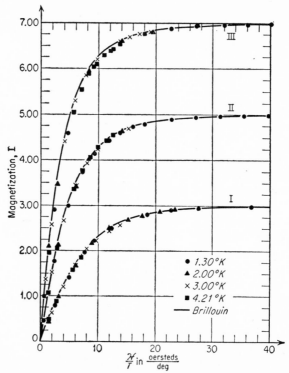

FIG. 16.4. Plot of magnetization I vs. $\mathcal{H}/T$ for (I) chromium potassium alum ($J = \frac{3}{2}$), (II) iron ammonium alum ($J = \frac{5}{2}$), and (III) gadolinium sulfate ($J = \frac{7}{2}$). The points are experimental results of W. E. Henry and the solid curves are graphs of the Brillouin function.

paramagnetic ions are so *dilute* that they interact with one another only very weakly. They therefore act like molecules of an ideal gas and their behavior in an external magnetic field may be represented by Brillouin's equation. The close agreement between measured values of I and Brillouin's formula is shown in Fig. 16.4 for three important paramagnetic crystals. Some physical properties of the most widely used paramagnetic salts are listed in Table 16.3. The term "gram-ionic weight" is the number of grams per mole in the case of the copper and the manganese salts, whereas it is the number of grams per half mole in all the other salts. The specific heat constant and the splitting factor, listed in the last two columns, will be explained later.

TABLE 16.3. PROPERTIES OF PARAMAGNETIC SALTS

Paramagnetic salt	Gram-ionic weight, M (gm)	Density, $\rho \left(\dfrac{\text{gm}}{\text{cm}^3}\right)$	Curie const., $C \left(\dfrac{\text{cm}^3 \cdot \text{deg}}{\text{gm ion}}\right)$	Sp. ht. const., A/R (deg^2)	Splitting factor δ/k, (°K)
Cerium magnesium nitrate, $2Ce(NO_3)_3 \cdot 3Mg(NO_3)_2 \cdot 24H_2O$	765		0.318	7.5×10^{-6}	0.00548
Chromium potassium alum, $Cr_2(SO_4)_3 \cdot K_2SO_4 \cdot 24H_2O$	499	1.83	1.86	0.016	0.245
Chromium methylammonium alum, $Cr_2(SO_4)_3 \cdot CH_3NH_3SO_4 \cdot 24H_2O$	492	1.645	1.87	0.0189	0.27
Copper potassium sulfate, $CuSO_4 \cdot K_2SO_4 \cdot 6H_2O$	442	2.22	0.445	0.00060	0.053
Iron ammonium alum, $Fe_2(SO_4)_3 \cdot (NH_4)_2SO_4 \cdot 24H_2O$	482	1.71	4.35	0.0142	0.20
Gadolinium sulfate, $Gd_2(SO_4)_3 \cdot 8H_2O$	373	3.010	7.85	0.32	1.35
Manganese ammonium sulfate, $MnSO_4 \cdot (NH_4)_2SO_4 \cdot 6H_2O$	391	1.83	4.36	0.033	0.32
Titanium cesium alum, $Ti_2(SO_4)_3 \cdot Cs_2SO_4 \cdot 24H_2O$	589	~2	0.118	3.9×10^{-5}	0.0125

16.5. Production of Very Low Temperatures by Adiabatic Demagnetization. When an attempt is made to lower the temperature of liquid helium II below about 1°K by pumping as rapidly as possible through a tube as wide as possible, the phenomenon of film creep provides a series of events equivalent to a heat leak. The film creeps up the pumping tube, evaporates at a place where the temperature is higher (thereby extracting heat), and then recondenses on the liquid (thereby giving up heat). The net effect is a transfer of heat to the liquid helium, whose temperature, therefore, cannot be reduced appreciably below 1°K with ordinary apparatus.

It was suggested independently by Debye and by Giauque in 1926 that the magnetic properties of certain paramagnetic salts could be used to obtain temperatures considerably below 1°K. The method suggested was the magnetocaloric effect, defined and explained in Art. 14.12. Experiments of this sort were first performed by Giauque in America and were then taken up by Kurti and Simon in England and by De Haas and Wiersma in Holland. In these experiments a paramagnetic salt is

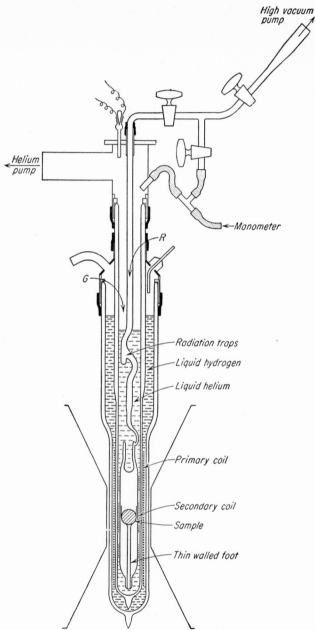

FIG. 16.5. Typical Leiden demagnetization cryostat.

cooled to as low a temperature as possible with the aid of liquid helium. A strong magnetic field is then applied, producing a rise of temperature in the substance and a consequent flow of heat to the surrounding helium, some of which is thereby evaporated. After a while, the substance is both strongly magnetized and as cold as possible. At this moment, the space surrounding the substance is evacuated. The magnetic field is now reduced to zero, and the temperature of the paramagnetic salt drops to a very low value.

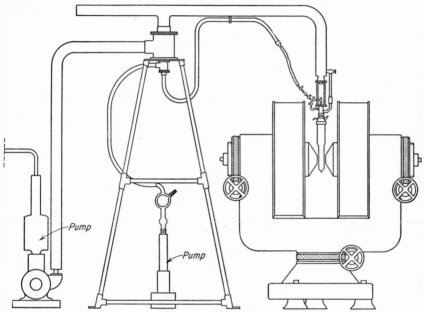

Fig. 16.6. Apparatus used in the Kamerlingh Onnes Laboratory at Leiden for adiabatic demagnetization.

The important details of the apparatus used by de Klerk, Steenland, and others at Leiden are shown in Fig. 16.5. The paramagnetic salt is either a single crystal, a pressed powder, or a mixture of small crystals in the form of either a sphere, as shown, or a spheroid. It rests on a glass pedestal in a glass vessel which communicates with the rest of the apparatus through tube R. The vessel is surrounded by liquid helium whose pressure (and therefore temperature) may be controlled through tube G. Surrounding the liquid helium is liquid hydrogen, the intervening space being evacuated. Helium gas is admitted through R into the vessel containing the paramagnetic salt before the magnet is switched on. The rise of temperature produced by switching on the magnet causes a flow of heat through this helium gas into the liquid helium. In other words, the helium gas is used as a conductor of heat to enable the paramagnetic salt to come to temperature equilibrium rapidly. It is therefore called the *exchange gas*. As soon as the temperature equilibrium is attained, the exchange gas is pumped out through the tube R, leaving the paramagnetic salt thermally insulated.

TABLE 16.4. TEMPERATURES ATTAINED BY ADIABATIC DEMAGNETIZATION OF VARIOUS PARAMAGNETIC SALTS

Experimenters	Date	Paramagnetic salt	Initial field, oersteds	Initial temp. °K	Final magnetic temp. T^*
Giauque and MacDougall	1933	Gadolinium sulfate	8,000	1.5	0.25
De Haas, Wiersma, and Kramers	1933	Cerium fluoride	27,600	1.35	0.13
		Dysprosium ethyl sulfate	19,500	1.35	0.12
		Cerium ethyl sulfate	27,600	1.35	0.085
De Haas and Wiersma	1934	Chromium potassium alum	24,600	1.16	0.031
	1935	Iron ammonium alum	24,075	1.20	0.018
		Alum mixture	24,075	1.29	0.0044
		Cesium titanium alum	24,075	1.31	0.0055
Kurti and Simon	1935	Gadolinium sulfate	5,400	1.15	0.35
		Maganese ammonium sulfate	8,000	1.23	0.09
		Iron ammonium alum	14,100	1.23	0.038
		Iron ammonium alum	8,300	1.23	0.072
		Iron ammonium alum	4,950	1.23	0.114
MacDougall and Giauque	1936	Gadolinium nitrobenzene sulfonate	8,090	0.94	0.098
Kurti, Lainé, Rollin, and Simon	1936	Iron ammonium alum	32,000	1.08	0.010
Kurti, Lainé, and Simon	1939	Iron ammonium alum	28,800	9.5	0.36
Ashmead	1939	Copper potassium sulfate	35,900	1.17	0.005

In the experiments of Kurti and Simon the adiabatic demagnetization is accomplished by switching the magnet off and wheeling it away. In the experiments at Leiden, the whole calorimeter is swung out of the magnetic field by means of the arrangement depicted in Fig. 16.6. The next step is to estimate the temperature. For this purpose, separate coils of wire surrounding the paramagnetic salt are used. The paramagnetic susceptibility $I/\mathscr{H}$, which is a function of the temperature, is measured by means of a special a-c bridge. A new temperature scale is now defined with the aid of Curie's equation. The new temperature T^*,

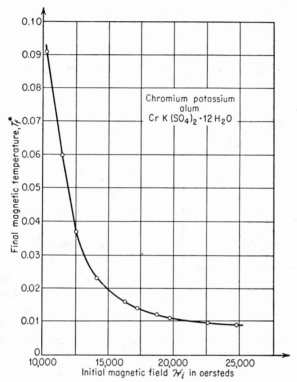

FIG. 16.7. De Klerk's results in the adiabatic demagnetization of chromium potassium alum.   (Initial temperature = 1.17°K.)

called the *magnetic temperature*, is defined as

$$T^* = \frac{\text{Curie's constant}}{\text{susceptibility}} = \frac{C\mathscr{H}}{I}.$$

It is seen that, in the region where Curie's law holds, T^* is the real Kelvin temperature, whereas, in the region around absolute zero, T^* is expected to differ somewhat from the Kelvin temperature.

The results of experiments on the cooling of paramagnetic salts by adiabatic demagnetization are given in Table 16.4, compiled by Burton, Grayson-Smith, and Wilhelm.

A series of results obtained by de Klerk is shown in Fig. 16.7, where the final magnetic temperature of chromium potassium alum is plotted against the initial magnetic field, the initial temperature being 1.17°K.

The lowest temperature reached up to the present writing (1956) was obtained by de Klerk, Steenland, and Gorter in Leiden with powdered mixed crystals of chromium alum and aluminum alum. The temperature, when converted to the Kelvin scale, is

$$\boxed{0.0014°\text{K.}}$$

16.6. Conversion of Magnetic Temperature into Kelvin Temperature. Adiabatic demagnetizations are carried out sufficiently slowly to approximate reversible processes. The behavior of a paramagnetic substance during an adiabatic demagnetization from a state i ($T = T_i$, $\mathscr{H} = \mathscr{H}_i$) to a state f ($T^* = T_f^*$, $\mathscr{H} = 0$) is represented conveniently on the T-$\mathscr{H}$ diagram shown in Fig. 16.8. The numbers on the ordinate axis above about 1°K are actual Kelvin temperatures as measured with the aid of a helium-vapor thermometer. Those below 1°K are magnetic temperatures. The substance passes through states of constant entropy during the demagnetization. It is

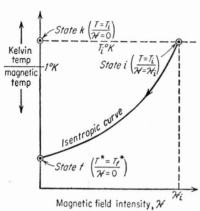

Fig. 16.8. Reversible adiabatic demagnetization of a paramagnetic solid.

clear that the entropy change from k to f is equal to the entropy change from k to i, or

$$s_f - s_k = s_i - s_k \qquad \text{(for 1 mole).}$$

The first step is to calculate $s_i - s_k$, which is the entropy change during a reversible isothermal process at the temperature T_i. Using the second $T\,ds$ equation,

$$T\,ds = c_{\mathscr{H}}\,dT + T\left(\frac{\partial i}{\partial T}\right)_{\mathscr{H}}d\mathscr{H},$$

and integrating from k to i, we get

$$s_i - s_k = \int_0^{\mathscr{H}_i}\left(\frac{\partial i}{\partial T}\right)_{\mathscr{H}}d\mathscr{H}.$$

The molar magnetization i can be calculated by Brillouin's equation as a function of T and $\mathscr{H}$; consequently, at $T = T_i$, $s_i - s_k$ is known as a function of $\mathscr{H}_i$. As a check on these calculated values, the heat evolved during an isothermal magnetization from zero field to a field $\mathscr{H}_i$ is measured. Upon dividing by T_i, $s_i - s_k$ is obtained. To every value of $\mathscr{H}_i$, however, there is a corresponding value of T_f^* attained by an adiabatic demagnetization from $\mathscr{H}_i$ to $\mathscr{H} = 0$. Since the entropy change $s_i - s_k$ is equal to $s_f - s_k$, we know $s_f - s_k$ as a function of T_f^*. Values obtained from the experiments and calculations of de Klerk on ½ mole of chromium potassium alum are given in Fig. 16.9. Since s_k refers to the state where $T = T_i$ and $\mathscr{H} = 0$, it is a constant; and since s_f refers to a point where $\mathscr{H} = 0$, the slope of the curve in Fig. 16.9 is evidently

$$\text{Slope} = \frac{1}{R}\left(\frac{\partial s}{\partial T_f^*}\right)_{\mathscr{H}=0}$$

and may be obtained at any desired value of T_f^*.

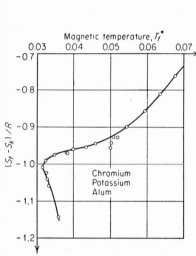

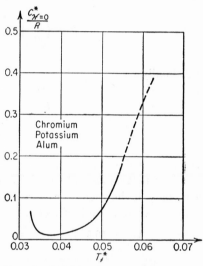

FIG. 16.9. Graph for obtaining values of $\frac{1}{R}\left(\dfrac{\partial s}{\partial T_f^*}\right)_{\mathscr{H}=0}$.

FIG. 16.10. Molar heat capacity at zero field as a function of magnetic temperature for chromium potassium alum. (De Klerk.)

Now consider 1 mole of a paramagnetic substance at the state f ($T^* = T_f^*$, $\mathscr{H} = 0$), and suppose an infinitesimal amount of energy is added, the field being kept zero and the magnetic temperature thus increased by an amount dT_f^*. In general,

$$\text{d}q = du - \mathscr{H}\, di;$$

but, at zero field, $dq = du$, and

$$\left(\frac{\text{d}q}{dT_f^*}\right)_{\mathscr{H}=0} = c_{\mathscr{H}=0}^* = \left(\frac{\partial u}{\partial T_f^*}\right)_{\mathscr{H}=0}$$

To measure $c_{\mathscr{H}=0}^*$, a known amount of energy must be supplied and the corresponding increase in the magnetic temperature must be measured.

In the experiments of Kurti and Simon, energy was added by the absorption of γ rays. De Klerk made use of the small ferromagnetic hysteresis possessed by paramagnetic salts at very low temperatures. De Klerk's results are shown in Fig. 16.10, where $c^*_{\mathcal{H}=0}/R$ is plotted against T^*_f. The values of $c^*_{\mathcal{H}=0}$ in this temperature range are enormous compared with those of a substance that obeys Debye's T^3 law.

We are now in a position to calculate the Kelvin temperature corresponding to any value of the magnetic temperature. Since

$$T \, ds = du - \mathcal{H} \, di,$$

then, at zero field, $T \, ds = du,$

$$T = \left(\frac{\partial u}{\partial s} \right)_{\mathcal{H}=0} = \frac{\left(\dfrac{\partial u}{\partial T^*_f} \right)_{\mathcal{H}=0}}{\left(\dfrac{\partial s}{\partial T^*_f} \right)_{\mathcal{H}=0}},$$

and, finally,

$$T = \frac{c^*_{\mathcal{H}=0}/R}{\dfrac{1}{R}\left(\dfrac{\partial s}{\partial T^*_f} \right)_{\mathcal{H}=0}}.$$

Numerical values are given in Table 16.5; the Kelvin temperatures corresponding to various values of T^*_f are shown in the last column. It is seen that, in the region of extremely low temperatures, the Kelvin temperature is from one-half to one-tenth the magnetic temperature.

TABLE 16.5. RELATION BETWEEN MAGNETIC AND KELVIN TEMPERATURE, USING CHROMIUM POTASSIUM ALUM

Magnetic temp., T^*	$\dfrac{c^*}{R}$	$\dfrac{1}{R}\left(\dfrac{\partial s}{\partial T^*_f} \right)_{\mathcal{H}=0}$	Kelvin temp., T
0.064	0.38	12.0	0.035
0.060	0.33	10.7	0.031
0.054	0.159	7.3	0.022
0.052	0.108	6.4	0.018
0.050	0.074	5.5	0.015
0.048	0.050	4.5	0.012
0.046	0.034	3.6	0.010
0.044	0.023	2.7	0.0088
0.042	0.016	2.25	0.0075
0.040	0.012	2.05	0.0065
0.038	0.011	2.6	0.0056
0.036	0.011	4.1	0.0047
0.034	0.024	6.1	0.0041
0.033	0.047	8.5	0.0039

We have seen that, when the magnetic temperature T^* is used as a thermometric parameter, the Kelvin temperature T is given by

$$T = \frac{(\mathrm{d}Q/\mathrm{d}T^*)_{\mathscr{H}=0}}{(\partial S/\partial T^*)_{\mathscr{H}=0}}.$$

The magnetic susceptibility, however, is not the only possible temperature-indicating property. In some preliminary experiments of Howling, Darnell, and Mendoza, the resistance R' of a carbon radio resistor was measured instead of T^* and the Kelvin temperature was obtained from the equation

$$T = \frac{(\mathrm{d}Q/\mathrm{d}R')_{\mathscr{H}=0}}{(\partial S/\partial R')_{\mathscr{H}=0}}.$$

16.7. Heat Capacities of Paramagnetic Salts. We have seen that Brillouin's equation holds for paramagnetic crystals in which there is only weak interaction among paramagnetic ions. For such crystals we may write $I = B\ (\mathscr{H}/T)$, where B designates Brillouin's function. The magnetic analogue of the equation (see Prob. 13.8)

$$\left(\frac{\partial U}{\partial P}\right)_T = -T\left(\frac{\partial V}{\partial T}\right)_P - P\left(\frac{\partial V}{\partial P}\right)_T$$

is

$$\left(\frac{\partial U}{\partial \mathscr{H}}\right)_T = T\left(\frac{\partial I}{\partial T}\right)_{\mathscr{H}} + \mathscr{H}\left(\frac{\partial I}{\partial \mathscr{H}}\right)_T.$$

Substituting for I the value $B(\mathscr{H}/T)$, we get

$$\left(\frac{\partial U}{\partial \mathscr{H}}\right)_T = T\left[B'\left(\frac{\mathscr{H}}{T}\right)\right]\left(-\frac{\mathscr{H}}{T^2}\right) + \mathscr{H}\left[B'\left(\frac{\mathscr{H}}{T}\right)\right]\left(\frac{1}{T}\right),$$

where B' represents the first derivative. Evidently $(\partial U/\partial \mathscr{H})_T = 0$, and

$$U = f(T) \text{ only.}$$

A paramagnetic substance whose magnetization is a function of $\mathscr{H}/T$ only is seen to have an *energy which is a function of temperature only*, like an ideal gas. Since $C_I = (\partial U/\partial T)_I$, it follows also that

$$C_I = f(T) \text{ only.}$$

Several of the paramagnetic salts have paramagnetic ions with two low-lying energy levels close together, separated by a small energy difference δ. At temperatures below 1°K, the Debye heat capacity due to lattice vibrations is negligibly small and practically all the ions are distributed between the two low-energy levels. A simple calculation in statistical mechanics, performed first by Schottky, gives rise to an expression for the molar heat capacity under these circumstances (temporarily dropping the subscript I)

$$\frac{c}{R} = \frac{\delta^2}{k^2T^2} \frac{e^{-\delta/kT}}{(1 + e^{-\delta/kT})^2},$$

where R is the universal gas constant and k is Boltzmann's constant.

If the Schottky equation is plotted, c/R is found to start at zero, rise rapidly to a maximum at $T = 0.4\delta/k$, and then decrease until, at values of T greater than δ/k, c/R varies inversely as T^2 according to the equation

$$\frac{c}{R} = \frac{\delta^2}{4k^2T^2} \qquad (T > \delta/k).$$

The experimental measurements of Gardner and Kurti on chromium methylamine alum shown in Fig. 16.11 fill in the entire Schottky curve

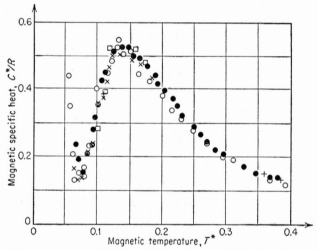

FIG. 16.11. The magnetic specific heat of chromium methylamine alum as a function of the magnetic temperature.

above 0.08°K. At a temperature of about 0.14°K, the heat capacity of a thimbleful of this salt is the same as that of 3 tons of copper at the same temperature! At temperatures above δ/k, a graph of c/R against $1/T^2$ should yield a straight line from whose slope the numerical value of δ/k may be obtained. Such a graph is shown for copper potassium sulfate in Fig. 16.12.

It is an interesting and important point that in cases where there are more than two closely spaced, low-lying energy levels and also even when various kinds of interaction take place among the ions, the heat capacity at temperatures that are not too low still varies inversely as the square of the temperature. A temperature range has always been found in which

$$\frac{c}{R} = \frac{A}{R}\frac{1}{T^2},$$

where A is a constant which is the sum of many complicated factors. Values of A/R are listed in the next-to-the-last column of Table 16.3 and the corresponding value of δ/k in the last column.

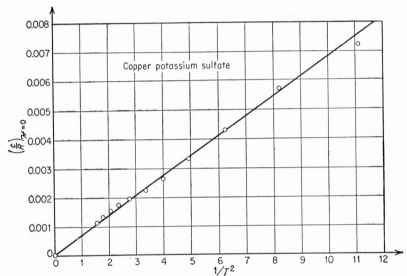

Fig. 16.12. Test of the relation $c/R \propto 1/T^2$.   (*Ashmead.*)

If we write the first law for a magnetic system and divide by dT, we get

$$\frac{dQ}{dT} = \frac{dU}{dT} - \mathscr{H}\frac{dI}{dT}.$$

If I is a function of $\mathscr{H}/T$ only, we have seen that U is a function of T only, and letting $\mathscr{H}$ be constant, we get

$$C_{\mathscr{H}} = C_I - \mathscr{H}\left(\frac{\partial I}{\partial T}\right)_{\mathscr{H}}.$$

Let us now calculate $C_{\mathscr{H}}$ for 1 mole of a paramagnetic salt in the temperature range in which (1) Curie's equation is obeyed and (2) C_I varies inversely as T^2.   Under these circumstances,

$$C_{\mathscr{H}} = \frac{A}{T^2} + \frac{C\mathscr{H}^2}{T^2},$$

and substituting this result into the thermodynamic equation for the magnetocaloric effect,

$$\frac{dT}{T} = -\frac{(\partial I/\partial T)_{\mathscr{H}}\, d\mathscr{H}}{C_{\mathscr{H}}},$$

the equation becomes

$$\frac{dT}{T} = \frac{(C\mathscr{H}/T^2)\, d\mathscr{H}}{A/T^2 + C\mathscr{H}^2/T^2} = \frac{1}{2}\frac{2\mathscr{H}\, d\mathscr{H}}{A/C + \mathscr{H}^2}.$$

Integrating from $(T_i,\, H_i)$ to $(T_f,\, 0)$, we get

$$\ln\frac{T_f}{T_i} = \frac{1}{2}\ln\frac{A/C}{A/C + \mathscr{H}_i^2}$$

or

$$\left(\frac{T_i}{T_f}\right)^2 = 1 + \frac{\mathscr{H}_i^2}{A/C}.$$

In Figs. 16.13 and 16.14 values of $(T_i/T_f)^2$ for gadolinium sulfate and chromium potassium alum are plotted against $\mathscr{H}_i^2$, and it is seen how

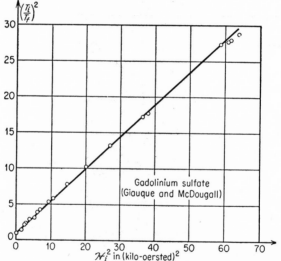

FIG. 16.13. Adiabatic demagnetization of gadolinium sulfate.

well the experimental results agree with the simple equation just derived when $\mathscr{H}_i$ is less than 10,000 oersteds. Notice that the ratio A/C has the dimensions of (oersted)^2, independent of the mass, and may be obtained experimentally from the slope of a line such as that in Figs. 16.13 or 16.14.

The properties of cerium magnesium nitrate are particularly noteworthy. Parallel to the axis of a crystal of this compound the magnetic susceptibility is practically zero, whereas perpendicular to this axis the susceptibility is quite reasonable in magnitude and *obeys Curie's equation all the way down to* 0.006°K: Starting at $T_i = 1°K$, $\mathcal{H}_i = 7130$ oersteds, the salt needs merely to be rotated from the parallel to the perpendicular position and its temperature will drop to 6 millidegrees!

16.8. The Magnetic Refrigerator.

At the conclusion of an adiabatic demagnetization, the temperature immediately starts to rise because of the unavoidable heat leak that is present in every cryostat, no matter how well designed. If the experiment under consideration

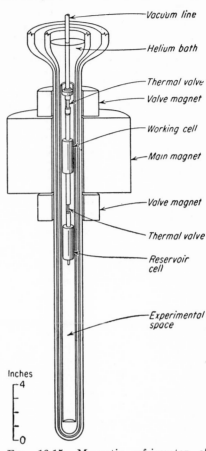

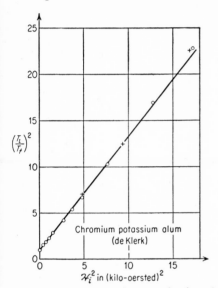

FIG. 16.14. Adiabatic demagnetization of chromium potassium alum.

FIG. 16.15. Magnetic refrigerator of Daunt and Heer.

can be performed quickly and does not itself involve too large a dissipation of energy into the system, adequate results may be obtained.   When, however, the experiment itself requires a dissipation of about 50 ergs/sec, a continuous refrigeration is needed.   For this purpose, Daunt and Heer designed a magnetic refrigerator, operating in a cycle, in which iron ammonium alum could be magnetized while in contact with one helium bath (the hot reservoir) and demagnetized when in contact with another helium bath (the cold reservoir).

A schematic diagram of the apparatus is shown in Fig. 16.15.   Notice that there are two thin metal rods marked "thermal valve."   These rods are made of lead and connect the paramagnetic salt contained in the "working cell" with the upper helium bath and with the lower "reservoir cell," respectively. At any temperature below 7.22°K lead becomes superconducting and, at the same time, becomes a very poor heat conductor. If, however, the superconductivity is removed with the aid of a magnetic field of only a few hundred oersteds (provided by the two "valve magnets"), the lead immediately becomes a good heat conductor.

During magnetization of the salt in the working cell the upper thermal valve is magnetized and the lower is not. During demagnetization, the reverse is the case. Each cycle takes about 2 min and at the end of about 30 min, the lower reservoir reached a temperature of about 0.20°K, with a heat extraction rate of about 70 ergs/sec. The design features of Daunt and Heer have been incorporated into a magnetic refrigerator constructed by A. D. Little Co. of Cambridge, Mass., composed of all necessary parts which perform automatically.

16.9. Nuclear Polarization and Alignment. The magnetic moment of the paramagnetic ions used in low-temperature demagnetizations is due to extranuclear electronic motions. Inside the nucleus there are particles whose motions also give rise to a magnetic moment, but it is about 10^{-3} that of the surrounding electrons. The lowest temperature achievable with the aid of electron magnetic moments seems to be about 0.001°K. It was first suggested by Gorter and by Simon that nuclear magnetism might be used to achieve still lower temperatures. This would require nuclear demagnetization from an initial field of about 50,000 oersteds and an initial temperature of about 0.01°K, in which case the final temperature might be as low as 10^{-5} or 10^{-6}°K!!

To perform this experiment, two large magnets are needed. Between the poles of one magnet there is placed the paramagnetic salt needed for the production of 0.01°K, and between the poles of the other the nuclear sample. The paramagnetic salt and the nuclear sample have to be far enough away so that their respective magnetic fields are independent of each other (from 10 to 20 cm), and yet have to be capable of being joined by a heat conductor. In addition to the fact that all materials are rather poor heat conductors at 0.01°K, there is the further difficulty of contact thermal resistance. In spite of these difficulties, Kurti and his coworkers at Oxford have succeeded in reaching the fabulous temperature of 18 millionths of a degree!

Other wonderful experiments, also, have been performed on nuclear magnets. To understand them, consider first the implications of the Brillouin equation $I = B(\mathcal{H}/T)$. If, say, 98 per cent magnetic saturation (orientation of electronic magnets) is achieved with a particular paramagnetic salt at a temperature of 1°K with a field of 10,000 oersteds, then, at a temperature of 0.01°K, a field of only 100 oersteds would be needed to produce the same orientation of the electronic magnets. In

other words, if the proper salt were used, starting at 1°K, a demagnetization from a field of 10,000 oersteds *not to zero field* but to a field of
100 oersteds, the temperature would drop to about 0.01°K, but the
orientation of the electronic magnets would still be considerable.   This,
of course, had been well known for a long time.   It occurred to Gorter
and, independently, to Rose that the aligned electronic magnets at 0.01°K
and in a weak field would give rise to a *unidirectional local field at the
nucleus of each ion* that would be much larger than any field achievable
in the laboratory, of the order of 100,000 oersteds or more, and would
therefore give rise to polarized nuclei which would also be aligned.

This experiment has been carried out several times by Roberts and
his coworkers at Oak Ridge.   They polarized Mn and Sm nuclei and
detected their polarization by measuring their ability to scatter polarized
slow neutrons from the Oak Ridge pile.

A clever modification of the Gorter and Rose method was suggested
by Bleaney who pointed out that, if polarization could be dispensed with,
alignment could still be achieved without any external magnetic field,
but making use of the axial, nonhomogeneous electric field present in a
single crystal.   Experiments of this sort were performed by Bleaney and
his coworkers at Oxford, and the alignment of radioactive cobalt nuclei
was detected by comparing the intensity of γ-ray emission parallel to
and at an angle to the alignment direction.   There was a difference of
as much as 40 per cent at the lowest temperatures.

It is seen therefore that magnetic cryogenic techniques have opened up
a new field of nuclear study which already has yielded much valuable
information.

16.10. Superfluidity of Liquid Helium II.   Helium gas at a pressure of 1 atm liquefies at 4.216°K.   If the temperature of a system consisting of liquid helium in equilibrium with its own vapor is lowered to
the λ point, 2.186°K, liquid helium II is formed.   As the temperature is
further reduced, the density of liquid helium II decreases, indicating
that the volume expansivity is negative.   The violent bubbling that
takes place by virtue of the unavoidable heat leak into a very cold liquid
at its boiling point ceases when helium passes through its λ point.   This
provides a simple visual method of observing the attainment of the λ
point and indicates an anomalously high thermal conductivity for liquid
helium II.

One of the most significant properties of liquid helium II is its abnormally low viscosity.   According to Poiseuille's law, the rate of flow of a
liquid through a tube or an annular space is inversely proportional to the
viscosity, other factors remaining constant.   If the rate of flow of liquid
helium through a fine annulus is measured as a function of temperature,
the solid curve of Fig. 16.16 is obtained.   At the λ point the rate of flow

increases abruptly and provides experimental evidence of a very low
viscosity. The result of a similar experiment on the light isotope of
helium of mass number 3 is shown in Fig. 16.16 as a dashed curve. No
such phenomenon has been observed for liquid helium 3.

A theory of liquid helium II was advanced by Landau in 1941 to
account for its peculiar behavior. Landau assumed that the energy
levels of liquid helium II (not of separate helium atoms) consisted of

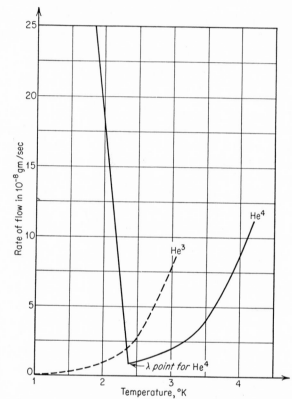

Fig. 16.16. Rate of flow of liquid helium 3 and of liquid helium 4 through a 7×10^{-5} cm
annulus.

two sets of overlapping continuous energy states: one representing the
levels for sound quanta, or *phonons*, and the other for quanta of vortex
motion, or *rotons*. The lowest phonon level was assumed to be below
the lowest roton level by an energy gap. On the basis of other assumptions Landau was able to construct a quantum hydrodynamics that
accounted quite well indeed for many of the properties of liquid helium II.

An equally plausible point of view was developed from quantum
statistical mechanics by F. London, who envisaged the formation of

liquid helium II from liquid helium I at the λ point as a peculiar type of quantum condensation, known as *Bose-Einstein condensation*. This is a phenomenon that takes place not in ordinary space like the familiar condensation but in momentum-space where the condensed particles have zero-point energy and momentum.

Many of the statements of both Landau's and London's theories rest on plausibility arguments rather than derivation from quantum theory. This situation has been considerably improved by the researches of Feynman, who has succeeded in deriving, on the basis of quantum statistics, the energy level and energy gap picture of Landau while at the same time retaining the Bose-Einstein condensation idea of London.

Both Landau's and London's points of view were redescribed by Tisza in picturesque language by a phenomenological theory of liquid helium II, known as the *two-fluid model* which, although not meant to be taken literally, has the virtue of simplicity, and has proved very helpful to experimentalists. According to this picture, liquid helium II is to be imagined as a mixture of two liquids:

1. Composed of normal atoms with normal viscosity.
2. Composed of superfluid atoms with zero-point energy and entropy and capable of moving through the normal atoms without friction or viscosity.

If ρ is the density of liquid helium II, ρ_n the density of the normal part, and ρ_s the density of the superfluid part,

$$\rho = \rho_n + \rho_s.$$

At the λ point all the atoms are normal and $\rho_n/\rho = 1$, whereas at absolute zero all the atoms are superfluid and $\rho_n/\rho = 0$.

If a disk or a set of concentric disks is set in oscillation in liquid helium II, the amplitude of oscillation will decrease with the time because of the viscosity of the liquid. If the disks are extremely close together, many of the normal atoms are dragged by the disks through the superfluid atoms, and, as a result, the moment of inertia of the disk system will depend on the density of normal atoms at the particular temperature chosen. By combining the results of these two experiments, and by applying plausible equations, Andronikashvilli was able to measure the ratio ρ_n/ρ as a function of the temperature. At lower temperatures, de Klerk, Hudson, and Pellam were able to infer values of ρ_n/ρ from their measurements of the speed of "second sound," a phenomenon in liquid helium II to be described later on. The combined results of all these measurements are shown in Fig. 16.17, where it may be seen that ρ_n/ρ varies as the fourth power of T up to about 0.6°K, and from there on the variation is more complicated. It is an interesting fact that the heat capacity and the thermal conductivity of liquid helium II also abruptly change their temperature dependence at 0.6°K. These facts lead us to believe that, at temperatures below 0.6°K, only phonons play a significant role.

Since ρ_n/ρ increases so markedly as the temperature rises, a temporary scarcity of superfluid atoms may be produced locally, i.e., in a small region of a vessel containing liquid II, if the temperature of that region is raised, either by heat leaking in from the outside, or by heat supplied by an electric heater. As a result, superfluid atoms diffuse into the region. This motion of superfluid atoms relative to normal atoms

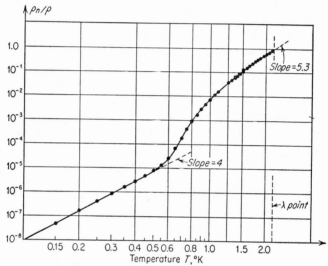

FIG. 16.17. Variation of normal fluid concentration with the temperature. Measurements of Andronikashvilli, de Klerk, Hudson, and Pellam.

accounts for the abnormally high heat conductivity of liquid helium II. It is more a transport of mass than a transport of heat.

In a mixture of liquid helium 4 and liquid helium 3 a temperature increase at one place causes a flow of superfluid He⁴ atoms to that place but not atoms of He³, since liquid He³ shows no superfluidity. This has been used to increase the concentration of He³ in a mixture to a value far above normal.

16.11. The Fountain Effect. One of the most peculiar phenomena of liquid helium II is the *fountain effect*, discovered by Allen and Jones in 1938. They observed that the level of liquid in a vessel, communicating through a narrow capillary to a surrounding bath of liquid, rose above that of the surrounding bath when heat was supplied electrically to the liquid in the vessel, as shown in Fig. 16.18. A more striking manifestation of this effect can be demonstrated with the apparatus shown in Fig. 16.19. The helium between the grains of finely ground emery was warmed by the radiation from a flashlight, and the consequent increase of pressure gave rise to a fountain of liquid helium which has been observed as high as 30 cm.

The fountain effect may be epitomized as follows: If two chambers or two parts of a vessel communicate with each other through a very

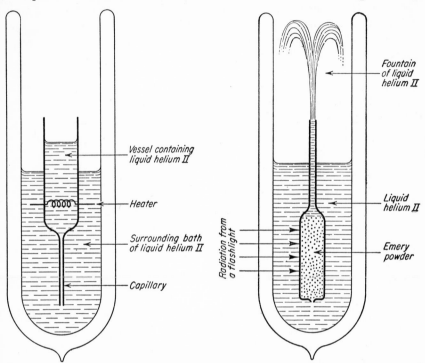

FIG. 16.18. Apparatus of Allen and Jones with which the fountain effect was first observed.

FIG. 16.19. Apparatus of Allen and Misener for showing the fountain effect.

narrow capillary, or a thin slit, or a small hole, or the spaces between a closely packed powder, etc., and the liquid helium II in one chamber is maintained at temperature T_1 and pressure P_1, then, if the temperature of the helium in the other chamber is maintained at T_2, the pressure will automatically become P_2, a positive temperature gradient giving rise to a positive pressure gradient. The numerical measure of the fountain effect is taken to be

$$f = \frac{P_2 - P_1}{T_2 - T_1},$$

or, as it will be shown later,

$$f = \left(\frac{\partial P}{\partial T}\right)_g,$$

where g is the Gibbs function.

When liquid helium II is transferred through a very small hole, slit, or capillary, it is generally accepted that only superfluid atoms are transported, carrying with them their zero-point energy and entropy. If we choose as a standard state for the calculation of entropy of liquid helium the state at absolute zero, and arbitrarily assign zero entropy to this state, then since liquid helium at absolute zero consists exclusively of superfluid atoms, we may ascribe zero entropy to superfluid atoms. Therefore, when liquid helium escapes through a narrow space, *no entropy is lost.*

Suppose two vessels, each containing liquid helium II, are connected by a narrow capillary, as shown in Fig. 16.20. If the vessels are maintained at different temperatures T_0 and T, respectively, with the aid of

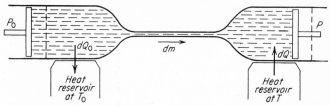

FIG. 16.20. Reversible transfer of mass dm of superfluid atoms.

suitable reservoirs, then for a given pressure on one mass of helium, there will exist a definite equilibrium pressure on the other. Suppose both pistons are moved to the right very slowly so that P_0 and T_0 are maintained constant on the left and P and T constant on the right, these being equilibrium values. Let the mass of liquid helium II on the right, m, increase by dm. Assuming that (1) only superfluid atoms, carrying no entropy, move through the capillary, and (2) there is no friction in, and no heat conduction through, the capillary, then each portion of helium undergoes an isothermal, isobaric, reversible change of mass.

It should be remarked that the behavior of a quantity of liquid helium II which loses superfluid atoms only, and thus loses no entropy *by virtue of this flow,* is entirely different from the behavior of the usual "open system" of classical thermodynamics where entropy *is* transferred by virtue of the flow of matter.

When the pistons move, only superfluid atoms flow through the capillary. Since these atoms carry no entropy, the entropy in the left-hand vessel is therefore distributed over a smaller mass and the temperature tends to rise. This is prevented, however, by the reservoir at constant temperature. Therefore, a flow of heat must take place to the reservoir. That is, when liquid helium II in the left-hand chamber loses superfluid atoms (loses mass), it loses no entropy through the capillary, but loses entropy to the reservoir of amount

$$s_0(m_0 - dm) - s_0 m_0 = -s_0 \, dm,$$

where s_0 is the specific entropy of liquid helium II at the constant temperature T_0 and constant pressure P_0. Since s_0 is a function of T_0 and P_0, it remains constant during the process.

The entropy change of the reservoir is $\text{d}Q_0/T_0$, where $\text{d}Q_0$ is the heat transferred from the liquid helium to the reservoir. Since the process is reversible, the sum of all the entropy changes is zero. Remembering once again that there is no entropy change accompanying the flow of matter, we have

$$\frac{\text{d}Q_0}{T_0} - s_0 \, dm = 0,$$

or
$$\text{d}Q_0 = T_0 s_0 \, dm.$$

Similarly, for the right-hand portion which gains dm grams of superfluid atoms, thereby gaining no entropy from the incoming atoms but gaining it instead from the reservoir, we have

$$\text{d}Q = Ts \, dm.$$

Considering the system as a whole,

$$\text{Net heat transferred} = Ts \, dm - T_0 s_0 \, dm,$$
$$\text{Net energy change} = (u - u_0) \, dm,$$
$$\text{Net work done} = (Pv - P_0 v_0) \, dm,$$

where u and v represent the specific energy and volume, respectively, at constant T and P; while u_0 and v_0 refer to constant T_0 and P_0. Obviously u, u_0, v, v_0 all remain constant during the process.

Applying the first law of thermodynamics, we get

$$Ts \, dm - T_0 s_0 \, dm = (u - u_0) \, dm + (Pv - P_0 v_0) \, dm,$$

$$\boxed{g_0 = g.}$$

Considering P_0 and T_0 on the left to remain constant, and varying P and T on the right, we have

$$dg = 0,$$

or
$$-s \, dT + v \, dP = 0,$$

and finally
$$\boxed{\left(\frac{\partial P}{\partial T}\right)_g = \frac{s}{v},}$$

the *fountain effect equation.* P is expressed in dynes per square centimeter, s in ergs per gram degree, and v in cubic centimeters per gram. If ρ is the density in grams per cubic centimeter and J is the mechanical equivalent of heat in ergs per calorie, the fountain effect equation may be written

$$\frac{1}{\rho J}\left(\frac{\partial P}{\partial T}\right)_g = s,$$

where both sides of the equation are expressed in calories per gram-degree K. Values of the entropy s may be calculated from data on the specific heat. Thus

$$s = \int_0^T \frac{c_P \, dT}{T}.$$

The experimental points and the entropy curve are shown in Fig. 16.21, where the agreement is seen to be satisfactory. Values of heat capacity and entropy obtained by Kramers, Wasscher, and Gorter are listed in Table 16.6.

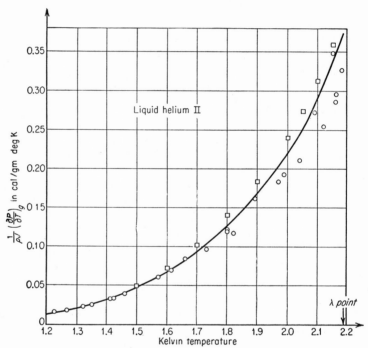

Fig. 16.21. Fountain effect in liquid helium II. Circles are experimental points of Meyer and Mellinck; squares those of Kapitza. Solid curve is entropy from measurements of Kramers, Wasscher, and Gorter.

16.12. Second Sound. According to the two-fluid theory of liquid helium II, the ratio of the number of normal to superfluid atoms depends strongly on temperature. A rapid, local temperature fluctuation gives rise to a rapid, local variation in the ratio ρ_n/ρ_s without altering the sum $\rho_n + \rho_s = \rho$. An ordinary longitudinal wave (loosely, ordinary sound) is the propagation of fluctuations in ρ throughout a medium. Fluctuations in the ratio ρ_n/ρ_s, *without change of* ρ, propagated through liquid helium II were predicted independently by Tisza and Landau and are called *second sound*. Second sound may be compared with ordinary sound in another way: In ordinary sound, vibrations of normal and super-fluid atoms *together* are propagated through a medium, whereas in second sound, vibrations of normal and superfluid atoms *relative to each other* are propagated.

Ordinary sound may be produced in liquid helium by a vibrating piston and, when so produced, is propagated with a speed $\mathcal{V}_1$ in agreement with the laws of classical physics. The temperature variation of $\mathcal{V}_1$ is shown

TABLE 16.6. HEAT CAPACITY AND ENTROPY OF LIQUID
HELIUM II (KRAMERS, WASSCHER, AND GORTER)

$T,\dagger$ °K	c, joule / gm · deg	s, joule / gm · deg	T, °K	c, joule / gm · deg	s, joule / gm · deg
0.60	0.0051	0.00169	1.45	0.944	0.162
0.65	0.0068	0.00215	1.50	1.127	0.197
0.70	0.0098	0.00276	1.55	1.330	0.238
0.75	0.0146	0.00358	1.60	1.572	0.284
0.80	0.0222	0.00475	1.65	1.83	0.336
0.85	0.0343	0.00644	1.70	2.11	0.395
0.90	0.0510	0.00885	1.75	2.46	0.461
0.95	0.0743	0.0122	1.80	2.80	0.535
1.00	0.1042	0.0168	1.85	3.19	0.617
1.05	0.142	0.0227	1.90	3.63	0.709
1.10	0.191	0.0304	1.95	4.27	0.812
1.15	0.250	0.0402	2.00	4.95	0.929
1.20	0.322	0.0523	2.05	5.82	1.061
1.25	0.410	0.0672	2.10	6.92	1.215
1.30	0.516	0.0853	2.15	8.61	1.40
1.35	0.634	0.1069	2.18	11.6	1.53
1.40	0.780	0.132	2.186	14.3	1.57

† Below 0.6°K, $c = 0.0235T^3$ joule/gm · deg, $s = 0.0078T^3$ joule/gm · deg.

in Fig. 16.22, where it may be seen that a striking discontinuity of slope occurs at the λ point.

Second sound may be produced by a temperature pulse or by periodic temperature fluctuations produced in a flat, disk-shaped heater by an appropriate electric current. This method is very simple but has the disadvantage of providing a continual supply of heat which boils away the liquid helium. To avoid this, it has been found possible to generate second sound by variations in temperature of a paramagnetic salt produced by superposing an alternating magnetic field on a steady field. Under these conditions, the temperature fluctuations are alternately above and below the ambient temperature, and there is no net input of heat.

The speed of second sound was first measured by Peshkov and later by Lane, Fairbank, and Fairbank; Osborne, Maurer, and Herlin; and Atkins and Osborne. The most recent measurements are those of de Klerk, Hudson, and Pellam. In some of the measurements, stationary second sound waves were set up in a cylindrical column of liquid helium II between two flat disks wound with resistance wire. An alternating electric current was used to produce the necessary temperature fluctuations in one disk, and the fluctuations in resistance produced by the temperature changes at the other disk served to detect the nodes or antinodes. In other measurements, a pulse of current in one disk caused

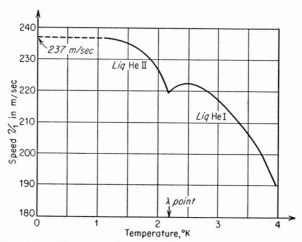

Fig. 16.22. Speed of ordinary sound in liquid helium. Measurements of Van Itterbeek and Forrez.

a temperature pulse to be propagated along a cylindrical column, and the velocity of this pulse was measured with electronic techniques.

The mathematical expression for the speed of second sound may be derived in a simple manner from the laws of thermodynamics, making use of the two-fluid model. Consider a column of liquid helium II indefinitely long, of cross-sectional area A, and at temperature T. Suppose that heat Q is supplied at one end by a source at temperature $T + \Delta T$ for a time τ. Both ΔT and τ may be chosen arbitrarily small. The temperature rise ΔT will be propagated along the column with a speed $\mathscr{V}_2$, the speed of second sound. It is assumed that the propagation takes place without dispersion and without attenuation. In time τ a column of length $\mathscr{V}_2\tau$ and of volume $\mathscr{V}_2\tau A$ will be affected. This volume of fluid, which we shall call the "system" is shown as the shaded region in Fig. 16.23.

The system differs from the rest of the liquid helium not only in temperature but also in the motions of the normal and superfluid atoms.

The normal atoms have a velocity v_n in the direction of propagation and the superfluid atoms have a velocity v_s in the opposite direction. The total momentum per unit volume is $\rho_n v_n + \rho_s v_s$, where ρ_n and ρ_s are the densities of normal and superfluid atoms, respectively, the total density ρ being equal to $\rho_n + \rho_s$. In the propagation of second sound, the total momentum per unit volume is zero, in contrast with first sound.

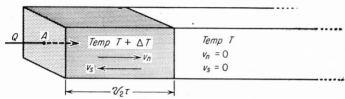

FIG. 16.23. Propagation of a second sound pulse in liquid helium II.

If H is the heat necessary to increase the temperature of the system by ΔT, then

$$H = \rho c \mathscr{V}_2 \tau A \, \Delta T, \tag{1}$$

where c is the specific heat capacity of the system. If, after the time interval τ, the heat source is turned off, the region of elevated temperature and relative motion of normal and superfluid atoms appears successively at neighboring points in the fluid, and thus is propagated with a speed $\mathscr{V}_2$. The energy H disappears at one place and appears at another. We may therefore speak of a "heat current" but this should not be confused with a convection or conduction current. The heat H produces a slight increase in the number of normal atoms and a consequent slight decrease in the number of superfluid atoms. The expression might therefore with more reason be called an "excitation energy current."

The contribution to the entropy change of the system due to the increase of temperature is

$$\Delta S = \rho c \mathscr{V}_2 \tau A \int_T^{T+\Delta T} \frac{dT}{T},$$

$$= \rho c \mathscr{V}_2 \tau A \ln\left(1 + \frac{\Delta T}{T}\right) = \rho c \mathscr{V}_2 \tau A \, \frac{\Delta T}{T},$$

$$= \frac{H}{T},$$

if we imagine ΔT small compared with T. Since this amount of entropy crosses area A in time τ, the "entropy current density" is $H/T\tau A$. According to the two-fluid model this entropy is carried by the normal atoms only, the superfluid atoms being assumed to possess zero entropy, referred to a standard state at absolute zero. Since the normal atoms, of density ρ_n, move with speed v_n and possess entropy per unit mass s_n, the entropy current density is given by $\rho_n s_n v_n$. But $\rho s = \rho_n s_n$, since

$s_s = 0$, and hence the entropy current density is equal to $\rho s v_n$, or

$$H = \rho s v_n \tau A T. \tag{2}$$

From Eqs. (1) and (2), it follows that

$$\frac{\Delta T}{T} = \frac{s v_n}{c \mathcal{V}_2},$$

and

$$\boxed{H \frac{\Delta T}{T} = \frac{\rho s^2 v_n^2 \tau A T}{c \mathcal{V}_2}.} \tag{3}$$

The kinetic energy K of the system may be calculated as follows:

$$\frac{K}{\mathcal{V}_{2\tau} A} = \frac{1}{2} \rho_n v_n^2 + \frac{1}{2} \rho_s v_s^2.$$

But

$$\rho_n v_n + \rho_s v_s = 0,$$

or

$$v_s = -\frac{\rho_n}{\rho_s} v_n,$$

whence

$$\frac{K}{\mathcal{V}_{2\tau} A} = \frac{1}{2} \rho_n \left(1 + \frac{\rho_n}{\rho_s}\right) v_n^2 = \frac{1}{2} \rho \frac{\rho_n}{\rho_s} v_n^2,$$

and

$$\boxed{K = \frac{1}{2} \rho \frac{\rho_n}{\rho_s} v_n^2 \mathcal{V}_{2\tau} A.} \tag{4}$$

If the source is turned off after time τ, this kinetic energy travels through the liquid without dissipation. Thus, at any moment, there exists a quantity of liquid of volume $\mathcal{V}_{2\tau} A$ with excitation energy per unit volume $H/\mathcal{V}_{2\tau} A = \rho c \, \Delta T$, and with kinetic energy per unit volume $K/\mathcal{V}_{2\tau} A = \frac{1}{2}\rho\rho_n v_n^2/\rho_s$. *Neither energy is transformed into the other; both coexist and remain constant in time, as they proceed through the liquid.*

To derive an expression for the speed of second sound it is merely necessary to find a relation between $H \, \Delta T/T$ and K. Let Q be the heat leaving the source at $T + \Delta T$, H be the heat necessary to raise the system in temperature by ΔT, and K the kinetic energy of the system. Then, from the first law of thermodynamics,

$$Q = H + K.$$

The entropy change of the source is

$$-\frac{Q}{T + \Delta T}.$$

The contribution to the entropy change of the system due to the temperature rise has already been shown to be

$$\frac{H}{T}.$$

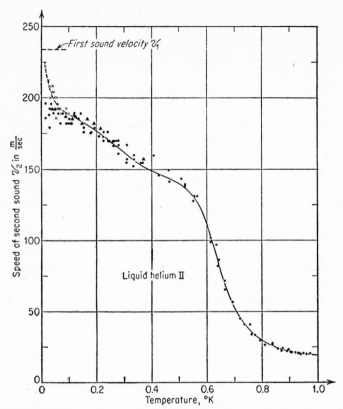

Fig. 16.24. Speed of second sound in liquid helium II as a function of temperature. (*De Klerk, Hudson, and Pellam.*)

The contribution to the entropy change of the system due to the *production* of kinetic energy is

$$- \frac{K}{T}.$$

Assuming, as usual, that the process is reversible, the total entropy change of the universe is zero, whence

$$- \frac{Q}{T + \Delta T} + \frac{H}{T} - \frac{K}{T} = 0.$$

Substituting for Q its value given by the first law, we get

$$- \frac{H}{T + \Delta T} - \frac{K}{T + \Delta T} + \frac{H}{T} - \frac{K}{T} = 0,$$

or

$$\frac{H \, \Delta T}{T^2} - \frac{2K}{T} = 0,$$

or

$$H \frac{\Delta T}{T} = 2K. \qquad (5)$$

Substituting the results of Eqs. (3) and (4) into Eq. (5), we get

$$\frac{\rho s^2 v_n^2 \tau A T}{c \mathcal{V}_2} = \rho \frac{\rho_n}{\rho_s} v_n^2 \mathcal{V}_2 \tau A,$$

or

$$\mathcal{V}_2 = \sqrt{\frac{\rho_s}{\rho_n} \frac{s^2 T}{c}},$$

which is the equation for the speed of second sound.

The temperature variation of the speed of second sound is shown in Fig. 16.24. Above 1°K, the speed remains fairly constant at a value of about 18 m/sec until almost 2°K. It then decreases to zero at the λ point. As the temperature goes below 0.6°K, it is seen that the speed of second sound, like other properties of liquid helium II, undergoes a change of slope.

Using the equation for the speed of second sound in conjunction with experimental measurements of $\mathcal{V}_2$, c, and s, de Klerk, Hudson, and Pellam calculated the temperature variation of ρ_n/ρ and it is these values that are plotted in Fig. 16.17.

16.13. The Creeping Film. It was observed by Kamerlingh Onnes in 1922 that the levels of liquid helium II in two concentric vessels placed

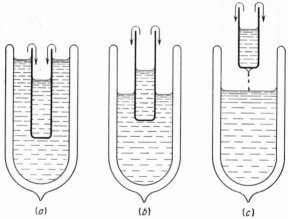

(a)   (b)   (c)

Fig. 16.25. Filling and emptying of a vessel by a creeping film of liquid helium II.

one within the other soon became equalized without any opening or communicating tube between the two vessels. Rollin showed that this phenomenon was due to a thin film that formed on any solid surface placed in liquid helium II. The film creeps with a definite critical velocity without friction from the higher to the lower level, as shown in Fig. 16.25(a), (b), and (c). Rough measurements indicate that the film is about 5×10^{-6} cm thick, or about 100 atomic layers.

Daunt and Mendelssohn proved that the rate at which the film creeps is independent of the difference of the two helium levels, but is determined by the temperature and the minimum periphery over which the film must pass. Defining the film transfer rate R as the volume of liquid moving per second per unit length of periphery, they showed that R is a function of T only, being zero at the λ point and approaching a constant as the temperature is lowered. Daunt and Mendelssohn's measurements were made by visual observation of the level of liquid helium II in a glass vessel as a function of the time, when it was filling and also when it was emptying.

A very extensive series of experiments on the rate of film creep over various surfaces was completed by B. Smith and Boorse in 1954. The vessel from which or into which the film creeped is represented schematically in Fig. 16.26. Between an outer metal cup S and an inner metal core C is an annular space for the liquid helium to enter or to leave. The liquid helium serves as a dielectric for the capacitor formed by S and C, and the level of the liquid in the annular space determines the capacitance, which in turn determines the frequency of a circuit of which the capacitor is part. As the level changes, the variation of frequency is made to produce a corresponding variation of voltage which is fed to a recording potentiometer.

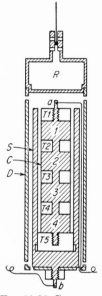

Fig. 16.26. Cross section of transport vessel–capacitor assembly of B. Smith and Boorse. (Not to scale.)

In Fig. 16.26 the vessel capacitor is shown surrounded by a radiation shield D and provided with a liquid helium reservoir R to ensure that the radiation shield was at a uniform temperature. Connections to the capacitor were made at points a and b.

The inner core C is separated into four metallic sections (numbered one to four) by means of five sections of insulating Teflon (numbered from $T1$ to $T5$). As the liquid level passes a metallic section a change of frequency takes place and this can be seen on the potentiometer record. As it passes a Teflon section, however, no change of frequency occurs. Knowing the volume of the annular space and reading time from the potentiometer record, the film creep rate over each of the four metal sections could be obtained.

The rate of film creep was measured at four average distances from the rim: 0.89, 2.23, 3.56, 4.89 cm; in the temperature range 1.1 to $2.1°K$; over aluminum, silver, copper, nickel, nickel silver, stainless steel, thorium, pyrex, quartz, and Lucite; and for various degrees of smoothness of the inside and outside surfaces of these materials. The main features of the results are shown in the graphs of Fig. 16.27. The film creep rate

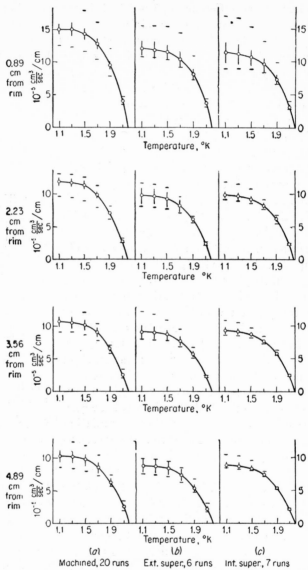

FIG. 16.27. Dependence of helium film creep rate on temperature, smoothness of finish, and distance from rim, averaged over various metals. Ext. super. and int. super. mean, respectively, externally superfinished and internally superfinished. (*B. Smith and Boorse.*)

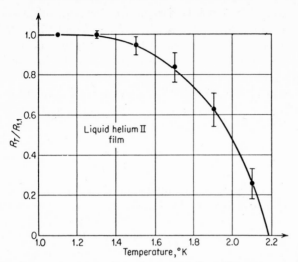

FIG. 16.28. Results of B. Smith and Boorse on the helium film creep rate as a function of temperature. The points are averages of 132 experiments on various metals with all heights and finishes and of 21 experiments on glass and quartz with all heights and finishes. The curve is a graph of $[1 - (T/T_\lambda)7]/[1 - (1.1/T_\lambda)7]$.

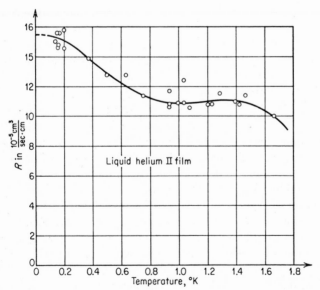

FIG. 16.29. Results of Ambler and Kurti on the helium film creep rate over glass at temperature below 1.6°K.

is always zero at the λ point, rises as the temperature is reduced, and reaches a constant value at 1.1°K of between 10 and 15 × 10⁻⁵ cm³/sec/ cm for all materials, rough or smooth. For any one degree of smoothness, the creep rate decreases as the distance of the helium level in the vessel from the rim increases.

It is shown in Fig. 16.28 that the temperature dependence of the creep rate averaged over all materials of all smoothnesses and over all distances from the rim, is represented well by the equation

$$\frac{R_T}{R_{1.1}} = \frac{1 - (T/T_\lambda)^7}{1 - (1.1/T_\lambda)^7},$$

where R_T is the creep rate at temperature T and $R_{1.1}$ that at 1.1°K.

Ambler and Kurti measured the creep rate over glass in the temperature range from 0.1 to 1.6°K, as shown in Fig. 16.29. The absolute value of the creep rate around 1.1°K is in agreement with the results of B. Smith and Boorse. Below 1°K, the creep rate is seen to rise only a small amount.

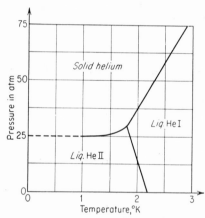

16.14. Solid Helium. When the internal energy of a simple crystal is calculated with the aid of statistical mechanics, it is found to consist of a temperature-dependent term, which approaches zero as T approaches zero, and a term independent of T. This latter term is known as the *zero-point energy*. It depends mainly on the strength of the interatomic forces and on the atomic mass. In the large majority of cases where interatomic forces and atomic mass are both great, the zero-point energy is small. Therefore, as the temperature of most substances is reduced, solidification may take place. In the case of helium, however, the zero-point energy is so large (about 60 cal/mole), because of small interatomic forces and small atomic mass, that a crystal under its own vapor pressure would be unstable. Under pressure, however, the reduction in volume brings the atoms nearer together so that the fields of force may interlock and a crystalline solid may form.

Fig. 16.30. Equilibrium diagram for solid-liquid helium, showing the upper triple point.

Solid helium has several of the characteristics of an ordinary solid. It is hard enough to block a capillary tube against a large pressure difference. Its specific heat roughly follows a Debye curve with a Debye temperature of about 25°K. In other respects, however, it differs markedly from ordinary solids. The phase diagram in the neighborhood of the upper triple point is shown in Fig. 16.30 and at high pressures and temperatures in Fig. 16.31. Notice that equilibrium between fluid and solid helium may be achieved at as high a temperature as 50°K, almost ten times the critical temperature.

The latent heat of fusion may be calculated from experimental measurements of $v'' - v'$ and of dP/dT, using Clapeyron's equation. The

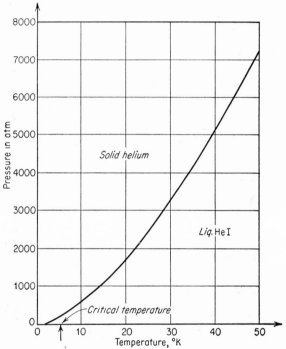

Fig. 16.31. Equilibrium diagram for solid-liquid helium at high temperatures and pressures. (*Holland, Huggill, Jones, and Simon.*)

results of such calculations by Simon and Swenson are shown in Fig. 16.32. Notice that, at the temperature of the upper triple point, the latent heat of fusion starts to decrease rapidly and becomes practically zero at about 1°K. Measurements of $v'' - v'$, however, indicate a constant value and hence, below about 1.7°K, an amazing thing occurs. The energy difference $u'' - u' = l_{fu} - P(v'' - v')$ becomes negative, indicating that the energy of solid helium is larger than that of liquid helium at the same temperature. The melting of solid helium at temperatures below about 1°K is a purely mechanical process, since there is practically no latent heat in this temperature region. An isothermal reduction in pressure produces melting and, conversely, an isothermal increase of pressure produces solidification.

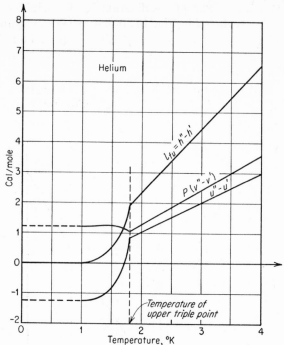

FIG. 16.32. Energy relations for liquid and solid helium, calculated with the aid of Clapeyron's equation and of the first law.

It was shown in Chap. 13 that the Debye characteristic temperature Θ depends on the melting temperature T_m, the molecular weight M, and the molar volume v, according to Lindemann's equation

$$\Theta = \text{const.} \frac{\sqrt{T_m/M}}{\sqrt[3]{v}}.$$

A large variation of T_m and corresponding v is possible with solid helium, as is shown in Table 16.7. It is noteworthy that Lindemann's equation holds quite well even when there is such a large variation of Θ.

TABLE 16.7. TEMPERATURE, VOLUME, AND
DEBYE Θ OF SOLID HELIUM

P, atm	T_m, °K	v, $\dfrac{cm^3}{mole}$	Θ, °K	$\dfrac{\Theta \sqrt[3]{v}}{\sqrt{T_m/M}}$
85	3.1	18.3	32	96
411	7.9	14.4	55	95
732	11.3	13.1	72	102
1420	17.3	11.6	92	100
2300	23.3	10.6	110	101

16.15. Helium of Mass Number Three.   The lighter isotope of helium, He^3, is found in natural helium with a concentration of about one part in a million.   The almost pure He^3 studied at the Los Alamos National Laboratory, at the Argonne National Laboratory, and at Ohio State University was obtained from the Isotopes Division of the U.S. Atomic Energy Commission.   It was prepared by radioactive decay of tritium which had been formed by neutron bombardment of deuterium, according to the reaction

$$_0n' + {}_1H^2 \rightarrow {}_1H^3 \rightarrow {}_2He^3 + {}_{-1}e^0.$$

Light helium is of particular theoretical interest since different theories predict different properties.   Thus, Landau's theory does not preclude

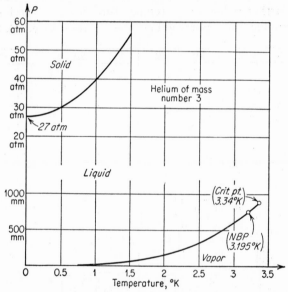

FIG. 16.33. Phase diagram of He^3.

superfluidity, whereas any theory based on statistical mechanics predicts properties in agreement with what is known as Fermi-Dirac statistics in which there is no condensation phenomenon to give rise to superfluidity. Although superfluidity in liquid He^3 has never been observed down to about 0.4°K, in apparent agreement with Fermi-Dirac statistics, nevertheless other properties such as heat capacity and magnetic susceptibility are not in agreement.   The problem of liquid He^3 is still (1956) quite baffling.

We have seen that ordinary helium, He^4, has two triple points neither of which is an equilibrium point for solid, liquid, and vapor.   A striking fact about light helium is that there are *no* triple points!   The phase diagram with the pressure axis distorted is shown in Fig. 16.33.   Notice that the critical point and the normal boiling point are only about one-tenth of a degree apart and also that He^3 requires a pressure of at least 27 atm to solidify.

There is some disagreement among experimenters about the heat capacity of liquid He^3. The results of Roberts and Sydoriak are represented by the empiric equation

$$c = 0.577 + 0.388T + 0.0613T^3$$

where c is in cal/mole · deg.

Some of the properties of mixtures of He^3 in He^4 are given in Art. 15.7.

16.16. Superconductivity. As the temperature is reduced, the electric resistance of many metals decreases until a residual value is reached. Further reduction in temperature down to the lowest values attainable produces no appreciable change in resistance. A few metals,

	I	II	III	IV	V	VI	VII	VIII		
1	1 H							2 He		
2	3 Li	4 Be	5 B	6 C	7 N	8 O	9 F	10 Ne		
3	11 Na	12 Mg	13 Al 1.197°	14 Si	15 P	16 S	17 Cl	18 A		
4	19 K	20 Ca	21 Sc	22 Ti 0.39°	23 V 4.89°	24 Cr	25 Mn	26 Fe	27 Co	28 Ni
	29 Cu	30 Zn 0.93°	31 Ga 1.10°	32 Ge	33 As	34 Se	35 Br	36 Kr		
5	37 Rb	38 Sr	39 Y	40 Zr 0.55°	41 Nb 8.9°	42 Mo	43 Tc 11.2°	44 Ru 0.47°	45 Rh 0.9°	46 Pd
	47 Ag	48 Cd 0.56°	49 In 3.40°	50 Sn 3.74°	51 Sb	52 Te	53 I	54 Xe		
6	55 Cs	56 Ba	57 La 4.8,5.8°	72 Hf 0.37°	73 Ta 4.38°	74 W	75 Re 1.70°	76 Os 0.71°	77 Ir	78 Pt
	79 Au	80 Hg 4.16°	81 Tl 2.39°	82 Pb 7.22°	83 Bi	84 Po	85 At	86 Rn		
7	87 Fr	88 Ra	89 Ac	90 Th 1.37°	91 Pa	92 U 1.1°	93 Np	94 Pu	95 Am	96 Cm

FIG. 16.34. Superconducting elements and their transition temperatures.

however, exhibit a most extraordinary behavior known as *superconductivity:* after the residual value of the resistance has been reached and the temperature is reduced, *the resistance suddenly decreases to zero.* Superconductivity is shown by 23 metals, 73 compounds, and 45 alloys. In the case of alloys and compounds, the transition from normal conductivity to superconductivity occurs over a fairly wide temperature interval, such as one or two degrees. In addition to this, the magnetic behavior of such superconductors is erratic and complicated, so that it is doubtful whether the methods of thermodynamics are applicable to them. We shall therefore limit ourselves in this chapter to pure metallic superconductors, which are shown in the periodic table of Fig. 16.34. The transition from normal resistance to zero resistance in the case of pure

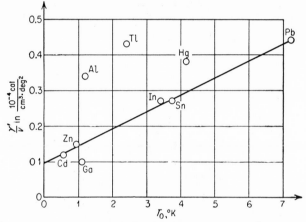

FIG. 16.35. Daunt's relation for the soft superconductors.

metals takes place in a very narrow temperature interval, about one one-hundredth of a degree or less, and hence the temperature T_0 at which a metal becomes superconducting can be measured with accuracy. Values of T_0 are printed below the chemical symbol for each superconductor in Fig. 16.34. It is an interesting fact that the superconducting elements lie mostly toward the middle of the periodic table. There are no superconductors with only one valence electron and there is also none with six valence electrons.

There are light superconducting elements that are physically soft and have a low melting point. They are known as the *soft superconductors* and they were found by Daunt to follow a simple linear relation shown in Fig. 16.35, where γ'/v (γ' is the electronic specific heat constant and v is the molar volume) is plotted against T_0. The other superconductors (which are known as *hard superconductors*) do not provide any regularity on Daunt's graph.

Matthias has given some evidence that the transition temperatures of some compounds and alloys depend in a regular way on a high power of the molar volume, on some power of the molecular weight, and on a function of the number of valence electrons. The function has a sort of maximum at 5, and another at 7. This relation does not seem to hold for elements, but the relevant data are presented in Table 16.8. The student might amuse himself by trying to find some regularity among the various values in this table.

TABLE 16.8. PROPERTIES OF SUPERCONDUCTING ELEMENTS

Element	No. of valence electrons	T_0, °K	M, $\dfrac{\text{gm}}{\text{mole}}$	v, $\dfrac{\text{cm}^3}{\text{mole}}$	γ', $\dfrac{10^{-4} \text{ cal}}{\text{mole} \cdot \text{deg}^2}$	Θ, °K	γ'/v, $\dfrac{10^{-4} \text{ cal}}{\text{cm}^3 \cdot \text{deg}^2}$
Al	3	1.20	27.0	9.93	3.4	375	0.34
Cd	2	0.56	112	13.0	1.6	165	0.12
Ga	3	1.10	69.7	11.8	1.2	240	0.10
Hf	4	0.37	179	13.5	6.6	213	0.49
Hg	2	4.16	201	14.0	5.3	69	0.38
In	3	3.40	115	15.8	4.2	109	0.27
La	3	4.8, 5.8	139	22.4	24	143	1.07
Nb	5	8.9	92.9	10.9	18	252	1.65
Os	8	0.71	190	8.45	5.6	.....	0.66
Pb	4	7.22	207	18.3	8.0	96	0.44
Re	7	1.70	186	9.07	5.9	210	0.65
Rh	9	0.9	103	8.30	11.0	350	1.33
Ru	8	0.47	102	8.40	8.0		0.95
Sn	4	3.74	119	16.3	4.4	195	0.27
Ta	5	4.38	181	10.9	13.6	230	1.25
Tc	7	11.2	99	8.6			
Th	4	1.37	232	19.8	12.1	168	0.61
Ti	4	0.39	47.9	10.6	8.3	430	0.78
Tl	3	2.39	204	17.3	7.5	87.9	0.43
U	3	1.1	238	12.5	26	200	2.08
V	5	4.89	51.0	8.39	22	338	2.62
Zn	2	0.93	65.4	9.20	1.4	235	0.15
Zr	4	0.55	91.2	14.1	3.9	265	0.28

If a superconducting element consists of several isotopes, it has been found that all the isotopes are superconductors but with slightly different transition temperatures. There is some theoretical foundation for the belief that the transition temperature should vary inversely as the square root of the isotopic mass number, or

$$T_0 \sqrt{M} = \text{const.}$$

Many measurements have been made on the isotopes of mercury, tin, thallium, and lead and the theoretical equation has been verified fairly

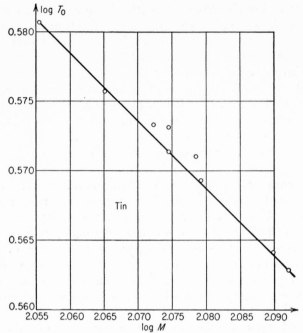

FIG. 16.36. Isotope effect in tin. The slope of the line is -0.49, or $T_0 M^{0.49} =$ const. The experiments were carried out at Cambridge, Oxford, Harwell, and the National Bureau of Standards.

well.   The best results are for tin and are given in Table 16.9 and Fig. 16.36.

TABLE 16.9. ISOTOPE EFFECT IN TIN

Average mass number, M	Transition temperature, T_0
113.6	3.808
116.2	3.764
118.1	3.744
118.7	3.727
118.7	3.742
119.8	3.724
120.0	3.709
123.0	3.665
123.6	3.654

The superconducting transition temperature depends also on pressure. In the case of tin, indium, lead, and mercury, the transition temperature is lowered as the pressure is raised, the derivative dT_0/dP being constant and about the same for these four superconductors, approximately $-4 \times$

10^{-5} deg/atm. For aluminum, the derivative is about -2.3×10^{-5} and for tantalum about -0.4×10^{-5} deg/atm. The behavior of thallium is anomalous. At low pressures, the derivative is positive at 1.2×10^{-5} deg/atm, whereas at pressures above 2400 atm the derivative becomes negative with the value -0.44×10^{-5} deg/atm.

The behavior of bismuth is most remarkable. At 1 atm, bismuth shows no superconductivity, whereas between 20,000 and 40,000 atmospheres bismuth becomes superconducting with a value of T_0 equal to 7°K. It is also a remarkable fact that very thin films of bismuth, of the order of 10^{-6} cm thick, are superconducting with a transition temperature of about 6°K.

16.17. Magnetic Properties of Superconductors. The most important phenomenon associated with superconductors is the fact that superconductivity may be destroyed by a magnetic field, either an external field or the field produced by a current flowing in the metal. In the case of a pure metal shaped into the form of a long, thin cylinder and placed longitudinally in a magnetic field, it is found that, as the field is increased, the temperature T remaining constant, the metal remains superconducting until a threshold field $\mathscr{H}_T$ is reached, at which, quite abruptly, the metal loses its superconductivity. The magnitude of the threshold field required to destroy superconductivity depends only on the temperature. Thus $\mathscr{H}_T$ is a function of T only, and is shown in Fig. 16.37. It should be noticed that each $\mathscr{H}_T$-T curve divides the $\mathscr{H}$-T plane into two regions, superconducting and normal, in a manner similar to a phase transition curve on a P-T diagram. All curves show the following properties:

1. The slope is always negative.
2. The slope at the point $T = T_0$, $\mathscr{H}_T = 0$ is finite.
3. The slope at $T = 0$, by extrapolation, is zero.

The relation between threshold field and temperature for metallic superconductors of extreme purity and free from strain is almost parabolic. To a first approximation

$$\mathscr{H}_T = \mathscr{H}_0 \left(1 - \frac{T^2}{T_0^2}\right),$$

where $\mathscr{H}_0$ is the field necessary to destroy superconductivity at absolute zero. Where accuracy is required equations such as the following are often used:

For tin,

$$\mathscr{H}_T = \mathscr{H}_0 \left[1 - 1.2117 \left(\frac{T}{T_0}\right)^2 + 0.2117 \left(\frac{T}{T_0}\right)^3\right].$$

For indium,

$$\mathcal{H}_T = \mathcal{H}_0 \left[1 - 1.1325 \left(\frac{T}{T_0} \right)^2 + 0.1325 \left(\frac{T}{T_0} \right)^3 \right].$$

For lead,

$$\mathcal{H}_T = \mathcal{H}_0 \left[1 - 0.91 \left(\frac{T}{T_0} \right)^2 + 0.09 \left(\frac{T}{T_0} \right)^4 \right].$$

The value of the slope, $d\mathcal{H}_T/dT$ at $T = T_0$, is important in the thermo-dynamic interpretation of the magnetic behavior of superconductors. This slope, along with values of T_0 and $\mathcal{H}_0$, are listed in Table 16.10.

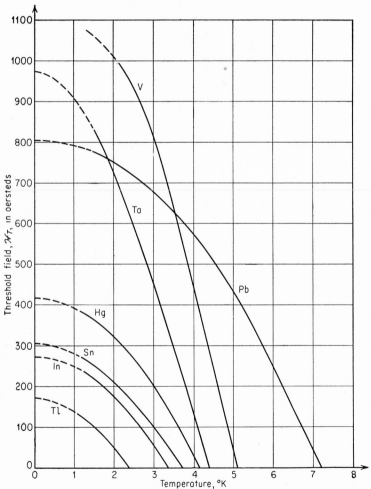

FIG. 16.37. Threshold field vs. temperature for a few superconductors.   (*Shoenberg.*)

In the case of a superconductor made of extremely pure metal in the shape of a long, thin cylinder, placed longitudinally in a magnetic field, the behavior of the magnetic induction $\mathscr{B}$ and the magnetization I, as the field is increased isothermally, is shown in Fig. 16.38. $\mathscr{H}_T$ is the

TABLE 16.10. MAGNETIC PROPERTIES OF
SUPERCONDUCTING ELEMENTS

Metal	T_0, °K	$\mathscr{H}_0$, oersteds	$\left(\dfrac{d\mathscr{H}_T}{dT}\right)_{T=T_0}$, oersteds/deg
Al	1.20	106	−163
Cd	0.56	28.8	− 86
Ga	1.10	50.3	− 93
Hf	0.37		
Hg	4.16	410	−194
In	3.40	280	−156
La	4.8, 5.8	1030	
Nb	8.9	1960	−453
Os	0.71	65	−183
Pb	7.22	812	−226
Re	1.70	188	−235
Rh	0.9		
Ru	0.47	46	−196
Sn	3.74	307	−147
Ta	4.38	860	−334
Tc	11.2		−350
Th	1.37	131	
Ti	0.39	100	−300
Tl	2.39	171	−126
U	1.1		
V	4.89	1340	−482
Zn	0.93	52.5	−121
Zr	0.55	46.6	−170

threshold field appropriate to the particular temperature chosen. It may be seen that, while the metal is superconducting, $\mathscr{B} = 0$ and, since

$$\mathscr{B} = \mathscr{H} + 4\pi \frac{I}{V},$$

it follows that

$$I = -\frac{V\mathscr{H}}{4\pi}.$$

Beyond the threshold field, however,

$$\mathscr{B} = \mathscr{H}, \quad \text{and} \quad I = 0.$$

From the graphs shown in Fig. 16.38 and $\mathcal{H}_T\text{-}T$ curves of Fig. 16.37, it may be suspected that the transition from superconductivity to normal conductivity at constant temperature and $\mathcal{H} = \mathcal{H}_T$ is a phase transition. Since experiment shows a latent heat for this change, we may conclude that the transition is of the first order. Defining a sort of "magnetic Gibbs function" G' by the equation

$$G' = U - TS - \mathcal{H}I,$$

we get

$$dG' = dU - T\,dS - \mathcal{H}\,dI$$
$$- S\,dT - I\,d\mathcal{H}.$$

But $T\,dS = dU - \mathcal{H}\,dI.$

Hence, $dG' = -S\,dT - I\,d\mathcal{H}.$

Now, for a phase transition at constant temperature T and constant magnetic field $\mathcal{H} = \mathcal{H}_T$, we see that G' remains constant, whence

$$G'^{(s)} = G'^{(n)}$$

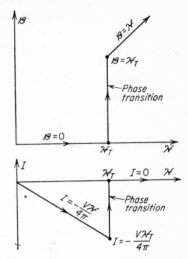

FIG. 16.38. Behavior of the magnetic induction $\mathcal{B}$ and the magnetization I of a superconductor when the field is increased isothermally.

where the superscript (s) stands for the superconducting phase and (n) for the normal phase. Similarly, for a transition at temperature $T + dT$ and field $\mathcal{H}_T + d\mathcal{H}_T$, we have

$$G'^{(s)} + dG'^{(s)} = G'^{(n)} + dG'^{(n)},$$

whence

$$dG'^{(s)} = dG'^{(n)},$$

or

$$-S^{(s)}\,dT - I^{(s)}\,d\mathcal{H}_T = -S^{(n)}\,dT - I^{(n)}\,d\mathcal{H}_T$$

and

$$-\frac{d\mathcal{H}_T}{dT} = \frac{S^{(n)} - S^{(s)}}{I^{(n)} - I^{(s)}}.$$

Since $S^{(n)} - S^{(s)} = L/T$, where L is the latent heat, and

$$I^{(n)} - I^{(s)} = 0 + \frac{V\mathcal{H}_T}{4\pi},$$

we get

$$-\frac{d\mathcal{H}_T}{dT} = \frac{4\pi L}{TV\mathcal{H}_T},$$

and finally,

$$\boxed{L = -\frac{TV\mathcal{H}_T}{4\pi}\frac{d\mathcal{H}_T}{dT}.}$$

The student should notice that this derivation is in all respects equivalent to the derivation of Clapeyron's equation. The value of $d\mathcal{H}_T/dT$ may be obtained from the $\mathcal{H}_T$-T curve, and hence L may be calculated. Values of L calculated in this way agree very well with those obtained calorimetrically. It is interesting that L vanishes at two extremes of temperature, namely, at $T = 0$, where $d\mathcal{H}_T/dT$ is also zero, and at $T = T_0$, where $\mathcal{H}_T = 0$.

The phase transition in zero field at $T = T_0$, as we have seen, takes place with no latent heat. The heat capacity at constant pressure, however, shows a discontinuous jump. It is therefore assumed that this is a second-order transition and that Ehrenfest's equations may be applied. Using the first equation

$$\frac{dP}{dT_0} = \frac{c_P^{(n)} - c_P^{(s)}}{T_0 v[\beta^{(n)} - \beta^{(s)}]},$$

we have, from experiments on tin,

$$\frac{dP}{dT_0} = -2.3 \times 10^{10} \text{ dynes/cm}^2 \cdot \text{deg},$$
$$T_0 = 3.74°\text{K},$$
$$c_P^{(n)} - c_P^{(s)} = -0.0029 \text{ cal/mole} \cdot \text{deg},$$
$$v = 16.3 \text{ cm}^3/\text{mole},$$

whence $$\beta^{(n)} - \beta^{(s)} = 0.87 \times 10^{-7} \text{ deg}^{-1},$$

which, unfortunately, is too small to measure, since each β is of the same order of magnitude. The change in compressibility, calculated from Ehrenfest's second equation, is also very small, so that experimental confirmation of the assumption that this transition is of the second order is at present lacking.

16.18. Heat Capacities of Superconductors. The apparatus for the measurement of the heat capacity of a superconducting metal differs from that for any ordinary metal only in the provision for a magnetic field to destroy superconductivity at temperatures below T_0. For this purpose, the sample, in the form of a cylinder about 10 cm long and 2 cm in diameter, is suspended in an evacuated chamber which is surrounded by liquid helium, another evacuated space, and then liquid nitrogen. All of this is in a large vacuum flask, or Dewar flask, which, at the bottom, is only about 5 cm in diameter so that it can fit conveniently between the pole faces of an electromagnet.

Temperature is measured usually with a carbon-resistance thermometer which is inserted into the sample, and heat is supplied by a momentary current in a heating coil wound around the sample. The experiments are tedious and difficult but they supply some of the most important information about superconductivity.

A typical set of experimental results is shown in Fig. 16.39 where the measurements on tin of Keesom and Van Laer in 1938 are compared with the work of Corak, Goodman, Satterthwaite, and Wexler in 1955. As is usual at low temperatures (see Chap. 13), $c_p = c_v = c$, and c/T is plotted against T^2, since the heat capacity of a normal metal is $\gamma'T + 464T^3/\Theta^3$. At values of T^2 less than $T_6^2(3.74)^2$, there are two separate graphs which cross each other. Below $T^2 = 9$, the graph marked normal is seen to be linear. This was obtained when the tin was placed in a suitable magnetic

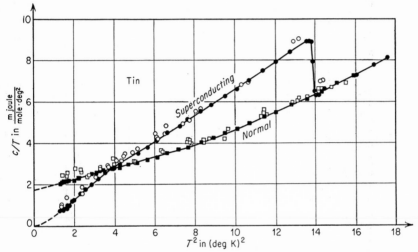

Fig. 16.39. Measurements of the heat capacity of tin by Keesom and Van Laer (open circles, super; open squares, normal), and by Corak, Goodman, Satterthwaite, and Wexler (solid circles, super; solid squares, normal).

field. From this line the electronic constant γ' and the Debye temperature Θ are obtained by measuring the intercept and slope, respectively, as explained in Chap. 13. Values of γ' and Θ for the superconducting metals are listed in Table 16.8.

The behavior of the heat capacity of a metal when it is superconducting is entirely different from that when it is normal. When c/T is plotted against T^2, the result is a curve such as the one marked superconducting in Fig. 16.39. Similar results for superconducting vanadium and tantalum obtained by Worley, Zemansky, and Boorse are shown in Fig. 16.40. Superconducting niobium, lanthanum, and aluminum behave in the same way.

X-ray diffraction studies of the crystal lattice of a metal before and after the superconducting transition indicate no change in any property of the crystal lattice. It is therefore assumed that a superconducting metal has the same Debye Θ as in the normal phase. If we subtract, therefore, the lattice heat capacity, $(464/\Theta^3)T^3$, from the superconducting heat capacity, we ought to get a heat capacity associated with the super-conducting electrons, $c_{el}^{(s)}$. Thus

$$c_{el}^{(s)} = c^{(s)} - \frac{464}{\Theta^3} T^3.$$

In Fig. 16.41, the logarithm of the ratio $c_{el}^{(s)}/\gamma' T_0$ for vanadium is plotted against T_0/T. Except for a region near $T = T_0$, the experimental points seem to lie on a straight line, indicating that the electronic contribution

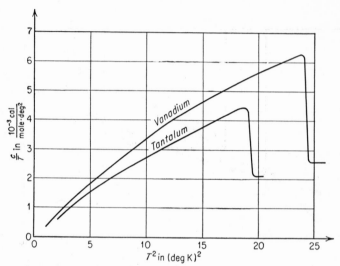

Fig. 16.40. Heat capacity of vanadium and tantalum in the superconducting phase (*Worley, Zemansky, and Boorse.*)

to the superconducting heat capacity obeys the equation

$$\frac{c_{el}^{(s)}}{\gamma' T_0} = ae^{-(bT_0/T)}.$$

Similar behavior has been observed for tin, aluminum, niobium, and tantalum. The constants a and b have approximately the same value for both vanadium and tin, with $a \sim 9$ and $b = 1.5$. For aluminum, however, $a = 6.9$ and $b = 1.28$.

It has been shown with the aid of the "magnetic Gibbs function" that, for a reversible transition from superconductivity to normal conductivity at temperature T and field $\mathcal{H} = \mathcal{H}_T$, an equation similar to Clapeyron's equation holds. Thus

$$-\frac{d\mathcal{H}_T}{dT} = \frac{S^{(n)} - S^{(s)}}{I^{(n)} - I^{(s)}},$$

or

$$S^{(n)} - S^{(s)} = -\frac{V}{4\pi} \mathcal{H}_T \frac{d\mathcal{H}_T}{dT}.$$

Differentiating both sides with respect to T and multiplying through by T, we get

$$T \frac{dS^{(n)}}{dT} - T \frac{dS^{(s)}}{dT} = - \frac{VT}{4\pi} \frac{d}{dT} \left(\mathscr{H}_T \frac{d\mathscr{H}_T}{dT} \right).$$

The terms on the left-hand side are heat capacities, so that, for 1 mole of material,

$$c^{(s)} - c^{(n)} = \frac{vT}{4\pi} \frac{d}{dT} \left(\mathscr{H}_T \frac{d\mathscr{H}_T}{dT} \right). \tag{1}$$

This is a very valuable equation but it must be used with care. If calorimetric measurements are particularly difficult, as they are with

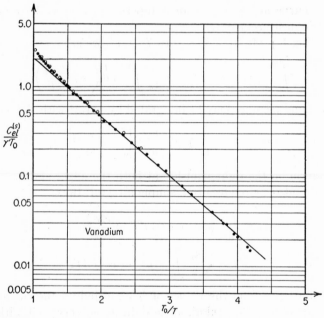

FIG. 16.41. Electronic contribution to the superconducting heat capacity of vanadium. (*Solid circles, Corak, Goodman, Satterthwaite, and Wexler; open circles, Worley, Zemansky, and Boorse.*)

mercury, it is necessary to use Eq. (1) in conjunction with magnetic measurements ($\mathscr{H}_T$ as a function of T) in order to find γ'. If the material is very pure and quite free from strain, the phase transition from superconductivity to normal conductivity may take place reversibly and the equation may be used with confidence. (The γ' of mercury in Table 16.8 was found in this way.)   It is, however, difficult to get some of the hard superconductors pure and strain-free. When this is the case and the measured values of $\mathscr{H}_T$ are introduced into Eq. (1), the calorimetric data so derived may be in error by a large factor.

Equation (1) may be used with more confidence to infer the magnetic properties of superconductors from calorimetric data. Thus, performing the differentiation indicated in Eq. (1), we get

$$c^{(s)} - c^{(n)} = \frac{vT}{4\pi}\left(\frac{d\mathcal{H}_T}{dT}\right)^2 + \frac{vT}{4\pi}\mathcal{H}_T\frac{d^2\mathcal{H}_T}{dT^2}.$$

At $T = T_0$, $\mathcal{H}_T = 0$ and the second member on the right is zero. Thus

$$\left(\frac{d\mathcal{H}_T}{dT}\right)_{T=T_0} = \sqrt{\frac{4\pi}{vT_0}(c^{(s)} - c^{(n)})_{T=T_0}},$$

and from this equation, known as *Rutgers equation*, the slope of the $\mathcal{H}_T$ vs. T curve at the transition temperature T_0 may be found from calorimetric measurements.

Integrating Eq. (1) from $T = 0$ to $T = T_0$, we get

$$\int_0^{T_0}(c^{(s)} - c^{(n)})\,dT = \frac{v}{4\pi}\int_{\mathcal{H}_0}^0 Td\left(\mathcal{H}_T\frac{d\mathcal{H}_T}{dT}\right).$$

The right-hand member may be integrated by parts† with the result that

$$\int_0^{T_0}(c^{(s)} - c^{(n)})\,dT = \frac{v}{4\pi}T\mathcal{H}_T\frac{d\mathcal{H}_T}{dT}\Big]_0^{T_0} - \frac{v}{4\pi}\int_{\mathcal{H}_0}^0 \mathcal{H}_T\frac{d\mathcal{H}_T}{dT}\,dT.$$

The first term on the right vanishes at both the upper and lower limits, and the second term reduces to a simple integral; thus

$$\int_0^{T_0}(c^{(s)} - c^{(n)})\,dT = \frac{v\mathcal{H}_0^2}{8\pi},$$

and

$$\mathcal{H}_0 = \sqrt{\frac{8\pi}{v}\int_0^{T_0}(c^{(s)} - c^{(n)})\,dT}.$$

With tin and vanadium the values of $\mathcal{H}_0$ and indeed the entire $\mathcal{H}_T$ vs. T curve calculated from calorimetric data agree very well with purely magnetic measurements.

16.19. Thermal Conductivity. The variation with temperature of the thermal conductivity of a nonmetal, quartz, is shown in Fig. 5.5. Similar curves are obtained for metals as shown in Fig. 5.6 for copper and aluminum. In the case of a metal above 1°K, the thermal conductivity is due mainly to electron scattering and obeys the equation

$$\frac{1}{k} = aT^2 + \frac{b}{T}.$$

The first term arises from the scattering of electrons by the crystal lattice and the second term by impurities which may be chemical (foreign atoms)

† $\int u\,dv = uv - \int v\,du.$

or physical (lattice defects).   Values of a and b for many metals are given in Table 16.11.   Below 1°K, the thermal conductivity of a metal varies as T^3 and is no longer due to the scattering of electrons.

TABLE 16.11. THERMAL CONDUCTIVITY OF METALS AT LOW TEMPERATURES

Constants in the Equation $\dfrac{1}{k} = aT^2 + \dfrac{b}{T}$ (H. M. Rosenberg)

Metal	$a,$ $\dfrac{10^{-5}\text{ cm}}{\text{watt}\cdot\text{deg}}$	$b,$ $\dfrac{\text{cm}\cdot\text{deg}^2}{\text{watt}}$	Metal	$a,$ $\dfrac{10^{-5}\text{ cm}}{\text{watt}\cdot\text{deg}}$	$b,$ $\dfrac{\text{cm}\cdot\text{deg}^2}{\text{watt}}$
Ag	4.3–5	0.3	Nb	50	58
Al	3.2	0.23	Ni	10.4	4.6
Au	19	1.13	Pb	290	0.10
Be	....	177	Pd	41	11.7
Cd	122–145	0.02	Pt	43	0.35
Ce	....	900	Rh	10.7	1.38
Co	10.5	7.9	Sn	60	0.12
Cu	2.5	0.35	Ta	79	25
Fe	9.5–10.2	9.6	Ti	454	82
Ga	160, 23, 87	4.7, 0.165, 2.22	Tl	537	0.1
In	185	0.35	U	790	93
Ir	4.6	0.75	V	124	310
La	....	740	W	9.3	5.8
Mg	8.5	1.05	Zn	30, 31, 34	0.7, 0.6
Mn	....	1200	Zr	125, 127	34
Mo	7.5	6.7			

When a metal becomes superconducting, its thermal conductivity drops markedly and approaches zero approximately as the cube of the temperature.   Heer and Daunt found, for example, that the thermal conductivity of superconducting tin at 0.65°K was $\frac{1}{40}$ that for normal tin, and in the case of tantalum at 0.55°K, the ratio was $\frac{1}{60}$.   The results of Heer and Daunt are summarized in Table 16.12.   It is an interesting fact that, approximately,

$$\frac{k^{(s)}}{k^{(n)}} = \left(\frac{T}{T_0}\right)^2.$$

TABLE 16.12. THERMAL CONDUCTIVITY OF NORMAL AND SUPERCONDUCTING METALS

Metal	Normal	Superconducting
Sn	$k^{(n)} = 0.041 \dfrac{\text{cal}}{\text{sec}\cdot\text{cm}\cdot\text{deg}^2} T$	$k^{(s)} = 0.0024 \dfrac{\text{cal}}{\text{sec}\cdot\text{cm}\cdot\text{deg}^4} T^3$
Ta	$k^{(n)} = 2.2 \dfrac{\text{cal}}{\text{sec}\cdot\text{cm}\cdot\text{deg}^2} T$	$k^{(s)} = 0.14 \dfrac{\text{cal}}{\text{sec}\cdot\text{cm}\cdot\text{deg}^4} T^3$

Since a superconducting metal may be made normal merely by applying a suitable magnetic field, a poor heat conductor may be instantly changed into a good heat conductor by closing a switch. This is the device used by Daunt and Heer in the magnetic refrigerator described in Art. 16.8.

16.20. The Third Law of Thermodynamics. We have seen how the Joule-Kelvin effect is employed to produce liquid helium at a temperature below 5°K. The rapid adiabatic vaporization of liquid helium then results in a further lowering of the temperature to about 1°K; and, finally,

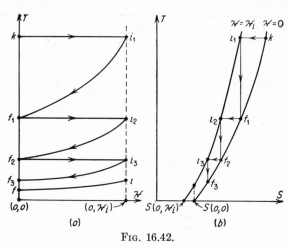

Fig. 16.42.

the magnetocaloric effect is used to lower the temperature of a paramagnetic salt to within about 0.001°K. It has been proposed, but not yet attempted, to obtain still lower temperatures by cyclic demagnetization, which may be understood with the aid of the temperature-field diagram of Fig. 16.42(a). After the original isothermal magnetization, shown by the line $k \to i_1$, the first adiabatic demagnetization $i_1 \to f_1$ may be used to provide enough material at temperature T_{f_1} to serve as a heat reservoir for the next isothermal magnetization $f_1 \to i_2$. A second adiabatic demagnetization $i_2 \to f_2$ gives rise to a lower temperature T_{f_2}, and so on. Among the difficulties that would arise in such an experiment, there is the fundamental problem of thermal contact during isothermal magnetization and thermal insulation during adiabatic demagnetization. The remarkable difference in thermal conductivity between a superconductor and a normal conductor (produced by applying a magnetic field to a superconductor) has been used by Daunt as a means for solving this experimental problem.

The question that naturally arises at this point is whether the magnetocaloric effect may be used to attain absolute zero. Experiments indicate that the final temperature achieved by an adiabatic demagnetization from a given constant initial field is roughly proportional to the initial temperature.   Thus, if the first demagnetization produces a temperature one-half that at the start, the second demagnetization from the same initial field will cut the temperature in half again, and so on.   Evidently, an infinite number of adiabatic demagnetizations would be required to attain absolute zero.   The colder a liquid is, the lower the vapor pressure, and the harder it is to produce further cooling by pumping away the vapor.   The fundamental feature of all cooling processes is that the lower the temperature achieved, the harder it is to go still lower.   Generalizing from experience, we may accept as true the statement that:

It is impossible by any procedure, no matter how idealized, to reduce any system to the absolute zero of temperature in a finite number of operations.

This is known as either *the principle of the unattainability of absolute zero*, or, following Fowler and Guggenheim, *the unattainability statement of the third law of thermodynamics*.   Just as in the case of the second law of thermodynamics, the third law has a number of alternative or equivalent statements.

Referring to Fig. 16.42(b), the initial isothermal, reversible magnetization $k \rightarrow i_1$ is attended by an entropy decrease.   The entropy decrease accompanying the second isothermal magnetization $f_1 \rightarrow i_2$ is seen to be smaller, and so on, for all successive isothermal magnetizations.   This follows from the fact that

$$S(T, \mathcal{H}_i) - S(T, 0) = \int_0^{\mathcal{H}_i} \left(\frac{\partial I}{\partial T}\right)_{\mathcal{H}} d\mathcal{H}$$

and the values of $(\partial I/\partial T)_{\mathcal{H}}$ decrease as T decreases.   In the case of a solid, the entropy change accompanying an isothermal reversible compression is given by

$$S(T, P_i) - S(T, 0) = - \int_0^{P_i} \left(\frac{\partial V}{\partial T}\right)_P dP$$

and also decreases as T decreases, since $(\partial V/\partial T)_P$ gets smaller.   The same is true of the entropy change associated with an isothermal transfer of electricity in a reversible cell.

Experimental evidence is very strong that for any isothermal, reversible process of a condensed system the accompanying entropy change is a function of the temperature which approaches zero as T approaches zero.   It is therefore accepted that:

The entropy change associated with any isothermal, reversible process of a condensed system approaches zero as the temperature approaches zero.

Let us call this theorem the Nernst-Simon statement of the third law of thermodynamics.   Both this statement and the unattainability statement have had a long and checquered career since the original paper by Nernst in 1907. It took 30 years of experimental and theoretical research, during which time there were periods of great confusion, before all differences of opinion were resolved and the statement was agreed upon. Since then, Simon has given another formulation of the third law in terms of the concept of a "subsystem" which requires for its understanding a knowledge of statistical mechanics.

Nernst originally stated, as the third law, that the temperature derivative of the change of Helmholtz function during an isothermal process approaches zero as the temperature approaches zero. He did not think in terms of entropy, and moreover was of the opinion that this statement and also the unattainability statement could be derived from the second law with the additional assumption that the heat capacities of all materials approached zero as the temperature approached zero. Nernst also maintained that both statements were true for all kinds of processes, both reversible and irreversible. It was mainly the experiments and arguments of Simon in the period from 1927 to 1937 that made precise the region of validity of the third law.

In order to show that the Nernst-Simon statement and the unattainability statement are equivalent, it is necessary to derive an equation for the limiting value of the entropy change accompanying an isothermal reversible process. Let us return to a paramagnetic salt and consider any isentropic demagnetization, $i \rightarrow f$, of Fig. 16.42(a). The entropy change between the point $T = 0$, $\mathcal{H} = \mathcal{H}_i$ and the state i is

$$S_i - S(0, \mathcal{H}_i) = \int_0^{T_i} \frac{C_{\mathcal{H}=\mathcal{H}_i}}{T} \, dT,$$

where $C_{\mathcal{H}}$ is the heat capacity at constant field, a positive quantity for all values of $\mathcal{H}$. The change in entropy between the origin and f is

$$S_f - S(0, 0) = \int_0^{T_f} \frac{C_{\mathcal{H}=0}}{T} \, dT.$$

Since $S_i = S_f$, and $S(0, \mathcal{H}_i) - S(0, 0) = \lim_{T \to 0} [S(T, \mathcal{H}_i) - S(T, 0)]$, we have

$$\lim_{T \to 0} [S(T, \mathcal{H}_i) - S(T, 0)] = \int_0^{T_f} \frac{C_{\mathcal{H}=0}}{T} \, dT - \int_0^{T_i} \frac{C_{\mathcal{H}=\mathcal{H}_i}}{T} \, dT. \quad (1)$$

To prove the equivalence of the unattainability and Nernst-Simon statements of the third law, we proceed in the same manner as in the case of the Kelvin-Planck and Clausius statements of the second law. Let

U = truth of the unattainability statement
$-U$ = falsity of the unattainability statement
N = truth of the Nernst-Simon statement
$-N$ = falsity of the Nernst-Simon statement

As before

$$U \equiv N,$$

when $-U \supset -N$ and $-N \supset -U.$

1. To prove that $-U \supset -N$, suppose that it is possible to find a value of T_i which makes $T_f = 0$, thereby violating the unattainability statement. Then, from Eq. (1), the left-hand member would be negative, thereby violating the Nernst statement.

2. To prove that $-N \supset -U$, suppose that the left-hand member of Eq. (1) had any negative value, thereby violating the Nernst-Simon statement. Then it would be possible to find a value of T_i in Eq. (1) which would make the second integral equal to this negative number. As a result, the first integral would vanish and T_f would be zero, thereby violating the unattainability statement. The fact that $-N \supset -U$ may also be readily seen from Fig. 16.42(b). If the point $S(0, \mathcal{H}_i)$ lies to the left of the point $S(0, 0)$, then the small vertical dashed line at the bottom of the figure represents one of many possible adiabatic demagnetizations which could be used to reach absolute zero.

This completes only half the proof of the equivalence of the two statements. The second half is concerned with the possibility of violating the Nernst-Simon statement by having the left-hand member of Eq. (1) assume positive values. In the case of a paramagnetic material, this is unthinkable, because it would mean that a magnetized state had a greater entropy or disorder than an unmagnetized one. Nevertheless, it is interesting to consider a paramagnetic material with the properties (1) an isothermal demagnetization produces a decrease in entropy, (2) an isentropic magnetization produces a drop in temperature. A material with such properties is represented on a T-$\mathcal{H}$ diagram in Fig. 16.43(a). For such a material

$$\lim_{T \to 0} [S(T, \mathcal{H}_i) - S(T, 0)] = \int_0^{T_i} \frac{C_{\mathcal{H}=0}}{T} \, dT - \int_0^{T_f} \frac{C_{\mathcal{H}=\mathcal{H}_i}}{T} \, dT.$$

If it were possible to find a value of T_i that would make $T_f = 0$, then the left-hand member would be positive. Thus $-U \supset -N$. On the other hand, if the left-hand member had any positive value, then by proper choice of T_i, the first integral could be made equal to this value, and the second integral would vanish, thereby making $T_f = 0$. Thus $-N \supset -U$. The truth of these statements may be readily seen in Fig. 16.43(b), where the vertical dashed line represents one of many adiabatic magnetizations which could be used to reach absolute zero.

It must be understood that these proofs were accomplished in terms of isothermal and adiabatic processes of a paramagnetic substance only for convenience and concreteness. By means of a slight change of symbolism, the same proofs may be applied to any system whatever, since all systems are capable of undergoing an isothermal, reversible decrease of entropy followed by a reversible adiabatic decrease of temperature. Furthermore, the Nernst-Simon statement also applies to materials in frozen metastable equilibrium, provided the isothermal process in question does not disturb this frozen equilibrium.

Referring again to Fig. 16.42(b), we recall that any isothermal magnetization, such as $k \to i_1$, $f_1 \to i_2$, etc., is attended by a liberation of heat, or, in other words, by a decrease in entropy. Thus $k \to i_1$ decreases

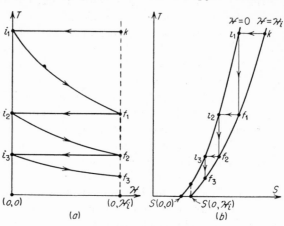

FIG. 16.43.

the entropy of the system a certain amount; then from i_1 to f_1 the entropy remains constant; then from f_1 to i_2 the entropy decreases further; and so on. If the entropy of the system at absolute zero is called the zero-point entropy, we see that a third equivalent statement of the third law is as follows:

It is impossible by any procedure, no matter how idealized, to reduce the entropy of a system to its zero-point value in a finite number of operations.

The equivalence of all three statements of the third law is demonstrated in a striking manner by the T-S diagram in Fig. 16.44.

There are many physical and chemical facts which substantiate the third law. For example, using Clapeyron's equation,

$$\frac{dP}{dT} = \frac{s^{(f)} - s^{(i)}}{v^{(f)} - v^{(i)}},$$

in conjunction with any phase change that takes place at low temperature, the statement that

$$\lim_{T \to 0} (s^{(f)} - s^{(i)}) = 0,$$

implies that

$$\lim_{T \to 0} \frac{dP}{dT} = 0,$$

since $v^{(f)} - v^{(i)}$ is not zero for a first-order phase transition. This is substantiated by all known sublimation curves, by the vaporization curve of liquid helium II, and by the melting curve of solid helium shown in Figs. 16.31 and 16.32. As a matter of fact dP/dT of solid helium approaches zero very rapidly, as shown by the experimental result of Simon and Swenson, that

$$\frac{dP}{dT} = 0.425T^7.$$

There are many other applications of the third law in the fields of physical chemistry and of statistical mechanics. For further study, the writings of Simon and of Guggenheim are recommended.

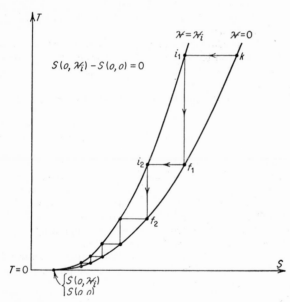

Fig. 16.44. T-S diagram for a paramagnetic substance to show the equivalence of the three statements of the third law.

PROBLEMS

16.1. A thermally insulated vessel contains liquid helium at 4.2°K and atmospheric pressure. Helium vapor is pumped away isentropically until the remaining liquid and vapor achieve a temperature of 1°K. What fraction of the initial amount of liquid helium evaporates during the process? (In the temperature range from 1 to 2.2°K, the specific heat of liquid helium equals $0.104T^{6.2}$ joules/gm · deg, and from 2.2 to 4.2°K, it remains approximately constant at about 2.5 joules/gm· deg. The heat of vaporization at 1°K is 20.1 joules/gm.)

16.2. Make a graph of the heat capacity of gadolinium sulfate as a function of T from 1.5° to 5°K and for values of $\mathscr{H}$ equal to 0, 1000, 2000, 3000, 4000, 5000 oersteds.

16.3. Cerium magnesium nitrate originally at 1.5°K is magnetized isothermally from zero field to 5000 oersteds. (a) What is the heat of magnetization per gram ion? It is then demagnetized adiabatically to a field of 1000 oersteds. (b) What is the final temperature? (c) What is the final heat capacity per gram ion?

16.4. At what initial temperature should iron ammonium alum be in order that an adiabatic demagnetization from an initial field of 10,000 oersteds to zero final field should yield a final temperature of 0.2°K?

16.5. A mixture of n gram ions of a paramagnetic salt and m gm of liquid helium at a temperature T_i undergoes an isothermal magnetization from zero field to a field $\mathcal{H}_i$. (a) Derive an expression for the amount of liquid helium that boils away. The mixture of n gram ions of paramagnetic salt and m' gm of liquid helium undergoes an adiabatic demagnetization from $\mathcal{H}_i$ to zero, the final temperature of the mixture being T_{ff}. (b) Treating the process as though the salt were insulated from the helium during the demagnetization and achieved the temperature T_f, and then exchanged heat with the helium until both were at T_{ff}, derive an equation for this process. [NOTE: The specific heat of helium below 0.6°K is 0.0235T^3 joules/g · deg, and above 0.6°K it is 0.104$T^{6.2}$ joules/gm · deg. The paramagnetic salt is always in the range where Curie's law holds and where its heat capacity varies inversely as the square of the temperature.]

16.6. Rewrite the fountain effect equation so that pressure is measured in centimeters of liquid helium, and entropy in joules per gram · degree. How high would the fountain be at 2°K when the temperature difference is 0.005 deg? [The density of liquid helium II is 0.14 gm/cm³.]

16.7. A column of liquid helium II is at a temperature of 1°K, at which $\rho_n/\rho = 0.0080$.

(a) Find ρ_s/ρ and ρ_s/ρ_n.

(b) With the aid of the values of c and s in Table 16.6, calculate the speed of second sound.

(c) A small region at one end of the column undergoes an increase of temperature of 0.01 deg. What is the speed of the normal atoms? Of the superfluid atoms?

16.8. How long would it take for a cylindrical bucket 2 cm high with inner diameter 2 mm filled with liquid helium II to empty by virtue of the creeping film (a) at 1.8°K; (b) at 2°K? The film rate at 1.1°K is 10^{-4} cm³/sec · cm.

16.9. (a) How much heat is absorbed by 100 cm³ of tin during the transition from the superconducting phase to the normal phase at 3°K?

(b) How much heat is absorbed by 50 cm³ of lead during such a transition at 6°K?

16.10. When a metal remains in the superconducting phase, show that (a) $C_I = C_{\mathcal{H}}$ and (b) there is no magnetocaloric effect.

16.11. Show that

$$c^{(s)} - c^{(n)} = \frac{vT}{8\pi} \frac{d^2}{dT^2} (\mathcal{H}_T^2).$$

16.12. (a) Prove that

$$\int_0^{T_0} \frac{c^{(s)}}{T} dT = \int_0^{T_0} \frac{c^{(n)}}{T} dT.$$

(b) Assuming

$$c^{(s)} = c_{e1}^{(s)} + \frac{464}{\Theta^3} T^3,$$

$$c^{(n)} = \gamma'T + \frac{464}{\Theta^3} T^3,$$

prove that

$$\int_0^1 \frac{c_{e1}^{(s)}}{\gamma'T} d\left(\frac{T}{T_0}\right) = 1.$$

(c) With the same assumptions as in (b), prove that

$$\int_0^1 \frac{c_{e1}^{(s)}}{\gamma' T_0} \, d\left(\frac{T}{T_0}\right) = \frac{1}{2} + \frac{v\mathcal{H}_0^2}{8\pi\gamma' T_0^2}.$$

16.13. At what temperature has silver its maximum thermal conductivity? Copper?

16.14. In Daunt and Heer's magnetic refrigerator at 0.5°K, what is the ratio of the thermal conductivity of lead in the normal phase to that in the superconducting phase?

16.15. Using the Nernst-Simon statement of the third law, prove that,

(a) In the case of a superconductor,

$$\lim_{T \to 0} \left(\frac{d\mathcal{H}_T}{dT}\right) = 0.$$

(b) In the case of a reversible cell, or a thermocouple,

$$\lim_{T \to 0} \left(\frac{d\mathcal{E}}{dT}\right) = 0.$$

(c) In the case of a surface film of liquid He³ or He⁴,

$$\lim_{T \to 0} \left(\frac{d\mathscr{A}}{dT}\right) = 0.$$

16.16. At $T = 0$, $(\partial S/\partial V)_{T=0} = 0$, and also

$$\frac{\partial}{\partial V}\left[\left(\frac{\partial S}{\partial V}\right)_T\right]_{T=0} = 0.$$

From this fact, prove that

$$\lim_{T \to 0} \left(\frac{\partial B}{\partial T}\right)_V = 0,$$

where B is the isothermal bulk modulus.

16.17. In the case of a solid whose equation of state is

$$Pv + G(v) = \Gamma u,$$

where $G(v)$ is a function of volume only and Γ is a constant, prove that c_v approaches zero as T approaches zero.

17

Chemical Thermodynamics

17.1. Dalton's Law. Imagine a homogeneous mixture of inert ideal gases at a temperature T, a pressure P, and a volume V. Suppose there are n_1 moles of gas A_1, n_2 moles of gas A_2, . . . , up to n_c moles of gas A_c. Since there is no chemical reaction, the mixture is in a state of equilibrium with the equation of state

$$PV = (n_1 + n_2 + \cdots + n_c) RT,$$

or

$$P = \frac{n_1}{V} RT + \frac{n_2}{V} RT + \cdots + \frac{n_c}{V} RT.$$

It is clear that the expression

$$\frac{n_k}{V} RT$$

represents the pressure that the kth gas would exert if it occupied the volume V alone. This is called the *partial pressure* of the kth gas and is denoted by p_k. Thus

$$p_1 = \frac{n_1}{V} RT, \qquad p_2 = \frac{n_2}{V} RT, \cdots, \qquad p_c = \frac{n_c}{V} RT,$$

and

$$P = p_1 + p_2 + \cdots + p_c.$$

The above equation expresses the fact that the total pressure of a mixture of ideal gases is equal to the sum of the partial pressures. This is *Dalton's law.*

Now

$$V = (n_1 + n_2 + \cdots + n_c) \frac{RT}{P}$$

$$= \Sigma n_k \frac{RT}{P},$$

and the partial pressure of the kth gas is

$$p_k = \frac{n_k}{V} RT.$$

Substituting the value for V, we get

$$p_k = \frac{n_k}{\Sigma n_k} P.$$

The ratio $n_k/\Sigma n_k$ is called the *mole fraction* of the kth gas and is denoted by x_k.   Thus

$$x_1 = \frac{n_1}{\Sigma n_k}, \qquad x_2 = \frac{n_2}{\Sigma n_k}, \cdots , \qquad x_c = \frac{n_c}{\Sigma n_k}$$

and $$p_1 = x_1 P, \qquad p_2 = x_2 P, \cdots , \qquad p_c = x_c P.$$

The mole fractions are convenient dimensionless quantities with which to express the composition of a mixture.   It is clear that

$$x_1 + x_2 + \cdots + x_c = \frac{n_1}{\Sigma n_k} + \frac{n_2}{\Sigma n_k} + \cdots + \frac{n_c}{\Sigma n_k}$$
$$= 1.$$

Hence, if all but one mole fraction is determined, the last can be calculated from the above equation.

17.2. Semipermeable Membrane. If a narrow tube of palladium is closed at one end and the open end is sealed into a glass tube, as shown in Fig. 17.1, the system may be pumped to a very high vacuum. If the palladium remains at room temperature, the vacuum may be maintained indefinitely. If, however, an ordinary bunsen burner is placed so that the blue cone surrounds part of the tube, the rest of the flame causing the palladium tube to become red-hot, hydrogen present in the blue cone will pass through the tube, but other gases will not.   Red-hot palladium is said to be a *semipermeable membrane*, permeable to hydrogen only. This is the simplest laboratory method of obtaining pure dry hydrogen.

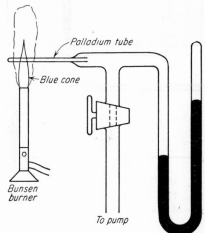

FIG. 17.1. Palladium tube permeable to hydrogen.

Experiment shows that hydrogen continues to flow through the red-hot palladium until the pressure of hydrogen in the vessel reaches a value equal to the partial pressure of the hydrogen in the flame.   When the flow stops, *membrane equilibrium* is said to exist.   Membrane equilibrium takes place when the partial pressure of the gas to which the membrane is permeable is the same on both sides of the membrane.   We shall suppose that there exists a special membrane permeable to each gas with which we have to deal. Whether this is actually so is not important. We shall make use of the principle of the semipermeable membrane as an ideal device for theoretical purposes.

17.3. Gibbs's Theorem. With the aid of a device equipped with two semipermeable membranes it is possible to conceive of separating in a reversible manner a mixture of two inert ideal gases. The vessel depicted in Fig. 17.2 is divided into two equal compartments by a rigid wall, which is a membrane permeable only to the gas A_1. Two pistons coupled so that they move together at a constant distance apart are constructed of materials such that one is impermeable to all gases (solid black) and the other permeable only to the gas A_2. The semipermeable membranes are shaded with horizontal lines. The initial state is depicted in Fig. 17.2(i). A mixture of A_1 and A_2 is in the left-hand chamber, and the right-hand chamber is evacuated.

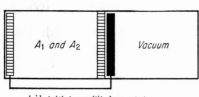

(i) Initial equilibrium state

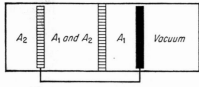

(k) Intermediate equilibrium state

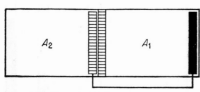

(f) Final equilibrium state

Fig. 17.2. Reversible isothermal separation of two inert ideal gases.

Now imagine pushing the coupled pistons to the right in such a manner that the following conditions are satisfied:

1. The motion is infinitely slow so that membrane equilibrium exists at all times.
2. There is no friction.
3. The whole system is kept at constant temperature.

These conditions define a *reversible isothermal process*. Consider the system at any intermediate state such as that depicted in Fig. 17.2(k). If p_1 and p_2 are the partial pressures, respectively, of A_1 and A_2 in the mixture, P_1 is the pressure of A_1 alone, and P_2 the pressure of A_2 alone, then the forces acting on the coupled pistons are

$$\text{Force to the left} = (p_1 + p_2) \times \text{area},$$
$$\text{Sum of the forces to the right} = (P_1 + P_2) \times \text{area}.$$

Since membrane equilibrium exists, $p_1 = P_1$ and $p_2 = P_2$, whence the resultant force acting on the coupled pistons is zero. After the pistons have moved all the way to the right, the gases are completely separated as shown in Fig. 17.2(f).

Since the resultant force was infinitesimal in the beginning and zero throughout the remainder of the process, $W = 0$. Also, since the process was isothermal and the internal energy of an ideal gas is a function of T only, $U_f = U_i$. Finally, since the process was both reversible and isothermal, the heat transferred Q is equal to $T(S_f - S_i)$. We have therefore the result that

$$T(S_f - S_i) = 0$$

and, since T is not zero,

$$S_i = S_f.$$

Now S_i is the entropy of the mixture at the temperature T and the volume V, while S_f is the sum of the entropies of the two gases each at the same temperature and each occupying the volume V alone. If we define the *partial entropy* of one of the gases of a mixture as the entropy that the gas would have if it occupied the whole volume alone at the same temperature, then we obtain the result that the *entropy of a mixture of ideal gases is the sum of the partial entropies.* This is known as *Gibbs's theorem.* The generalization for any number of gases is obvious.

17.4. Entropy of a Mixture of Inert Ideal Gases. Imagine a number of inert ideal gases separated from one another by suitable partitions, all the gases being at the same temperature T and pressure P. Suppose there are n_1 moles of gas A_1, n_2 moles of A_2, etc., up to n_c moles of A_c. Before the partitions are removed, the entropy of the whole system S_i is the sum of the separate entropies. The entropy of 1 mole of the kth gas at the temperature T and pressure P is

$$s_k = \int c_{Pk} \frac{dT}{T} + s_{0k} - R \ln P,$$

and therefore

$$S_i = \sum n_k \left(\int c_{Pk} \frac{dT}{T} + s_{0k} - R \ln P \right)$$

$$= R \sum n_k \left(\frac{1}{R} \int c_{Pk} \frac{dT}{T} + \frac{s_{0k}}{R} - \ln P \right).$$

It is convenient to represent the first two terms within the parentheses by σ, thus:

$$\sigma_k = \frac{1}{R} \int c_{Pk} \frac{dT}{T} + \frac{s_{0k}}{R}.$$

Then $S_i = R \, \Sigma \, n_k (\sigma_k - \ln P).$

After the partitions are removed, the temperature and pressure remain the same because there is no chemical reaction, but the gases diffuse and, by Gibbs's theorem, the entropy of the mixture is the sum of the partial entropies. Now the partial entropy of the kth gas is the entropy that the kth gas would have if it occupied the whole volume alone at the same temperature, in which case it would exert a pressure equal to the partial pressure p_k. Therefore the total entropy of the mixture is

$$S_f = R\Sigma n_k(\sigma_k - \ln p_k).$$

Since $p_k = x_k P$,

$$\boxed{S_f = R\Sigma n_k(\sigma_k - \ln P - \ln x_k).}$$

The change of entropy due to the diffusion of any number of inert gases is therefore equal to

$$\boxed{S_f - S_i = -R\Sigma n_k \ln x_k.}$$

Every one of the mole fractions is a number less than unity with a negative logarithm. The whole expression is therefore positive, as it should be. Since

$$x_k = \frac{n_k}{\Sigma n} = \frac{n_k RT}{\Sigma n RT} = \frac{n_k Pv}{PV} = \frac{n_k v}{V},$$

we may write

$$S_f - S_i = n_1 R \ln \frac{V}{n_1 v} + n_2 R \ln \frac{V}{n_2 v} + \cdots.$$

The above result shows that the entropy change due to the diffusion of any number of ideal gases is the same as that which would take place if each gas were caused to undergo a free expansion from the volume that it occupies alone at T and P to the volume of the mixture at the same T and P. The validity of this result was assumed in Chap. 10 in order to calculate the entropy change of the universe when two ideal gases diffuse. The assumption is therefore seen to be justified.

As an example, consider the diffusion of 1 mole of helium and 1 mole of neon. Then

$$S_f - S_i = -R(1 \ln \tfrac{1}{2} + 1 \ln \tfrac{1}{2})$$
$$= 2R \ln 2.$$

In this expression there are no quantities such as heat capacities or entropy constants that distinguish one gas from another. The result is the same for the diffusion of any two inert ideal gases, no matter how similar or dissimilar they are. If, however, the two gases are identical, the concept of diffusion has no meaning, and there is no entropy change. From the microscopic point of view, this means that the diffusion of any two dissimilar gases brings about the same degree of disorder whereas the diffusion of two identical gases introduces no element of disorder.

The application of mathematics to the macroscopic processes of nature usually gives rise to continuous results. Our experience suggests that, as the two diffusing gases become more and more alike, the entropy change due to diffusion should get smaller and smaller, approaching zero as the gases become identical.   The fact that this is not the case is known as *Gibbs's paradox*.   The paradox has been resolved by Bridgman in the following way: To recognize that two gases are dissimilar requires a set of experimental operations.   These operations become more and more difficult as the gases become more and more alike, but, at least in principle, the operations are possible.   In the limit, when the gases become identical, there is a discontinuity in the instrumental operations inasmuch as no instrumental operation exists by which the gases may be distinguished.   Hence a discontinuity in a function, such as that of an entropy change, is to be expected.

17.5. Gibbs Function of a Mixture of Inert Ideal Gases.   The enthalpy and the entropy of 1 mole of an ideal gas at the temperature T and the pressure P are

$$h = h_0 + \int c_P \, dT,$$

$$s = \int c_P \frac{dT}{T} + s_0 - R \ln P,$$

and therefore the molar Gibbs function $g = h - Ts$ is equal to

$$g = h_0 + \int c_P \, dT - T \int c_P \frac{dT}{T} - Ts_0 + RT \ln P.$$

Applying the formula for integration by parts,†

$$\int c_P \, dT - T \int c_P \frac{dT}{T} = -T \int \frac{\int c_P \, dT}{T^2} \, dT,$$

we get

$$g = h_0 - T \int \frac{\int c_P \, dT}{T^2} \, dT - Ts_0 + RT \ln P$$

$$= RT \left(\frac{h_0}{RT} - \frac{1}{R} \int \frac{\int c_P \, dT}{T^2} \, dT - \frac{s_0}{R} + \ln P \right).$$

It is convenient to denote the first three of the terms within parentheses by ϕ, thus:

$$\phi = \frac{h_0}{RT} - \frac{1}{R} \int \frac{\int c_P \, dT}{T^2} \, dT - \frac{s_0}{R}.$$

† We have

$$uv = \int u \, dv + \int v \, du$$

where

$$u = \frac{1}{T}, \qquad v = \int c_P \, dT,$$

$$du = -\frac{dT}{T^2}, \qquad dv = c_P \, dT.$$

The molar Gibbs function of an ideal gas may therefore be written

$$g = RT(\phi + \ln P)$$

where ϕ is a function of T only.

Consider a number of inert ideal gases separated from one another, all at the same T and P. Suppose there are n_1 moles of gas A_1, n_2 moles of A_2, etc., up to n_c moles of A_c. Before the gases are mixed, the Gibbs function of the system G is the sum of the separate Gibbs functions, or

$$G_i = \Sigma n_k g_k$$
$$= RT\Sigma n_k(\phi_k + \ln P)$$

where the summation extends from $k = 1$ to $k = c$. To express the Gibbs function after mixing G_f, it is necessary merely to replace the total pressure P by the partial pressure p_k. (Why?) Thus,

$$G_f = RT\Sigma n_k(\phi_k + \ln p_k)$$
$$= RT\Sigma n_k(\phi_k + \ln P + \ln x_k).$$
Therefore, $$G_f - G_i = RT\Sigma n_k \ln x_k,$$

where the expression on the right is a negative quantity. It is seen therefore that the Gibbs function after diffusion is less than the Gibbs function before diffusion. This will be shown later to be an expression of a general law that holds for all irreversible processes that take place at constant T and P.

We have shown that the Gibbs function of a mixture of inert ideal gases at the temperature T and pressure P is

$$G = RT\Sigma n_k(\phi_k + \ln P + \ln x_k),$$

where

$$\phi = \frac{h_0}{RT} - \frac{1}{R} \int \frac{\int c_P \, dT}{T^2} \, dT - \frac{s_0}{R}.$$

17.6. Chemical Equilibrium. Consider a homogeneous mixture of 1 mole of hydrogen and 1 mole of oxygen at room temperature and at atmospheric pressure. It is a well-known fact that this mixture will remain indefinitely at the same temperature, pressure, and composition. The most careful measurements over a long period of time will disclose no appreciable spontaneous change of state. One might be inclined to deduce from this that such a mixture represents a system in a state of thermodynamic equilibrium. This, however, is not the case. If a small piece of platinized asbestos is introduced or if an electric spark is created across two electrodes, an explosion takes place involving a sudden change in the temperature, the pressure, and the composition. If at the end of the explosion the system is brought back to the same temperature and pressure, it will be found that the composition is now $\frac{1}{2}$ mole of oxygen, no measurable amount of hydrogen, and 1 mole of water vapor.

The piece of material such as platinized asbestos by whose agency a chemical reaction is started is known as a *catalyst*. If chemical combination is started in a mixture of 1 mole of hydrogen and 1 mole of oxygen with different amounts and different kinds of catalysts and the

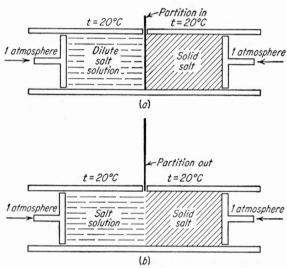

Fig. 17.3. Transport of matter across the boundary between two phases.

final composition of the mixture is measured in each case, it is found that (1) the final composition does not depend upon the amount of catalyst used; (2) the final composition does not depend on the kind of catalyst used; (3) the catalyst itself is the same at the end of the reaction as at the beginning.   These results lead us to the following conclusions:

1. The initial state of the mixture is a state of mechanical and thermal equilibrium but not of chemical equilibrium.

2. The final state is a state of thermodynamic equilibrium.

3. The transition from the initial nonequilibrium state to the final equilibrium state is accompanied by a chemical reaction that is too slow to be measured when it takes place spontaneously.   Through the agency of the catalyst the reaction is caused to take place more rapidly.

Imagine a vessel divided into two compartments by a removable partition as shown in Fig. 17.3(a). Suppose that one compartment contains a dilute solution of sodium chloride and water which is maintained at a pressure of 1 atm and at a temperature of 20°C, the mole fraction of the salt being, say, 0.01. Under these conditions the solution is in thermodynamic equilibrium. Suppose that the other compartment contains solid salt in equilibrium also at a pressure of 1 atm and a temperature of 20°C. Now imagine that the partition is removed [Fig. 17.3(b)] and that the pressure and temperature of the whole system are kept constant at the original values. Experiment shows that some solid salt dissolves, i.e., the mole fraction of the salt in the solution increases spontaneously at constant pressure and temperature. After a while, the change ceases and the mole fraction is found to be about 0.1.

Focusing our attention on the solution from the moment it was put in contact with the solid salt, we are led to the following conclusions:

1. The initial state of the solution (at the moment it was put in contact with the solid salt) is one of mechanical and thermal equilibrium but not of chemical equilibrium.

2. The final state of the solution is a state of thermodynamic equilibrium.

3. The transition from the initial nonequilibrium state to the final equilibrium state is accompanied by a transport of a chemical constituent into the solution.

17.7. Thermodynamic Description of Nonequilibrium States. A *phase* is defined as a system or a portion of a system composed of any number of chemical constituents satisfying the requirements that (1) it is homogeneous and (2) it has a definite boundary. The hydrogen-oxygen mixture described in Art. 17.6 is a gaseous phase of two chemical constituents and of constant mass. The salt solution is a liquid phase of two chemical constituents whose mass, when it is in contact with the solid-salt phase, is variable. Although the initial states of both these phases are nonequilibrium states, it is possible to describe them in terms of thermodynamic coordinates. Since each phase is in mechanical and thermal equilibrium, a definite P and T may be ascribed to each; since each has a definite boundary, each has a definite volume; and since each is homogeneous, the composition of each phase may be described by specifying the number of moles of each constituent. In general, a phase consisting of c chemical constituents in mechanical and thermal equilibrium may be described with the aid of the coordinates P, V, T, $n_1, n_2, \ldots , n_c$.

Under a given set of conditions a phase may undergo a change of state in which some or all of these coordinates change. While this is going on, the phase passes through states not of thermodynamic equilibrium but of mechanical and thermal equilibrium only. These states are connected by an equation of state that is a relation among P, V, T, and the n's. Whether a phase is in chemical equilibrium or not, it has a definite internal energy and enthalpy. Both U and H may be regarded as functions of P, V, T, and the n's; and, upon eliminating one of the coordinates by means of the equation of state, U and H may be expressed as a function of any two of P, V, and T and all the n's.   Since entropy is a measure of the molecular disorder of the system, the entropy of a phase that is not in chemical equilibrium must have a meaning.   We shall assume that the entropy of a phase and therefore the Helmholtz and Gibbs functions also can be expressed as functions of any two of P, V, and T and all the n's.

During a change of state the n's, which determine the composition of the phase, change either by virtue of a chemical reaction or by virtue of a transport of matter across the boundaries between phases, or both. In general, under given conditions, there is a set of values of the n's for which the phase is in chemical and therefore in thermodynamic equilibrium.   The functions that express the properties of a phase when it is not in chemical equilibrium must obviously reduce to those for thermodynamic equilibrium when the equilibrium values of the n's are substituted.   We are therefore led to assume that *any property of a phase in mechanical and thermal equilibrium can be represented by a function of any two of P, V, T, and the n's of the same form as that used to denote the same property when the phase is in thermodynamic equilibrium.*

Consider, for example, a phase consisting of a mixture of ideal gases. When the gases are inert, the equation of state is

$$PV = \Sigma n_k RT,$$

the entropy is

$$S = R\Sigma n_k(\sigma_k - \ln P - \ln x_k),$$

and the Gibbs function is

$$G = RT\Sigma n_k(\phi_k + \ln P + \ln x_k).$$

According to the assumption just made, these same equations may be used in connection with an ideal gas phase in mechanical and thermal equilibrium when the gases are chemically active, when the phase is in contact with other phases, or under both conditions, whether chemical equilibrium exists or not.   Under these conditions the n's and x's are variables.   Whether they all independent variables or not is a question that cannot be answered until the conditions under which a change of state takes place are specified.   It is clear that, if the mass of the phase remains constant and the gases are inert, the n's and x's are constants. If the mass of the phase remains constant and the gases are chemically active, then it will be shown that each n and therefore each x is a function of only one independent variable, the degree of reaction.   If the mass of the phase is variable, the number of n's that are independent depends on the number of other phases in contact with the original phase and on the chemical constituents of these other phases.

A system composed of two or more phases is called a *heterogeneous system*. Any extensive property such as V, U, S, H, A, or G of any one of the phases may be expressed as a function of, say, T, P, and the n's of that phase. Thus, for the Gibbs function of the first phase,

$$G^{(1)} = \text{function of } (T, P, n_1^{(1)}, n_2^{(1)}, \cdots);$$

for the second phase,

$$G^{(2)} = \text{function of } (T, P, n_1^{(2)}, n_2^{(2)}, \cdots);$$

etc. The Gibbs function of the whole heterogeneous system is therefore

$$G = G^{(1)} + G^{(2)} + \cdots.$$

This result holds for any extensive property of a heterogeneous system.

17.8. Conditions for Chemical Equilibrium. Consider any chemical system of constant mass, either homogeneous or heterogeneous, in mechanical and thermal equilibrium but not in chemical equilibrium. Suppose that the system is in contact with a reservoir at temperature T and undergoes an infinitesimal irreversible process involving an exchange of heat dQ with the reservoir. The process may involve a chemical reaction or a transport of matter between phases or both. Let dS denote the entropy change of the system and dS_0 the entropy change of the reservoir. The total entropy change of the universe is therefore $dS_0 + dS$; and since the performance of an irreversible process is attended by an increase in the entropy of the universe, we may write

$$dS_0 + dS > 0.$$

Since

$$dS_0 = -\frac{dQ}{T},$$

we have

$$-\frac{dQ}{T} + dS > 0,$$

or

$$dQ - T\,dS < 0.$$

During the infinitesimal irreversible process the internal energy of the system changes by an amount dU, and an amount of work $P\,dV$ is performed. The first law can therefore be written in its usual form,

$$dQ = dU + P\,dV,$$

and the inequality becomes

$$\boxed{dU + P\,dV - T\,dS < 0.}$$

This inequality holds during any infinitesimal portion and therefore during all infinitesimal portions of the irreversible process. According to the assumption made in the preceding article, U, V, and S may all be regarded as functions of thermodynamic coordinates.

During the irreversible process for which the above inequality holds, some or all of the coordinates may change. If we restrict the irreversible process by imposing the condition that two of the thermodynamic coordinates shall remain constant, then the inequality can be reduced to a simpler form. Suppose, for example, that the internal energy and the volume remain constant. Then the inequality reduces to $dS > 0$, which means that the entropy of a system at constant U and V increases during an irreversible process, approaching a maximum at the final state of equilibrium. This result, however, is obvious from the entropy principle, since a system at constant U and V is isolated and is therefore, so to speak, its own universe. The two most important sets of conditions are the following:

1. *If T and V are constant*, the inequality reduces to

$$d(U - TS) < 0,$$
or
$$dA < 0,$$

expressing the result that *the Helmholtz function of a system at constant T and V decreases during an irreversible process*, becoming a minimum at the final equilibrium state.

2. *If T and P are constant*, the inequality reduces to

$$d(U + PV - TS) < 0,$$
or
$$dG < 0,$$

expressing the result that *the Gibbs function of a system at constant T and P decreases during an irreversible process*, becoming a minimum at the final equilibrium state.

The student will recall that the condition for equilibrium of a conservative mechanical system is that the potential energy shall be a minimum. The Helmholtz and Gibbs functions are therefore seen to play a similar role in thermodynamics. For this reason Gibbs called the function A the "thermodynamic potential at constant volume" and the function G the "thermodynamic potential at constant pressure."

17.9. Use of the Helmholtz Function to Prove that $(\partial P/\partial V)_T < 0$. In discussing the important equation

$$C_P - C_V = -T \left(\frac{\partial V}{\partial T} \right)_P^2 \left(\frac{\partial P}{\partial V} \right)_T$$

in Art. 13.6, the remark was made that $(\partial P/\partial V)_T$ is always negative. It will now be proved for any system of constant mass. Consider the system depicted symbolically in Fig. 17.4.   At first, each half of the system is in equilibrium as well as the entire system.   Suppose now the left half is compressed by an amount δv and the right half expanded by the same amount, each half remaining at constant temperature and the *total* volume remaining constant.

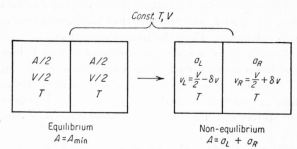

FIG. 17.4. Transition from a state of thermodynamic equilibrium to a state characterized by a lack of mechanical equilibrium.

The Helmholtz function of the left half, a_L, may now be expanded in a Taylor's series about its equilibrium value $A_{min}/2$, as follows

$$a_L = \frac{A_{min}}{2} - \left(\frac{\partial a}{\partial v}\right)_T \delta v + \frac{1}{2}\left(\frac{\partial^2 a}{\partial v^2}\right)_T (\delta v)^2 - \cdots ,$$

which may be terminated after the squared term if δv is small enough. But there is no difference between the behavior of half the system and that of the whole system, or

$$\left(\frac{\partial a}{\partial v}\right)_T = \left(\frac{\partial A}{\partial V}\right)_T.$$

Hence $$a_L = \frac{A_{min}}{2} - \left(\frac{\partial A}{\partial V}\right)_T \delta v + \frac{1}{2}\left(\frac{\partial^2 A}{\partial V^2}\right)_T (\delta v)^2.$$

Similarly for the right half,

$$a_R = \frac{A_{min}}{2} + \left(\frac{\partial A}{\partial V}\right)_T \delta v + \frac{1}{2}\left(\frac{\partial^2 A}{\partial V^2}\right)_T (\delta v)^2.$$

Adding these two equations, the total Helmholtz function of the system *in the nonequilibrium state* is

$$a_L + a_R = A_{min} + \left(\frac{\partial^2 A}{\partial V^2}\right)_T (\delta v)^2,$$

or $$a_L + a_R - A_{min} = \delta A_{T,V} = \left(\frac{\partial^2 A}{\partial V^2}\right)_T (\delta v)^2.$$

The relation between A and the volume v of either half of the system at constant T and V is shown in Fig. 17.5.   Since $\delta A_{T,V}$ is positive, it follows that

$$\left(\frac{\partial^2 A}{\partial V^2}\right)_T > 0.$$

But

$$\left(\frac{\partial A}{\partial V}\right)_T = -P,$$

and hence, finally,

$$\left(\frac{\partial P}{\partial V}\right)_T < 0.$$

This is *the condition for mechanical stability.*

17.10. Thermodynamic Equations for a Phase. Consider a phase composed of c chemical constituents of which there are n_1 moles of substance A_1, n_2 moles of A_2, ⋯ , n_c moles of A_c, the phase being in thermal equilibrium at the temperature T and in mechanical equilibrium at the pressure P.   The Gibbs function of the phase can be written

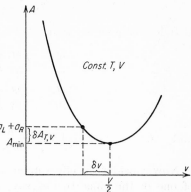

Fig. 17.5. Dependence of the Helmholtz function of the entire system on the volume of half of it, when the total volume and the temperature are constant.

$$G = \text{function of } (T, P, n_1, n_2, \cdots , n_c).$$

If the constituents are inert, the phase is in chemical and therefore in thermodynamic equilibrium.   Imagine the performance of an infinitesimal *reversible* process in which the temperature and pressure are changed by dT and dP, respectively, and the numbers of moles of the various constituents are altered by the amounts dn_1, dn_2, ... , dn_c.   Since we have assumed that the constituents are inert, the changes in the n's are to be regarded as accomplished by the reversible addition or withdrawal of the constituents with the aid of suitable semipermeable membranes.   The resulting change in the Gibbs function of the phase is given by

$$dG = \frac{\partial G}{\partial T} dT + \frac{\partial G}{\partial P} dP + \frac{\partial G}{\partial n_1} dn_1 + \frac{\partial G}{\partial n_2} dn_2 + \cdots + \frac{\partial G}{\partial n_c} dn_c,$$

where it is understood that G is a function of T, P, and the n's and that each partial derivative implies that all variables other than the one indicated are to be kept constant.

As a special case, consider an infinitesimal reversible process in which all the dn's are zero.   Under these conditions, the composition and the mass of the phase remain constant, and the equation becomes

$$dG = \frac{\partial G}{\partial T} dT + \frac{\partial G}{\partial P} dP \quad \text{(constant composition and mass).}$$

But, for this case, it has already been shown that

$$dG = -S\,dT + V\,dP.$$

It follows, therefore, that

$$\frac{\partial G}{\partial T} = \left(\frac{\partial G}{\partial T}\right)_{P,n_1,n_2,\cdots,n_c} = -S,$$

$$\frac{\partial G}{\partial P} = \left(\frac{\partial G}{\partial P}\right)_{T,n_1,n_2,\cdots,n_c} = V,$$

and $\quad dG = -S\,dT + V\,dP + \dfrac{\partial G}{\partial n_1}\,dn_1 + \dfrac{\partial G}{\partial n_2}\,dn_2 + \cdots + \dfrac{\partial G}{\partial n_c}\,dn_c.$

Now consider the effect upon the Gibbs function when a small amount of one of the constituents, say, the kth constituent, A_k, is introduced into the phase, T, P, and the other n's remain constant. If dn_k moles of A_k are introduced, the effect on the Gibbs function is expressed by the partial derivative

$$\mu_k = \frac{\partial G}{\partial n_k},$$

where μ_k is called the *chemical potential* of the kth constituent of the phase in question. A chemical potential of one constituent is a function of T, P, and *all* the n's. If a substance is not present in a phase, it does not follow that its chemical potential is zero. The chemical potential is a measure of the effect on the Gibbs function when a substance *is* introduced. Even though the substance is not present in the phase, there is always the possibility of introducing it, in which case the Gibbs function would be altered and the value of μ would be finite. We may now write

$$dG = -S\,dT + V\,dP + \mu_1\,dn_1 + \mu_2\,dn_2 + \cdots + \mu_c\,dn_c$$

for an infinitesimal change in the Gibbs function of any phase consisting of inert constituents.

Suppose, now, that the constituents are chemically active. Changes in the n's may now take place because of a chemical reaction. Although the phase is always considered to be in thermal and mechanical equilibrium, an infinitesimal process involving a change in T, P, and the n's will, in general, be irreversible, since chemical equilibrium may not exist. In accordance with our previous assumption as to the form of the expressions denoting properties of a phase in thermal and mechanical equilibrium but not in chemical equilibrium, *we shall assume that the equation*

$$\boxed{\begin{aligned} dG &= -S\,dT + V\,dP + \mu_1\,dn_1 + \mu_2\,dn_2 + \cdots + \mu_c\,dn_c \\ &= -S\,dT + V\,dP + \Sigma\mu_k\,dn_k \end{aligned}} \tag{1}$$

correctly expresses the change in the Gibbs function for **any** *infinitesimal process, in which the n's may be caused to change either by the transfer of constituents to or from the phase or by the agency of a chemical reaction, or both.*

Imagine a phase at constant T and P in which all constituents are increased in the same proportion. Since the Gibbs function is an extensive quantity, it also will be increased in the same proportion. Infinitesimal changes in the mole numbers in the same proportion are represented by

$$dn_1 = n_1\, d\lambda, \qquad dn_2 = n_2\, d\lambda, \cdot \cdot \cdot , \qquad dn_c = n_c\, d\lambda,$$

and the corresponding change in G is

$$dG = G\, d\lambda,$$

where $d\lambda$ is the proportionality factor. Since

$$dG_{T,P} = \mu_1\, dn_1 + \mu_2\, dn_2 + \cdot \cdot \cdot + \mu_c\, dn_c,$$

we have

$$G\, d\lambda = \mu_1 n_1\, d\lambda + \mu_2 n_2\, d\lambda + \cdot \cdot \cdot + \mu_c n_c\, d\lambda,$$

or

$$\boxed{\begin{aligned} G &= \mu_1 n_1 + \mu_2 n_2 + \cdot \cdot \cdot + \mu_c n_c \\ &= \Sigma \mu_k n_k. \end{aligned}} \qquad (2)$$

Equation (2) shows that *the chemical potentials are intensive quantities;* for if all the n's are increased in the same proportion at constant T and P, the μ's must remain constant in order that G increase in the same proportion.

17.11. Chemical Potentials. The chemical potentials play a fundamental role in chemical thermodynamics. The chemical potential of the kth constituent of a phase is defined as

$$\mu_k = \frac{\partial G}{\partial n_k}$$

and is a function of T, P, and all the n's. In order that μ_k may be an intensive quantity, it is clear that the n's must be combined in such a way that, when all of them are multiplied by the same factor, the value of μ_k remains the same. Now the mole fraction of the kth constituent,

$$x_k = \frac{n_k}{\Sigma n},$$

satisfies that requirement, and hence it is to be expected that μ_k is a function of T, P, and x_k. The actual form of the function depends, of course, on the nature of the phase. Consider the following phases:

1. *Phase Consisting of Only One Constituent.*   In this simple but not trivial case,

$$G = \mu n$$

and
$$\mu = \frac{G}{n} = g;$$

i.e., the chemical potential is the molar Gibbs function and is a function of T and P only.

2. *Phase Consisting of a Mixture of Ideal Gases.*   In this case we have, from Art. 17.5,

$$G = RT\Sigma n_k(\phi_k + \ln P + \ln x_k)$$

which, when compared with the general equation

$$G = \Sigma n_k\mu_k,$$

shows that the chemical potential of one ideal gas in a mixture of ideal gases is

$$\mu = RT(\phi + \ln P + \ln x),$$

which may be written in the two alternative forms

$$\mu = RT(\phi + \ln p),$$
$$\mu = g + RT \ln x.$$

3. *Phase Consisting of an Ideal Solution.*   An ideal solution is defined as one in which the chemical potential of each constituent is of the form

$$\mu_k = g_k + RT \ln x_k$$

where g_k is the Gibbs function of 1 mole of the kth constituent in the pure state, expressed as a function of T and P.

4. *Phase Consisting of a Dilute Solution.*   In the case of a dilute solution in which the mole fraction of the solvent x_0 is very much larger than each of the mole fractions of the solutes x_1, x_2, . . . , it can be shown that, for the solvent,

$$\mu_0 = g_0 + RT \ln x_0,$$

where g_0 is the molar Gibbs function of the solvent in the pure state, expressed as a function of T and P.   For any one of the solutes,

$$\mu_k = g_{0k} + RT \ln x_k,$$

where g_{0k} is a function of T and P only but depends upon the nature of the solvent as well as upon the solute.

5. *Other Phases.*   By defining functions known as fugacity and activity coefficients it is possible to express the chemical potentials of constituents of a mixture of real gases and also of concentrated solutions.   This is beyond the scope of this book.

We shall assume that it is always possible to express the chemical potential of any constituent of any phase as a function of T, P, and the x of that constituent. It will be a surprise to the student to discover how much valuable information can be obtained with the aid of this assumption, without knowing the exact expressions for the chemical potentials of the constituents of a phase.

17.12. Degree of Reaction. If we introduce into a vessel a mixture of any arbitrary number of moles of water vapor, hydrogen, and oxygen, the chemical reaction that is capable of taking place is indicated by the notation

$$H_2O \rightleftharpoons H_2 + \tfrac{1}{2}O_2,$$

where the quantity that is written on the left is called an *initial constituent* and those on the right *final constituents*. The numbers that precede the chemical symbols and that "balance" the equation (it is understood that both H_2O and H_2 are preceded by unity) are called the *stoichiometric coefficients* and are proportional to the numbers of moles of the constituents that *change* during the reaction. Thus, if 1 mole of water vapor dissociates, then 1 mole of hydrogen and $\tfrac{1}{2}$ mole of oxygen are formed; or if 0.1 mole of water vapor dissociates, then 0.1 mole of hydrogen and 0.05 mole of oxygen are formed; or, if n_0 moles of water vapor dissociate, n_0 being any number whatever, then n_0 moles of hydrogen and $n_0/2$ moles of oxygen are formed. Similarly, if the reaction proceeds to the left to the extent that n_0' moles of hydrogen combine with $n_0'/2$ moles of oxygen, then n_0' moles of water vapor are formed.

In general, suppose we have a mixture of four substances whose chemical symbols are A_1, A_2, A_3, and A_4. Let A_1 and A_2 be the initial constituents and A_3 and A_4 the final constituents, the reaction being represented by

$$\nu_1 A_1 + \nu_2 A_2 \rightleftharpoons \nu_3 A_3 + \nu_4 A_4.$$

We have chosen four substances only for convenience. The equations to be developed are of such a character that they can easily be applied to reactions in which any number of substances participate. The ν's are the stoichiometric coefficients, which are always positive integers or fractions.

Suppose we start with arbitrary amounts of *both* initial and final constituents. If we imagine the reaction to proceed completely to the right, at least one of the initial constituents, say, A_1, will completely disappear. Then it is possible to find a positive number n_0 such that the original number of moles of each of the initial constituents is expressed in the form

$$n_1(\text{original}) = n_0\nu_1,$$
$$n_2(\text{original}) = n_0\nu_2 + N_2,$$

where N_2 is a constant representing the number of moles of A_2 that cannot combine. If we imagine the reaction to proceed completely to the left, at least one of the final constituents, say, A_3, will completely disappear. In this event, another positive number n_0' may be found such that the original number of moles of each final constituent is expressed in the form

$$n_3(\text{original}) = n_0'\nu_3,$$
$$n_4(\text{original}) = n_0'\nu_4 + N_4.$$

If the reaction is imagined to proceed completely to the left, there is the maximum amount possible of each initial constituent and the minimum amount of each final constituent. Thus,

$$n_1(\text{max}) = (n_0 + n_0')\nu_1, \qquad n_3(\text{min}) = 0,$$
$$n_2(\text{max}) = (n_0 + n_0')\nu_2 + N_2, \qquad n_4(\text{min}) = N_4.$$

If the reaction is imagined to proceed completely to the right, there is the minimum amount possible of each initial constituent and the maximum amount of each final constituent. Thus,

$$n_1(\text{min}) = 0, \qquad n_3(\text{max}) = (n_0 + n_0')\nu_3,$$
$$n_2(\text{min}) = N_2, \qquad n_4(\text{max}) = (n_0 + n_0')\nu_4 + N_4.$$

Suppose the reaction proceeds partially either to the right or to the left to such an extent that there are n_1 moles of A_1, n_2 moles of A_2, n_3 moles of A_3, and n_4 moles of A_4 present at a given moment. We define the *degree of reaction* ϵ in terms of any one of the initial constituents, say, A_1, as the fraction

$$\epsilon = \frac{n_1(\text{max}) - n_1}{n_1(\text{max}) - n_1(\text{min})}.$$

It follows from this definition that $\epsilon = 0$ when the reaction is completely to the left and $\epsilon = 1$ when the reaction is completely to the right. When the reaction consists in the dissociation of one initial constituent, ϵ is called the *degree of dissociation;* when it consists in the ionization of one initial constituent, ϵ is called the *degree of ionization.* Expressing $n_1(\text{max})$ and $n_1(\text{min})$ in terms of the constants that express the original amounts of the constituents, we get

$$\epsilon = \frac{(n_0 + n_0')\nu_1 - n_1}{(n_0 + n_0')\nu_1},$$

and, solving for n_1,

$$n_1 = (n_0 + n_0')\nu_1(1 - \epsilon).$$

The number of moles of each of the constituents is therefore given by the expressions

$$n_1 = (n_0 + n_0')\nu_1(1 - \epsilon), \qquad n_3 = (n_0 + n_0')\nu_3\epsilon,$$
$$n_2 = (n_0 + n_0')\nu_2(1 - \epsilon) + N_2, \qquad n_4 = (n_0 + n_0')\nu_4\epsilon + N_4.$$

When a chemical reaction takes place, all the n's change, but not independently. The restrictions imposed upon the n's are given by the above relations. These equations are therefore examples of *equations of constraint*.

The equations of constraint are equally valid whether the system is heterogeneous or homogeneous. If each constituent is present in, say, φ different phases, with $n_1^{(1)}$ moles of constituent A_1 in phase (1) and $n_1^{(2)}$ moles of the same constituent in phase (2), etc., then the total number of moles of constituent A_1 is

$$n_1 = n_1^{(1)} + n_1^{(2)} + \cdots + n_1^{(\varphi)} = (n_0 + n_0')\nu_1(1 - \epsilon),$$

etc., for the other constituents. For the present, however, we shall limit ourselves to homogeneous systems, reserving heterogeneous systems for Chap. 19.

Since all the n's are functions of ϵ only, it follows that, in a homogeneous system, all the mole fractions are functions of ϵ only. An example will show how simple these expressions are when the starting conditions are simple. Consider a vessel containing n_0 moles of water vapor only, with no hydrogen or oxygen present. If dissociation occurs until the degree of dissociation is ϵ, then the n's and the x's are shown as functions of ϵ in Table 17.1. Since the chemical potential of each gas in the mixture is a function of T, P, and x, it follows that every chemical potential is a function of T, P, and ϵ.

TABLE 17.1. $H_2O \rightleftharpoons H_2 + \frac{1}{2}O_2$

A	ν	n	x
$A_1 = H_2O$	$\nu_1 = 1$	$n_1 = n_0(1 - \epsilon)$	$x_1 = \dfrac{1 - \epsilon}{1 + \dfrac{\epsilon}{2}}$
$A_3 = H_2$	$\nu_3 = 1$	$n_3 = n_0\epsilon$	$x_3 = \dfrac{\epsilon}{1 + \dfrac{\epsilon}{2}}$
$A_4 = O_2$	$\nu_4 = \dfrac{1}{2}$	$n_4 = \dfrac{n_0\epsilon}{2}$ $\Sigma n = n_0\left(1 + \dfrac{\epsilon}{2}\right)$	$x_4 = \dfrac{\epsilon/2}{1 + \dfrac{\epsilon}{2}}$

If the reaction is imagined to proceed to an infinitesimal extent, the degree of reaction changing from ϵ to $\epsilon + d\epsilon$, the various n's will change by the amounts

$$dn_1 = -(n_0 + n_0')\nu_1 \, d\epsilon, \qquad dn_3 = (n_0 + n_0')\nu_3 \, d\epsilon,$$
$$dn_2 = -(n_0 + n_0')\nu_2 \, d\epsilon, \qquad dn_4 = (n_0 + n_0')\nu_4 \, d\epsilon.$$

These equations show that the changes in the n's are proportional to the ν's, the factor of proportionality being, for the initial constituents, $-(n_0 + n_0') \, d\epsilon$ and, for the final constituents, $+(n_0 + n_0') \, d\epsilon$. Another way of writing them is as follows,

$$\frac{dn_1}{-\nu_1} = \frac{dn_2}{-\nu_2} = \frac{dn_3}{\nu_3} = \frac{dn_4}{\nu_4} = (n_0 + n_0') \, d\epsilon,$$

which shows perhaps more clearly that the dn's are proportional to the ν's.

17.13. Equation of Reaction Equilibrium. Consider a homogeneous phase consisting of arbitrary amounts of the four constituents A_1, A_2, A_3, and A_4, capable of undergoing the reaction

$$\nu_1 A_1 + \nu_2 A_2 \rightleftharpoons \nu_3 A_3 + \nu_4 A_4.$$

Suppose that the phase is at a uniform temperature T and pressure P. If n_1, n_2, n_3, and n_4 denote the numbers of moles of each constituent that are present at any moment and μ_1, μ_2, μ_3, and μ_4 the respective chemical potentials, then the Gibbs function of the mixture is

$$G = \mu_1 n_1 + \mu_2 n_2 + \mu_3 n_3 + \mu_4 n_4.$$

The n's are given by the equations of constraint,

$$n_1 = (n_0 + n_0')\nu_1(1 - \epsilon), \qquad n_3 = (n_0 + n_0')\nu_3\epsilon,$$
$$n_2 = (n_0 + n_0')\nu_2(1 - \epsilon) + N_2, \qquad n_4 = (n_0 + n_0')\nu_4\epsilon + N_4;$$

and the μ's are functions of T, P, and ϵ. It therefore follows that G is a function of T, P, and ϵ.

Let us imagine that the reaction is allowed to take place at constant T and P. Under these conditions, the Gibbs function decreases; i.e., during an infinitesimal change in ϵ from ϵ to $\epsilon + d\epsilon$,

$$dG_{T,P} < 0.$$

We have shown that, for any infinitesimal change to which a phase in thermal and mechanical equilibrium is subjected,

$$dG = -S \, dT + V \, dP + \mu_1 \, dn_1 + \mu_2 \, dn_2 + \cdots .$$

Therefore, for this mixture of four constituents,

$$dG_{T,P} = \mu_1 \, dn_1 + \mu_2 \, dn_2 + \mu_3 \, dn_3 + \mu_4 \, dn_4,$$

with the equations of constraint in differential form,

$$dn_1 = -(n_0 + n_0')\nu_1 \, d\epsilon, \qquad dn_3 = (n_0 + n_0')\nu_3 \, d\epsilon,$$
$$dn_2 = -(n_0 + n_0')\nu_2 \, d\epsilon, \qquad dn_4 = (n_0 + n_0')\nu_4 \, d\epsilon.$$

Substituting, we obtain a general expression for any infinitesimal change of the Gibbs function at constant T and P. Thus,

$$dG_{T,P} = (n_0 + n_0')(-\nu_1\mu_1 - \nu_2\mu_2 + \nu_3\mu_3 + \nu_4\mu_4)\, d\epsilon.$$

It follows from this equation that when the reaction proceeds spontaneously to the right, so that $d\epsilon$ is positive, then, in order that $dG_{T,P} < 0$,

$$\nu_1\mu_1 + \nu_2\mu_2 > \nu_3\mu_3 + \nu_4\mu_4 \qquad \text{(reaction to right)}.$$

Conversely, if the reaction proceeds spontaneously to the left,

$$\nu_1\mu_1 + \nu_2\mu_2 < \nu_3\mu_3 + \nu_4\mu_4 \qquad \text{(reaction to left)}.$$

The mixture will be in equilibrium at the given T and P when the Gibbs function is a minimum at which an infinitesimal change in ϵ will produce no change in the Gibbs function. Therefore, for $dG_{T,P} = 0$ at equilibrium, we have

$$\boxed{\nu_1\mu_1 + \nu_2\mu_2 = \nu_3\mu_3 + \nu_4\mu_4} \qquad \text{(at equilibrium)},$$

which is called the *equation of reaction equilibrium*. It should be noted that this equation contains only intensive variables. Evidently, to determine the composition of a homogeneous mixture after the reaction has come to equilibrium, it is necessary merely to substitute the appropriate expressions for the chemical potentials into the equation of reaction equilibrium. This will be done in the case of ideal gases in the next chapter.

PROBLEMS

17.1. A mixture of 3 moles of helium, 4 moles of neon, and 5 moles of argon is at a pressure of 1 atm and a temperature of 300°K. Calculate (a) the volume; (b) the various mole fractions; (c) the various partial pressures; (d) the change of entropy due to mixing; (e) the change in the Gibbs function due to mixing.

17.2. n_1 moles of an ideal monatomic gas at temperature T_1 and pressure P are in one compartment of an insulated container. In an adjoining compartment separated by an insulating partition are n_2 moles of another ideal monatomic gas at temperature T_2 and pressure P. When the partition is removed,

(a) Show that the final pressure of the mixture is P.

(b) Calculate the entropy change when the gases are identical.

(c) Calculate the entropy change when the gases are different.

17.3. n_1 moles of an ideal gas at pressure P_1 and temperature T are in one compartment of an insulated container. In an adjoining compartment, separated by a partition, are n_2 moles of an ideal gas at pressure P_2 and temperature T. When the partition is removed,

(a) Calculate the final pressure of the mixture.

(b) Calculate the entropy change when the gases are identical.

(c) Calculate the entropy change when the gases are different.

(d) Prove that the entropy change in (c) is the same as that which would be produced by two independent free expansions.

17.4. Calculate the entropy change of the universe due to the diffusion of two ideal gases (1 mole of each) at the same temperature and pressure, by calculating $\int dQ/T$ over a series of reversible processes involving the use of the apparatus depicted in Fig. 17.2.

17.5. What is the minimum amount of work required to separate 1 mole of air at 27°C and 1 atm pressure (assumed composed of $\frac{1}{5}O_2$ and $\frac{4}{5}N_2$) into O_2 and N_2 each at 27°C and 1 atm pressure?

17.6. Prove Gibbs's theorem by using the apparatus depicted in Fig. 17.2 in such a way that the gases are separated reversibly and adiabatically.

17.7. Consider the system depicted in Fig. 17.6 in which the whole system and also each half are in equilibrium. Consider a process to take place in which each half of the system remains at the constant volume $V/2$, but a small amount of heat

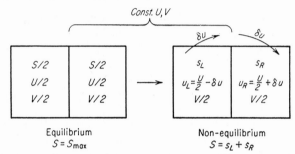

FIG. 17.6. Transition from a state of thermodynamic equilibrium to a state characterized by a lack of thermal equilibrium.

δu (at constant volume $dQ = dU$) is extracted from the left half and transferred to the right half, as shown in Fig. 17.6. Realizing that

$$\left(\frac{\partial s}{\partial u}\right)_v = \left(\frac{\partial S}{\partial U}\right)_V,$$

(a) Expand the entropy of the left half s_L by means of Taylor's series about the equilibrium value $S_{\max}/2$, terminating the series after the squared term. Do the same for s_R.

(b) Show that

$$\delta S_{U,V} = s_L + s_R - S_{\max} = \left(\frac{\partial^2 S}{\partial U^2}\right)_V (\delta u)^2.$$

(c) Show that $C_V > 0$, which is the *condition for thermal stability*.

17.8. (a) Show that the molar Helmholtz function of an ideal gas is

$$a = u_0 - T \int \frac{\int c_V \, dT}{T^2} \, dT - T s_0 - RT \ln v.$$

(b) Show that the Helmholtz function of a mixture of inert ideal gases is

$$A = \Sigma n_k (a_k + RT \ln x_k).$$

(c) Show that the change in the Helmholtz function due to diffusion is

$$A_f - A_i = RT \Sigma n_k \ln x_k.$$

17.9. Prove that, for an irreversible cycle,

$$_I\oint \frac{dQ}{T} < 0.$$

17.10. By means of the equations

$$dG = -S\,dT + V\,dP + \Sigma\mu_k\,dn_k$$

and
$$G = \Sigma\mu_k n_k,$$

prove that

(a) $-S\,dT + V\,dP = \Sigma n_k\,d\mu_k.$

(b) $-s\,dT + v\,dP = \Sigma x_k\,d\mu_k.$

17.11. Show that, if the internal energy of a phase is expressed as a function of S, V, $n_1, n_2, \ldots, n_c$,

(a) $dU = T\,dS - P\,dV + \Sigma\mu_k\,dn_k,$

where $\mu_k = (\partial U/\partial n_k)_{S,V,\text{ other } n\text{'s}}.$

(b) $U = TS - PV + \Sigma\mu_k n_k.$

(c) $-S\,dT + V\,dP = \Sigma n_k\,d\mu_k.$

17.12. Show that, if the Helmholtz function of a phase is expressed as a function of $T, V, n_1, n_2, \ldots, n_c$,

(a) $dA = -S\,dT - P\,dV + \Sigma\mu_k\,dn_k,$

where $\mu_k = (\partial A/\partial n_k)_{T,V,\text{ other } n\text{'s}}.$

(b) $A = -PV + \Sigma\mu_k n_k.$

(c) $-S\,dT + V\,dP = \Sigma n_k\,d\mu_k.$

17.13. Prove that

(a) $Td\left(\dfrac{A}{T}\right) = -\dfrac{U}{T}\,dT - P\,dV + \Sigma\mu_k\,dn_k.$

(b) $d(PV) = S\,dT + P\,dV + \Sigma n_k\,d\mu_k.$

(These formulas are of importance in statistical mechanics.)

17.14. Show that, for an ideal gas in a mixture of ideal gases,

$$d\mu_k = \frac{\mu_k - h_k}{T}\,dT + v_k\,dP + RT\,d\ln x_k.$$

17.15. In Fig. 17.7 is depicted a gaseous system in a vessel divided into two compartments by means of a porous diaphragm. The left-hand compartment was originally maintained at a constant temperature $T + \Delta T$ slightly larger than that on the

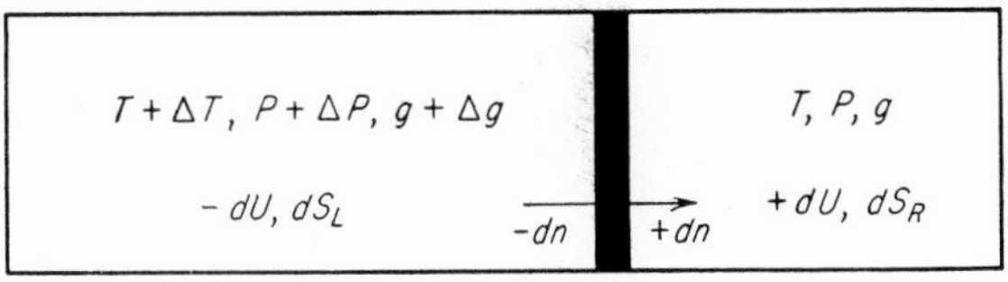

FIG. 17.7. Thermal effusion through a porous diaphragm.

right. After a while, a pressure difference was set up, as indicated, somewhat like the fountain effect in liquid helium, but with the difference that a transfer of gas from one compartment to the other is irreversible.

Imagine the adiabatic, irreversible transfer of dn moles of gas from the left to the right, each compartment remaining at constant T, P, and V, but undergoing an infinitesimal change in S and U.

(a) Using the equation in Prob. 17.11(a),

$$T \, dS = dU + P \, dV - g \, dn$$

calculate dS_L, the entropy change of the gas in the left compartment, and dS_R, that for the right.

(b) Show that, if dn is transferred in time $d\tau$

$$\frac{d(S_L + S_R)}{d\tau} = -I_u \Delta \left(\frac{1}{T}\right) - I_n \Delta \left(\frac{g}{T}\right),$$

where $I_u = dU/d\tau$ and $I_n = dn/d\tau$.

(c) Express $-I_u$ and $-I_n$ as linear functions of both $\Delta(1/T)$ and $\Delta(g/T)$ with coefficients L_{11}, L_{12}, L_{21}, L_{22}, as in Art. 14.10.

(d) Show that

$$\frac{L_{12}}{L_{22}} = \left(\frac{I_u}{I_n}\right)_{\Delta T = 0} = \left(\frac{dU}{dn}\right)_{\Delta T = 0} = u^*.$$

(e) Show that

$$\frac{L_{21}}{L_{22}} = -\left[\frac{\Delta(g/T)}{\Delta(1/T)}\right]_{I_n = 0}$$

(f) Show that

$$\frac{\Delta(g/T)}{\Delta(1/T)} = h - vT \frac{\Delta P}{\Delta T}.$$

(g) Using Onsager's reciprocal relation show that

$$\left(\frac{\Delta P}{\Delta T}\right)_{I_n = 0} = \frac{u^* + h}{vT}.$$

Compare this result with that of Prob. 14.19(f).

17.16. Starting with n_0 moles of CO and n_0 moles of H_2O capable of undergoing the reaction

$$CO + H_2O \rightleftharpoons CO_2 + H_2$$

in the gaseous phase, set up a table of values of A, ν, n, and x, similar to that of Table 17.1.

17.17. Starting with n_0 moles of H_2S and $2n_0$ moles of H_2O, capable of undergoing the reaction

$$H_2S + 2H_2O \rightleftharpoons 3H_2 + SO_2$$

in the gaseous phase, set up a table of values of A, ν, n, and x, similar to that of Table 17.1.

18

Ideal Gas Reactions

18.1. Law of Mass Action. It has been shown that when four substances which are capable of undergoing the reaction

$$\nu_1 A_1 + \nu_2 A_2 \rightleftharpoons \nu_3 A_3 + \nu_4 A_4,$$

and which constitute a homogeneous phase at constant temperature and pressure, come to equilibrium, the equation of reaction equilibrium

$$\nu_1 \mu_1 + \nu_2 \mu_2 = \nu_3 \mu_3 + \nu_4 \mu_4$$

must be satisfied. If the constituents are ideal gases, then the chemical potentials are given by the expressions of the type

$$\mu_k = RT(\phi_k + \ln P + \ln x_k)$$

where the ϕ's are functions of the temperature only. Substituting in the equation of reaction equilibrium, we get

$$\nu_1(\phi_1 + \ln P + \ln x_1) + \nu_2(\phi_2 + \ln P + \ln x_2)$$
$$= \nu_3(\phi_3 + \ln P + \ln x_3) + \nu_4(\phi_4 + \ln P + \ln x_4)$$

Rearranging terms,

$$\nu_3 \ln x_3 + \nu_4 \ln x_4 - \nu_1 \ln x_1 - \nu_2 \ln x_2$$
$$+ (\nu_3 + \nu_4 - \nu_1 - \nu_2) \ln P = -(\nu_3\phi_3 + \nu_4\phi_4 - \nu_1\phi_1 - \nu_2\phi_2),$$

or
$$\ln \frac{x_3^{\nu_3} x_4^{\nu_4}}{x_1^{\nu_1} x_2^{\nu_2}} P^{\nu_3 + \nu_4 - \nu_1 - \nu_2} = -(\nu_3\phi_3 + \nu_4\phi_4 - \nu_1\phi_1 - \nu_2\phi_2).$$

The right-hand member is a quantity whose value depends only on the temperature. Denoting it by $\ln K$, where K is known as the *equilibrium constant*,

$$\ln K = -(\nu_3\phi_3 + \nu_4\phi_4 - \nu_1\phi_1 - \nu_2\phi_2),$$

we get finally

$$\boxed{\left(\frac{x_3^{\nu_3} x_4^{\nu_4}}{x_1^{\nu_1} x_2^{\nu_2}}\right)_{\epsilon = \epsilon_e} P^{\nu_3 + \nu_4 - \nu_1 - \nu_2} = K,}$$

which is called *the law of mass action.* K has the dimensions of pressure raised to the $(\nu_3 + \nu_4 - \nu_1 - \nu_2)$th power. The fraction involving the equilibrium values of the x's is a function of the equilibrium value of ϵ, that is, ϵ_e, and hence the law of mass action is seen to be a relation among ϵ_e, P, and T.

It is obvious that, if there are more than two initial constituents and two final constituents, the law of mass action becomes

$$\left(\frac{x_3^{\nu_3} x_4^{\nu_4} \cdots}{x_1^{\nu_1} x_2^{\nu_2} \cdots}\right)_{\epsilon=\epsilon_e} P^{\nu_3+\nu_4+\cdots-\nu_1-\nu_2-\cdots} = K,$$

where K is given by

$$\ln K = -(\nu_3\phi_3 + \nu_4\phi_4 + \cdots - \nu_1\phi_1 - \nu_2\phi_2 - \cdots).$$

18.2. Experimental Determination of Equilibrium Constants. It has been pointed out that a mixture of hydrogen and oxygen will remain indefinitely without reacting at atmospheric pressure and at room temperature. If, however, the temperature is raised considerably, water vapor forms and equilibrium takes place quickly. If, now, the mixture is cooled very suddenly so as not to disturb the equilibrium, an analysis of the composition of the mixture yields the values of the mole fractions corresponding to equilibrium at the high temperature. The equilibrium has, so to speak, been "frozen." Sometimes a flow method is used. The reacting gases are mixed in known proportions at a low temperature, and the mixture is caused to flow slowly through a long reacting tube at a desired temperature. The gases remain at this temperature a sufficient time for equilibrium to take place. The mixture is then allowed to flow through a capillary, where it is suddenly cooled. The equilibrium values of the mole fractions are then measured by the methods of chemical analysis.

It is a consequence of the law of mass action that the equilibrium constant corresponding to a given temperature is independent of the amounts of products which are originally mixed. For example, in the case of the "water-gas" reaction,

$$CO_2 + H_2 \rightleftharpoons CO + H_2O,$$

the law of mass action requires that, at equilibrium,

$$\frac{x_{CO} x_{H_2O}}{x_{CO_2} x_{H_2}} P^{1+1-1-1} = K$$

or

$$\frac{x_{CO} x_{H_2O}}{x_{CO_2} x_{H_2}} = \text{const.}$$

at a constant temperature, independent of the starting conditions. Starting with arbitrary amounts of CO_2 and H_2, and maintaining the temperature constant at $1259°K$, the equilibrium values of the mole fractions are given in Table 18.1, where it may be seen that K is quite constant.

TABLE 18.1. EQUILIBRIUM DATA FOR THE WATER-GAS REACTION
$CO_2 + H_2 \rightleftharpoons CO + H_2O$ at $1259°K$

Original mixture		Equilibrium mixture			$K = \dfrac{x_{CO}x_{H_2O}}{x_{CO_2}x_{H_2}}$
x_{CO_2}	x_{H_2}	x_{CO_2}	$x_{CO} = x_{H_2O}$	x_{H_2}	
0.101	0.899	0.0069	0.094	0.805	1.60
0.310	0.699	0.0715	0.2296	0.4693	1.58
0.491	0.509	0.2122	0.2790	0.2295	1.60
0.609	0.391	0.3443	0.2645	0.1267	1.60
0.703	0.297	0.4750	0.2282	0.0685	1.60

The water-gas reaction is an example of a reaction that does not involve a change in the total number of moles. If such a reaction were to take place at constant temperature and pressure, there would be no change in volume. There are, however, many reactions in which the total number of moles varies. In such cases, it is possible to measure the value of the degree of reaction at equilibrium by merely measuring the volume (or the density) of the mixture at equilibrium. If ϵ_e is known, the equilibrium constant can then be calculated. As an example of this procedure, consider the dissociation of nitrogen tetroxide according to the equation

$$N_2O_4 \rightleftharpoons 2NO_2.$$

If we start with n_0 moles of N_2O_4 at temperature T and pressure P, the initial volume V_0 is

$$V_0 = n_0 \frac{RT}{P}.$$

If V_e denotes the volume at equilibrium, the temperature and pressure remaining the same, then

$$V_e = [n_0(1 - \epsilon_e) + 2n_0\epsilon_e] \frac{RT}{P},$$

where ϵ_e is the value of the degree of dissociation at equilibrium. This can be written

$$V_e = (1 + \epsilon_e)V_0,$$

or

$$\epsilon_e = \frac{V_e}{V_0} - 1.$$

Since the density ρ is inversely proportional to the volume, we get finally

$$\epsilon_e = \frac{\rho_0}{\rho_e} - 1.$$

Now, at equilibrium,

$$x_{N_2O_4} = \frac{n_0(1 - \epsilon_e)}{n_0(1 + \epsilon_e)}, \qquad x_{NO_2} = \frac{2n_0\epsilon_e}{n_0(1 + \epsilon_e)},$$

and therefore the law of mass action becomes

$$\frac{\left(\dfrac{2\epsilon_e}{1+\epsilon_e}\right)^2}{\dfrac{1-\epsilon_e}{1+\epsilon_e}}\,P = K,$$

or

$$\frac{4\epsilon_e^2}{1-\epsilon_e^2}\,P = K.$$

The pressure is always measured in atmospheres. Numerical data for this reaction are given in Table 18.2, where it is seen that, at the constant temperature of 323°K, the equilibrium constant remains fairly constant for three different values of the pressure.

TABLE 18.2. $N_2O_4 \rightleftharpoons 2NO_2$

Temp., °K	P, atm	ρ_0 (air = 1)	ρ_e (air = 1)	$\epsilon_e = \dfrac{\rho_0}{\rho_e} - 1$	$K = \dfrac{4\epsilon_e^2}{1-\epsilon_e^2}P$, atm
	0.124	3.179	1.788	0.777	0.752
323	0.241	3.179	1.894	0.678	0.818
	0.655	3.179	2.144	0.483	0.797

There are many other methods of measuring equilibrium constants. For a complete account of this important branch of physical chemistry the student is referred to an advanced treatise.

18.3. Heat of Reaction. The equilibrium constant is defined by the equation

$$\ln K = -(\nu_3\phi_3 + \nu_4\phi_4 - \nu_1\phi_1 - \nu_2\phi_2).$$

Differentiating $\ln K$ with respect to T, we get

$$\frac{d}{dT}\ln K = -\left(\nu_3\frac{d\phi_3}{dT} + \nu_4\frac{d\phi_4}{dT} - \nu_1\frac{d\phi_1}{dT} - \nu_2\frac{d\phi_2}{dT}\right).$$

Since

$$\phi = \frac{h_0}{RT} - \frac{1}{R}\int\frac{\int c_P\,dT}{T^2}\,dT - \frac{s_0}{R},$$

we have

$$\frac{d\phi}{dT} = -\frac{h_0}{RT^2} - \frac{\int c_P\,dT}{RT^2}$$

$$= -\frac{1}{RT^2}\left(h_0 + \int c_P\,dT\right)$$

$$= -\frac{h}{RT^2}.$$

Therefore, $\dfrac{d}{dT} \ln K = \dfrac{1}{RT^2}\,(\nu_3 h_3 + \nu_4 h_4 - \nu_1 h_1 - \nu_2 h_2)$,

where all the h's refer to the same temperature T and the same pressure P. The right-hand term has a simple interpretation. If ν_1 moles of A_1 and ν_2 moles of A_2 are converted at constant temperature and pressure into ν_3 moles of A_3 and ν_4 moles of A_4, the heat transferred would be equal to the final enthalpy $\nu_3 h_3 + \nu_4 h_4$ minus the initial enthalpy $\nu_1 h_1 + \nu_2 h_2$. Calling this heat the *heat of reaction*, and denoting it by ΔH, we have

$$\Delta H = \nu_3 h_3 + \nu_4 h_4 - \nu_1 h_1 - \nu_2 h_2,$$

and

$$\boxed{\dfrac{d}{dT}\ln K = \dfrac{\Delta H}{RT^2}.}$$

The preceding equation is called the *van't Hoff isobar* and is one of the most important equations in chemical thermodynamics.

Rewriting the equation as follows

$$\frac{d \ln K}{dT/T^2} = \frac{\Delta H}{R},$$

or

$$\frac{d \ln K}{d\,\dfrac{1}{T}} = -\frac{\Delta H}{R},$$

we get

$$\Delta H = -2.30R\,\frac{d \log K}{d\,\dfrac{1}{T}}.$$

The van't Hoff isobar enables one to calculate the heat of reaction at any desired temperature or within any desired temperature range, once the temperature variation of the equilibrium constant is known. If only two values of K, say, K_1 and K_2, have been measured at two neighboring temperatures T_1 and T_2, the average heat of reaction within this temperature range is

$$\Delta H = -2.30R\,\frac{\log K_1 - \log K_2}{1/T_1 - 1/T_2}$$

$$= 4.573\,\frac{T_1 T_2}{T_1 - T_2}\log\frac{K_1}{K_2}.$$

For example, in the case of the dissociation of hydrogen iodide, the equilibrium constants are 0.02016 and 0.01642 at 730.8 and 666.8°K, respectively. The average heat of reaction within these two temperatures is therefore

$$\Delta H = \frac{4.573 \times 730.8 \times 666.8}{64} \log \frac{0.02016}{0.01642}$$
$$= 34{,}800 \times 0.08778$$
$$= 3050 \text{ cal to dissociate 2 moles of HI}$$
$$= 1525 \text{ cal/mole.}$$

If measurements of K are made at several different temperatures, the heat of reaction may be obtained more accurately by graphical means. Since

$$\Delta H = -4.573 \frac{d \log K}{d \frac{1}{T}},$$

it follows that the slope of the curve obtained by plotting $\log K$ against $1/T$, multiplied by 4.573, is the heat of reaction at the temperature corresponding to the point chosen. As a rule, $\log K$ can be measured only within a small temperature range, in which case the curve is usually a straight line. As an example of this procedure, consider the dissociation of water vapor according to the reaction

$$H_2O \rightleftharpoons H_2 + \tfrac{1}{2}O_2.$$

Starting with n_0 moles of water vapor and no hydrogen or oxygen, the mole fractions corresponding to any value ϵ of the degree of dissociation are shown in Table 17.1. At equilibrium,

$$\left(\frac{x_3^{\nu_3} x_4^{\nu_4}}{x_1^{\nu_1}}\right)_{\epsilon=\epsilon_e} P^{\nu_3+\nu_4-\nu_1} = K,$$

or

$$\frac{\dfrac{\epsilon_e}{1+\dfrac{\epsilon_e}{2}}\left(\dfrac{\dfrac{\epsilon_e}{2}}{1+\dfrac{\epsilon_e}{2}}\right)^{\tfrac{1}{2}}}{\dfrac{1+\epsilon_e}{1+\dfrac{\epsilon_e}{2}}} P^{\tfrac{1}{2}} = K,$$

or

$$\frac{\epsilon_e^{\tfrac{3}{2}}}{(2+\epsilon_e)^{\tfrac{1}{2}}(1-\epsilon_e)} P^{\tfrac{1}{2}} = K.$$

When ϵ_e is very much smaller than unity, this equation reduces to

$$K = \sqrt{\frac{\epsilon_e^3 P}{2}}.$$

In Table 18.3 experimental values of ϵ_e are given at a number of temperatures and at constant atmospheric pressure. along with the corresponding values of K, log K, and $1/T$. The graph of log K against $1/T$ is shown in Fig. 18.1, where it is seen that the points lie on a straight line with a slope equal to $-13,100$. It follows, therefore, that the heat of dissociation at the average temperature of about $1900°K$ is equal to

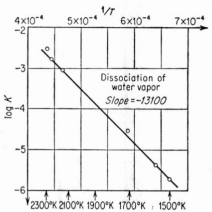

$$\Delta H = -4.573 \times -13,100$$
$$= 59,800 \text{ cal/mole.}$$

It is rather difficult to measure accurately the heat of reaction by a direct calorimetric method. Most heats of reaction are obtained either with the aid of the van't Hoff isobar or by means of a reversible cell. If ΔH is positive, the reaction is said to be *endothermic*; if negative, *exothermic*.

FIG. 18.1. Graph of log K against $1/T$ for the dissociation of water vapor.

18.4. Temperature Dependence of the Heat of Reaction. In a few cases in which it is possible to measure the equilibrium constant over a very wide temperature range, the graph of log K against $1/T$ is found to have a variable slope, indicating that the heat of reaction depends on the temperature. Such a graph, however, is impossible to obtain in most cases since, at low temperatures, a reaction either does not proceed or, if it does, the equilibrium value of the degree of reaction is too small to measure. Thus, in the case of the dissociation of water vapor, the degree of dissociation at room temperature and atmospheric pressure is

TABLE 18.3. $H_2O \rightleftharpoons H_2 + \frac{1}{2}O_2$ ($P = 1$ ATM)

Temp., °K	ϵ_e measured	$K = \dfrac{\epsilon_e^{3/2}P^{1/2}}{(2 + \epsilon_e)^{1/2}(1 - \epsilon_e)},$ (atm)$^{1/2}$	log K	$\dfrac{1}{T}$
1500	1.97×10^{-4}	1.95×10^{-6}	-5.71	6.67×10^{-4}
1561	$3.4 \ \times 10^{-4}$	4.48×10^{-5}	-5.36	6.41×10^{-4}
1705	$1.2 \ \times 10^{-3}$	2.95×10^{-5}	-4.53	5.87×10^{-4}
2155	$1.2 \ \times 10^{-2}$	$9.0 \ \times 10^{-4}$	-3.05	4.64×10^{-4}
2257	1.77×10^{-2}	1.67×10^{-3}	-2.78	4.43×10^{-4}
2300	$2.6 \ \times 10^{-2}$	2.95×10^{-3}	-2.53	4.35×10^{-4}

about 10^{-27}, which means that, under these conditions, not even one molecule of H_2O dissociates.

To obtain the heat of reaction at any desired temperature, it is necessary to know the temperature dependence of the heat capacities of all the reacting gases.   Since

$$\Delta H = \nu_3 h_3 + \nu_4 h_4 - \nu_1 h_1 - \nu_2 h_2,$$

and $$h = h_0 + \int c_P \, dT,$$

then

$$\Delta H = \nu_3 h_{03} + \nu_4 h_{04} - \nu_1 h_{01} - \nu_2 h_{02}$$
$$+ \int (\nu_3 c_{P3} + \nu_4 c_{P4} - \nu_1 c_{P1} - \nu_2 c_{P2}) \, dT.$$

Denoting the constant part by ΔH_0 thus,

$$\Delta H_0 = \nu_3 h_{03} + \nu_4 h_{04} - \nu_1 h_{01} - \nu_2 h_{02},$$

we get

$$\boxed{\Delta H = \Delta H_0 + \int (\nu_3 c_{P3} + \nu_4 c_{P4} - \nu_1 c_{P1} - \nu_2 c_{P2}) \, dT.}$$

The integral can be determined by substituting for the c_P's the empiric equations expressing their temperature dependence.   If, therefore, ΔH is known at one temperature, ΔH_0 can be calculated and the equation may be used to provide ΔH at any temperature.

For example, in the case of the dissociation of water vapor, approximate empiric expressions for the c_P's of H_2O, H_2, and O_2 are given in Art. 6.6.   After numerical substitution,

$$\Delta H = \Delta H_0 + 0.940T + 0.00165T^2 - 0.00000074T^3.$$

At $T = 1900°K$, $\Delta H = 59,800$ cal/mole.   Therefore,

$$\Delta H_0 = 59,800 - 1790 - 5960 + 5080$$
$$= 57,100 \text{ cal/mole.}$$

Therefore, the temperature dependence of the heat of dissociation of water vapor is given by the equation

$$\Delta H = 57,100 + 0.940T + 0.00165T^2 - 0.00000074T^3.$$

Values of ΔH_0 for the most fundamental ideal gas reactions are given in Table 18.6.

Some chemical reactions may be expressed as the result of two or more reactions.   If ΔH_0 is known for each of the separate reactions, then the ΔH_0 of the resultant reaction may be calculated.   For example,

$$h_0(H_2) + \tfrac{1}{2}h_0(O_2) - h_0(H_2O) = 57,100,$$
$$h_0(CO) + \tfrac{1}{2}h_0(O_2) - h_0(CO_2) = 66,800,$$

and, by subtracting one equation from the other,

$$h_0(CO_2) + h_0(H_2) - h_0(CO) - h_0(H_2O) = -9700.$$

In standard chemical notation this is written

$$H_2O \rightleftharpoons H_2 + \tfrac{1}{2}O_2 \qquad \Delta H_0 = 57,100$$
$$\underline{CO_2 \rightleftharpoons CO + \tfrac{1}{2}O_2 \qquad \Delta H_0 = 66,800}$$
$$CO + H_2O \rightleftharpoons CO_2 + H_2 \qquad \Delta H_0 = -9,700.$$

It is obvious that ΔH at any convenient temperature such as ΔH_{298} may be treated in the same way.

18.5. Temperature Dependence of the Equilibrium Constant. The equilibrium constant is defined by the equation

$$\ln K = -(\nu_3\phi_3 + \nu_4\phi_4 - \nu_1\phi_1 - \nu_2\phi_2),$$

where
$$\phi = \frac{h_0}{RT} - \frac{1}{R}\int \frac{\int c_P\, dT}{T^2}\, dT - \frac{s_0}{R}.$$

We have, therefore,

$$\ln K = -\frac{1}{RT}\left(\nu_3 h_{03} + \nu_4 h_{04} - \nu_1 h_{01} - \nu_2 h_{02}\right)$$

$$+ \frac{1}{R}\int \frac{\int (\nu_3 c_{P3} + \nu_4 c_{P4} - \nu_1 c_{P1} - \nu_2 c_{P2})\, dT}{T^2}\, dT$$

$$+ \frac{1}{R}\left(\nu_3 s_{03} + \nu_4 s_{04} - \nu_1 s_{01} - \nu_2 s_{02}\right).$$

Recognizing that

$$\Delta H_0 = \nu_3 h_{03} + \nu_4 h_{04} - \nu_1 h_{01} - \nu_2 h_{02}$$

and setting

$$\Delta S_0 = \nu_3 s_{03} + \nu_4 s_{04} - \nu_1 s_{01} - \nu_2 s_{02},$$

the equation becomes

$$\boxed{\begin{aligned} \ln K = \\ -\frac{\Delta H_0}{RT} + \frac{1}{R}\int \frac{\int (\nu_3 c_{P3} + \nu_4 c_{P4} - \nu_1 c_{P1} - \nu_2 c_{P2})\, dT}{T^2}\, dT + \frac{\Delta S_0}{R}, \end{aligned}}$$

which is sometimes known as *Nernst's equation*.

As an example of the use of Nernst's equation, consider the dissociation of water vapor. After numerical substitution, we get

$$R \ln K = -\frac{\Delta H_0}{T} + 0.940 \ln T + 0.00165 T - 0.00000037 T^2 + \Delta S_0.$$

From Table 18.3 we find that, at $2155°K$,

$$\ln K = -2.30 \times 3.05,$$

and, from the preceding article, $\Delta H_0 = 57,100$. When these values are substituted in the preceding equation, the unknown constant ΔS_0 is found to be 3.50.   Therefore, the equilibrium constant for the dissociation of water vapor may be calculated at any temperature from the equation

$$R \ln K = -\frac{57,100}{T} + 0.940 \ln T + 0.00165T - 0.00000037T^2 + 3.50.$$

Using this equation, we find that, at 298°K, $\ln K = -93.7$.   We shall see in the next article why it is important to know the value of $\ln K_{298}$ for all reactions.

An interesting application of Nernst's equation was made by Megh Nad Saha to the thermal ionization of a monatomic gas.   If a monatomic gas is heated to a high enough temperature, some ionization occurs and the atoms, ions, and electrons may be regarded as a mixture of three

TABLE 18.4. $A \rightleftharpoons A^+ + e$

A	ν	n	x
$A_1 = A$	$\nu_1 = 1$	$n_1 = n_0(1 - \epsilon_e)$	$x_1 = \dfrac{1 - \epsilon_e}{1 + \epsilon_e}$
$A_3 = A^+$	$\nu_3 = 1$	$n_3 = n_0\epsilon_e$	$x_3 = \dfrac{\epsilon_e}{1 + \epsilon_e}$
$A_4 = e$	$\nu_4 = 1$	$n_4 = n_0\epsilon_e$	$x_4 = \dfrac{\epsilon_e}{1 + \epsilon_e}$
	$\nu_3 + \nu_4 - \nu_1 = 1$	$\Sigma n = n_0(1 + \epsilon_e)$	

ideal monatomic gases, undergoing the reaction

$$A \rightleftharpoons A^+ + e.$$

Starting with n_0 moles of atoms alone, the state of affairs at equilibrium is shown in Table 18.4.   For this reaction,

$$\ln K = \ln \frac{x_3^{\nu_3} x_4^{\nu_4}}{x_1^{\nu_1}} P^{\nu_3 + \nu_4 - \nu_1}$$

$$= \ln \frac{\dfrac{\epsilon_e}{1 + \epsilon_e} \dfrac{\epsilon_e}{1 + \epsilon_e}}{\dfrac{1 - \epsilon_e}{1 + \epsilon_e}} P,$$

or
$$\ln K = \ln \frac{\epsilon_e^2}{1 - \epsilon_e^2} P. \qquad (1)$$

It can be shown that ΔH_0 is the amount of energy necessary to ionize 1 mole of atoms.   If we denote the ionization potential of the atom in volts by E, then

$$\Delta H_0 = \frac{E(\text{volts}) \times 1.59 \times 10^{-19} \dfrac{\text{coulomb}}{\text{electron}} \times 6.06 \times 10^{23} \dfrac{\text{electrons}}{\text{mole}}}{4.19 \dfrac{\text{joule}}{\text{cal}}}$$

$$= 23{,}070E \text{ cal/mole.} \tag{2}$$

Since the three gases are monatomic, each c_P is equal to $\frac{5}{2}R$. Therefore, $\nu_3 c_{P3} + \nu_4 c_{P4} - \nu_1 c_{P1} = \frac{5}{2}R$, and

$$\frac{1}{R} \int \frac{\int (\nu_3 c_{P3} + \nu_4 c_{P4} - \nu_1 c_{P1})\, dT}{T^2}\, dT = \frac{5}{2}\ln T. \tag{3}$$

Let us put

$$\frac{\Delta S_0}{R} = \ln B. \tag{4}$$

Introducing the results (1), (2), (3), and (4) into Nernst's equation, we get

$$\ln \frac{\epsilon_e^2}{1 - \epsilon_e^2} P = -\frac{23{,}070E}{RT} + \frac{5}{2}\ln T + \ln B.$$

Expressing P in atmospheres, changing to common logarithms, and introducing the value of B from statistical mechanics, Saha finally obtained the formula

$$\log \frac{\epsilon_e^2}{1 - \epsilon_e^2} P(\text{atm}) = -\frac{23{,}070E}{4.573T} + \frac{5}{2}\log T + \log \frac{\omega_i \omega_e}{\omega_a} - 6.491,$$

where ω_i, ω_e, and ω_a are constants that refer, respectively, to the ion, the electron, and the atom.

In order to apply Saha's equation to a specific problem, it is necessary to know the ionization potential and the ω's. A complete discussion of these quantities is beyond the scope of this book. Values of these constants for a few elements are listed in Table 18.5. The constant ω for an electron is 2. Saha applied his equation to the determination of the temperature of a stellar atmosphere. The spectrum of a star con-

TABLE 18.5. VALUES OF E AND ω

Element	E, volts	ω_a	ω_i
Na	5.12	2	1
Cs	3.87	2	1
Ca	6.09	1	2
Cd	8.96	1	2
Zn	9.36	1	2
Tl	6.07	2	1

tains lines which originate from atoms (arc lines) and also those which originate from ions (spark lines). A comparison of the intensity of a spark line with that of an arc line, both referring to the same element, gives rise to a value of the degree of ionization ϵ_e. Treating a star as a sphere of ideal gas, it is possible to obtain an estimate of the pressure of a stellar atmosphere. Since all the other quantities are known, the temperature can be calculated.

18.6. Gibbs Function Change.   It was shown in Art. 17.5 that the molar Gibbs function of an ideal gas at the temperature T and pressure P is equal to

$$g = RT(\phi + \ln P).$$

If we have four gases that can engage in the reaction

$$\nu_1 A_1 + \nu_2 A_2 \rightleftharpoons \nu_3 A_3 + \nu_4 A_4,$$

we define the Gibbs function change of the reaction ΔG by the expression

$$\Delta G = \nu_3 g_3 + \nu_4 g_4 - \nu_1 g_1 - \nu_2 g_2,$$

where the g's refer to the gases completely separated at T, P. It should be emphasized that ΔG is defined in terms of the separate Gibbs functions of the gases, not in terms of the mixture. Among American chemists ΔG is known as the *free-energy change*. The connection between ΔG and the behavior of the gases when mixed is shown by introducing the values of the g's. Thus,

$$\Delta G = RT(\nu_3 \phi_3 + \nu_4 \phi_4 - \nu_1 \phi_1 - \nu_2 \phi_2) + RT \ln P^{\nu_3 + \nu_4 - \nu_1 - \nu_2}.$$

But $\ln K = -(\nu_3 \phi_3 + \nu_4 \phi_4 - \nu_1 \phi_1 - \nu_2 \phi_2).$

Therefore, $\Delta G = -RT \ln K + RT \ln P^{\nu_3 + \nu_4 - \nu_1 - \nu_2}.$

The student will recall that K also contains the factor P raised to the $(\nu_3 + \nu_4 - \nu_1 - \nu_2)$th power. It follows, therefore, that the above equation will be satisfied when both P's are measured in the same units, whatever the units are. If we express P as usual in atmospheres and calculate ΔG when each gas is at a pressure of 1 atm, the second term on the right drops out. Under these conditions ΔG is known as the *standard Gibbs function change* and is denoted by $\Delta G°$. Therefore,

$$\boxed{\Delta G° = -RT \ln K.}$$

To calculate $\Delta G°$ at a low temperature such as 298°K, we may proceed in either of two ways.

1. Use Nernst's equation to calculate $\ln K_{298}$, and then multiply by $-RT$. Thus, in the case of the dissociation of water vapor, $\ln K_{298}$ was found to be -93.7. Therefore,

$$\Delta G°_{298} = -1.986 \times 298 \times -93.7$$
$$= 55,500 \text{ cal/mole.}$$

2. Introduce into the equation $\Delta G° = -RT \ln K$ the value of $\ln K$ given by Nernst's equation, thereby obtaining the equation

$$\Delta G° = \Delta H_0 - T \int \frac{\int (\nu_3 c_{P3} + \nu_4 c_{P4} - \nu_1 c_{P1} - \nu_2 c_{P2})\, dT}{T^2}\, dT - T\,\Delta S_0$$

from which $\Delta G°$ may be calculated directly, once the constant ΔS_0 has been determined. In the case of the dissociation of water vapor, this equation becomes

$$\Delta G° = 57{,}100 - 0.940T \ln T - 0.00165T^2 + 0.00000037T^3 - 3.50T.$$

Similar equations have been obtained for other reactions, and values of ΔS_0 and $\Delta G°_{298}$ have been computed. Values of ΔH_0, ΔS_0, and $\Delta G°_{298}$ for the most fundamental ideal gas reactions are given in Table 18.6.

TABLE 18.6. FUNDAMENTAL IDEAL GAS REACTIONS

Reaction	ΔH_0, cal/mole	ΔS_0, cal/mole · deg	$\Delta G°_{298}$, cal/mole
$H_2 \rightleftharpoons 2H$	102,000	1.17	96,500
$HCl \rightleftharpoons \frac{1}{2}H_2 + \frac{1}{2}Cl_2$	21,900	-5.31	22,700
$HBr \rightleftharpoons \frac{1}{2}H_2 + \frac{1}{2}Br_2$	12,000	-5.74	12,900
$HI \rightleftharpoons \frac{1}{2}H_2 + \frac{1}{2}I_2$	1,270	-5.01	2,000
$HO \rightleftharpoons \frac{1}{2}N_2 + \frac{1}{2}O_2$	-21,600	-2.50	-20,900
$H_2O \rightleftharpoons H_2 + \frac{1}{2}O_2$	57,100	3.50	55,500
$H_2S \rightleftharpoons H_2 + \frac{1}{2}S_2$	19,200	1.65	17,000
$CO_2 \rightleftharpoons CO + \frac{1}{2}O_2$	66,800	4.46	61,800
$NO_2 \rightleftharpoons NO + \frac{1}{2}O_2$	14,200	2.73	8,900
$SO_2 \rightleftharpoons \frac{1}{2}S_2 + O_2$	83,300	0.9	78,600
$NH_3 \rightleftharpoons \frac{1}{2}N_2 + \frac{3}{2}H_2$	9,500	9.61	3,910
$SO_2 \rightleftharpoons SO_2 + \frac{1}{2}O_2$	22,600	21.36	16,200
$N_2O_4 \rightleftharpoons 2NO_2$	13,600	41.6	1,200

Both ΔS_0 and $\Delta G°_{298}$ may be added and subtracted in the same manner as ΔH_0. For example,

$$\begin{array}{ll} H_2O \rightleftharpoons H_2 + \frac{1}{2}O_2 & \Delta G°_{298} = 55{,}500 \\ CO_2 \rightleftharpoons CO + \frac{1}{2}O_2 & \Delta G°_{298} = 61{,}800 \\ \hline CO + H_2O \rightleftharpoons CO_2 + H_2 & \Delta G°_{298} = -6300. \end{array}$$

Therefore, for the resultant reaction,

$$\ln K_{298} = \frac{-\Delta G°_{298}}{RT} = \frac{6300}{1.986 \times 298} = 10.64,$$

and $K_{298} = 42{,}700$, from which the value of the degree of reaction at equilibrium may be calculated. Therefore, if the ΔG's of some reactions are known, the exact behavior of other reactions may be calculated.

18.7. Affinity. Let us imagine that ν_1 moles of A_1 and ν_2 moles of A_2 are mixed at uniform temperature T and pressure P and that chemical reaction takes place, thereby forming constituents A_3 and A_4. At any moment, when the degree of reaction is ϵ, the Gibbs function of the mixture is

$$G = \mu_1 n_1 + \mu_2 n_2 + \mu_3 n_3 + \mu_4 n_4,$$

where
$$n_1 = \nu_1(1 - \epsilon), \qquad n_3 = \nu_3 \epsilon,$$
$$n_2 = \nu_2(1 - \epsilon), \qquad n_4 = \nu_4 \epsilon,$$

and each chemical potential is a function of T, P, and ϵ. It follows that

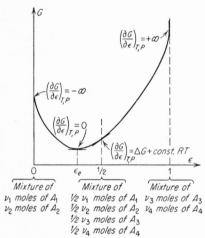

G is a function of T, P, and ϵ, and therefore, at constant T and P, G is a function of ϵ only. The graph of G against ϵ has somewhat the form shown in Fig. 18.2.

At the equilibrium point where $\epsilon = \epsilon_e$, the curve has a minimum at which

$$\left(\frac{\partial G}{\partial \epsilon}\right)_{T,P} = 0 \qquad (\text{at } \epsilon = \epsilon_e).$$

FIG. 18.2. Graph of G against ϵ at constant T and P.

The slopes of the curve at the points $\epsilon = 0$ and $\epsilon = 1$ may be calculated from the equation derived in Art. 17.12, namely,

$$dG_{T,P} = (n_0 + n_0')(\nu_3\mu_3 + \nu_4\mu_4 - \nu_1\mu_1 - \nu_2\mu_2)\, d\epsilon,$$

which becomes in this case

$$\left(\frac{\partial G}{\partial \epsilon}\right)_{T,P} = \nu_3\mu_3 + \nu_4\mu_4 - \nu_1\mu_1 - \nu_2\mu_2.$$

Since
$$\mu_k = RT(\phi_k + \ln P + \ln x_k),$$
and
$$g_k = RT(\phi_k + \ln P),$$

the chemical potential may be written in the convenient form

$$\mu_k = g_k + RT \ln x_k.$$

Therefore,

$$\left(\frac{\partial G}{\partial \epsilon}\right)_{T,P} = \nu_3 g_3 + \nu_4 g_4 - \nu_1 g_1 - \nu_2 g_2$$
$$+ RT(\nu_3 \ln x_3 + \nu_4 \ln x_4 - \nu_1 \ln x_1 - \nu_2 \ln x_2)$$

or
$$\left(\frac{\partial G}{\partial \epsilon}\right)_{T,P} = \Delta G + RT \ln \frac{x_3^{\nu_3} x_4^{\nu_4}}{x_1^{\nu_1} x_2^{\nu_2}}.$$

It should be borne in mind that the x's in this equation are not equilibrium values but correspond to *any* value of ϵ. Now, when $\epsilon = 0$, there are no final constituents, and therefore both x_3 and x_4 are zero. Hence,

$$\left(\frac{\partial G}{\partial \epsilon}\right)_{T,P} = -\infty \qquad (\text{at } \epsilon = 0).$$

On the other hand, when $\epsilon = 1$, there are no initial constituents and therefore x_1 and x_2 are zero. Hence,

$$\left(\frac{\partial G}{\partial \epsilon}\right)_{T,P} = +\infty \qquad (\text{at } \epsilon = 1).$$

The graph in Fig. 18.2 has these properties.

Consider the point $\epsilon = \frac{1}{2}$ at which there are $\nu_1/2$ moles of A_1, $\nu_2/2$ moles of A_2, $\nu_3/2$ moles of A_3, and $\nu_4/2$ moles of A_4. At this point the constituents are present in proportion to their stoichiometric coefficients, and the mole fractions are

$$x_1 = \frac{\nu_1}{\Sigma\nu}, \qquad x_3 = \frac{\nu_3}{\Sigma\nu},$$

$$x_2 = \frac{\nu_2}{\Sigma\nu}, \qquad x_4 = \frac{\nu_4}{\Sigma\nu}.$$

The slope of the curve at this point indicates whether such a mixture is in equilibrium or not. If this slope is positive, the equilibrium point is to the left; i.e., when both the initial and final constituents are mixed, there will be a tendency for the reaction to proceed to the left, causing initial constituents to be formed. Conversely, if the slope of the curve at $\epsilon = \frac{1}{2}$ is negative, the equilibrium point is to the right; or when both initial and final constituents are mixed, there will be a tendency for the reaction to proceed to the right, causing final constituents to be formed. Finally, if this slope is zero, a mixture of both initial and final constituents is in equilibrium, and there is no tendency for the reaction to proceed at all.

It is seen, therefore, that the *sign* of the slope of the G-ϵ curve at $\epsilon = \frac{1}{2}$ is an indication of the behavior of a system composed of initial and final constituents mixed in proportion to their stoichiometric coefficients. Furthermore, it is obvious from the curve that the *magnitude* of this slope is a measure of the departure from or nearness to equilibrium of such a mixture. We shall call the slope of the G-ϵ curve at the point $\epsilon = \frac{1}{2}$ the *affinity* of the reaction, which is equal to

$$\left(\frac{\partial G}{\partial \epsilon}\right)_{T,P} (\epsilon = \tfrac{1}{2}) = \Delta G + RT \ln \frac{\left(\dfrac{\nu_3}{\Sigma\nu}\right)^{\nu_3}\left(\dfrac{\nu_4}{\Sigma\nu}\right)^{\nu_4}}{\left(\dfrac{\nu_1}{\Sigma\nu}\right)^{\nu_1}\left(\dfrac{\nu_2}{\Sigma\nu}\right)^{\nu_2}}.$$

This equation is true at all temperatures and pressures. Let us choose $T = 298°K$ and $P = 1$ atm. Then,

$$\frac{\partial G}{\partial \epsilon}\begin{bmatrix} \epsilon = \tfrac{1}{2} \\ T = 298°K \\ P = 1\,\text{atm} \end{bmatrix} = \Delta G^{\circ}_{298} + 1.986 \times 298 \ln \frac{\left(\dfrac{\nu_3}{\Sigma\nu}\right)^{\nu_3}\left(\dfrac{\nu_4}{\Sigma\nu}\right)^{\nu_4}}{\left(\dfrac{\nu_1}{\Sigma\nu}\right)^{\nu_1}\left(\dfrac{\nu_2}{\Sigma\nu}\right)^{\nu_3}}.$$

The last term on the right is a constant for each reaction. In the case of the dissociation of water vapor and also the dissociation of CO_2, it is equal to -477. When all the ν's are unity, it is zero. In general, its value is less than 500 cal, whereas it can be seen from Table 18.6 that ΔG°_{298} is usually many thousands of calories. Consequently, ΔG°_{298} has much more effect on the quantity $\partial G/\partial \epsilon$ than the other term. We may therefore write

$$\frac{\partial G}{\partial \epsilon}\begin{bmatrix} \epsilon = \tfrac{1}{2} \\ T = 298°K \\ P = 1\,\text{atm} \end{bmatrix} \sim \Delta G^{\circ}_{298}.$$

Therefore *the standard Gibbs function change at 298°K is an indication of the direction and amount to which a reaction will proceed at this temperature.* For example, since ΔG°_{298} for the water-vapor reaction is a large positive number, this means that the equilibrium point is far to the left of $\epsilon = \tfrac{1}{2}$ and therefore ϵ_e is very small. Again, since ΔG°_{298} is a large negative number for the reaction $NO \rightleftharpoons \tfrac{1}{2}N_2 + \tfrac{1}{2}O_2$, it follows that the equilibrium point is far to the right of $\epsilon = \tfrac{1}{2}$, and therefore ϵ_e is almost unity.

18.8. Displacement of Equilibrium Due to a Change in Temperature or Pressure. The equilibrium value of the degree of reaction was obtained by setting $(\partial G/\partial \epsilon)_{T,P}$ equal to zero. This, however, is the condition that G be a maximum as well as a minimum. In order to verify that G is a minimum, it is necessary to show that $(\partial^2 G/\partial \epsilon^2)_{T,P}$ is positive at the equilibrium point. For a mixture of arbitrary amounts of four chemically active ideal gases, we have

$$\left(\frac{\partial G}{\partial \epsilon}\right)_{T,P} = (n_0 + n_0')\left(\Delta G + RT \ln \frac{x_3^{\nu_3}x_4^{\nu_4}}{x_1^{\nu_1}x_2^{\nu_2}}\right)$$

for all values of ϵ. Therefore, since ΔG is a function of T and P only,

$$\left(\frac{\partial^2 G}{\partial \epsilon^2}\right)_{T,P} = (n_0 + n_0')RT \frac{d}{d\epsilon}\ln \frac{x_3^{\nu_3}x_4^{\nu_4}}{x_1^{\nu_1}x_2^{\nu_2}}.$$

The right-hand member of this equation can be easily evaluated for any value of ϵ [the details of this calculation constitute Prob. 18.14(a)], and is found to be

$$\frac{d}{d\epsilon} \ln \frac{x_3^{\nu_3} x_4^{\nu_4}}{x_1^{\nu_1} x_2^{\nu_2}} = \frac{n_0 + n_0'}{\Sigma n_k} \left[\frac{\nu_1^2}{x_1} + \frac{\nu_2^2}{x_2} + \frac{\nu_3^2}{x_3} + \frac{\nu_4^2}{x_4} - (\Delta\nu)^2 \right],$$

where $\Delta\nu = \nu_3 + \nu_4 - \nu_1 - \nu_2$. It may be proved rigorously that the expression in brackets is positive for all values of the ν's and x's. The proof, however, is rather lengthy. If we do not insist upon complete generality but choose as starting conditions $n_0\nu_1$ moles of A_1 and $n_0\nu_2$ moles of A_2, with no amount of A_3 and A_4, then the preceding equation reduces to the simple form [this calculation constitutes Prob. 18.14(c)]

$$\frac{d}{d\epsilon} \ln \frac{x_3^{\nu_3} x_4^{\nu_4}}{x_1^{\nu_1} x_2^{\nu_2}} = \frac{n_0}{\Sigma n_k} \frac{(\nu_1 + \nu_2)(\nu_3 + \nu_4)}{\epsilon(1 - \epsilon)}.$$

Since the right-hand member of this equation is always positive for all ν's and all values of ϵ, it follows that $(\partial^2 G/\partial\epsilon^2)_{T,P}$ is always positive and hence, when $\epsilon = \epsilon_e$, G is a minimum and not a maximum. It will be seen that this plays an important role in determining the displacement of equilibrium when the temperature or the pressure is changed.

Let us consider first the effect on the equilibrium value of the degree of reaction of a change of temperature at constant pressure. We know that at equilibrium the law of mass action provides us with a relation among T, ϵ_e, and P, which may be written in the form

$$\ln K = \ln \left(\frac{x_3^{\nu_3} x_4^{\nu_4}}{x_1^{\nu_1} x_2^{\nu_2}} \right)_{\epsilon = \epsilon_0} + (\nu_3 + \nu_4 - \nu_1 - \nu_2) \ln P,$$

where $\ln K$ is a function of T only and the first term on the right is a function of ϵ_e only. Now,

$$\left(\frac{\partial\epsilon_e}{\partial T} \right)_P = \left(\frac{\partial\epsilon_e}{\partial \ln K} \right)_P \left(\frac{\partial \ln K}{\partial T} \right)_P$$

$$= \frac{\dfrac{d \ln K}{dT}}{\left(\dfrac{\partial \ln K}{\partial\epsilon_e} \right)_P}.$$

Using the van't Hoff isobar to evaluate the numerator and the law of mass action to evaluate the denominator, we get

$$\boxed{\left(\frac{\partial\epsilon_e}{\partial T} \right)_P = \frac{\Delta H}{RT^2 \dfrac{d}{d\epsilon_e} \ln \dfrac{x_3^{\nu_3} x_4^{\nu_4}}{x_1^{\nu_1} x_2^{\nu_2}}}.} \tag{1}$$

Since we have already mentioned that the denominator on the right is positive, it follows that the sign of $(\partial\epsilon_e/\partial T)_P$ is determined by the sign of ΔH. Therefore, *an increase of temperature at constant pressure causes a shift in the equilibrium value of the degree of reaction in the direction in which the heat of reaction is absorbed.*

To determine the effect of a change of pressure at constant temperature, we write

$$\left(\frac{\partial \epsilon_e}{\partial P}\right)_T = -\left(\frac{\partial \epsilon_e}{\partial \ln K}\right)_P \left(\frac{\partial \ln K}{\partial P}\right)_{\epsilon_e}$$

$$= -\frac{\left(\dfrac{\partial \ln K}{\partial P}\right)_{\epsilon_e}}{\left(\dfrac{\partial \ln K}{\partial \epsilon_e}\right)_P}.$$

Using the law of mass action to evaluate both numerator and denominator, we get

$$\left(\frac{\partial \epsilon_e}{\partial P}\right)_T = -\frac{\nu_3 + \nu_4 - \nu_1 - \nu_2}{P \dfrac{d}{d\epsilon_e} \ln \dfrac{x_3^{\nu_3} x_4^{\nu_4}}{x_1^{\nu_1} x_2^{\nu_2}}}. \tag{2}$$

The numerator on the right is proportional to the change in the number of moles of the constituents as the reaction proceeds to the right. If it is positive, this means that the volume increases at constant T and P. Therefore, *an increase of pressure at constant temperature causes a shift in the equilibrium value of the degree of reaction in the direction in which a decrease of volume takes place.*

18.9. Heat Capacity of Reacting Gases in Equilibrium. Let us consider, as usual, a mixture of arbitrary amounts of four ideal gases capable of undergoing the reaction

$$\nu_1 A_1 + \nu_2 A_2 \rightleftharpoons \nu_3 A_3 + \nu_4 A_4.$$

At equilibrium, the enthalpy of the mixture is

$$H = \Sigma n_k h_k$$

where

$$n_1 = (n_0 + n_0')\nu_1(1 - \epsilon_e), \qquad n_3 = (n_0 + n_0')\nu_3\epsilon_e,$$
$$n_2 = (n_0 + n_0')\nu_2(1 - \epsilon_e) + N_2, \qquad n_4 = (n_0 + n_0')\nu_4\epsilon_e + N_4,$$

and ϵ_e is the equilibrium value of the degree of reaction. Suppose that an infinitesimal change of temperature takes place *at constant pressure* in such a way that equilibrium is maintained. Then ϵ_e will change to the value $\epsilon_e + d\epsilon_e$, and the enthalpy will change by the amount

$$dH_P = \Sigma n_k \, dh_k + \Sigma h_k \, dn_k.$$

Since $dh_k = c_{Pk} \, dT$ and $dn_k = \pm (n_0 + n_0')\nu_k \, d\epsilon_e$,

$$dH_P = \Sigma n_k c_{Pk} \, dT + (n_0 + n_0')(\nu_3 h_3 + \nu_4 h_4 - \nu_1 h_1 - \nu_2 h_2) \, d\epsilon_e,$$

and the heat capacity of the reacting gas mixture is

$$C_P = \left(\frac{\partial H}{\partial T}\right)_P = \sum n_k c_{Pk} + (n_0 + n_0') \Delta H \left(\frac{\partial \epsilon_e}{\partial T}\right)_P.$$

From the preceding article,

$$\left(\frac{\partial \epsilon_e}{\partial T}\right)_P = \frac{\Delta H}{RT^2 \dfrac{d}{d\epsilon_e} \ln \dfrac{x_3^{\nu_3} x_4^{\nu_4}}{x_1^{\nu_1} x_2^{\nu_2}}},$$

and consequently

$$C_P = \sum n_k c_{Pk} + (n_0 + n_0') \frac{(\Delta H)^2}{RT^2 \dfrac{d}{d\epsilon_e} \ln \dfrac{x_3^{\nu_3} x_4^{\nu_4}}{x_1^{\nu_1} x_2^{\nu_2}}}.$$

As an example, consider the equilibrium mixture of H_2O vapor, H_2, and, O_2 caused by the dissociation of 1 mole of H_2O at 1 atm and 1900°K. We have $n_0 = 1$, $n_0' = 0$, $\Delta H = 59{,}800$ cal/mole, $R = 1.99$ cal/mole · deg, $\epsilon_e = 3.2 \times 10^{-3}$, $\Sigma n_k = n_0(1 + \epsilon_e/2)$, $\nu_1 = 1$, $\nu_2 = 0$, $\nu_3 = 1$, $\nu_4 = \frac{1}{2}$, and

$$\frac{d}{d\epsilon_e} \ln \frac{x_3^{\nu_3} x_4^{\nu_4}}{x_1^{\nu_1} x_2^{\nu_2}} = \frac{n_0}{\Sigma n_k} \frac{(\nu_1 + \nu_2)(\nu_3 + \nu_4)}{\epsilon_e(1 - \epsilon_e)}.$$

Hence

$$\begin{aligned}
C_P - \sum n_k c_{Pk} &= \frac{(\Delta H)^2(1 + \epsilon_e/2)\epsilon_e(1 - \epsilon_e)}{RT^2(\nu_1 + \nu_2)(\nu_3 + \nu_4)} \\
&= \frac{(59{,}800)^2 \times 3.2 \times 10^{-3}}{1.99 \times (1900)^2 \times \frac{3}{2}} \\
&= 1.03 \text{ cal/deg.}
\end{aligned}$$

PROBLEMS

18.1. Show that the law of mass action may be written

$$\frac{p_3^{\nu_3} p_4^{\nu_4}}{p_1^{\nu_1} p_2^{\nu_2}} = K,$$

where the p's are the equilibrium values of the partial pressures.

18.2. Starting with n_0 moles of NO, which dissociates according to the equation $NO \rightleftharpoons \frac{1}{2}N_2 + \frac{1}{2}O_2$, show that at equilibrium

$$K = \frac{1}{2} \frac{\epsilon_e}{1 - \epsilon_e}.$$

18.3. Starting with n_0 moles of NH_3, which dissociates according to the equation $NH_3 \rightleftharpoons \frac{1}{2}N_2 + \frac{3}{2}H_2$, show that at equilibrium

$$K = \frac{\sqrt{27}}{4} \frac{\epsilon_e^2}{1 - \epsilon_e^2} P.$$

18.4. A mixture of $n_0\nu_1$ moles of A_1 and $n_0\nu_2$ moles of A_2 at temperature T and pressure P occupies a volume V_0. When the reaction

$$\nu_1 A_1 + \nu_2 A_2 \rightleftharpoons \nu_3 A_3 + \nu_4 A_4$$

has come to equilibrium at the same T and P, the volume is V_e. Show that

$$\epsilon_e = \frac{V_e - V_0}{V_0}\,\frac{\nu_1 + \nu_2}{\nu_3 + \nu_4 - \nu_1 - \nu_2}.$$

18.5. At 35°C and 1 atm the degree of dissociation of N_2O_4 at equilibrium is 0.27.
(a) Calculate K.
(b) Calculate ϵ_e at the same temperature when the pressure is 100 mm.
(c) The equilibrium constant for the dissociation of N_2O_4 has the values 0.664 and 0.141 at the temperatures 318 and 298°K, respectively. Calculate the average heat of reaction within this temperature range.

18.6. The equilibrium constant of the reaction $SO_3 \rightleftharpoons SO_2 + \frac{1}{2}O_2$ has the following values:

Kelvin temperature	800	900	1000	1105
Equilibrium constant	0.0319	0.153	0.540	1.59

Determine the average heat of dissociation graphically.

18.7. Calculate the degree of ionization of cesium vapor at 10^{-6} atm at the two temperatures 2260 and 2520°K.

18.8. Calculate the degree of ionization of calcium vapor in the sun's chromosphere. The temperature and pressure of the sun's chromosphere are approximately 6000°K and 10^{-10} atm, respectively.

18.9. (a) Show that

$$\Delta G = \Delta H + T\left(\frac{\partial \Delta G}{\partial T}\right)_P.$$

(b) Show that

$$\Delta G = -RT \ln \frac{x_3^{\nu_3} x_4^{\nu_4}}{x_1^{\nu_1} x_2^{\nu_2}}$$

where the x's are equilibrium values.

18.10. Calculate the heat capacity of the equilibrium mixture of Prob. 18.7 at the temperature of 2260°K.

18.11. When 1 mole of HI dissociates according to the reaction

$$HI \rightleftharpoons \tfrac{1}{2}H_2 + \tfrac{1}{2}I_2$$

at $T = 675$°K, $K = 0.0174$, and $\Delta H = 1410$ cal/mole. Calculate $(\partial \epsilon_e/\partial T)_P$ at this temperature.

18.12. Starting with ν_1 moles of A_1 and ν_2 moles of A_2, show that
(a) At any value of ϵ,

$$G = \epsilon(\nu_3\mu_3 + \nu_4\mu_4 - \nu_1\mu_1 - \nu_2\mu_2) + \nu_1\mu_1 + \nu_2\mu_2.$$

(b) At equilibrium,

$$G(\text{min}) = \nu_1\mu_{1e} + \nu_2\mu_{2e},$$

where the subscript e denotes an equilibrium value,

(c) $\dfrac{G - G(\text{min})}{RT} = \epsilon \left(\ln \dfrac{x_3^{\nu_3} x_4^{\nu_4}}{x_1^{\nu_1} x_2^{\nu_2}} - \ln \dfrac{x_{3e}^{\nu_3} x_{4e}^{\nu_4}}{x_{1e}^{\nu_1} x_{2e}^{\nu_2}} \right) + \ln x_1^{\nu_1} x_2^{\nu_2} - \ln x_{1e}^{\nu_1} x_{2e}^{\nu_2}.$

(d) At $\epsilon = 0$,

$$\dfrac{G_0 - G(\text{min})}{RT} = \ln \left(\dfrac{\nu_1}{\nu_1 + \nu_2} \right)^{\nu_1} \left(\dfrac{\nu_2}{\nu_1 + \nu_2} \right)^{\nu_2} - \ln x_{1e}^{\nu_1} x_{2e}^{\nu_2}.$$

(e) At $\epsilon = 1$,

$$\dfrac{G_1 - G(\text{min})}{RT} = \ln \left(\dfrac{\nu_3}{\nu_3 + \nu_4} \right)^{\nu_3} \left(\dfrac{\nu_4}{\nu_3 + \nu_4} \right)^{\nu_4} - \ln x_{3e}^{\nu_3} x_{4e}^{\nu_4}.$$

18.13. In the case of the ionization of a monatomic gas, show that

(a) $\dfrac{G - G(\text{min})}{RT} = \epsilon \left(\ln \dfrac{\epsilon^2}{1 - \epsilon^2} - \ln \dfrac{\epsilon_e^2}{1 - \epsilon_e^2} \right) + \ln \dfrac{1 - \epsilon}{1 + \epsilon} - \ln \dfrac{1 - \epsilon_e}{1 + \epsilon_e}.$

(b) At $\epsilon = 0$,

$$\dfrac{G_0 - G(\text{min})}{RT} = - \ln \dfrac{1 - \epsilon_e}{1 + \epsilon_e}.$$

(c) At $\epsilon = 1$,

$$\dfrac{G_1 - G(\text{min})}{RT} = \ln \dfrac{1}{4} - \ln \dfrac{\epsilon_e^2}{(1 + \epsilon_e)^2}.$$

(d) Plot $[G - G(\text{min})]/2.30RT$ against ϵ for the ionization of cesium vapor at $2260°K$ and 10^{-6} atm, using the result of Prob. 18.7.

18.14. (a) Prove that, for a mixture of reacting ideal gases,

$$\dfrac{d}{d\epsilon} \ln \dfrac{x_3^{\nu_3} x_4^{\nu_4}}{x_1^{\nu_1} x_2^{\nu_2}} = \dfrac{n_0 + n_0'}{\Sigma n_k} \dfrac{1}{\psi},$$

where

$$\dfrac{1}{\psi} = \dfrac{\nu_1^2}{x_1} + \dfrac{\nu_2^2}{x_2} + \dfrac{\nu_3^2}{x_3} + \dfrac{\nu_4^2}{x_4} - (\Delta\nu)^2$$

$$\Delta\nu = \nu_3 + \nu_4 - \nu_1 - \nu_2.$$

(b) If we start with $n_0\nu_1$ moles of A_1, $n_0\nu_2$ moles of A_2, and no A_3 or A_4, show that

$$\psi = \dfrac{\epsilon(1 - \epsilon)}{(\nu_1 + \nu_2)(\nu_3 + \nu_4)}.$$

18.15. Prove that, for a mixture of reacting ideal gases *in equilibrium*,

(a) $\left(\dfrac{\partial V}{\partial P} \right)_T = - \dfrac{V}{P} - \dfrac{(n_0 + n_0')RT(\Delta\nu)^2}{P^2 \dfrac{d}{d\epsilon_e} \ln \dfrac{x_3^{\nu_3} x_4^{\nu_4}}{x_1^{\nu_1} x_2^{\nu_2}}}.$

(b) $\left(\dfrac{\partial V}{\partial T} \right)_P = \dfrac{V}{T} + \dfrac{(n_0 + n_0') \Delta\nu \, \Delta H}{PT \dfrac{d}{d\epsilon_e} \ln \dfrac{x_3^{\nu_3} x_4^{\nu_4}}{x_1^{\nu_1} x_2^{\nu_2}}}.$

(c) $\left(\dfrac{\partial P}{\partial T} \right)_{\epsilon_e} = - \dfrac{P \, \Delta H}{RT^2 \, \Delta\nu}.$

18.16. Prove that, for a mixture of reacting ideal gases *in equilibrium*,

$$dS = \sum n_k \left[\sum x_k c_{Pk} + \frac{\psi(\Delta H)^2}{RT^2} \right] \frac{dT}{T} - R \sum n_k \left[1 + \frac{\psi \Delta H \Delta \nu}{RT} \right] \frac{dP}{P}.$$

18.17. The heat of sublimation of 1 mole of a solid is equal to

$$l_{su} = T(s''' - s').$$

Substituting for l_{su} its value given by Kirchhoff's equation, and using the equations

$$s''' = \int c_p''' \frac{dT}{T} - R \ln P + s_0''',$$

$$s' = \int_0^T c_p' \frac{dT}{T} + s_0',$$

where s_0' is the molar entropy of a solid at absolute zero, derive the equation

$$\ln P = -\frac{l_0}{RT} + \frac{1}{R} \int \frac{\int c_p''' \, dT}{T^2} \, dT - \frac{1}{R} \int_0^T \frac{\int_0^T c_p' \, dT}{T^2} \, dT + \frac{s_0''' - s_0'}{R}.$$

Compare this equation with the one in Art. 15.5 and show that

$$s_0''' = Ri + s_0'.$$

Apply this equation to the materials that undergo a chemical reaction and use the chemical Δ notation, to get

$$\Delta S_0''' = R \, \Delta i + \Delta S_0'.$$

Explain how *experimental measurements* of $\Delta S_0'''$ and Δi may be used to check the validity of the third law of thermodynamics.

19

Heterogeneous Systems

19.1. Thermodynamic Equations for a Heterogeneous System.

It was shown in Art. 17.9 that the Gibbs function of any homogeneous phase, consisting of c constituents and in thermal and mechanical equilibrium at the temperature T and pressure P, is equal to

$$G = \Sigma \mu_k n_k, \qquad (1)$$

where each chemical potential is a function of T, P, and the mole fraction of the respective constituent, and the summation is taken over all the constituents. Furthermore, if the phase undergoes an infinitesimal process involving a change of temperature dT, a change of pressure dP, and changes in each one of the n's, the accompanying change in the Gibbs function is equal to

$$dG = -S\, dT + V\, dP + \Sigma \mu_k\, dn_k. \qquad (2)$$

Suppose we have a heterogeneous system of φ phases, all homogeneous and all at the uniform temperature T and pressure P. Let us denote constituents as usual by subscripts and phases by superscripts. The total Gibbs function of the heterogeneous system G is the sum of the Gibbs functions of all the phases; i.e.,

$G = \Sigma \mu_k^{(1)} n_k^{(1)}$ over all the constituents of the 1st phase,

$\quad + \Sigma \mu_k^{(2)} n_k^{(2)}$ over all the constituents of the 2d phase,

$$\cdots\cdots\cdots\cdots\cdots\cdots\cdots\cdots\cdots\cdots\cdots\cdots\cdots\cdots\cdots\cdots$$

$\quad + \Sigma \mu_k^{(\varphi)} n_k^{(\varphi)}$ over all the constituents of the φth phase. $\qquad$ (I)

If an infinitesimal process takes place in which *all* the phases undergo a change in temperature dT and a change in pressure dP, then the change in the Gibbs function is

$$dG = -S^{(1)}\, dT + V^{(1)}\, dP + \Sigma \mu_k^{(1)}\, dn_k^{(1)} \quad \text{(for the 1st phase)}$$
$$\quad -S^{(2)}\, dT + V^{(2)}\, dP + \Sigma \mu_k^{(2)}\, dn_k^{(2)} \quad \text{(for the 2d phase)}$$

$$\cdots\cdots\cdots\cdots\cdots\cdots\cdots\cdots\cdots\cdots\cdots\cdots\cdots\cdots\cdots\cdots$$

$$\quad -S^{(\varphi)}\, dT + V^{(\varphi)}\, dP + \Sigma \mu_k^{(\varphi)}\, dn_k^{(\varphi)} \quad \text{(for the } \varphi \text{th phase)}.$$

This equation evidently reduces to

$$dG = -S\,dT + V\,dP + \Sigma\mu_k^{(1)}\,dn_k^{(1)} + \Sigma\mu_k^{(2)}\,dn_k^{(2)} + \cdots$$
$$+ \Sigma\mu_k^{(\varphi)}\,dn_k^{(\varphi)}, \quad \text{(II)}$$

where S and V are the entropy and volume, respectively, of the whole heterogeneous system.

The problem of the equilibrium of a heterogeneous system is to obtain an equation or a set of equations among the μ's that hold when all the phases are in chemical equilibrium. If the system is assumed to approach equilibrium at constant T and P, then, at equilibrium, G is a minimum, and the problem can be stated thus: *To render G a minimum at constant T and P, subject to whatever conditions are imposed on the n's by virtue of the constraints of the system.* The mathematical condition that G be a minimum at constant T and P is that

$$dG_{T,P} = 0.$$

Hence, the equation that must be satisfied at equilibrium is

$$dG_{T,P} = \Sigma\mu_k^{(1)}\,dn_k^{(1)} + \Sigma\mu_k^{(2)}\,dn_k^{(2)} + \cdots + \Sigma\mu_k^{(\varphi)}\,dn_k^{(\varphi)} = 0,$$

where the dn's are not all independent but are connected by equations of constraint.

To return for a moment to the system treated in Chap. 17, namely, one phase consisting of a mixture of chemically active substances, we found that the equations of constraint were of such a simple form that, by direct substitution, G could be expressed as a function of T, P, and only one other independent variable ϵ and that $dG_{T,P}$ could be expressed in terms of only one differential $d\epsilon$, thus:

$$dG_{T,P} = (n_0 + n_0')(\nu_3\mu_3 + \nu_4\mu_4 - \nu_1\mu_1 - \nu_2\mu_2)\,d\epsilon.$$

At equilibrium, when $dG_{T,P} = 0$, only one equation, the equation of reaction equilibrium, was obtained.

In the case of a heterogeneous system, however, the situation is more complicated. In the first place there is, as a rule, more than one independent variable besides T and P. In the second place, the equations of constraint are usually of such a nature that it is either impossible or exceedingly cumbersome to attempt by direct substitution to express G in terms of the independent variables only and dG in terms of differentials of these independent variables. Finally, instead of only one equation of equilibrium, there may be several, depending on the type of heterogeneous system.

We are therefore confronted with a type of problem that is not usually handled in an elementary course in calculus, namely, to render a function of any number of variables an extremum (either a minimum or a maximum) subject to any number and any kind of equations of constraint. This problem can be solved by a simple and elegant method due to Lagrange, known as *Lagrange's method of multipliers*.

19.2. Lagrange's Method of Multipliers. Let us consider for the sake of simplicity a function f of only four variables y_1, y_2, y_3, and y_4 that is to be rendered an extremum, subject to the equations of constraint

$$\psi_1(y_1, y_2, y_3, y_4) = 0,$$
$$\psi_2(y_1, y_2, y_3, y_4) = 0.$$

Since there are two equations of constraint, only two of the four y's are independent. Taking the differential of the function f and equating it to zero, we get

$$\frac{\partial f}{\partial y_1} dy_1 + \frac{\partial f}{\partial y_2} dy_2 + \frac{\partial f}{\partial y_3} dy_3 + \frac{\partial f}{\partial y_4} dy_4 = 0.$$

Taking the differential of the equations of constraint, we get

$$\frac{\partial \psi_1}{\partial y_1} dy_1 + \frac{\partial \psi_1}{\partial y_2} dy_2 + \frac{\partial \psi_1}{\partial y_3} dy_3 + \frac{\partial \psi_1}{\partial y_4} dy_4 = 0,$$
$$\frac{\partial \psi_2}{\partial y_1} dy_1 + \frac{\partial \psi_2}{\partial y_2} dy_2 + \frac{\partial \psi_2}{\partial y_3} dy_3 + \frac{\partial \psi_2}{\partial y_4} dy_4 = 0.$$

Multiplying the first of the above two equations by λ_1 and the second by λ_2, we have the three equations

$$\frac{\partial f}{\partial y_1} dy_1 + \frac{\partial f}{\partial y_2} dy_2 + \frac{\partial f}{\partial y_3} dy_3 + \frac{\partial f}{\partial y_4} dy_4 = 0,$$
$$\lambda_1 \frac{\partial \psi_1}{\partial y_1} dy_1 + \lambda_1 \frac{\partial \psi_1}{\partial y_2} dy_2 + \lambda_1 \frac{\partial \psi_1}{\partial y_3} dy_3 + \lambda_1 \frac{\partial \psi_1}{\partial y_4} dy_4 = 0,$$
$$\lambda_2 \frac{\partial \psi_2}{\partial y_1} dy_1 + \lambda_2 \frac{\partial \psi_2}{\partial y_2} dy_2 + \lambda_2 \frac{\partial \psi_2}{\partial y_3} dy_3 + \lambda_2 \frac{\partial \psi_2}{\partial y_4} dy_4 = 0,$$

where λ_1 and λ_2 are unknown arbitrary functions of y_1, y_2, y_3, and y_4, known as *Lagrangian multipliers*. Adding the three equations, we get

$$\left(\frac{\partial f}{\partial y_1} + \lambda_1 \frac{\partial \psi_1}{\partial y_1} + \lambda_2 \frac{\partial \psi_2}{\partial y_1}\right) dy_1 + \left(\frac{\partial f}{\partial y_2} + \lambda_1 \frac{\partial \psi_1}{\partial y_2} + \lambda_2 \frac{\partial \psi_2}{\partial y_2}\right) dy_2$$
$$+ \left(\frac{\partial f}{\partial y_3} + \lambda_1 \frac{\partial \psi_1}{\partial y_3} + \lambda_2 \frac{\partial \psi_2}{\partial y_3}\right) dy_3 + \left(\frac{\partial f}{\partial y_4} + \lambda_1 \frac{\partial \psi_1}{\partial y_4} + \lambda_2 \frac{\partial \psi_2}{\partial y_4}\right) dy_4 = 0.$$

Now the values to be ascribed to the multipliers λ_1 and λ_2 may be chosen at will. Let us choose λ_1 and λ_2 such that the first two parentheses vanish. This provides two equations

$$\frac{\partial f}{\partial y_1} + \lambda_1 \frac{\partial \psi_1}{\partial y_1} + \lambda_2 \frac{\partial \psi_2}{\partial y_1} = 0,$$
$$\frac{\partial f}{\partial y_2} + \lambda_1 \frac{\partial \psi_1}{\partial y_2} + \lambda_2 \frac{\partial \psi_2}{\partial y_2} = 0,$$

which serve to determine the values of λ_1 and λ_2. We are then left with the equation

$$\left(\frac{\partial f}{\partial y_3} + \lambda_1 \frac{\partial \psi_1}{\partial y_3} + \lambda_2 \frac{\partial \psi_2}{\partial y_3}\right) dy_3 + \left(\frac{\partial f}{\partial y_4} + \lambda_1 \frac{\partial \psi_1}{\partial y_4} + \lambda_2 \frac{\partial \psi_2}{\partial y_4}\right) dy_4 = 0.$$

Since two of the four y's are independent, let us regard y_3 and y_4 as the independent variables. It follows then that

$$\frac{\partial f}{\partial y_3} + \lambda_1 \frac{\partial \psi_1}{\partial y_3} + \lambda_2 \frac{\partial \psi_2}{\partial y_3} = 0,$$

$$\frac{\partial f}{\partial y_4} + \lambda_1 \frac{\partial \psi_1}{\partial y_4} + \lambda_2 \frac{\partial \psi_2}{\partial y_4} = 0.$$

These two equations plus the two equations of constraint constitute four equations that determine the extremal values of y_1, y_2, y_3, and y_4.

It is obvious that this method may be applied to a function of any number of coordinates subject to any number of equations of constraint. The method of Lagrangian multipliers can be summarized as follows:

1. Write down the differential of the function, and equate it to zero.

2. Take the differential of each equation of constraint, and multiply by as many different Lagrangian multipliers as there are equations of constraint.

3. Add all the equations, factoring the sum so that each differential appears only once.

4. Equate the coefficient of each differential to zero.

19.3. Phase Rule without Chemical Reaction. Consider a heterogeneous system of c chemical constituents that do not combine chemically with one another. Suppose that there are φ phases, each one of which is in contact with every other phase in such a way that there are no impediments to the transport of any constituent from one phase to another. Let us assume temporarily that every constituent is present in every phase. As usual, constituents will be denoted by subscripts and phases by superscripts. As we have shown previously, the Gibbs function of the whole heterogeneous system is

$$G = \sum_{1}^{c} n_k^{(1)} \mu_k^{(1)} + \sum_{1}^{c} n_k^{(2)} \mu_k^{(2)} + \cdots + \sum_{1}^{c} n_k^{(\varphi)} \mu_k^{(\varphi)},$$

where all the summations extend from $k = 1$ to $k = c$, since all the constituents are present in all the phases. G is a function of T, P, and the n's of which there are $c\varphi$ in number. Not all these n's, however, are independent. Since there are no chemical reactions, the only way in which the n's may change is by the transport of the constituents from one phase to another, in which case the total number of moles of each constituent remains constant. We have, therefore, as our equations of constraint,

$$n_1^{(1)} + n_1^{(2)} + \cdots + n_1^{(\varphi)} = \text{const.},$$
$$n_2^{(1)} + n_2^{(2)} + \cdots + n_2^{(\varphi)} = \text{const.},$$

$$n_c^{(1)} + n_c^{(2)} + \cdots + n_c^{(\varphi)} = \text{const.}$$

In order to find the equations of chemical equilibrium, it is necessary to render G a minimum at constant T and P, subject to these equations of constraint. Applying Lagrange's method, we have

$$dG = \mu_1^{(1)} dn_1^{(1)} + \cdots + \mu_c^{(1)} dn_c^{(1)} + \cdots + \mu_1^{(\varphi)} dn_1^{(\varphi)} + \cdots + \mu_c^{(\varphi)} dn_c^{(\varphi)} = 0$$
$$\lambda_1\ dn_1^{(1)} \qquad\qquad\qquad + \cdots + \lambda_1\ dn_1^{(\varphi)} \qquad\qquad = 0$$

$$\lambda_c\ dn_c^{(1)} + \cdots \qquad\qquad\qquad\qquad + \lambda_c\ dn_c^{(\varphi)} = 0$$

where there are c Lagrangian multipliers, one for each equation of constraint. Adding and equating each coefficient of each dn to zero, we get

$$\mu_1^{(1)} = -\lambda_1, \qquad \mu_1^{(2)} = -\lambda_1, \cdots, \qquad \mu_1^{(\varphi)} = -\lambda_1,$$
$$\mu_2^{(1)} = -\lambda_2, \qquad \mu_2^{(2)} = -\lambda_2, \cdots, \qquad \mu_2^{(\varphi)} = -\lambda_2,$$

$$\mu_c^{(1)} = -\lambda_c, \qquad \mu_c^{(2)} = -\lambda_c, \cdots, \qquad \mu_c^{(\varphi)} = -\lambda_c,$$

or

$$\mu_1^{(1)} = \mu_1^{(2)} = \cdots = \mu_1^{(\varphi)},$$
$$\mu_2^{(1)} = \mu_2^{(2)} = \cdots = \mu_2^{(\varphi)},$$

$$\mu_c^{(1)} = \mu_c^{(2)} = \cdots = \mu_c^{(\varphi)}.$$

These are the *equations of phase equilibrium.* They express the important fact that, at equilibrium, the chemical potential of a constituent in one phase must be equal to the chemical potential of the same constituent in every other phase.

As a simple example, suppose we have only one constituent present in two phases. Then

$$dG_{T,P} = \mu_1^{(1)} dn_1^{(1)} + \mu_1^{(2)} dn_1^{(2)};$$

and since $dn_1^{(2)} = -dn_1^{(1)}$,

$$dG_{T,P} = [\mu_1^{(1)} - \mu_1^{(2)}] dn_1^{(1)}.$$

Now, before equilibrium is reached, suppose there is a flow of matter from phase (1) to phase (2). Then $dn_1^{(1)}$ is negative; and since this flow is irreversible, $dG_{T,P}$ must be negative. Therefore, *while the flow is taking place,*

$$\mu_1^{(1)} > \mu_1^{(2)} \qquad \text{[flow of matter from phase (1) to phase (2)]}.$$

Obviously, the transfer of matter ceases when the two chemical potentials become equal. The chemical potentials of a constituent in two neighboring phases may be compared with the temperatures and pressures of these phases, thus:

1. If the temperature of phase (1) is greater than that of phase (2), there is a flow of heat that ceases when the temperatures are equal, i.e., when thermal equilibrium is established.

2. If the pressure of phase (1) is greater than that of phase (2), there is a "flow" of work that ceases when the pressures are equal, i.e., when mechanical equilibrium is established.

3. If the chemical potential of a constituent of phase (1) is greater than that of phase (2), there is a flow of that constituent which ceases when the chemical potentials are equal, i.e., when chemical equilibrium is established.

The equations of phase equilibrium expressing the equality of the chemical potentials of any one constituent in all the φ phases are obviously $\varphi - 1$ in number. Therefore, for c constituents, there are altogether $c(\varphi - 1)$ equations among the μ's.

Following out the procedure of Lagrange's method, we should complete our solution of the problem by solving the $c(\varphi - 1)$ equations of phase equilibrium and the c equations of constraint for the φc values of the n's that make G a minimum. These values should, of course, be functions of the parameters T and P. We find, however, that the equations do not contain the n's in such fashion as to determine their values, because of the fact that the equations of equilibrium are equations among the chemical potentials, which are intensive quantities and depend on the x's, which contain the n's in the special form

$$x_k = \frac{n_k}{\Sigma n}.$$

This is another way of saying that the chemical potential for a constituent in a phase depends on the composition of that phase but on its total mass.

There are many *different* sets of n's that satisfy the equations of phase equilibrium and give rise to the same minimum value of the Gibbs function. This may be seen from the fact that

$$G = \mu_1^{(1)}n_1^{(1)} + \cdots + \mu_c^{(1)}n_c^{(1)} + \cdots + \mu_1^{(\varphi)}n_1^{(\varphi)} + \cdots + \mu_c^{(\varphi)}n_c^{(\varphi)},$$

but at equilibrium the chemical potentials of the same constituent are the same in all phases and hence may be written without any superscripts. Factoring out the μ's, we get

$$G(\text{min}) = \mu_1[n_1^{(1)} + \cdots + n_1^{(\varphi)}] + \cdots + \mu_c[n_c^{(1)} + \cdots + n_c^{(\varphi)}],$$

and therefore *the minimum value of the Gibbs function is the same for many different distributions of the total mass among the phases.* Since, therefore, we cannot find the values of the n's at equilibrium, we may inquire as to whether we can obtain *any* precise information about a heterogeneous system in equilibrium.

As we have seen, the state of the system at equilibrium is determined by the temperature, the pressure, and $c\varphi$ mole fractions. Hence,

$$\text{Total number of variables} = c\varphi + 2.$$

Among these variables there are two types of equations: (1) equations of phase equilibrium of which there are $c(\varphi - 1)$ in number and (2) equations of the type $\Sigma x = 1$, one for each phase, and therefore φ such equations altogether. Hence,

$$\text{Total number of equations} = c(\varphi - 1) + \varphi.$$

If there are as many equations as there are variables, then the temperature, pressure, and composition of the whole system at equilibrium are determined. Such a system is called *nonvariant* and is said to have zero variance. If the number of variables exceeds the number of equations by one, then the equilibrium of the system is not determined until one of the variables is arbitrarily chosen. Such a system is called *monovariant* and is said to have a variance of 1. In general, *the excess of variables over equations is called the variance, f.* Thus,

$$\text{Variance} = (\text{number of variables}) - (\text{number of equations})$$

or $\qquad f \quad = \quad (c\varphi + 2) \qquad - \qquad [c(\varphi - 1) + \varphi]$

whence $\qquad \boxed{f = c - \varphi + 2.}$

This is known as the *phase rule* and was first derived in 1875 by Josiah Willard Gibbs, who was then professor of mathematical physics at Yale University. The phase rule arose from a general theory of the equilibrium of heterogeneous systems that Gibbs developed during the years 1875 to 1878 and published in an obscure journal, *The Transactions of the Connecticut Academy.* The original paper, entitled "On the Equilibrium of Heterogeneous Substances," was almost 300 pages long. In it, Gibbs considered not only chemical effects, but also those produced by gravity, capillarity, and nonhomogeneous strains. It stands today as one of the most profound contributions to the world of human thought and, along with Gibbs's researches in vector analysis and statistical mechanics, places him with the greatest of the world's geniuses.

It is a simple matter to remove the restriction that every constituent must be present in every phase. Suppose that constituent A_1 is absent from phase (1). Then the equation of equilibrium that exists when the constituent is present, namely,

$$\mu_1^{(1)} = -\lambda_1,$$

is now lacking. However, to describe the composition of the first phase, we need one mole fraction fewer than before. Therefore, since both the number of equations and the number of variables have been reduced by one, the difference is the same and the phase rule remains unchanged.

To remove the second restriction, that no chemical reaction takes place, is more difficult and requires solving the problem *de novo*. Before this is done, however, it is worth while to consider a few simple applications of the phase rule in its present form.

19.4. Simple Applications of the Phase Rule. As simple examples of the use of the phase rule, we shall consider a pure substance, a simple eutectic, and a freezing mixture.

1. *Pure Substance.* In the case of a pure substance such as water, the phase rule merely confirms what is already known. If there are two phases in equilibrium, say, solid and vapor, the variance is 1. There is one equation of equilibrium, namely,

$$\mu'(T, P) = \mu'''(T, P),$$

where one prime stands for solid and three primes for vapor. We have already shown that, when a phase consists of only one constituent, the chemical potential is equal to the molar Gibbs function. Hence,

$$g' = g'''$$

is the equation of equilibrium among the two coordinates T and P, which will be recognized as the equation of the sublimation curve. If three phases are in equilibrium, the system is nonvariant, the two equations of equilibrium

$$g' = g''',$$
$$g'' = g''',$$

serving to determine both T and P. The phase rule shows that the maximum number of phases of a one-constituent system that can exist in equilibrium is three. The various triple points of water confirm this result.

2. *Simple Eutectic.* Let us consider a system of two constituents that neither combine to produce a compound nor form a solid solution but that, in the liquid phase, are miscible in all proportions. A mixture of

gold and thallium has these properties. Suppose we have a liquid alloy consisting of 40 per cent thallium and 60 per cent gold in an evacuated chamber originally at about 1000°C. A mixture of thallium and gold vapors will constitute the vapor phase, and we shall have $c = 2$ and $\varphi = 2$. It follows that the variance is 2; and hence, the composition and temperature having been chosen, the vapor pressure is determined. If the temperature is now progressively lowered, a solid phase of pure gold will separate from the liquid at a temperature of about 600°C, and the percentage of thallium in the solution is thus increased. At any given concentration there will be one and only one temperature at which the three phases, vapor mixture, liquid solution, and solid gold, will be in equilibrium, because now $c = 2$ and $\varphi = 3$; therefore, $f = 1$.

By covering the metals with a piston on which any desired pressure may be exerted, we may exclude the vapor phase and study the variance of the system when only solid and liquid phases are present. In this way, the temperatures and compositions at which equilibrium exists among various phases may be measured and the results plotted on a phase diagram such as that shown in Fig. 19.1.

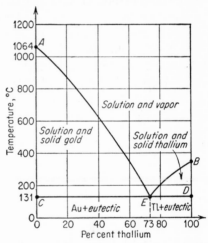

FIG. 19.1. Phase diagram for the eutectic system of gold and thallium.

Point A is the melting point (strictly speaking, the triple point) of pure gold, and B that of pure thallium. When the two phases, solution and vapor, are present, the system is divariant; and equilibrium may exist at any temperature and composition represented by a point in the *region* above AEB. When the three phases, solution, vapor, and solid gold, are present, the system is monovariant; and equilibrium may exist only at those temperatures and compositions represented by points on the *curve* AE. Similarly, curve BE represents temperatures and compositions at which the monovariant system consisting of the three phases, solution, vapor, and solid thallium, is in equilibrium. The complete curve AEB is known as the *liquidus*.

At E, there are four phases present, solution, vapor, solid gold, and solid thallium. Hence $c = 2$, $\varphi = 4$, and $f = 0$, or the system is nonvariant. This is known as the *eutectic point*, and the composition at this point as the eutectic composition.

Solution and solid gold may coexist at all temperatures and compositions represented by points in region ACE. Below line CE, however, no liquid can exist, and the system consists of a solid with the eutectic mixture plus free gold. Solution and solid thallium coexist in region BED, and below ED we have eutectic plus free thallium. Line CED is known as the *solidus*.

There are many different types of eutectic system, each with phase diagrams of different character. All of them, however, may be understood completely in terms of the phase rule. For further details, the student is advised to read "The Phase Rule and Phase Reactions" by S. T. Bowden, a well-written and well-illustrated work.

3. *Freezing Mixture.* A number of years ago, before the commercial use of solid carbon dioxide ("dry ice") as a cooling agent, foods such as ice cream used to be packed in a container surrounded by a mixture of ice and common salt. If the mixture was thermally insulated and covered, it maintained a constant temperature of about $-21°C$. Another practice that is still current today is to melt the ice that forms on the sidewalk by sprinkling salt on it. These phenomena may be clearly understood on the basis of the phase rule.

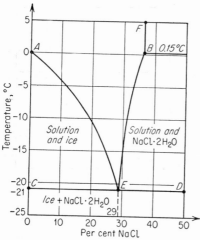

FIG. 19.2. Phase diagram for the mixture NaCl and H_2O.

Consider the phase diagram of NaCl and water shown in Fig. 19.2. A is the triple point of pure water, and B is the transition point where the dihydrate $NaCl·2H_2O$ changes into NaCl. Except for the upper right-hand portion of the figure, the diagram is in all respects similar to the simple eutectic diagram of Fig. 19.1. At all points on AE, the system is monovariant and consists of the three phases, solution, vapor, and ice. Similarly, on EB, we have solution, vapor, and dihydrate. Point E is the eutectic point, which, since in this case the system contains water, is called the *cryohydric point*. The mixture of dihydrate and water that forms at the cryohydric point is called a *cryohydrate*.

Only at points below the solidus CED can ice and $NaCl·2H_2O$ exist as solids together. Consequently, when they are mixed at a temperature above $-21°C$ (as on the sidewalk), they are not in equilibrium, and as a result the ice melts and the salt dissolves. It should be mentioned at this point that if the system is open to the air at atmospheric pressure then there is one more constituent, air, which would ordinarily increase the variance by 1. Since, however, the pressure is constant, this extra variance is used up, and the system behaves as before.

If, ice, salt, water, and vapor at 0°C are together in a thermally insulated container, they are not in equilibrium and some ice will melt and dissolve some salt. But this saturated solution will be too concentrated to be in equilibrium with ice. Ice will therefore melt, lowering the concentration of the solution, which will then dissolve more salt. While this is going on, the temperature of the whole system automatically and spontaneously decreases until the temperature of −21°C is reached. Such a system is known as a *freezing mixture*.

At the transition point B, where NaCl forms, there are three constituents, and hence one might expect a maximum of five phases to coexist. This, however, is not the case, because a chemical reaction

$$NaCl \cdot 2H_2O \rightleftharpoons NaCl + \text{solution}$$

takes place. We shall see in the next article that the presence of this reaction causes the system to behave as if there were only two constituents, so that only four phases coexist at the point B, solid $NaCl \cdot 2H_2O$, solid NaCl, solution, and vapor.

There are a number of freezing mixtures that are often used for preserving materials at low temperatures. These are listed in Table 19.1.

TABLE 19.1. FREEZING MIXTURES

First constituent	Second constituent	Lowest temperature, °C
NH_4Cl	Ice	−15.4
NaCl	Ice	−21
Alcohol	Ice	−30
$CaCl_2 \cdot 6H_2O$	Ice	−55
Alcohol	Solid CO_2	−72
Ether	Solid CO_2	−77

19.5. Phase Rule with Chemical Reaction. Let us consider a heterogeneous system composed of arbitrary amounts of c constituents, assuming, for the sake of simplicity, that four of the constituents are chemically active, capable of undergoing the reaction

$$\nu_1 A_1 + \nu_2 A_2 \rightleftharpoons \nu_3 A_3 + \nu_4 A_4.$$

Suppose that there are φ phases and, as only a temporary assumption, that all the constituents are present in all the phases. As before, the Gibbs function of the system is

$$G = \sum_1^c \mu_k^{(1)} n_k^{(1)} + \sum_1^c \mu_k^{(2)} n_k^{(2)} + \cdots + \sum_1^c \mu_k^{(\varphi)} n_k^{(\varphi)}.$$

The equations of constraint for those constituents which do not react are of the same type as before; i.e., they express the fact that the total number of moles of each inert constituent is constant. In the case of the chemically active constituents, however, the total number of moles of any one is not constant but is a function of the degree of reaction. Hence, the equations of constraint are

$$n_1^{(1)} + n_1^{(2)} + \cdots + n_1^{(\varphi)} = (n_0 + n_0')\nu_1(1 - \epsilon),$$
$$n_2^{(1)} + n_2^{(2)} + \cdots + n_2^{(\varphi)} = (n_0 + n_0')\nu_2(1 - \epsilon) + N_2,$$
$$n_3^{(1)} + n_3^{(2)} + \cdots + n_3^{(\varphi)} = (n_0 + n_0')\nu_3\epsilon,$$
$$n_4^{(1)} + n_4^{(2)} + \cdots + n_4^{(\varphi)} = (n_0 + n_0')\nu_4\epsilon + N_4,$$
$$n_5^{(1)} + n_5^{(2)} + \cdots + n_5^{(\varphi)} = \text{const.},$$
$$\cdot \quad \cdot \qquad \qquad \cdot \qquad \cdot$$
$$\cdot \quad \cdot \qquad \qquad \cdot \qquad \cdot$$
$$\cdot \quad \cdot \qquad \qquad \cdot \qquad \cdot$$
$$n_c^{(1)} + n_c^{(2)} + \cdots + n_c^{(\varphi)} = \text{const.},$$

where n_0, n_0', N_2, and N_4 have their usual meaning. Applying Lagrange's method, we get the equations below (reading across pages 462 and 463).

$$\mu_1^{(1)} dn_1^{(1)} + \cdots + \mu_4^{(1)} dn_4^{(1)} + \cdots + \mu_c^{(1)} dn_c^{(1)} + \cdots +$$
$$\lambda_1 dn_1^{(1)} \qquad\qquad\qquad\qquad\qquad + \cdots +$$
$$\lambda_2 dn_2^{(1)} \qquad\qquad\qquad\qquad + \cdots +$$
$$\lambda_3 dn_3^{(1)} \qquad\qquad\qquad + \cdots +$$
$$\lambda_4 dn_4^{(1)} \qquad\qquad + \cdots +$$
$$\lambda_5 dn_5^{(1)} \qquad + \cdots +$$
$$\cdot \qquad\qquad \cdot \quad \cdot$$
$$\cdot \qquad\qquad \cdot \quad \cdot$$
$$\cdot \qquad\qquad \cdot \quad \cdot$$
$$\lambda_c dn_c^{(1)} + \cdots +$$

Adding, and equating coefficients of the dn's to zero, we get the usual $c(\varphi - 1)$ equations of phase equilibrium,

$$\mu_1^{(1)} = \mu_1^{(2)} = \cdots = \mu_1^{(\varphi)},$$
$$\mu_2^{(1)} = \mu_2^{(2)} = \cdots = \mu_2^{(\varphi)},$$
$$\cdot \qquad \cdot \qquad \cdot$$
$$\cdot \qquad \cdot \qquad \cdot$$
$$\mu_c^{(1)} = \mu_c^{(2)} = \cdots = \mu_c^{(\varphi)}.$$

Equating the coefficient of $d\epsilon$ to zero, we get an extra equation of equilibrium, namely,

$$\lambda_1 \nu_1 + \lambda_2 \nu_2 - \lambda_3 \nu_3 - \lambda_4 \nu_4 = 0,$$

which, since $\lambda_1 = -\mu_1$ of any phase, $\lambda_2 = -\mu_2$ of any phase, etc., becomes

$$\nu_1 \mu_1 + \nu_2 \mu_2 = \nu_3 \mu_3 + \nu_4 \mu_4.$$

This equation will be recognized as the equation of reaction equilibrium, which, in the case of ideal gases, was found to lead to the law of mass action.

The rest of the argument follows the same lines as before. There are $c(\varphi - 1)$ equations of phase equilibrium, 1 equation of reaction equilibrium, and φ equations of the type $\Sigma x = 1$. Hence, the total number of equations is

$$c(\varphi - 1) + 1 + \varphi.$$

Since the variables are the same as before, namely, T, P, and the x's,

---

$$\mu_1^{(\varphi)} \, dn_1^{(\varphi)} + \cdots + \mu_4^{(\varphi)} \, dn_4^{\varphi'} + \cdots + \mu_c^{(\varphi)} \, dn_c^{(\varphi)} \qquad = 0$$

$$\lambda_1 \, dn_1^{(\varphi)} \qquad\qquad +\lambda_1(n_0 + n_0')\nu_1 \, d\epsilon = 0$$

$$\qquad \lambda_2 \, dn_2^{(\varphi)} \qquad\qquad +\lambda_2(n_0 + n_0')\nu_2 \, d\epsilon = 0$$

$$\qquad\qquad \lambda_3 \, dn_3^{(\varphi)} \qquad\qquad -\lambda_3(n_0 + n_0')\nu_3 \, d\epsilon = 0$$

$$\qquad\qquad\qquad \lambda_4 \, dn_4^{(\varphi)} \qquad\qquad -\lambda_4(n_0 + n_0')\nu_4 \, d\epsilon = 0$$

$$\qquad\qquad\qquad\qquad \lambda_5 \, dn_5^{(\varphi)} \qquad\qquad = 0$$

$$\vdots \qquad\qquad\qquad \vdots$$

$$\qquad\qquad\qquad\qquad\qquad \lambda_c \, dn_c^{(\varphi)} \qquad\qquad = 0$$

---

of which there are in number $c\varphi + 2$, the variance is

$$f = c\varphi + 2 - [c(\varphi - 1) + 1 + \varphi]$$

or

$$f = (c - 1) - \varphi + 2.$$

The phase rule in this case is seen to be different, in that $c - 1$ now stands where c formerly stood. For the reason given before, this form of the phase rule remains unchanged when every constituent is not present in every phase. We see therefore that when there are c constituents, present in arbitrary amounts, and only one chemical reaction, there is one extra equation of equilibrium and the variance is reduced by 1. It is obvious that if there were two independent chemical reactions there would be two extra equations of equilibrium, whence the phase rule would become $f = (c - 2) - \varphi + 2$. For r independent reactions, we would have

$$f = (c - r) - \varphi + 2.$$

The argument up to now has been based on the fact that only three kinds of equations have existed among the variables T, P, and the x's: equations of phase equilibrium, equations of reaction equilibrium, and equations of the type $\Sigma x = 1$. It often happens, however, that a chemical reaction takes place in such a manner that additional equations expressing further restrictions upon the x's are at hand. Suppose, for example, we put an arbitrary amount of solid NH_4HS into an evacuated chamber and two new constituents form according to the reaction

$$NH_4HS \rightleftharpoons NH_3 + H_2S.$$

Since gaseous NH_3 and H_2S are in the same phase, the restriction always exists that

$$x_{NH_3} = x_{H_2S}.$$

This constitutes a fourth type of equation to be added to the three listed at the beginning of this paragraph.

Another example of additional restricting equations among the x's is provided by the phenomenon of dissociation in solution. Suppose that we have a heterogeneous system one of whose phases is a solution of salt 2 in solvent 1. Suppose that the salt dissociates according to the scheme shown in Fig. 19.3(a). All the ions, of course, remain in the liquid phase, and no precipitate is formed. Consequently, we have the equation

$$x_3 = x_4,$$

which expresses the fact that the solution is electrically neutral. If multiple dissociation takes place according to the scheme shown in Fig. 19.3(b), then there are three independent restricting equations among the x's, namely,

$$x_3 = x_8 + x_6 + x_4,$$
$$x_5 = x_8 + x_6,$$
$$x_7 = x_8.$$

Adding these equations, we get the *dependent* equation

$$x_3 + x_5 + x_7 = 3x_8 + 2x_6 + x_4,$$

expressing the fact of electrical neutrality.

Let us call equations of the preceding type *restricting equations,* and let us suppose that z of them are independent. Then we may list four types of equations among T, P, and the x's, thus:

1. Equations of phase equilibrium [$c(\varphi - 1)$ in number].
2. Equations of reaction equilibrium (r in number).
3. Equations of the type $\Sigma x = 1$ (φ in number).
4. Restricting equations (z in number).

Hence, the total number of equations is

$$c(\varphi - 1) + r + \varphi + z;$$

and, as usual, the total number of variables is $c\varphi + 2$. Therefore,

$$f = c\varphi + 2 - [c(\varphi - 1) + r + \varphi + z]$$

or

$$f = (c - r - z) - \varphi + 2.$$

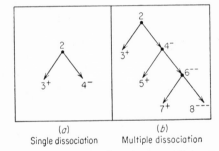

(a)   (b)
Single dissociation   Multiple dissociation

Fig. 19.3. Dissociations of a salt that give rise to additional restricting equations among the mole fractions.

If we define the *number of components c' as the total number of constituents minus the number of independent reactions minus the number of independent restricting equations,* i.e.,

$$\boxed{c' = c - r - z,}$$

we may always write the phase rule in the same form, thus:

$$\boxed{f = c' - \varphi + 2.}$$

19.6. Determination of the Number of Components. The problem of determining the number of components in a heterogeneous system may be somewhat difficult for the beginner. As a result of experience with the behavior of typical heterogeneous systems, the physical chemist is able to determine the number of components by counting the smallest number of constituents whose specification is sufficient to determine the composition of every phase. The validity of this working rule rests upon a few fundamental facts whose truth we shall demonstrate rigorously in this article.

EXAMPLE I. First let us consider a heterogeneous system consisting of a liquid phase composed of a solution of the salt NaH_2PO_4 in water and a vapor phase composed of water vapor. It is important to show that, *so long as no precipitate is formed by virtue of a reaction between the salt and the water, no matter what else we assume to take place in the solution, the number of components is two.*

1. *Neglecting All Dissociation.* There are two constituents, no chemical reactions, and no restricting equations. Hence,

$$c' = 2 - 0 - 0 = 2.$$

2. *Assuming Single Dissociation of the Salt.* There are four constituents, NaH_2PO_4, H_2O, Na^+, $H_2PO_4^-$; one chemical reaction

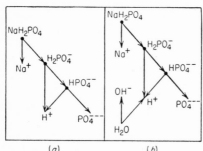

$$NaH_2PO_4 \rightleftharpoons Na^+ + H_2PO_4^-,$$

and one restricting equation

$$x_{Na^+} = x_{H_2PO_4^-}.$$

Hence, $c = 4 - 1 - 1 = 2$.

3. *Assuming Multiple Dissociation of the Salt.* There are seven constituents and three independent chemical reactions, as shown in Fig. 19.4(a), and two independent restricting equations,

(a)   (b)
Dissociation of NaH_2PO_4 Dissociation of NaH_2PO_4
                              and H_2O

FIG. 19.4. Multiple dissociation of NaH_2PO_4 with and without dissociation of H_2O.

$$x_{Na^+} = x_{PO_4^{---}} + x_{HPO_4^{--}} + x_{H_2PO_4^-},$$
$$x_{H^+} = 2x_{PO_4^{---}} + x_{HPO_4^{--}}.$$

(By adding the two equations, the *dependent* equation expressing electrical neutrality of the solution is obtained.) Hence, $c' = 7 - 3 - 2 = 2$.

4. *Assuming Dissociation of the Water Also.* There are eight constituents and four independent chemical reactions, as shown in Fig. 19.4(b), and two independent restricting equations,

$$x_{Na^+} = x_{PO_4^{---}} + x_{HPO_4^{--}} + x_{H_2PO_4^-}$$
and
$$x_{H^+} = 2x_{PO_4^{---}} + x_{HPO_4^{--}} + x_{OH^-}.$$

Hence, $c' = 8 - 4 - 2 = 2$.

5. *Assuming Association of the Water.* A ninth constituent $(H_2O)_2$ is formed as a result of a fifth independent reaction,

$$H_2O \rightleftharpoons \frac{1}{2}(H_2O)_2.$$

There are still the same two independent restricting equations, and hence $c' = 9 - 5 - 2 = 2$.

It is clear, therefore, that it is a matter of indifference as to what chemical changes take place in the solution. The number of components is always two, provided that no precipitate forms.

EXAMPLE II. To investigate the effect of precipitate, let us consider a mixture of $AlCl_3$ and water. In this case, the $AlCl_3$ combines with the water to form $Al(OH)_3$, some of which precipitates out of the solution, according to the reaction shown in Fig. 19.5. There are eight constituents and only four independent reactions. At first thought, one might imagine that there are five independent reactions, but if we write the equations of reaction equilibrium corresponding to the four dissociations:

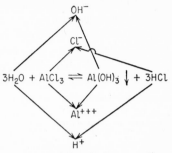

FIG. 19.5. Dissociation, reaction, and precipitation that occur when $AlCl_3$ is dissolved in water.

$$3\mu_{H_2O} = 3\mu_{H^+} + 3\mu_{OH^-},$$
$$\mu_{AlCl_3} = \mu_{Al^{+++}} + 3\mu_{Cl^-},$$
$$\mu_{Al(OH)_3} = \mu_{Al^{+++}} + 3\mu_{OH^-},$$
$$3\mu_{HCl} = 3\mu_{H^+} + 3\mu_{Cl^-},$$

and add the first two and subtract the sum of the last two, we get

$$3\mu_{H_2O} + \mu_{AlCl_3} = \mu_{Al(OH)_3} + 3\mu_{HCl},$$

which is the equation of reaction equilibrium corresponding to the reaction

$$3H_2O + AlCl_3 \rightleftharpoons Al(OH)_3 + 3HCl,$$

which is therefore seen to be a *dependent* reaction.

Since some of the $Al(OH)_3$ has precipitated out, there is only one restricting equation, namely, that expressing the electrical neutrality of the solution,

$$3x_{Al^{+++}} + x_{H^+} = x_{OH^-} + x_{Cl^-}.$$

Consequently, $c' = 8 - 4 - 1 = 3$, and we have an interesting situation where a heterogeneous system, formed originally by mixing two substances, has three components.

EXAMPLE III. As a last example, let us consider a system consisting of water vapor and a water solution containing arbitrary amounts of $NaCl$ and KNO_3 in water.

1. *Neglecting All Dissociations.* There are five constituents, H_2O, $NaCl$, KNO_3, $NaNO_3$, KCl; one reaction,

$$NaCl + KNO_3 \rightleftharpoons NaNO_3 + KCl;$$

and one restricting equation,

$$x_{\text{NaNO}_3} = x_{\text{KCl}}.$$

Hence, $c' = 5 - 1 - 1 = 3$.

2. *Considering All Reactions.* There are 11 (constituents, which undergo the reactions

$$H_2O \rightleftharpoons H^+ + OH^-,$$
$$NaCl \rightleftharpoons Na^+ + Cl^-,$$
$$KNO_3 \rightleftharpoons K^+ + NO_3^-,$$
$$NaNO_3 \rightleftharpoons Na^+ + NO_3^-,$$
$$KCl \rightleftharpoons K^+ + Cl^-.$$

It should be noticed that the reaction

$$NaCl + KNO_3 \rightleftharpoons NaNO_3 + KCl$$

is not independent of the preceding five but that its equation of reaction equilibrium may be obtained by adding the second and third and subtracting the sum of the fourth and fifth.

There are three restricting equations. The first,

$$x_{\text{Na}^+} + x_{\text{NaNO}_3} = x_{\text{Cl}^-} + x_{\text{KCl}},$$

expresses the fact that the amount of sodium lost by the NaCl (to form Na^+ and $NaNO_3$) is equal to the amount of chlorine lost by the NaCl (to form Cl^- and KCl). The second,

$$x_{\text{K}^+} + x_{\text{KCl}} = x_{\text{NO}_3^-} + x_{\text{NaNO}_3},$$

expresses the corresponding fact concerning the loss of potassium and nitrate from KNO_3. The third is

$$x_{\text{H}^+} = x_{\text{OH}^-}.$$

(The dependent equation of electrical neutrality is obtained by adding these three equations.) Hence, $c' = 11 - 5 - 3 = 3$.

In the event that we start with arbitrary amounts of all five substances, H_2O, NaCl, KNO_3, $NaNO_3$, and KCl, there are still 11 constituents and five independent reactions, but only two restricting equations, namely,

$$x_{\text{Na}^+} + x_{\text{K}^+} + x_{\text{H}^+} = x_{\text{Cl}^-} + x_{\text{NO}_3^-} + x_{\text{OH}^-},$$

expressing electrical neutrality, and

$$x_{\text{H}^+} = x_{\text{OH}^-}.$$

Hence, $c' = 11 - 5 - 2 = 4$.

19.7. Displacement of Equilibrium. Consider a heterogeneous system of φ phases and c constituents, four of which undergo the reaction

$$\nu_1 A_1 + \nu_2 A_2 \rightleftharpoons \nu_3 A_3 + \nu_4 A_4.$$

Any infinitesimal process involving a change in temperature, pressure, and composition of the phases is accompanied by a change in the Gibbs function equal to

$$dG = -S\,dT + V\,dP + \mu_1^{(1)}\,dn_1^1 + \cdots + \mu_c^{(1)}\,dn_c^{(1)}$$
$$+ \cdots + \mu_1^{(\varphi)}\,dn_1^{(\varphi)} + \cdots + \mu_c^{(\varphi)}\,dn_c^{(\varphi)}.$$

In general, during such an infinitesimal change, there is neither equilibrium among the phases nor equilibrium with regard to the chemical reaction. Complete chemical equilibrium would require both phase equilibrium and reaction equilibrium. *Suppose we assume phase equilibrium only.* Then,

$$\mu_1^{(1)} = \mu_1^{(2)} = \cdots = \mu_1^{(\varphi)},$$
$$\mu_2^{(1)} = \mu_2^{(2)} = \cdots = \mu_2^{(\varphi)},$$

$$\cdot \qquad \cdot \qquad \cdot$$
$$\cdot \qquad \cdot \qquad \cdot$$
$$\cdot \qquad \cdot \qquad \cdot$$

$$\mu_c^{(1)} = \mu_c^{(2)} = \cdots = \mu_c^{(\varphi)},$$

and the change in the Gibbs function becomes

$$dG = -S\,dT + V\,dP + \mu_1[dn_1^{(1)} + \cdots + dn_1^{(\varphi)}]$$
$$+ \cdots + \mu_4[dn_4^{(1)} + \cdots + dn_4^{(\varphi)}] + \mu_5[dn_5^{(1)} + \cdots + dn_5^{(\varphi)}]$$
$$+ \cdots + \mu_c[dn_c^{(1)} + \cdots + dn_c^{(\varphi)}].$$

But

$$dn_1^{(1)} + \cdots + dn_1^{(\varphi)} = -(n_0 + n_0')\nu_1\,d\epsilon,$$
$$dn_2^{(1)} + \cdots + dn_2^{(\varphi)} = -(n_0 + n_0')\nu_2\,d\epsilon,$$
$$dn_3^{(1)} + \cdots + dn_3^{(\varphi)} = +(n_0 + n_0')\nu_3\,d\epsilon,$$
$$dn_4^{(1)} + \cdots + dn_4^{(\varphi)} = +(n_0 + n_0')\nu_4\,d\epsilon,$$
$$dn_5^{(1)} + \cdots + dn_5^{(\varphi)} = 0,$$

$$\cdot \qquad \cdot \qquad \cdot$$
$$\cdot \qquad \cdot \qquad \cdot$$
$$\cdot \qquad \cdot \qquad \cdot$$

$$dn_c^{(1)} + \cdots + dn_c^{(\varphi)} = 0.$$

Therefore, the change in the Gibbs function during an infinitesimal process in which there is phase equilibrium but not reaction equilibrium is given by

$$dG = -S\,dT + V\,dP + (n_0 + n_0')(\nu_3\mu_3 + \nu_4\mu_4 - \nu_1\mu_1 - \nu_2\mu_2)\,d\epsilon.$$

Since, under these circumstances G is a function of T, P, and ϵ, it follows that

$$\frac{\partial G}{\partial T} = -S,$$

$$\frac{\partial G}{\partial P} = V,$$

$$\frac{\partial G}{\partial \epsilon} = (n_0 + n_0')(\nu_3\mu_3 + \nu_4\mu_4 - \nu_1\mu_1 - \nu_2\mu_2).$$

When reaction equilibrium exists at temperature T and pressure P, we must have $\partial G/\partial \epsilon = 0$ at $\epsilon = \epsilon_e$. If we go to a slightly different equilibrium state at temperature $T + dT$ and pressure $P + dP$, then the new degree of reaction will be $\epsilon_e + d\epsilon_e$ and the change in $\partial G/\partial \epsilon$ during this process is zero. Therefore

$$d\left(\frac{\partial G}{\partial \epsilon}\right) = 0.$$

But

$$d\left(\frac{\partial G}{\partial \epsilon}\right) = \frac{\partial^2 G}{\partial T\,\partial \epsilon}\,dT + \frac{\partial^2 G}{\partial P\,\partial \epsilon}\,dP + \frac{\partial^2 G}{\partial \epsilon^2}\,d\epsilon = 0$$

$$= \frac{\partial}{\partial \epsilon}\left(\frac{\partial G}{\partial T}\right)dT + \frac{\partial}{\partial \epsilon}\left(\frac{\partial G}{\partial P}\right)dP + \frac{\partial^2 G}{\partial \epsilon^2}\,d\epsilon = 0$$

$$= -\frac{\partial S}{\partial \epsilon}\,dT + \frac{\partial V}{\partial \epsilon}\,dP + \frac{\partial^2 G}{\partial \epsilon^2}\,d\epsilon = 0.$$

Solving for $d\epsilon = d\epsilon_e$, we get

$$d\epsilon_e = \frac{\partial S/\partial \epsilon}{\partial^2 G/\partial \epsilon^2}\,dT - \frac{\partial V/\partial \epsilon}{\partial^2 G/\partial \epsilon^2}\,dP.$$

Recognizing that, at thermodynamic equilibrium, $dQ = T\,dS$ or

$$\left(\frac{dQ}{d\epsilon}\right)_{T,P} = T\left(\frac{\partial S}{\partial \epsilon}\right)_{T,P},$$

we get

$$\left(\frac{\partial \epsilon_e}{\partial T}\right)_P = \frac{(dQ/d\epsilon)_{T,P}}{T\,(\partial^2 G/\partial \epsilon^2)_{T,P}}, \tag{1}$$

$$\left(\frac{\partial \epsilon_e}{\partial P}\right)_T = -\frac{(\partial V/\partial \epsilon)_{T,P}}{(\partial^2 G/\partial \epsilon^2)_{T,P}}. \tag{2}$$

Since at thermodynamic equilibrium G is a minimum, $\partial^2 G/\partial \epsilon^2$ is positive. Equation (1) therefore states that an increase of temperature at constant pressure always causes a reaction to proceed in the direction in which heat is absorbed at constant T and P, whereas, from Eq. (2), we see that an increase of pressure at constant temperature causes a reaction to proceed in the direction in which the volume decreases at constant T and P.

PROBLEMS

19.1. All the lettered points in Fig. 19.6 lie in one plane. The line CD separates the plane into two regions: on the left a wave has the speed v and on the right the speed v'. Show by Lagrange's method that the time for the wave to travel the path APB is a minimum when $v/v' = \sin \varphi / \sin \varphi'$.

19.2. A hot metal of mass m, specific heat c_P, and temperature T_i is immersed in a cooler liquid of mass m', specific heat c'_P, and temperature T'_i. The entire system is thermally insulated. If the final temperature of the metal is T_f and that of the liquid is T'_f, show by Lagrange's method that the condition for the entropy change of the universe to be a maximum is that $T_f = T'_f$.

19.3. A box contains an extremely large number N of molecules. The total entropy is

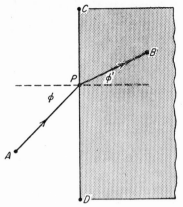

$$S = k \ln B,$$

where

$$B = \frac{N!}{n_1! n_2! n_3! \, \cdots}$$

FIG. 19.6.

and the n's are the number of molecules in the various cells of the phase space. Using Stirling's formula

$$\ln x! = x \ln x - x$$

and employing Lagrange's method, render the entropy a maximum, subject to the equations of constraint

$$n_1 + n_2 + n_3 + \cdots = N = \text{const.},$$
$$n_1 u_1 + n_2 u_2 + n_3 u_3 + \cdots = U = \text{const.},$$

where the u's are the average energies associated with the various cells of the phase space and are constants. Prove that

$$n_k = \alpha e^{-\beta u_k},$$

where α and β are undetermined functions.

19.4. Consider a homogeneous mixture of four ideal gases capable of undergoing the reaction

$$\nu_1 A_1 + \nu_2 A_2 \rightleftharpoons \nu_3 A_3 + \nu_4 A_4.$$

How many components are there if one starts with
(a) Arbitrary amounts of A_1 and A_2 only.
(b) Arbitrary amounts of all four gases.
(c) ν_1 moles of A_1 and ν_2 moles of A_2 only.

19.5. Consider a system composed of a solid phase of calcium carbonate, $CaCO_3$, a solid phase of calcium oxide, CaO, and a gaseous phase consisting of a mixture of CO_2, $CaCO_3$ vapor, and CaO vapor, all three constituents being present initially in arbitrary amounts. These are the substances that are present in a limekiln, where the reaction

$$CaCO_3 \rightleftharpoons CaO + CO_2$$

takes place.
(a) How many components are there, and what is the variance?
(b) Assuming the gaseous phase to be a mixture of ideal gases, show that

$$\frac{p_{CaO} p_{CO_2}}{p_{CaCO_3}} = K.$$

(c) If solid $CaCO_3$ is introduced into an evacuated chamber, how many components are there, and what is the variance?

19.6. Solid ammonium hydrosulphide, NH_4HS, is mixed with arbitrary amounts of gaseous NH_3 and H_2S, forming a three-constituent system of two phases, undergoing the reaction

$$NH_4HS \rightleftharpoons NH_3 + H_2S.$$

(a) How many components are there, and what is the variance?

(b) Assuming that the gaseous phase is a mixture of ideal gases, show that

$$\frac{p_{NH_3} p_{H_2S}}{p_{NH_4HS}} = K.$$

(c) If solid NH_4HS is placed in an evacuated chamber, how many components are there, and what is the variance?

19.7. How many components are there in a system composed of arbitrary amounts of water, sodium chloride, and barium chloride?

19.8. At high temperature the following reactions take place: $C + CO_2 \rightleftharpoons 2CO$ and $CO_2 + H_2 \rightleftharpoons CO + H_2O$. How many components are there if we start with

(a) Arbitrary amounts of C, CO_2, H_2.

(b) Arbitrary amounts of C, CO_2, H_2, CO, and H_2O.

19.9. Consider a system consisting of a pure liquid phase in equilibrium with a gaseous phase composed of a mixture of the vapor of the liquid and an inert gas that is insoluble in the liquid. Suppose that the inert gas (sometimes called the *foreign gas*) can flow into or out of the gaseous phase so that the total pressure can be varied at will.

(a) How many components are there, and what is the variance?

(b) Assuming the gaseous phase to be a mixture of ideal gases, show that

$$g'' = RT(\phi + \ln p),$$

where g'' is the molar Gibbs function of the liquid and ϕ and p refer to the vapor.

(c) Suppose a little more foreign gas is added, thus increasing the pressure from P to $P + dP$, at constant temperature. Show that

$$v'' \, dP = RT \frac{dp}{p},$$

where v'' is the molar volume of the liquid, which is practically constant.

(d) Integrating at constant temperature from an initial state where there is no foreign gas to a final state where the total pressure is P and the partial vapor pressure is p, show that

$$\ln \frac{p}{P_0} = \frac{v''}{RT} (P - P_0) \qquad \text{(Gibbs equation)}$$

where P_0 is the vapor pressure when no foreign gas is present.

(e) In the case of water at $0°C$, at which $P_0 = 4.57$ mm, show that, when there is sufficient air above the water to make the total pressure equal to 10 atm, $p = 4.61$ mm.

19.10. The Gibbs function G of a liquid phase consisting of a solvent and very small amounts of several solutes is

$$G = \mu_0 n_0 + \mu_1 n_1 + \mu_2 n_2 + \cdots$$

where the subscript zero refers to the solvent, and

$$\mu_k = g_k + RT \ln x_k.$$

Heterogeneous Systems

473

(a) Using the relation $V = (\partial G/\partial P)_T$, show that

$$V = \Sigma n_k v_k.$$

(b) Using the relation $H = G - T(\partial G/\partial T)_P$, show that

$$H = \Sigma n_k h_k,$$

which means that there is no heat of dilution.

19.11. A very small amount of sugar is dissolved in water, and the solution is in equilibrium with pure water vapor.

(a) Show that the equation of phase equilibrium is

$$g''' = g'' + RT \ln (1 - x)$$

where g''' is the molar Gibbs function of water vapor, g'' the molar Gibbs function of pure liquid water, and x the mole fraction of the sugar in solution.

(b) For an infinitesimal change in x at constant temperature, show that

$$(v''' - v'') \, dP = RT \, d \ln (1 - x).$$

(c) Assuming the vapor to behave like an ideal gas and regarding v'' as constant, integrate the preceding equation at constant temperature from an initial state $x = 0$, $P = P_0$, to a final state $x = x$, $P = P_x$, and derive

$$\ln \frac{P_x}{P_0} = \ln (1 - x) + \frac{v''}{RT} (P_x - P_0).$$

P_0 is the vapor pressure of the pure liquid, and P_x the vapor pressure of the dilute solution.

(d) Justify neglecting the last term on the right, and show that

$$P_x = P_0(1 - x) \qquad \text{(Raoult's law)}$$

or

$$\frac{P_0 - P_x}{P_0} = x.$$

19.12. Consider the system of Prob. 19.11, and let x stand for the mole fraction of the sugar.

(a) For an infinitesimal change in x at constant pressure, show that

$$-s''' \, dT = -s'' \, dT + R \ln (1 - x) \, dT + RT \, d \ln (1 - x).$$

(b) Substituting for $R \ln (1 - x)$ the value obtained from the equation of phase equilibrium, show that (a) reduces to

$$0 = \frac{h''' - h''}{T} \, dT + RT \, d \ln (1 - x).$$

(c) Taking into account that $x \ll 1$ and calling $h''' - h''$ the latent heat of vaporization l_{va}, show that the elevation of the boiling point is

$$\Delta T = \frac{RT^2}{l_{va}} x.$$

19.13. A very small amount of sugar is dissolved in water, and the solution is in equilibrium with pure ice. The equation of phase equilibrium is

$$g' = g'' + RT \ln (1 - x),$$

where g' = molar Gibbs function of pure ice
  g'' = molar Gibbs function of pure water
  x = mole-fraction of sugar in solution

(a) For an infinitesimal change in x at constant pressure, show that

$$-s'\, dT = -s''\, dT + R \ln (1 - x)\, dT + RT\, d \ln (1 - x).$$

(b) Substituting for $R \ln (1 - x)$ the value obtained from the equation of phase equilibrium, show that (a) reduces to

$$\frac{h'' - h'}{T}\, dT = RT\, d \ln (1 - x).$$

(c) Taking into account that $x \ll 1$ and calling $h'' - h'$ the heat of fusion, l_{fu}, show that the depression of the freezing point is

$$\Delta T = -\frac{RT^2}{l_{fu}}\, x.$$

Bibliography

Temperature

American Institute of Physics, "Temperature," Vol. II, Reinhold, 1956

Physical Thermodynamics

J. K. Roberts and A. R. Miller, "Heat and Thermodynamics," Blackie, 1951
M. Planck, "Theory of Heat," Macmillan, 1932
F. W. Sears, "Thermodynamics," Addison-Wesley, 1953
W. P. Allis and M. A. Herlin, "Thermodynamics and Statistical Mechanics," McGraw-Hill, 1952
F. D. Rossini (editor), "Thermodynamics and Physics of Matter," Princeton, 1955

Chemical Thermodynamics

J. W. Gibbs, "Collected Works," Vol. I, Longmans, 1928
F. W. MacDougall, "Thermodynamics and Chemistry," Wiley, 1939
E. A. Guggenheim, "Thermodynamics," Interscience, 1949
I. Prigogine and R. Defay, "Chemical Thermodynamics," Longmans, 1954
K. G. Denbigh, "Principles of Chemical Equilibrium," Cambridge, 1955

Engineering Thermodynamics

J. H. Keenan, "Thermodynamics," Wiley, 1941
J. F. Lee and F. W. Sears, "Thermodynamics," Addison-Wesley, 1955
H. J. Stoever, "Engineering Thermodynamics," Wiley, 1951
E. Schmidt, "Thermodynamics," Oxford, 1949
E. F. Obert, "Thermodynamics," 2d ed., McGraw-Hill, 1957

Special Applications of Thermodynamics

S. T. Bowden, "Phase Rule and Phase Reactions," Macmillan, 1938
W. H. McAdams, "Heat Transmission," 3d ed., McGraw-Hill, 1954
D. Shoenberg, "Superconductivity," Cambridge, 1952

C. G. B. Garrett, "Magnetic Cooling," Harvard, 1954

C. J. Gorter (editor), "Progress in Low Temperature Physics," Interscience, 1955

C. F. Squire, "Low Temperature Physics," McGraw-Hill, 1953

F. Simon, "The Third Law of Thermodynamics," Handbuch der Physik, X, p. 350; *Ergebnisse der exakten Naturwissenschaften*, **9**, 222, 1930; 40th Guthrie Lecture of the London Physical Society, 1956

Index